THE
HANDY
SCIENCE
ANSWER
BOOK

THE HANDY

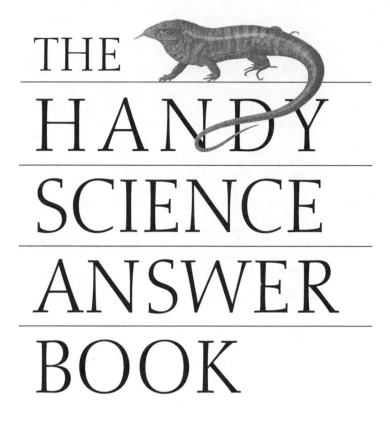

SCIENCE

ANSWER

BOOK

Second Edition

Compiled by the Science and Technology Department
of the Carnegie Library of Pittsburgh

BARNES & NOBLE BOOKS
NEW YORK

THE HANDY SCIENCE ANSWER BOOK

Copyright © 1997 by The Carnegie Library of Pittsburgh

This edition published by Barnes & Noble, Inc.,
by arrangement with Visible Ink Press LLC.

2004 Barnes & Noble Books

ISBN 0-7607-4651-6

Printed and bound in the United States of America

05 06 07 08 MC 9 8 7 6 5 4 3

Contents

INTRODUCTION *XI*
ACKNOWLEGMENTS *XIII*
CREDITS *XV*

PHYSICS AND CHEMISTRY

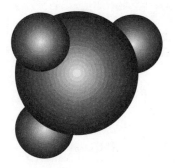

Energy, motion, force, and heat *1*
Light, sound, and other waves *6*
Matter *10*
Chemical elements, etc. *15*
Measurement, methodology, etc. *23*

SPACE

Universe *29*
Stars *31*
Planets and moons *40*
Comets, meteorites, etc. *51*
Observation and measurement 56
Exploration *58*

v

EARTH

Air *71*

Physical characteristics, etc. *73*

Water *76*

Land *84*

Volcanoes and earthquakes *93*

Observation and measurement *98*

CLIMATE AND WEATHER

Temperature *103*

Air phenomena *105*

Wind *110*

Precipitation *119*

Weather prediction *123*

MINERALS AND OTHER MATERIALS

Rocks and minerals *127*

Metals *133*

Natural substances *138*

Man-made products *143*

ENERGY

Non-nuclear fuels *155*

Nuclear power *163*

Measures and measurement *167*

Consumption and conservation *170*

ENVIRONMENT

Ecology, resources, etc. *177*

Extinct and endangered plants and animals *187*

Pollution *193*

Recycling, conservation, and waste *201*

BIOLOGY

Evolution and genetics *209*

Life processes, structures, etc. *220*

Classification, measurement, and terms *223*

Fungi, bacteria, algae, etc. *227*

PLANT WORLD

Physical characteristics, functions, etc. *231*

Trees and shrubs *233*

Flowers and other plants *238*

Gardening, farming, etc. *245*

ANIMAL WORLD

Physical characteristics, etc. *259*

Names *266*

Insects, spiders, etc. *270*

Aquatic life *277*

Reptiles and amphibians *281*

Birds *283*

Mammals *291*

Pets *301*

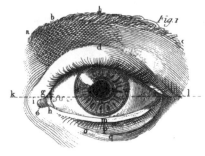

HUMAN BODY

Functions, processes, and characteristics *311*

Bones, muscles, and nerves *322*

Organs and glands *326*

Body fluids *330*

Skin, hair, and nails *334*

Senses and sense organs *336*

HEALTH AND MEDICINE

Health hazards, risks, etc. *343*

First aid, poisons, etc. *352*

Diseases, disorders, and other health problems *357*

Health care *373*

Diagnostic equipment, tests, etc. *377*

Drugs, medicines, etc. *379*

Surgery and other non-drug treatments *388*

WEIGHTS, MEASURES, TIME, TOOLS, AND WEAPONS

Weights, measures, and measurement *393*

Time *402*

Tools, machines, and processes *416*

Weapons *423*

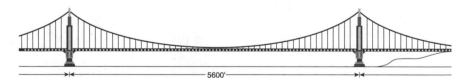

BUILDINGS, BRIDGES, AND OTHER STRUCTURES

Buildings and building parts *429*

Roads, bridges, and tunnels *437*

Miscellaneous structures *442*

BOATS, TRAINS, CARS, AND PLANES

Boats and ships *447*

Trains and trolleys *452*

Motor vehicles *455*

Aircraft *467*

Military vehicles *472*

COMMUNICATIONS

Symbols, writing, and codes *475*

Radio and television *480*

Telecommunications, recording, etc.
    486

Computers *490*

GENERAL SCIENCE AND TECHNOLOGY

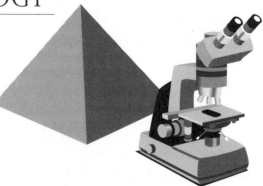

Numbers *505*

Mathematics *508*

Terms and theories *519*

Further Reading   *523*

Index   *547*

Introduction

We live in an age of scientific and technological urgency, chatting on the Internet, cooking in microwave ovens, and keeping track of voice mail, E mail, and what we call "snail" mail when its delivery takes, say, a whole day or so. From the trivial to the complex, gizmos and whatchamacallits dominate modern life. Information whizzes by faster than a speeding bullet. Discoveries are made daily, hourly, by the minute. The horizons of knowledge are becoming mighty distant for many of us. That quizzical staring into space and idle scratching of the head are symptoms of the condition known as *information overload*. Though not life-threatening, it certainly is frustrating.

Wouldn't it be great if someone would just collect the answers to some of life's mysteries? Like, just what is a syzygy? Why is the sky blue? How deep is the ocean? What are PCBs? What is genetic engineering? When did the Ice Age begin? When did it end? Why do the hands on a clock go "clockwise"? Does rock music kill plants? Why do cats like catnip? Why do a Siamese cat's eyes glow red? How long do specific animals live? What is a male lobster called? How many miles of veins do I have? What is the purpose of goosebumps? What is dead reckoning? Why don't the tires on an airplane blow out when the airplane lands? Why do AM radio stations have a wider broadcast range at night? How does that fax machine work? What is a computer "virus" and how is it spread? What do those lines in a Universal Product Code mean?

The Handy Science Answer Book is just such a collection. Each year, the staff of the Science and Technology Department at the Carnegie Library of Pittsburgh receives more than 111,000 reference questions and inquiries by the telephone, through the mail, and from personal in-house contact. Even though armed with 390,000 books, 425,000 bound periodicals, and thousands of government documents, technical reports, and microfiche, the Department finds that it requires a special file to answer these questions quickly and reliably. Some of this wealth of cumulative information has been in existence for at least 44 years—as far back as any of the current Carnegie staff can remember. It may even date back to 1905, the year when the Carnegie Library of Pittsburgh became the first major public library in the United States to establish a separate Science and Technology Department. The gems from the ready reference file are shared with you in *The Handy Science Answer Book*.

This second edition of *Handy Science* provides answers to more than 1,400 unusual, interesting, or frequently asked questions in the areas of science, pseudo science, and technology. We've added more than 300 completely new questions, and updated and expanded hundreds more. In addition, 100 illustrations and many tables augment the text. In some ways, science touches so much of our lives—whether it be our environment, our homes, our workplaces, right down to our physical bodies themselves—that it can become difficult to categorize what actually constitutes science. *Handy Science* makes no particular effort to restrict the questions to pure science, but focuses on those questions that have achieved noteworthiness either through their popularity, the time-consuming nature of their research, or their uniqueness.

The Carnegie staff has verified figures and dates to the best of their ability. Keep in mind that even in science, figures can seem to be in conflict; many times such discrepancies may be attributable to the authority perspective, or more commonly, to the results of simple mathematical rounding of figures. Occasionally, the figure or date listed is a consensus of the consulted sources; other times the discrepancy is noted and alternatives given. *Handy Science* rounds off figures whenever it seems that such precision is unnecessary. When designating eras, *Handy Science* uses the abbreviation C.E. ("of the common era") instead of the more familiar A.D. (*anno Domini,* "in the year of the Lord"), and B.C.E. ("before the common era") in place of B.C. ("before Christ").

The answers are written in non-technical language and provide either a succinct response or a more elaborate explanation, depending on the nature of the question. Definitions to scientific terminology are given within the answer itself, and both metric and U.S. customary measurements are listed. Following the main Q&A section are suggestions for further reading (most of which were used to answer various questions) and the index.

So, when you're stuck wondering how, exactly, a chimney differs from a flue, or whether there's any bird that can fly upside down, or how dalmatians became firehouse dogs, reach for *Handy Science.* Or if you suddenly need to know the life span of a chimpanzee (51 years maximum) or the number of horses in the world (65,292,000) or how many muscles it takes to produce a smile (17) or a frown (43), reach for *Handy Science.* You'll find it downright handy.

Acknowledgments

Many people have made significant contributions to the second edition of *The Handy Science Answer Book*. Margery Peffer gave her best performance ever during this revision project. She realized early on the scope and magnitude of the work and completed it with wisdom, insight, and professionalism. I especially appreciated her calmness when all our efforts seemed to be confirming Murphy's Law. Thanks, Marge. I want to thank the staff librarians in the Science and Technology Department for their sustained endeavors and words of encouragement. They include: Joan Anderson, Naomi Balaban, Aimee deChambeau, Janet Horsch, Susan Horvath, Marilyn Megahan, Blanche McManus, Dorothy Melamed, David Murdock, Gregory Pomrenke, Charles Quinn, and Donna Strawbridge.

Mary Shields did a great job of preparing every question from handwritten entry to final format on disk. She proofed every question, verified all citations, solved numerous problems relating to questions, and kept track of tens of thousands of photocopies.

Students in my "Science and Technology Resources and Services" classes at the University of Pittsburgh's School of Library and Information Science contributed some interesting and challenging questions over the last few years. Bob Wienand and Chuck Sabatos provided some difficult questions in chemistry that we're still trying to answer.

I thank Bob Croneberger, Loretta O'Brien, and Gladys Shapera Maharam, senior library administrators, at the Carnegie Library of Pittsburgh for their interest and encouragement.

In addition, I've enjoyed working with science editor Bridget Travers and appreciate her task of seeing this project to completion. At Visible Ink Press, thanks to senior editor Christa Brelin and to Mikal Ansari, Randy Bassett, Jim Craddock, Buffy May Fairchild, Pam Hayes, Shanna Heilveil, David Kunath, Bryan Lassner, Evi Seoud, Devra Sladics, Kim Smilay, and Sue Stefani. For fine proofreading, thank you Sharon Remington; for fetching design, thanks Mary Krzewinski; and for excellent typesetting, thanks Marco Di Vita of the Graphix Group.

Finally, thanks to my wife, Sandi, and sons, Andrew and Michael, for their encouragement, patience, and understanding—especially when I was late for dinner.

James E. Bobick
Head, Science and Technology Department
Carnegie Library of Pittsburgh

Credits

Line art illustrations by Hans & Cassady of Westerville, Ohio.

Photographs of nine-banded armadillo, monarch butterfly, sundew, and Grand Canyon National Park provided by Robert J. Huffman/Field Mark Publications. Additional photographs provided by the Library of Congress, the National Aeronautics and Space Administration, the National Park Service, the U.S. Department of Agriculture, and the U.S. Fish and Wildlife Service.

THE
HANDY
SCIENCE
ANSWER
BOOK

PHYSICS AND CHEMISTRY

ENERGY, MOTION, FORCE, AND HEAT

See also: Energy

How is **"absolute zero"** defined?

Absolute zero is the theoretical temperature at which all substances have zero thermal energy. Originally conceived as the temperature at which an ideal gas at constant pressure would contract to zero volume, absolute zero is of great significance in thermodynamics and is used as the fixed point for absolute temperature scales. Absolute zero is equivalent to 0°K, -459.67°F, or -273.15°C.

The velocity of a substance's molecules determines its temperature; the faster the molecules move, the more volume they require, and the higher the temperature becomes. The lowest actual temperature ever reached was two-billionth of a degree above absolute zero (2×10^{-9}K) by a team at the Low Temperature Laboratory in the Helsinki University of Technology, Finland, in October, 1989.

Does **hot water freeze faster** than cold?

A bucket of hot water will not freeze faster than a bucket of cold water. However, a bucket of water that *has been* heated or boiled, then allowed to cool to the same temperature as the bucket of cold water, may freeze faster. Heating or boiling drives out some of the air bubbles in water; because air bubbles cut down thermal conductivity, they can inhibit freezing. For the same reason, previously heated water forms denser ice than unheated water, which is why hot-water pipes tend to burst before cold-water pipes.

1

What is **superconductivity**?

Superconductivity is a condition in which many metals, alloys, organic compounds, and ceramics conduct electricity without resistance, usually at low temperatures. Heinke Kamerlingh Omnes, a Dutch physicist, discovered superconductivity in 1911, but it was not until 1972 that the modern theory regarding the phenomenon was developed by three American physicists—John Bardeen, Leon N. Cooper, and John Robert Schrieffer. Known as the *BCS theory* after the three scientists, it postulates that superconductivity occurs in certain materials because the electrons in them, rather than remaining free to collide with imperfections and scatter, form pairs that can flow easily around imperfections and do not lose their energy. A variety of uses have been proposed for this phenomenon, including switching devices that control electronic circuits in computers; devices that measure extremely small magnetic fields for medical diagnosis; and the means to develop powerful superconducting magnets used to build particle accelerators.

What is **inertia**?

Inertia is a tendency of all objects and matter in the universe to stay still, or if moving, to continue moving in the same direction, unless acted on by some outside force. This forms the first law of motion formulated by Isaac Newton (1642–1727). To move a body at rest, enough external force must be used to overcome the object's inertia; the larger the object is, the more force is required to move it. In his *Philosophae Naturalis Principia Mathematica*, published in 1687, Newton sets forth all three laws of motion. Newton's second law is that the force to move a body is equal to its mass times its acceleration ($F = MA$), and the third law states that for every action there is an equal and opposite reaction.

Isaac Newton.

Why do **golf balls** have dimples?

The dimples minimize the drag (a force that makes a body lose energy as it moves through a fluid), allowing the ball to travel further than a smooth ball would. The air, as it passes a dimpled ball, tends to cling to the ball longer, reducing the eddies or wake effect that drain the ball's energy. The dimpled ball can travel up to 300 yards

Why does a boomerang return to its thrower?

Two well-known scientific principles dictate the characteristic flight of a boomerang: (1) the force of lift on a curved surface caused by air flowing over it; and (2) the unwillingness of a spinning gyroscope to move from its position.

When a person throws a boomerang properly, he or she causes it to spin vertically. As a result, the boomerang will generate lift, but it will be to one side rather than upwards. As the boomerang spins vertically and moves forward, air flows faster over the top arm at a particular moment than over the bottom arm. Accordingly, the top arm produces more lift than the bottom arm and the boomerang tries to twist itself, but because it is spinning fast, it acts like a gyroscope and turns to the side in an arc. If the boomerang stays in the air long enough, it will turn a full circle and return to the thrower. Every boomerang has a built-in orbit diameter, which is not affected by a person throwing the boomerang harder or spinning it faster.

(275 meters), but a smooth ball only goes 70 yards (65 meters). A ball can have 300 to 500 dimples that can be 0.01 inch (0.25 millimeter) deep. Another effect to get distance is to give the ball a backspin. With a backspin there is less air pressure on the top of the ball, so the ball stays aloft longer (much like an airplane).

What is **Maxwell's demon**?

An imaginary creature who, by opening and shutting a tiny door between two volumes of gases, could, in principle, concentrate slower molecules in one (making it colder) and faster molecules in the other (making it hotter), thus breaking the second law of thermodynamics. Essentially this law states that heat does not naturally flow from a colder body to a hotter body; work must be expended to make it do so. This hypothesis was formulated in 1871 by James C. Maxwell (1831–1879), who is considered to be the greatest theoretical physicist of the 19th century. The demon would bring about an effective flow of molecular kinetic energy. This excess energy would be useful to perform work and the system would be a perpetual motion machine. About 1950, the French physicist Léon Brillouin disproved Maxwell's hypothesis by demonstrating that the decrease in entropy resulting from the demon's actions would be exceeded by the increase in entropy in choosing between the fast and slow molecules.

Who is the founder of the science of **magnetism**?

The English scientist William Gilbert (1544–1603) regarded the Earth as a giant magnet, and investigated its magnetic field terms of dip and variation. He explored many other magnetic and electrostatic phenomena. The Gilbert (symbol Gb), a unit of magnetism, is named for him.

William Gilbert.

John H. Van Vleck (1899–1980), an American physicist, made significant contributions to modern magnetic theory. He explained the magnetic, electrical, and optical properties of many elements and compounds with the ligand field theory, demonstrated the effect of temperature on paramagnetic materials (called Van Vleck paramagnetism), and developed a theory on the magnetic properties of atoms and their components.

When was **spontaneous combustion** first recognized?

Spontaneous combustion is the ignition of materials stored in bulk. This is due to internal heat build-up caused by oxidation (generally a reaction in which electrons are lost, specifically when oxygen is combined with a substance, or when hydrogen is removed from a compound). Because this oxidation heat cannot be dissipated into the surrounding air, the temperature of the material rises until the material reaches its ignition point and bursts into flame.

A Chinese text written before 290 C.E. recognized this phenomenon in a description of the ignition of stored oiled cloth. The first Western recognition of spontaneous combustion was by J. P. F. Duhamel in 1757, when he discussed the gigantic conflagration of a stack of oil-soaked canvas sails drying in the July sun. Before spontaneous combustion was recognized, such events were usually blamed on arsonists.

What is **phlogiston**?

Phlogiston was a name used in the 18th century to identify a supposed substance given off during the process of combustion. The phlogiston theory was developed in the early 1700s by the German chemist and physicist, Georg Ernst Stahl (1660–1734).

In essence, Stahl held that combustible material such as coal or wood was rich in a material substance called "phlogiston." What remained after combustion was without phlogiston and could no longer burn. The rusting of metals also involved a transfer of phlogiston. This accepted theory explained a great deal previously unknown to chemists. For instance, metal smelting was consistent with the phlogiston theory. Charcoal in burning lost weight. Thus the loss of phlogiston either decreased or increased weight.

The French chemist Antoine Laurent Lavoisier (1743–1794) demonstrated that the gain of weight when a metal turned to a calx was just equal to the loss of weight of the air in the vessel. Lavoisier also showed that part of the air (oxygen) was indispensable to combustion, and that no material would burn in the absence of oxygen. The transition from Stahl's phlogiston theory to Lavoisier's oxygen theory marks the birth of modern chemistry at the end of the 18th century.

What is the **kindling point** of paper?

Paper ignites at 450°F (230°C).

What is an **adiabatic process**?

It is any thermodynamic process in which no heat transfer takes place between a system and its surrounding environment.

Does **water running down a drain** rotate in a different direction in the Northern and Southern Hemispheres?

If water runs out from a perfectly symmetrical bathtub, basin, or toilet bowl, in the Northern Hemisphere it would swirl counterclockwise; in the Southern Hemisphere, the water would run out clockwise. This is due to the Coriolis effect (the Earth's rotation influencing any moving body of air or water). However, some scientists think that the effect does not work on small bodies of water. Exactly on the equator, the water would run straight down.

What is a **Leyden jar**?

A Leyden jar, the earliest form of capacitor, is a device for storing an electrical charge. First described in 1745 by E. Georg van Kleist (c.1700–1748), it was also used by Pieter van Musschenbroek (1692–1761), a professor of physics at the University of Leyden. The device came to be known as a Leyden jar and was the first device that could store large amounts of electric charge. The jars contained an inner wire electrode in contact with water, mercury, or wire. The outer electrode was a human hand holding the jar. An improved version coated the jar inside and outside with separate metal foils with the inner foil connected to a conducting rod and terminated in a conducting sphere. This eliminated the need for the liquid electrolyte. In use, the jar was normally charged from an electrostatic generator. The Leyden jar is still used for classroom demonstrations of static electricity.

LIGHT, SOUND, AND OTHER WAVES

What is the **speed of light**?

The figure is 186,282 miles (299,792 kilometers) per second.

What are the **primary colors** in light?

Color is determined by the wavelength of its light (the distance between one crest of the light wave and the next). Those colors that blend to form "white light" are from shortest wave length to longest: red, orange, yellow, green, blue, indigo, and violet. All these monochromatic colors, except indigo, occupy large areas of the spectrum (entire range of wavelengths produced when a beam of electromagnetic radiation is broken up). These colors can be seen when a light beam is refracted through a prism. Some consider the primary colors to be six monochromatic colors that occupy large areas of the spectrum: red, orange, yellow, green, blue, and violet. Many physicists recognize three primary colors: red, yellow, and blue; or red, green, and blue, or red, green, and violet. All other colors can be made from these by adding two primary colors in various proportions. Within the spectrum, scientists have discovered 55 distinct hues. Infra-red and ultraviolet rays at each end of the spectrum are invisible to the human eye.

Why does the color of clothing appear different in sunlight than it does in a store under fluorescent light?

White light is a blend of all the colors, and each color has a different wavelength. Although sunlight and fluorescent light both appear as "white light," they each contain slightly different mixtures of these varying wavelengths. When sunlight and fluorescent light (white light) are absorbed by a piece of clothing, only some of the wavelengths (composing white light) reflect from the clothing. When the retina of the eye perceives the "color" of the clothing, it is really perceiving these reflected wavelengths. The mixture of wavelengths determines the color perceived. This is why an article of clothing sometimes appears to be a different color in the store than it does on the street.

What were **Anders Ångström's** contributions to the development of **spectroscopy**?

Swedish physicist and astronomer Anders Jonas Ångström (1814–1874) was one of the founders of spectroscopy. His early work provided the foundation for spectrum analysis (analysis of the ranges of electromagnetic radiation emitted or absorbed). He investigated the sun spectra as well as that of the Aurora Borealis. In 1868, he established measurements for wavelengths of greater than 100 Frauenhofer. In 1907, the angstrom (Å, equal to 10^{-10}m), a unit of wavelength measurement, was officially adopted.

Why was the **Michelson-Morley** experiment important?

This experiment on light waves, first carried out in 1881 by physicists Albert A. Michelson (1852–1931) and E. W. Morley (1838–1923) in the United States, is one of the historically significant experiments in physics and led to the development of Einsteins's theory of relativity. The original experiment, using the Michelson interferometer, attempted to detect the velocity of the Earth with respect to the hypothetical "luminiferous ether," a medium in space proposed to carry light waves. The procedure measured the speed of light in the direction of the Earth and the speed of light at right angles to the Earth's motion. No difference was found. This result discredited the ether theory and ultimately led to the proposal by Albert Einstein (1879–1955) that the speed of light is a universal constant.

Why does a **double sonic boom** occur when the space shuttle enters the atmosphere?

As long as an airborne object, such as a plane, is moving below the speed of sound (called Mach 1), the disturbed air remains well in front of the craft. But as the craft passes Mach 1 and is flying at supersonic speeds, a sharp air pressure rise occurs in front of the craft. In a sense the air molecules are crowded together and collectively impact. What is heard is a claplike thunder called a sonic boom or a supersonic bang. There are many shocks coming from a supersonic aircraft but these shocks usually combine to form two main shocks, one coming from the nose and one from the aft end of the aircraft. Each of the shocks moves at different velocities. If the time difference between the two shock waves is greater than 0.10 seconds apart, two sonic booms will be heard. This usually occurs when the aircraft ascends quickly. If the aircraft ascends more slowly, the two booms will sound like only one boom to the observer.

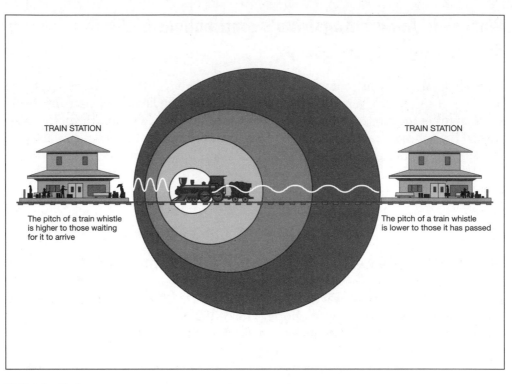

TRAIN STATION

The pitch of a train whistle is higher to those waiting for it to arrive

TRAIN STATION

The pitch of a train whistle is lower to those it has passed

The Doppler effect.

What causes the sounds that are heard in a **seashell**?

When a seashell is held to an an ear, the sounds heard are ambient, soft sounds that have been resonated and thereby amplified by the seashell's cavity. The extreme sensitivity of the human ear to sound is illustrated by the seashell resonance effect.

What is the **Doppler effect**?

The Austrian physicist, Christian Doppler (1803–1853) in 1842 explained the phenomenon of the apparent change in wavelength of radiation—such as sound or light—emitted either by a moving body (source) or by the moving receiver. The frequency of the wave-lengths increases and the wavelength becomes shorter as the moving source approaches, producing high-pitched sounds and bluish light (called blue shift). Likewise as the source recedes from the receiver the frequency of the wavelengths decreases, the sound is pitched lower and light appears reddish (called red shift). This Doppler effect is commonly demonstrated by the whistle of an approaching train or jet aircraft.

There are three differences between acoustical (sound) and optical (light) Doppler effects: The optical frequency change is not dependent on which is moving—

the source or observer—nor is it affected by the medium through which the waves are moving, but acoustical frequency is affected by such conditions. Optical frequency changes are affected if the source or observer moves at right angles to the line connecting the source and observer. Observed acoustical changes are not affected in such a situation. Applications of the Doppler phenomenon include the Doppler radar and the measurement by astronomers of the motion and direction of celestial bodies.

What is a **decibel**?

A decibel is a measure of the relative loudness or intensity of sound. A 20 decibel sound is 10 times louder than a 10 decibel sound; 30 decibels is 100 times louder, etc. One decibel is the smallest difference between sounds detectable by the human ear.

Decibel Level	Equivalent
10	Light whisper
20	Quiet conversation
30	Normal conversation
40	Light traffic
50	Typewriter, Loud conversation
60	Noisy office
70	Normal traffic, Quiet train
80	Rock music, Subway
90	Heavy traffic, Thunder
100	Jet plane at takeoff

What is the sound frequency of the **musical scale**?

EQUAL TEMPERED SCALE

Note	Frequency	Note	Frequency
C♭	261.63	G	392.00
C#	277.18	G#	415.31
D	293.67	A	440.00
D#	311.13	A#	466.16
E	329.63	B	493.88
F	349.23	C n	523.25
F#	369.99		

Notes: ♭ indicates flat; # indicates sharp; n indicates return to natural.

The lowest frequency distinguishable as a note is about 20 hertz. The highest audible frequency is about 20,000 hertz. A hertz (symbol Hz) is a unit of frequency that measures the number of the wave cycles per second frequency of a periodic phenomenon whose periodic time is one second (cycles per second).

What is the **speed of sound**?

The speed of sound is not a constant; it varies depending on the medium in which it travels. The measurement of sound velocity in the medium of air must take into account many factors, including air temperature, pressure, and purity. At sea level and 32°F (0°C), scientists do not agree on a standard figure; estimates range from 740 to 741.5 miles (1191.6 to 1193.22 kilometers) per hour. As air temperature rises, sound velocity increases. Sound travels faster in water than in air and even faster in iron and steel. Sounds traveling a mile in air for five seconds, will travel the same distance in one second underwater and travel one-third of a second in steel.

What are the characteristics of **alpha, beta, and gamma radiation**?

Radiation is a term that describes all the ways energy is emitted by the atom as x-rays, gamma rays, neutrons, or as charged particles. Most atoms, being stable, are nonradioactive; but some are unstable and give off either particles or gamma radiation. Substances bombarded by radioactive particles can become radioactive and yield alpha particles, beta particles, and gamma rays.

> *Alpha particles*, first identified by Antoine Henri Becquerel (1852–1908), have a positive electrical charge and consist of two protons and two neutrons. Because of their great mass, alpha particles can travel only a short distance, around two inches (five centimeters) in air, and can be stopped by a sheet of paper.

> *Beta particles*, identified by Ernest Rutherford (1871–1937), are extremely high-speed electrons or protons that move at the speed of light. They can travel far in air and can pass through solid matter several millimeters thick.

> *Gamma rays*, identified by Marie (1867–1934) and Pierre Curie (1859–1906), are similar to x-rays, but usually have a shorter wave length. These rays, which are bursts of protons, or very short-wave electromagnetic radiation, travel at the speed of light. They are much more penetrating than either the alpha or beta particles and can go through seven inches (18 centimeters) of lead.

MATTER

What is the **fourth state of matter**?

Plasma, a mixture of free electrons and ions or atomic nuclei, is sometimes referred to as a "fourth state of matter." Plasmas occur in thermonuclear reactions as in the sun, in fluorescent lights, and in stars. When gas temperature is raised high enough the collision of atoms become so violent that electrons are knocked loose from their nuclei. The result of a gas having loose, negatively charged electrons and heavier, positively charged nuclei is called a plasma.

All matter is made up of atoms. Animals and plants are organic matter; minerals and water are inorganic matter. Whether matter appears as a solid, liquid, or gas depends on how the molecules are held together in their chemical bonds. Solids have a rigid structure in the atoms of the molecules; in liquids the molecules are close together but not packed; in a gas, the molecules are widely spaced and move around, occasionally colliding but usually not interacting. These states—solid, liquid, and gas—are the first three states of matter.

Who is generally regarded as the discoverer of the electron, the proton, and the neutron?

The British physicist, Sir Joseph John Thomson (1856–1940), in 1897 researched electrical conduction in gases, which led to the important discovery that cathode rays consisted of negatively charged particles called electrons. The discovery of the electron inaugurated the electrical theory of the atom, and this with other work entitled Thomson to be regarded as the founder of modern atomic physics.

Ernest Rutherford (1871–1937) discovered the proton in 1919. He also predicted the existence of the neutron, later discovered by his colleague, James Chadwick (1891–1974). Chadwick was awarded the 1935 Nobel Prize for physics for this discovery.

How did the quark get its name?

This theoretical particle, considered to be the fundamental unit of matter, was named by Murray Gell-Mann (b. 1929) an American theoretical physicist and Nobel Prize winner. Its name was initially a playful tag that Gell-Mann invented, sounding something like "kwork." Later Gell-Mann came across the line "Three quarks for Master Marks" in James Joyce's *Finnegan's Wake*, and the tag became known as a quark. There are six kinds or

Murray Gell-Mann.

11

"flavors" (up, down, strange, charm, bottom, and top) of quarks, and each "flavor" has three varieties or "colors" (red, blue, and green). All eighteen types have different electric charges (a basic characteristic of all elementary particles). Three quarks form a proton (having one unit of positive electric charge) or a neutron (zero charge), and two quarks (a quark and an antiquark) form a meson. Like all known particles, a quark has its anti-matter opposite, known as an antiquark (having the same mass but opposite charge).

What are the **subatomic particles**?

Subatomic particles are particles that are smaller than atoms. Historically, subatomic particles were considered to be electrons, protons, and neutrons. However, the difinition of subatomic particles has now been expanded to include elementary particles, which are the particles so small that they do not appear to be made of more minute units. The physical study of such particles became possible only during the twentieth century with the development of increasingly sophisticated apparatus. Many new particles have been discovered in the last half of the twentieth century.

A number of proposals have been made to organize the particles by their spin, their mass, or their common properties. One system is now commonly known as the Standard Model. This system recognizes two basic types of fundamental particles: quarks and leptons. Other force-carrying particles are called bosons. Photons, gluons, and weakons are bosons. Leptons include electrons, muons, taus, and three kinds of neutrinos. Quarks never occur alone in nature. They always combine to form particles called hadrons. According to the Standard Model, all other subatomic particles consist of some combination of quarks and their antiparticles. A proton, for example, is thought to consist of two up quarks and their antiparticles.

What are **colligative properties**?

Colligative properties are properties of solutions that depend on the number of particles present in the solution and not on characteristics of the particles themselves. Colligative properties include depression of freezing point and elevation of boiling point. For living systems, perhaps the most important colligative property is osmotic pressure.

What substance, other than water, is **less dense as a solid** than as a liquid?

Only bismuth and water share this characteristic. Density (the mass per unit volume or mass/volume) refers to how compact or crowded a substance is. For instance, the density of water is 1 g/cm³ (gram per cubic centimeter) or 1 kg/l (kilogram per liter);

the density of a rock is 3.3 g/cm³; pure iron is 7.9 gs/cm³; and the Earth (as a whole) is 5.5 g/cm³ (average). Water as a solid (i.e., ice) floats; which is a good thing, otherwise ice would sink to the bottom of every lake or stream.

Why is **liquid water** more dense than ice?

Pure liquid water is most dense at 39.2°F (3.98°C) and decreases in density as it freezes. The water molecules in ice are held in a relatively rigid geometric pattern by their hydrogen bonds, producing an open, porous structure. Liquid water has fewer bonds; therefore, more molecules can occupy the same space, making liquid water more dense than ice.

What does **half-life** mean?

Half-life is the time it takes for the number of radioactive nuclei originally present in a sample to decrease to one half of their original number. Thus, if a sample has a half-life of one year, its radioactivity will be reduced to half its original amount at the end of a year and to one quarter at the end of two years. The half-life of a particular radionuclide is always the same, independent of temperature, chemical combination, or any other condition.

Natural radiation was discovered in 1896 by the French physicist Henri Becquerel. His discovery initiated the science of nuclear physics.

Who made the **first organic compound to be synthesized** from inorganic ingredients?

In 1828, Friedrich Wöhler (1800–1882) synthesized urea from ammonia and cyanic acid. This synthesis dealt a deathblow to the vital-force theory, which held that definite and fundamental differences existed between organic and inorganic compounds. The Swedish chemist Johan Jakob Berzelius (1779–1848) proposed that the two classes of compounds were produced from their elements by entirely different laws. Organic compounds were produced under the influence of a vital force and so were incapable of being prepared artificially. This distinction ended with Wöhler's synthesis.

Who is known as the founder of **crystallography**?

The French priest and mineralogist, René-Just Haüy (1743–1822), is called the father of crystallography. In 1781 Haüy had a fortunate accident when he dropped a piece of calcite and it broke into small fragments. He noticed that the fragments broke along straight planes that met at constant angles. He hypothesized that each crystal was

What is a chemical garden and how is one made?

Mix 4 tablespoons of bluing, 4 tablespoons of salt, and 1 tablespoon household ammonia. Pour this mixture over pieces of coal or brick in a suitable dish or bowl. Put several drops of red or green ink or mercurochrome on various parts of the coal and leave undisturbed for several days.

A crystal garden—a dishful of crystals that grow like plants and look like coral—will begin to appear. How soon the crystals will begin to appear depends on the temperatures and humidity in the room. Before long, crystals will be growing all over the briquettes, on the side of the dish, and down onto the plate. The crystals will be pure white with a snow-like texture.

built up of successive additions of what is now called a unit cell to form a simple geometric shape with constant angles. An identity or difference in crystalline form implied an identity or difference in chemical composition. This was the beginning of the science of crystallography.

By the early 1800s many physicists were experimenting with crystals; in particular, they were fascinated by their ability to bend light and separate it into its component colors. An important member of the emerging field of optical mineralogy was the British scientist David Brewster, who succeeded in classifying most known crystals according to their optical properties.

The work of French chemist Louis Pasteur during the mid 1800s became the foundation for crystal polarimetry—a method by which light is polarized, or aligned to a single plane. Pierre Curie and his brother Jacques discovered another phenomenon displayed by certain crystals called piezoelectricity. It is the creation of an electrical potential by squeezing certain crystals.

Perhaps the most important application of crystals is in the science of x-ray crystallography. Experiments in this field were first conducted by the German physicist Max von Laue. This work was perfected by William Henry Bragg (1862–1942) and William Lawrence Bragg (1890–1971) who were awarded the Nobel Prize in physics for their work. The synthesis of penicillin and insulin were made possible by the use of x-ray crystallography.

CHEMICAL ELEMENTS, ETC.

See also: Metals and Other Materials

Who are some of the **founders of modern chemistry**?

Several contenders share this honor:

Swedish chemist Jöns Jakob Berzelius (1779–1848) devised chemical symbols, determined atomic weights, contributed to the atomic theory, and discovered several new elements. Between 1810 and 1816, he described the preparation, purification, and analysis of 2,000 chemical compounds. Then he determined atomic weights for 40 elements. He simplified chemical symbols, introducing a notation (still used today)—letters with numbers—that replaced the pictorial symbols his predecessors used. He discovered cerium (in 1803, with Wilhelm Hisinger), selenium (1818), silicon (1824), and thorium (1829).

Robert Boyle (1627–1691), a British natural philosopher, is considered one of the founders of modern chemistry. Best known for his discovery of Boyle's Law (volume of a gas is inversely proportional to its pressure at constant temperature), he was a pioneer in the use of experiments and the scientific method. A founder of the Royal Society, he worked to remove the mystique of alchemy from chemistry to make it a pure science.

The French chemist Antoine-Laurent Lavoisier (1743–1794) is regarded as another founder of modern chemistry. His wide-ranging contributions include the discrediting of the phlogiston theory of combustion, which had been for so long a stumbling block to a true understanding of chemistry. He established modern terminology for chemical substances and did the first experiments in quantitative organic analysis. He is sometimes credited with having discovered or established the law of conservation of mass in chemical reactions.

John Dalton (1766–1844), an English chemist, proposed an atomic theory of matter that became a basic theory of modern chemistry. His theory, first proposed in 1803, states that each chemical element is composed of its own kind of atoms, all with the same relative weight.

Who developed the **periodic table**?

Dmitri Ivanovich Mendeleyev (1834–1907) was a Russian chemist whose name will always be linked with his outstanding achievement, the development of the periodic table. He was the first chemist really to understand that all elements are related members of a single ordered system. He changed what had been a highly fragmented and speculative branch of chemistry into a true, logical science. His nomination for the 1906 Nobel Prize for chemistry failed by one vote, but his name became recorded in perpetuity 50 years later when element 101 was called mendelevium.

According to Mendeleyev, the properties of the elements, as well as those of their compounds, are periodic functions of their atomic weights (in the 1920s, it was discovered that atomic number was the key rather than weight). Mendeleyev compiled the first true periodic table listing all the 63 (then-known) elements. In order to make the table work, Mendeleyev had to leave gaps, and he predicted that further elements would eventually be discovered to fill them. Three were discovered in Mendeleyev's lifetime: gallium, scandium, and germanium.

Dimitri Mendeleyev.

There are 94 naturally occurring elements; of the 15 remaining elements (elements 95 to 109), 10 are undisputed. By 1984, over 6.8 million chemical compounds had been produced from these elements; 65 thousand of them in common use.

What are the **alkali metals**?

These are the elements at the left of the periodic table: lithium (Li, element 3), potassium (K, element 19), rubidium (Rb, element 37), cesium (Cs, element 55), francium (Fr, element 87), and sodium (Na, element 11). The alkali metals are sometimes called the sodium family of elements, or Group I elements. Because of their great chemical reactivity (easily form positive ions), none exist in nature in the elemental state.

What are the **alkaline Earth metals**?

These are beryllium (Be, element 4), magnesium (Mg, element 12), calcium (Ca, element 20), strontium (Sr, element 38), barium (Ba, element 56), and radium (Ra, element 88). The alkaline Earth metals are also called Group II elements. Like the alkali metals, they are never found as free elements in nature and are moderately reactive metals. Harder and less volatile than the alkali metals, these elements all burn in air.

What are the **transition elements**?

The transition elements are the 10 subgroups of elements between Group II and Group XIII, starting with period 4. They include gold (Au, element 79), silver (Ag, element 47), platinum (Pt, element 78), iron (Fe, element 26), copper (Cu, element 29), and other metals. All transition elements are metals. Compared to alkali and alkaline Earth met-

The periodic table.

als, they are usually harder and more brittle and have higher melting points. Transition metals are also good conductors of heat and electricity. They have variable valences, and compounds of transition elements are often colored. Transition elements are so named because they comprise a gradual shift from the strongly electropositive elements of Groups I and II to the electronegative elements of Groups VI and VII.

What are the **transuranic chemical elements** and the currently proposed names for elements 102–109?

Transuranium elements are those elements in the periodic system with atomic numbers greater than 92. The names for elements 102–109 have been under review by the International Union of Pure & Applied Chemistry (IUPAC).

Elements 93–103

Element Number	Name	Symbol
93	Neptunium	Np
94	Plutonium	Pu

Element Number	Name	Symbol
95	Americum	Am
96	Curium	Cm
97	Berkelium	Bk
98	Californium	Cf
99	Einsteinium	Es
100	Fermium	Fm
101	Mendelevium	Md

Elements 102–109

Element Number	Proposed Names (by discovery group)	IUPAC name	Symbol
102	Nobelium (Swedish) Joliotium (Russian)	Nobelium	No
103	Lawrencium (American)	Lawrencium	Lr
104	Rutherfordium (American) Kurchatovium (Russian)	Dubnium	Db
105	Hahnium (American) Nielsbohrium (Russian)	Joliotium	Jl
106	Seaborgium (American)	Rutherfordium	Rf
107	Nielsborium (German)	Bohrium	Bh
108	Hassium (German)	Hahnium	Hn
109	Meitnerium (German)	Meitnerium	Mt

Which elements are the "noble metals"?

The noble metals are gold (Au, element 79), silver (Ag, element 47), mercury (Hg, element 80), and the platinum group, which includes platinum (Pt, element 78), palladium (Pd, element 46), iridium (Ir, element 77), rhodium (Rh, element 45), ruthenium (Ru, element 44), and osmium (Os, element 76). The term refers to those metals highly resistant to chemical reaction or oxidation (resistant to corrosion) and is contrasted to "base" metals, which are not so resistant. The term has its origins in ancient alchemy whose goals of transformation and perfection were pursued through the different properties of metals and chemicals. The term is not synonymous with "precious metals," although a metal, like platinum, may be both.

The platinum group metals have a variety of uses. In the United States more than 95% of all platinum group metals are used for industrial purposes. While platinum is a coveted material for jewelry making, it is also used in the catalytic converters of automobiles to control exhaust emissions, as are rhodium and palladium. Rhodium can also be alloyed with platinum and palladium for use in furnace windings, thermocouple elements and in aircraft spark-plug electrodes. Osmium is used in the manufacture of pharmaceuticals and in alloys for instrument pivots and long-life phonograph needles.

What is a philosopher's stone?

A philosopher's stone was the name of a substance believed by medieval alchemists to have the power to change baser metals into gold or silver. It had, according to some, the power of prolonging life and of curing all injuries and diseases. The pursuit of it by alchemists led to the discovery of several chemical substances; however, the magical philosopher's stone has since proved fictitious.

What are some chemical elements whose **symbols** are not derived from their English names?

Modern Name	Symbol	Older Name
antimony	Sb	stibium
copper	Cu	cuprum
gold	Au	aurum
iron	Fe	ferrum
lead	Pb	plumbum
mercury	Hg	hydrargyrum
potassium	K	kalium
silver	Ag	argentum
sodium	Na	natrium
tin	Sn	stannum
tungsten	W	wolfram

Which elements are **liquid at room temperature**?

Mercury ("liquid silver," Hg, element 80) and bromine (Br, element 35) are liquid at room temperature 68° to 70°F (20° to 25°C). Gallium (Ga, element 31) with a melting point of 85.6°F (29.8°C) and cesium (Cs, element 55) with a melting point of 83°F (28.4°C), are liquids at slightly above room temperature.

What is **Harkin's rule**?

Atoms having even atomic numbers are more abundant in the universe than are atoms having odd atomic numbers. Chemical properties of an element are determined by its atomic number, which is the number of protons in the atom's nucleus.

Which chemical element is the **most abundant in the universe**?

Hydrogen (H, element 1) makes up about 75% of the mass of the universe. It is estimated that more than 90% of all atoms in the universe are hydrogen atoms. Most of the rest are helium (He, element 2) atoms.

Which chemical elements are the **most abundant on Earth**?

Oxygen (O, element 8) is the most abundant element in the Earth's crust, waters, and atmosphere. It composes 49.5% of the total mass of these compounds. Silicon (Si, element 14) is the second most abundant element. Silicon dioxide and silicates make up about 87% of the materials in the Earth's crust.

Why are the **rare gases** and **rare Earth elements** called "rare"?

Rare gases refers to the elements helium, neon, argon, krypton, and xenon. They are rare in that they are gases of very low density ("rarified") at ordinary temperatures and are found only scattered in minute quantities in the atmosphere and in some substances. In addition, rare gases have zero valence and normally will not combine with other elements to make compounds.

Rare Earth elements are elements numbered 58 through 71 in the periodic table plus yttrium (Y, element 39) and thorium (Th, element 90). They are called "rare Earths" because they are difficult to extract from monazite ore, where they occur. The term has nothing to do with scarcity or rarity in nature.

Which elements have the **most isotopes**?

The elements with the most isotopes, with 36 each, are xenon (Xe) with nine stable isotopes (identified from 1920 to 1922) and 27 radioactive isotopes (identified from 1939 to 1981), and cesium (Cs) with one stable isotope (identified in 1921) and 35 radioactive isotopes (identified from 1935 to 1983).

The element with the least number of isotopes is hydrogen (H), with three isotopes, including two stable ones—protium (identified in 1920) and deuterium (identified in 1931)—and one radioactive isotope—tritium (first identified in 1934, but later considered a radioactive isotope in 1939).

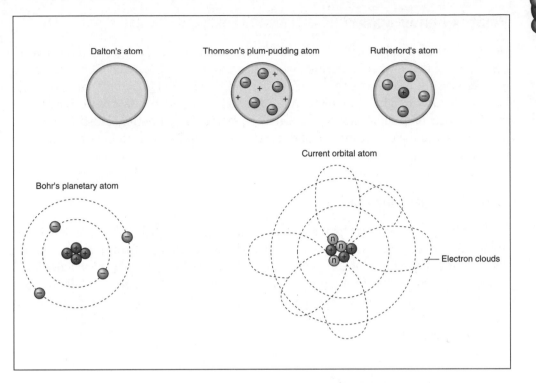

Hydrogen isotopes.

Which element has the **highest density**?

Either osmium or iridium is the element with the highest density; however, scientists have yet to gather enough conclusive data to choose between the two. When traditional methods of measurement are employed, osmium generally appears to be the densest element. Yet, when calculations are made based upon the space lattice, which may be a more reliable method given the nature of these elements, the density of iridium is 22.65 compared to 22.61 for osmium.

What is the **density of air**?

The density of dry air is 1.29 grams per liter at 32°F (0°C) at average sea level and a barometric pressure of 29.92 inches of mercury (760 millimeters).

The weight of one cubic foot of dry air at one atmosphere of barometric pressure is:

Temperature (Fahrenheit)	Weight per cubic foot (pounds)
50°	0.07788
60°	0.07640
70°	0.07495

What is **heavy water**?

Heavy water, also called deuterium oxide (D_2O), is composed of oxygen and two hydrogen atoms in the form of deuterium, which has about twice the mass of normal hydrogen. As a result, heavy water has a molecular weight of about 20, while ordinary water has a molecular weight of about 18. Approximately one part heavy water can be found in 6,500 parts of ordinary water, and it may be extracted by fractional distillation. It is used in thermonuclear weapons and nuclear reactors and as an isotopic tracer in studies of chemical and biochemical processes.

What is a **Lewis acid**?

Named after the American chemist Gilbert Newton Lewis (1875–1946), the Lewis theory defines an *acid* as a species that can accept an electron pair from another atom, and a *base* as a species that can donate an electron pair to complete the valence shell of another atom. Hydrogen ion (proton) is the simplest substance that will do this, but Lewis acids include many compounds—such as boron trifluoride (BF_3) and aluminum chloride ($AlCl_3$)—that can react with ammonia, for example, to form an addition compound or Lewis salt.

What are the **gas laws**?

The gas laws are physical laws concerning the behavior of gases. They include *Boyle's law,* which states that the volume of a given mass of gas at a constant temperature is inversely proportional to its pressure; and *Charles's law,* which states that the volume of a given mass of gas at constant pressure is directly proportional to its absolute temperature. These two laws can be combined to give the *General* or *Universal gas law,* which may be expressed as:

$$\frac{(\text{pressure} \times \text{volume})}{\text{temperature}} = \text{constant}$$

Avogardro's law states that equal volumes of all gases contain the same number of particles if they all have the same pressure and temperature.

The laws are not obeyed exactly by any real gas, but many common gases obey them under certain conditions, particularly at high temperatures and low pressures.

Which chemical is **used in greater quantities** than any other?

Sodium chloride (NaCl), or salt, has over 14,000 uses, and is probably used in greater quantities and for more applications than any other chemical.

Which chemicals are used today as **embalming fluids**?

During the 19th century embalming became a common practice in the United States, and generally salts of heavy metals such as arsenic, antimony, lead, mercury, and copper were used to preserve the corpse and inhibit bacterial growth. By the early 1900s, however, laws were passed prohibiting the use of metal salts in embalming. Formaldehyde soon became the compound of choice and continues to be the most common preservative in embalming fluids. Its continued popularity is due to low cost, availability in usable form, and simplicity of use. It also provides good cell preservation under a variety of pH conditions. Generally, a mortician, after draining the corpse of bodily fluids, injects it with a solution of formaldehyde in water. Various buffers are also present in the solution to counteract the formation of "formaldehyde pigments" on the body. Concerns over the possible carcinogenic effects of formaldehyde, as well as its tendancy to turn a corpse's skin an ashen grey, have instigated numerous attempts at finding a replacement. Glutaraldehyde was first used in 1955, but in spite of some distinct advantages, formaldehyde is still the embalming fluid of choice.

MEASUREMENT, METHODOLOGY, ETC.

What were some of the leading contributions of **Albert Einstein**?

Albert Einstein (1879–1955) was the principal founder of modern theoretical physics; his theory of relativity (speed of light is a constant and not relative to the observer or source of light), and the relationship of mass and energy ($e=mc^2$), fundamentally changed human understanding of the physical world.

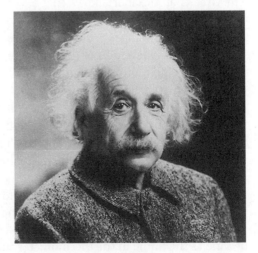

During a single year in 1905, he produced three landmark papers. These papers dealt with the nature of particle movement known as Brownian motion, the quantum nature of electromagnetic radiation as demonstrated by the photoelectric effect, and the special theory of relativity. Although Einstein is probably best known for the last of these works, it was for his quantum explanation of the photoelectric effect that he was awarded the 1921 Nobel Prize in physics. His stature as a scientist, together with his strong humanitarian stance on major

Albert Einstein.

political and social issues, made him one of the outstanding men of the twentieth century.

Who is generally regarded as the founder of quantum mechanics?

The German mathematical physicist, Werner Karl Heisenberg (1901–1976), is regarded as the father of quantum mechanics (theory of small-scale physical phenomena). His theory of uncertainty in 1927 overturned traditional classical mechanics and electromagnetic theory regarding energy and motions when applied to subatomic particles such as electrons and parts of atomic nuclei. The theory states that it is impossible to specify precisely both the position and the simultaneous momentum (mass × volume) of a particle, but they could only be predicted. This meant that a result of an action can only be expressed in terms of probability that a certain effect will occur, not certainty.

Werner Karl Heisenberg.

Who invented the thermometer?

The Greeks of Alexandria knew that air expanded as it was heated, and it is known that Hero of Alexandria (first century C.E.) and Philo of Byzantium made simple thermometers or "thermoscopes," but they were not real thermometers. In 1592, Galileo (1564–1642) made a kind of thermometer that also functioned as a barometer, but in 1612, his friend Santorio Santorio (1561–1636) first adapted the air thermometer (a device in which a colored liquid was driven down by the expansion of air) to measure the body's temperature change during illness and recovery. Still, it was not until 1713 that Daniel Fahrenheit (1686–1736) began developing a thermometer having a fixed scale. He worked out his scale from two "fixed" points: the melting point of ice and the heat of the healthy human body. He realized that the melting point of ice was a constant temperature, whereas the freezing point of water varied. Fahrenheit put his thermometer into a mixture of ice, water, and salt (which he marked off as 0°) and using this as a starting point, marked off melting ice at 32° and blood heat at 96°. In 1835, it was discovered that normal blood measured 98.6°F. Sometimes, Fahrenheit used spirit of wine as the liquid in the thermometer tube, but more often he used specially purified mercury. Later, the boiling point of water (212°F) became the upper fixed point.

What is the **Kelvin** temperature scale?

Temperature is the level of heat in a gas, liquid, or solid. The freezing and boiling points of water are used as standard reference levels in both the metric (centigrade or Celsius) and the English system (Fahrenheit). In the metric system, the difference between freezing and boiling is divided into 100 equal intervals called degree Celsius or degree centigrade (°C). In the English system, the intervals are divided into 180 units, with one unit called degree Fahrenheit (°F). But temperature can be measured from absolute zero (no heat, no motion); this principle defines thermodynamic temperature and establishes a method to measure it upward. This scale of temperature is called the Kelvin temperature scale, after its inventor, William Thomson, Lord Kelvin (1824–1907), who devised it in 1848. The Kelvin (symbol K) has the same magnitude as the degree Celsius (the difference between freezing and boiling water is 100 degrees), but the two temperatures differ by 273.15 degrees (absolute zero, which is -273.15°C on the Celsius scale). Below is a comparison of the three temperatures:

Characteristic	K°	C°	F°
Absolute zero	0	-273.15	-459.67
Freezing point of water	273.15	0	32
Normal human body temperature	310.15	37	98.6
Boiling point of water	373.15	100	212

To convert Celsius to Kelvin: Add 273.15 to the temperature($K = C + 273.15$). To convert Fahrenheit to Celsius: Subtract 32 from the temperature and multiply the difference by 5; then divide the product by 9 ($C = 5/9[F - 32]$). To convert Celsius to Fahrenheit: Multiply the temperature by 1.8, then add 32 ($F = 9/5C + 32$ or $F = 1.8C + 32$).

What was unusual about the original **Celsius** temperature scale?

In 1742, the Swedish astronomer Anders Celsius (1701–1744) set the freezing point of water at 100°C and the boiling point of water at 0°C. It was Carolus Linnaeus (1707–1778), who reversed the scale, but a later textbook attributed the modified scale to Celsius and the name has remained.

How are **Celsius** temperatures **converted into** **Fahrenheit** temperatures?

The formulas for converting Celsius or Centigrade temperatures into Fahrenheit (and the reverse) are as follows:

$$F = (C \times 9/5) + 32$$
$$C = (F - 32) \times 5/9$$

Some useful comparisons of the two scales:

Temperature	Fahrenheit	Celsius or Centigrade
Absolute zero	-459.67	-273.15
Point of equality	-40.0	-40.0
Zero fahrenheit	0.0	-17.8
Freezing point of water	32.0	0.0
Normal human blood temperature	98.4	36.9
100 degrees F	100.0	37.8
Boiling point of water (at standard pressure)	212.0	100.0

What is STP?

The abbreviation STP is often used for *s*tandard *t*emperature and *p*ressure. As a matter of convenience, scientists have chosen a specific temperature and pressure as standards for comparing gas volumes. The standard temperature is 0°C (273°K) and the standard pressure is 760 torr (one atmosphere).

How did the electrical term ampere originate?

It was named for André Marie Ampère (1775–1836), the physicist who formulated the basic laws of the science of electrodynamics. The *ampere* (symbol A), often abbreviated as "amp," is the unit of electric current, defined at the constant current, that, maintained in two straight parallel infinite conductors placed one meter apart in a vacuum, would produce a force between the conductors of 2×10^{-7} newton per meter. For example, the amount of current flowing through a 100-watt light bulb is 1 amp; through a toaster, 10 amps; a TV set, 3 amps; a car battery, 50 amps (while cranking). A newton (symbol N) is defined as a unit of force needed to accelerate one kilogram by one meter second^{-2}, or $1N = 1Kg^{MS-2}$.

How did the electrical unit volt originate?

The unit of voltage is the volt, named after Alessandro Volta (1745–1827), the Italian scientist who built the first modern battery. (A battery, operating with a lead rod and vinegar, was also manufactured in Egypt several thousand years ago.) Voltage measures the force or "oomph" with which electrical charges are pushed through a material. Some common voltages are 1.5 volts for a flashlight battery; 12 volts for a car battery; 115 volts for ordinary household receptacles and 230 volts for a heavy-duty household receptacle.

How did the electrical unit **watt** originate?

Named for the Scottish engineer and inventor James Watt (1736–1819), the watt is used to measure electric power. An electric device uses one watt when one volt of electric current drives one ampere of current through it.

What is a **mole** in chemistry?

A mole (symbol Mol), a fundamental measuring unit for the amount of a substance, refers to either a gram atomic weight or a gram molecular weight of a substance. It is the quantity of a substance that contains 6.02×10^{23} atoms, molecules, or formula units of that substance. This number is called Avogadro's number or constant after Amedeo Avogadro (1776–1856) who is considered to be one of the founders of physical science.

What is **Mole Day**?

Mole Day was organized by the National Mole Day Foundation to promote an awareness and enthusiasm for chemistry. It is celebrated each year on October 23rd.

How does **gram atomic weight** differ from **gram formula weight**?

Gram atomic weight is the amount of an *element* (substance made up of atoms having the same atomic number) equal to its atomic weight (the number of protons) in grams. Gram formula weight is an amount of a *compound* (a combination of elements) equal to its formula weight in grams.

SPACE

UNIVERSE

What was the **Big Bang**?

The Big Bang theory is the explanation most commonly accepted by astronomers for the origin of the universe. It proposes that the universe began as the result of an explosion—the Big Bang—15 to 20 billion years ago. Two observations form the basis of this cosmology. First, as Edwin Hubble (1889–1953) demonstrated, the universe is expanding uniformly, with objects at greater distances receding at greater velocities. Secondly, the Earth is bathed in a glow of radiation that has the characteristics expected from a remnant of a hot primeval fireball. This radiation was discovered by Arno A. Penzias (b. 1933) and Robert W. Wilson (b. 1936) of Bell Telephone Laboratories. In time, the matter created by the Big Bang came together in huge clumps to form the galaxies. Smaller clumps within the galaxies formed stars. Parts of at least one clump became a group of planets—our solar system.

How **old** is the **universe**?

Recent data collected by the Hubble Space Telescope suggests that the universe may only be eight billion years old. This contradicts the previous belief the universe was somewhere between 15 billion and 20 billion years old. The earlier figure was derived from the concept that the universe has been expanding at the same rate since its birth at the Big Bang. The rate of expansion is a ratio known as Hubble's constant. It is calculated by dividing the speed at which the galaxy is moving away from the Earth by its distance from the Earth. By inverting Hubble's Constant, that is, dividing the distance of a galaxy by its recessional speed, the age of the universe can be calculated. The estimates of both the velocity and distance of galaxies from the Earth are subject to uncertainties and not all scientists accept that the universe has always expanded at the same rate. Therefore, many still hold that the age of the universe is open to question.

Who is **Stephen Hawking**?

Hawking (b. 1943), a British physicist and mathematician, is considered to be the greatest theoretical physicist of the late 20th century. In spite of being severely handicapped by amyotrophic lateral sclerosis (ALS), he has made major contributions to scientific knowledge about black holes and the origin and evolution of the universe though his research into the nature of space-time and its anomalies. For instance, Hawking proposed that a black hole could emit thermal radiation and predicted that a black hole would disappear after all its mass has been converted into radiation (called "Hawking's radiation"). A current objective of Hawking is to synthesize quantum mechanics and relativity theory into a theory of quantum gravity. He is also the author of several books, including the popular best-selling work *A Brief History of Time*.

What are **quasars**?

The name quasar is short for *quasi-stellar radio source*. Quasars appear to be stars, but they have large red shifts in their spectra indicating that they are receding from the Earth at great speeds, some at up to 90% of the speed of light. Their exact nature is still unknown, but many believe quasars to be the cores of distant galaxies, the most distant objects yet seen. Quasars were first identified in 1963 by astronomers at the Palomar Observatory in California.

What is a **syzygy**?

A syzygy is a configuration that occurs when three celestial bodies lie in a straight line, such as the sun, Earth, and moon during a solar or lunar eclipse. The particular syzygy when a planet is on the opposite side of the Earth from the sun is called an opposition.

Which **galaxy** is closest to us?

The Andromeda Galaxy is the galaxy closest to the Milky Way galaxy, where Earth is located. It is estimated to be 2.2 million light years away from Earth. Bigger than the Milky Way, Andromeda is a spiral-shaped galaxy that is also the brightest in Earth's sky.

STARS

What is a **binary star**?

A binary star is a pair of stars revolving around a common center of gravity. About half of all stars are members of either binary star systems or multiple star systems, which contain more than two stars.

The bright star Sirius, about 8.6 light years away, is composed of two stars, one about 2.3 times the mass of the sun, the other a white dwarf star about 980 times the mass of Jupiter. Alpha Centauri, the nearest star to Earth after the sun, is actually three stars: Alpha Centauri A and Alpha Centauri B, two sunlike stars, orbit each other, and Alpha Centauri C, a low mass red star, orbits around them.

What is a black hole?

When a star with a mass greater than about four times that of the sun collapses even the neutrons cannot stop the force of gravity. There is nothing to stop the contraction and the star collapses forever. The material is so dense that nothing—not even light—can escape. The American physicist John Wheeler, in 1967, gave this phenomenon the name "black hole." Since no light escapes from a black hole, it cannot be observed directly. However, if a black hole existed near another star, it would draw matter from the other star into itself and, in effect, produce x-rays. In the constellation of Cygnus, there is a strong x-ray source, named Cygnus X-1. It is near a star, and the two revolve around each other. The unseen x-ray source has the gravitational pull of at least 10 suns and is believed to be a black hole. Another type of black hole, a primordial black hole, may also exist dating from the time of the Big Bang when regions of gas and dust were highly compressed.

There are four other possible black holes: a Schwarzschild black hole has no charge and no angular momentum; a Reissner-Nordstrom black hole has charge but no angular momentum; a Kerr black hole has angular momentum but no charge; and a Kerr-Newman black hole has charge and angular momentum.

What is a **pulsar**?

A pulsar is a rotating neutron star that gives off sharp regular pulses of radio waves at rates ranging from 0.001 to four seconds. Stars burn by fusing hydrogen into helium. When they use up their hydrogen, their interiors begin to contract. During this contraction, energy is released and the outer layers of the star are pushed out. These layers are large and cool; the star is now a red giant. A star with more than twice the mass of the sun will continue to expand, becoming a supergiant. At that point, it may blow up in an explosion called a supernova. After a supernova, the remaining material of the star's core may be so compressed that the electrons and protons become neutrons. A star 1.4 to four times the mass of the sun can be compressed into a neutron star only about 12 miles (20 kilometers) across. Neutron stars rotate very fast. The neutron star at the center of the Crab Nebula spins 30 times per second.

A pulsar is formed by the collapse of a star with 1.4 to four times the mass of the sun. Some of these neutron stars emit radio signals from their magnetic poles in a direction that reaches Earth. These signals were first detected by Jocelyn Bell (b. 1943) of Cambridge University in 1967. Because of their regularity some people speculated that they were extraterrestrial beacons constructed by alien civilizations. This theory was eventually ruled out and the rotating neutron star came to be accepted as the explanation for these pulsating radio sources, or pulsars.

What does the **color of a star** indicate?

The color of a star gives an indication of its temperature and age. Stars are classified by their spectral type. From oldest to youngest and hottest to coolest, the types of stars are:

| Type | Color | Temperature | |
		Farenheit	Celsius
O	Blue	45,000–75,000	25,000–40,000
B	Blue	20,800–45,000	11,000–25,000
A	Blue-White	13,500–20,000	7,500–11,000
F	White	10,800–13,500	6,000–7,500
G	Yellow	9,000–10,800	5,000–6,000
K	Orange	6,300–9,000	3,500–5,000
M	Red	5,400–6,300	3,000–3,500

Each type is further subdivided on a scale of 0–9. The sun is a type G2 star.

Which stars are the **brightest**?

The brightness of a star is called its magnitude. Apparent magnitude is how bright a star appears to the naked eye. The lower the magnitude, the brighter the star. On a clear night, stars of about magnitude +6 can be seen with the naked eye. Large telescopes can detect objects as faint as +27. Very bright objects have negative magnitudes; the sun is -26.8.

Star	Constellation	Apparent Magnitude
Sirius	Canis Major	-1.47
Canopus	Carina	-0.72
Arcturus	Boötes	-0.06
Rigil Kentaurus	Centaurus	+0.01
Vega	Lyra	+0.04
Capella	Auriga	+0.05
Rigel	Orion	+0.14
Procyon	Canis Minor	+0.37
Betelgeuse	Orion	+0.41
Achernar	Eridanus	+0.51

What is the **Milky Way**?

The Milky Way is a hazy band of light that can be seen encircling the night sky. This light comes from the stars that make up the Milky Way galaxy, the galaxy to which the sun and the Earth belong. Galaxies are huge systems of stars separated from one another by largely empty space. Astronomers estimate that the Milky Way galaxy contains at least 100 billion stars and is about 100,000 light years in diameter. The galaxy is shaped like a phonograph record with a central bulge, or nucleus, and spiral arms curving out from the center.

What is the **Big Dipper**?

The Big Dipper is a group of seven stars that are part of the constellation Ursa Major. They appear to form a sort of spoon with a long handle. The group is known as the Plough in Great Britain. The Big Dipper is almost always visible in the northern hemisphere. It serves as a convenient reference point when locating other stars; for example, an imaginary line drawn from the two end stars of the dipper leads to Polaris, the North Star.

Where is the **North Star**?

If an imaginary line is drawn from the North Pole into space, it will reach a star called Polaris, or the North Star, less than one degree away from the line. As the Earth rotates on its axis, Polaris acts as a pivot-point around which all the stars visible in the northern hemisphere appear to move, while Polaris itself remains motionless.

What is the **summer triangle**?

The summer triangle is the triangle formed by the stars Deneb, Vega, and Altair as seen in the summer Milky Way.

How many **constellations** are there and how were they named?

Constellations are groups of stars that seem to form some particular shape, that of a person, animal, or object. They only appear to form this shape and be close to each other from Earth; in actuality the stars in a constellation are often very distant from each other. There are 88 recognized constellations whose boundaries were defined in the 1920s by the International Astronomical Union.

Various cultures in all parts of the world have had their own constellations. However, because modern science is predominantly a product of Western culture, many of the constellations represent characters from Greek and Roman mythology. When Europeans began to explore the southern hemisphere in the 16th and 17th centuries, they derived some of the new star patterns from the technological wonders of their time, such as the microscope.

Names of constellations are usually given in Latin. Individual stars in a constellation are usually designated with Greek letters in the order of brightness; the brightest star is alpha, the second brightest is beta, and so on. The genitive, or possessive, form of the constellation name is used, thus Alpha Orionis is the brightest star of the constellation Orion.

Constellation	Genitive	Abbreviation	Meaning
Andromeda	Andromedae	And	Chained Maiden
Antlia	Antliae	Ant	Air Pump
Apus	Apodis	Aps	Bird of Paradise
Aquarius	Aquarii	Aqr	Water Bearer
Aquila	Aquilae	Aql	Eagle
Ara	Arae	Ara	Altar
Aries	Arietis	Ari	Ram
Auriga	Aurigae	Aur	Charioteer
Boötes	Boötis	Boo	Herdsman
Caelum	Caeli	Cae	Chisel
Camelopardalis	Camelopardalis	Cam	Giraffe
Cancer	Cancri	Cnc	Crab
Canes Venatici	Canum Venaticorum	CVn	Hunting Dogs
Canis Major	Canis Majoris	CMa	Big Dog
Canis Minor	Canis Minoris	CMi	Little Dog

Capricornus	Capricorni	Cap	Goat
Carina	Carinae	Car	Ship's Keel
Cassiopeia	Cassiopeiae	Cas	Queen of Ethiopia
Centaurus	Centauri	Cen	Centaur
Cepheus	Cephei	Cep	King of Ethiopia
Cetus	Ceti	Cet	Whale
Chamaeleon	Chamaeleonis	Cha	Chameleon
Circinus	Circini	Cir	Compass
Columba	Columbae	Col	Dove
Coma Berenices	Comae Berenices	Com	Berenice's Hair
Corona Australis	Coronae Australis	CrA	Southern Crown
Corona Borealis	Coronae Borealis	CrB	Northern Crown
Corvus	Corvi	Crv	Crow
Crater	Crateris	Crt	Cup
Crux	Crucis	Cru	Southern Cross
Cygnus	Cygni	Cyg	Swan
Delphinus	Delphini	Del	Dolphin
Dorado	Doradus	Dor	Goldfish
Draco	Draconis	Dra	Dragon
Equuleus	Equulei	Equ	Little Horse
Eridanus	Eridani	Eri	River Eridanus
Fornax	Fornacis	For	Furnace
Gemini	Geminorum	Gem	Twins
Grus	Gruis	Gru	Crane
Hercules	Herculis	Her	Hercules
Horologium	Horologii	Hor	Clock
Hydra	Hydrae	Hya	Hydra, Greek monster
Hydrus	Hydri	Hyi	Sea Serpent
Indus	Indi	Ind	Indian
Lacerta	Lacertae	Lac	Lizard
Leo	Leonis	Leo	Lion
Leo Minor	Leonis Minoris	LMi	Little Lion
Lepus	Leporis	Lep	Hare
Libra	Librae	Lib	Scales
Lupus	Lupi	Lup	Wolf
Lynx	Lyncis	Lyn	Lynx
Lyra	Lyrae	Lyr	Lyre or Harp
Mensa	Mensae	Men	Table Mountain
Microscopium	Microscopii	Mic	Microscope
Monoceros	Monocerotis	Mon	Unicorn
Musca	Muscae	Mus	Fly
Norma	Normae	Nor	Carpenter's Square
Octans	Octanis	Oct	Octant

35

Constellation	Genitive	Abbreviation	Meaning
Ophiuchus	Ophiuchi	Oph	Serpent Bearer
Orion	Orionis	Ori	Orion, the Hunter
Pavo	Pavonis	Pav	Peacock
Pegasus	Pegasi	Peg	Winged Horse
Perseus	Persei	Per	Perseus, a Greek hero
Phoenix	Phoenicis	Phe	Phoenix
Pictor	Pictoris	Pic	Painter
Pisces	Piscium	Psc	Fish
Piscis Austrinus	Piscis Austrini	PsA	Southern Fish
Puppis	Puppis	Pup	Ship's Stern
Pyxis	Pyxidis	Pyx	Ship's Compass
Reticulum	Reticuli	Ret	Net
Sagitta	Sagittae	Sge	Arrow
Sagittarius	Sagittarii	Sgr	Archer
Scorpius	Scorpii	Sco	Scorpion
Sculptor	Sculptoris	Scl	Sculptor
Scutum	Scuti	Sct	Shield
Serpens	Serpentis	Ser	Serpent
Sextans	Sextantis	Sex	Sextant
Taurus	Tauri	Tau	Bull
Telescopium	Telescopii	Tel	Telescope
Triangulum	Trianguli	Tri	Triangle
Triangulum	Triangli Australis	TrA	Southern Australe Triangle
Tucana	Tucanae	Tuc	Toucan
Ursa Major	Ursae Majoris	UMa	Big Bear
Ursa Minor	Ursae Minoris	UMi	Little Bear
Vela	Velorum	Vel	Ship's Sail
Virgo	Virginis	Vir	Virgin
Volans	Volantis	Vol	Flying Fish
Vulpecula	Vulpeculae	Vul	Little Fox

What is the **largest constellation**?

Hydra is the largest constellation, extending from Gemini to the south of Virgo. It has a recognizable long line of stars. The name "hydra" is derived from the watersnake monster killed by Hercules in ancient mythology.

Which star is the **closest to Earth**?

The sun, at a distance of 92,955,900 miles (149,598,000 kilometers), is the closest star to the Earth. After the sun, the closest stars are the members of the triple star system known as Alpha Centauri (Alpha Centauri A, Alpha Centauri B, and Alpha Centauri C, sometimes called Proxima Centauri). They are 4.3 light years away.

What is the **sun made of**?

The sun is an incandescent ball of gases. Its mass is 1.8×10^{27} tons or 1.8 octillion tons (a mass 330,000 times as great as the Earth).

Element	% of mass
Hydrogen	73.46
Helium	24.85
Oxygen	0.77
Carbon	0.29
Iron	0.16
Neon	0.12
Nitrogen	0.09
Silicon	0.07
Magnesium	0.05
Sulfur	0.04
Other	0.10

How **hot** is the sun?

The center of the sun is about 27,000,000°F (15,000,000°C). The surface, or photosphere, of the sun is about 10,000°F (5,500°C). Magnetic anomolies in the photosphere cause cooler regions that appear to be darker than the surrounding surface. These sunspots are about 6,700°F (4,000°C). The sun's layer of lower atmosphere, the chromosphere, is only a few thousand miles thick. At the base, the chromosphere is about 7,800°F (4,300°C), but its temperature rises with altitude to the corona, the sun's outer layer of atmosphere, which has a temperature of about 1,800,000°F (1,000,000°C).

When will the **sun die**?

The sun is approximately 4.5 billion years old. About five billion years from now, the sun will have burned all of its hydrogen fuel into helium. As this process occurs, the sun will change from the yellow dwarf as we know it to a red giant. Its diameter will extend well beyond the orbit of Venus, and even possibly beyond the orbit of Earth. In either case, the Earth will be burned to a cinder.

What is the **ecliptic**?

Ecliptic refers to the apparent yearly path of the sun through the sky with respect to the stars. In the spring, the ecliptic in the northern hemisphere is angled high in the evening sky. In fall, the ecliptic lies much closer to the horizon.

Why does the **color of the sun** vary?

Sunlight contains all the colors of the rainbow, which blend to form white light, making sunlight appear white. At times, some of the color wavelengths, especially blue, become scattered in the Earth's atmosphere and the sunlight appears colored. When the sun is high in the sky, some of the blue rays are scattered in the Earth's atmosphere. At such times, the sky looks blue and the sun appears to be yellow. At sunrise or sunset, when the light must follow a longer path through the Earth's atmosphere, the sun looks red (red having the longest wavelengths).

How long does it take **light from the sun** to reach the Earth?

Sunlight takes about eight minutes and 20 seconds to reach the Earth, traveling at 186,282 miles (299,792 kilometers) per second.

How long is a **solar cycle**?

The solar cycle is the periodic change in the number of sun spots. The cycle is taken as the interval between successive minima and is about 11.1 years. During an entire cycle, solar flares, sunspots, and other magnetic phenomena move from intense activity to relative calm and back again. The solar cycle is one area of study to be carried out by up to 10 ATLAS space missions designed to probe the chemistry and physics of the atmosphere. These studies of the solar cycle will yield a more detailed picture of the Earth's atmosphere and its response to changes in the sun.

What is the **sunspot cycle**?

It is the fluctuating number of sunspots on the sun during an 11-year period. The variation in the number of sunspots seems to correspond with the increase or decrease in the number of solar flares. An increased number of sunspots means an increased number of solar flares.

When do **solar eclipses** happen?

A solar eclipse occurs when the moon passes between the Earth and the sun and all three bodies are aligned in the same plane. When the moon completely blocks Earth's view of the sun and the umbra, or dark part of the moon's shadow, reaches the Earth, a total eclipse occurs. A total eclipse happens only along a narrow path 100 to 200 miles (160 to 320 kilometers) wide called the track of totality. Just before totality, the only parts of the sun that are visible are a few points of light called Baily's beads shining through valleys on the moon's surface. Sometimes, a last bright flash of sunlight is seen—the diamond ring effect. During totality, which averages 2.5 minutes, but may last up to 7.5 minutes, the sky is dark and stars and other planets are easily seen. The corona, the sun's outer atmosphere, is also visible.

If the moon does not appear large enough in the sky to completely cover the sun, it appears silhouetted against the sun with a ring of sunlight showing around it. This is an annular eclipse. Because the sun is not completely covered, its corona cannot be seen and although the sky may darken, it will not be dark enough to see the stars.

During a partial eclipse of the sun, the penumbra of the moon's shadow strikes the Earth. A partial eclipse can also be seen on either side of the track of totality of an annular or total eclipse. The moon will cover part of the sun and the sky will not darken noticeably during a partial eclipse.

What is the safest way to **view a solar eclipse**?

Punch a pinhole in an index card and hold it two to three feet in front of another index card. The eclipse can be viewed safely through the hole. Encase the index card contraption in a box, using aluminum foil with a pinhole, and you'll see a sharper image of the eclipse. You may also purchase special glasses with aluminized Mylar lenses. Damage to the retina can occur if the eclipse is viewed with other contraptions like photographic filters, exposed film, smoked glass, camera lenses, telescopes, or binoculars.

When will the **next total solar eclipse** be visible from the United States?

It will occur on August 21, 2017, sweeping a path 70 miles (113 kilometers) wide from Salem, Oregon to Charleston, South Carolina.

What is a **sun dog**?

A sun dog is also known as a mock sun, false sun, or the 22° parhelia. It is a bright spot of light that sometimes appears on either side of the sun at the same distance above the horizon as the sun, and is separated from the sun by an angle of 22°.

What is **solar wind**?

Solar wind is caused by the expansion of gases in the sun's outermost atmosphere, the corona. Because of the corona's extremely high temperature of 4,000,000°F **39**

(2,200,000°C), the gases heat up and their atoms start to collide. The atoms lose electrons and become electrically charged ions. These ions create the solar wind. Solar wind has a velocity of 310 miles (500 kilometers) per second, and its density is approximately 82 ions per cubic inch (five ions per cubic centimeter). Because the Earth is surrounded by strong magnetic forces, its magnetosphere, it is protected from the solar wind particles. In 1959, the Soviet spacecraft *Luna 2* acknowledged the existence of solar wind and made the first measurements of its properties.

PLANETS AND MOONS

See also: The Earth

How old is the **solar system**?

It is is currently believed to be 4.5 billion years old. The Earth and the rest of the solar system formed from an immense cloud of gas and dust. Gravity and rotational forces caused the cloud to flatten into a disc and much of the cloud's mass to drift into the

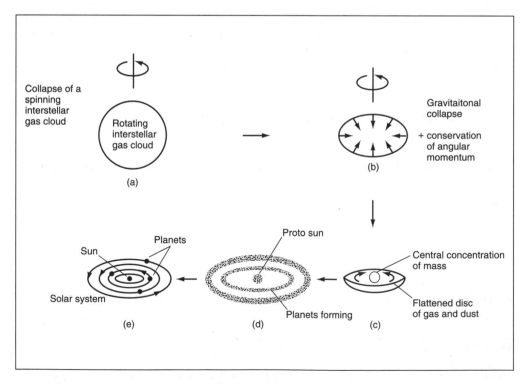

Collapse of a spinning interstellar gas cloud

Rotating interstellar gas cloud

(a)

Gravitaitonal collapse

+ conservation of angular momentum

(b)

Proto sun

Central concentration of mass

Flattened disc of gas and dust

(c)

Planets forming

(d)

Sun

Planets

Solar system

(e)

The evolution of the solar system from a gas cloud (a) to its present-day structure (e).

center. This material became the sun. The left-over parts of the cloud formed small bodies called planetesimals. These planetesimals collided with each other, gradually forming larger and larger bodies, some of which became the planets. This process is thought to have taken about 25 million years.

How **far are the planets** from the sun?

The planets revolve around the sun in elliptical orbits, with the sun at one focus of the ellipse. Thus, a planet is at times closer to the sun than at other times. The distances given below are the average distance from the sun, starting with Mercury, the planet closest to the sun, and moving outward.

Planet	Average distance	
	Miles	**Kilometers**
Mercury	35,983,000	57,909,100
Venus	67,237,700	108,208,600
Earth	92,955,900	149,598,000
Mars	141,634,800	227,939,200
Jupiter	483,612,200	778,298,400
Saturn	888,184,000	1,427,010,000
Uranus	1,782,000,000	2,869,600,000
Neptune	2,794,000,000	4,496,700,000
Pluto	3,666,000,000	5,913,490,000

How long do the planets take to go **around the sun**?

Planet	Period of revolution	
	Earth days	**Earth years**
Mercury	88	0.24
Venus	224.7	0.62
Earth	365.26	1.00
Mars	687	1.88
Jupiter	4,332.6	11.86
Saturn	10,759.2	29.46
Uranus	30,685.4	84.01
Neptune	60,189	164.8
Pluto	90,777.6	248.53

What are the **diameters** of the planets?

Planet	Diameter	
	Miles	Kilometers
Mercury	3,031	4,878
Venus	7,520	12,104
Earth	7,926	12,756
Mars	4,221	6,794
Jupiter	88,846	142,984
Saturn	74,898	120,536
Uranus	31,763	51,118
Neptune	31,329	50,530
Pluto	1,423	2,290

Note: All diameters are as measured at the planet's equator.

What are the **colors** of the planets?

Planet	Color
Mercury	Orange
Venus	Yellow
Earth	Blue, brown, green
Mars	Red
Jupiter	Yellow, red, brown, white
Saturn	Yellow
Uranus	Green
Neptune	Blue
Pluto	Yellow

Which planets have **rings**?

Jupiter, Saturn, Uranus, and Neptune all have rings. Jupiter's rings were discovered by *Voyager 1* in March, 1979. The rings extend 80,240 miles (129,130 kilometers) from the center of the planet. They are about 4,300 miles (7,000 kilometers) in width and less than 20 miles (30 kilometers) thick. A faint inner ring is believed to extend to the edge of Jupiter's atmosphere.

Saturn has the largest, most spectacular set of rings in the solar system. That the planet is surrounded by a ring system was first recognized by the Dutch astronomer Christiaan Huygens (1629–1695) in 1659. Saturn's rings are 169,800 miles (273,200 kilometers) in diameter, but less than 10 miles (16 kilometers) thick. There are six different rings, the largest of which appear to be divided into thousands of ringlets. The rings appear to be composed of pieces of water ice ranging in size from tiny grains to blocks several tens of yards in diameter.

In 1977 when Uranus occulted (passed in front of) a star, scientists observed that the light from the star flickered or winked several times before the planet itself covered the star. The same flickering occurred in reverse order after the occultation. The reason for this was determined to be a ring around Uranus. Nine rings were initially identified, and *Voyager 2* observed two more in 1986. The rings are thin, narrow, and very dark.

Voyager 2 also discovered a series of at least four rings around Neptune in 1989. Some of the rings appear to have arcs, areas where there is a higher density of material than at other parts of the ring.

Who discovered **Saturn's rings**?

Unbeknownst to him, Galileo was probably the first to discover Saturn's rings in 1610. Because his telescope was small, Galileo could not see the rings properly and assumed they were satellites. In 1656, Christiaan Huygens discovered a ring around Saturn with a more powerful telescope. Later, in 1675, Jean Domenique Cassini distinguished two rings around Saturn. Still later, more rings were discovered and, as recently as 1980, ringlets were observed.

What is the **gravitational force** on each of the planets, the moon, and the sun relative to the Earth?

If the gravitational force on the Earth is taken as 1, the comparative forces are

Sun	27.9
Mercury	0.37
Venus	0.88
Earth	1.00
Moon	0.16
Mars	0.38
Jupiter	2.64
Saturn	1.15
Uranus	0.93
Neptune	1.22
Pluto	0.06

Weight comparisons can be made by using this table. If a person weighed 100 pounds (45.36 kilograms) on Earth, then the weight of the person on the Moon would be 16 pounds (7.26 kilograms) or 100×0.16.

Is **a day** the same on all the planets?

No. A day, the period of time it takes for a planet to make one complete turn on its axis, varies from planet to planet. Venus, Uranus, and Pluto display retrograde motion, that is to say, they rotate in the opposite direction from the other planets. The table below lists the length of the day for each planet.

Planet	Earth days	Length of day	
		Hours	Minutes
Mercury	58	15	30
Venus	243		32
Earth		23	56
Mars		24	37
Jupiter		9	50
Saturn		10	39
Uranus		17	14
Neptune		16	03
Pluto	6	09	18

Which planets are called **"inferior"** planets and which are **"superior"** planets?

An inferior planet is one whose orbit is nearer to the sun than Earth's orbit is. Mercury and Venus are the inferior planets. Superior planets are those whose orbits around the sun lie beyond that of Earth. Mars, Jupiter, Saturn, Uranus, Neptune, and Pluto are the superior planets. The terms have nothing to do with the quality of an individual planet.

What are the **Jovian** and **terrestrial** planets?

Jupiter, Saturn, Uranus, and Neptune are the Jovian (the adjectival form for the word "Jupiter"), or Jupiter-like, planets. They are giant planets, composed primarily of light elements such as hydrogen and helium.

Mercury, Venus, Earth, and Mars are the terrestrial (derived from "terra," the Latin word for "earth"), or Earth-like, planets. They are small in size, have solid surfaces, and are composed of rocks and iron. Pluto appears to be a terrestrial-type planet as well, but it may have a different origin from the other planets.

What is unique about the **rotation** of the planet **Venus**?

Unlike Earth and most of the other planets, Venus rotates in a retrograde, or opposite, direction with relation to its orbital motion about the sun. It rotates so slowly that

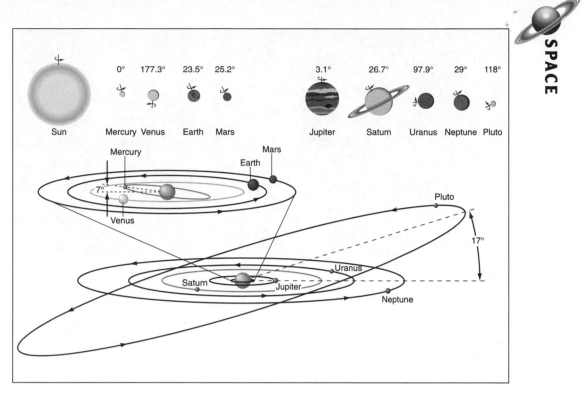

Schematic of the present-day solar system.

only two sunrises and sunsets occur each Venusian year. Uranus and Pluto's rotation are also retrograde.

Is it true that the **rotation speed of the Earth** varies?

The rotation speed is at its maximum in late July and early August and at its minimum in April; the difference in the length of the day is about 0.0012 second. Since about 1900 the Earth's rotation has been slowing at a rate of approximately 1.7 seconds per year. In the geologic past the Earth's rotational period was much faster; days were shorter and there were more days in the year. About 350 million years ago, the year had 400 to 410 days; 280 million years ago, a year was 390 days long.

Is it true that the **Earth is closer to the sun in winter than in summer in the northern hemisphere?**

Yes. However, the Earth's axis, the line around which the planet rotates, is tipped 23.5° with respect to the plane of revolution around the sun. When the Earth is closest to the sun (its perihelion, about January 3), the northern hemisphere is tilted away from

45

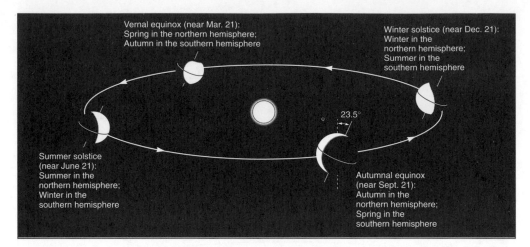

The seasons.

the sun. This causes winter in the northern hemisphere while the southern hemisphere is having summer. When the Earth is farthest from the sun (its aphelion, around July 4), the situation is reversed, with the northern hemisphere tilted towards the sun. At this time, it is summer in the northern hemisphere and winter in the southern hemisphere.

What is the **circumference of the Earth**?

The Earth is an oblate ellipsoid—a sphere slightly flattened at the poles and bulging at the equator. The distance around the Earth at the equator is 24,902 miles (40,075 kilometers). The distance around the Earth through the poles is 24,860 miles (40,008 kilometers).

What is the **precession** of the **equinoxes**?

The "precession of the equinoxes" is the 26,000-year circular movement of the Earth's axis. It is caused by the bulging at the equator, which makes the Earth's axis twist in such a way that the North and South Poles complete a circle every 26,000 years. Every year when the sun crosses the equator at the time of the equinox, it is in a slightly different position than the previous year. This movement proceeds eastward until a circle is completed.

Is there **life on Mars**?

Three experiments conducted on the composition of the Martian soil and atmosphere, carried out by the Viking Lander in July 1976, offered no evidence of life on Mars.

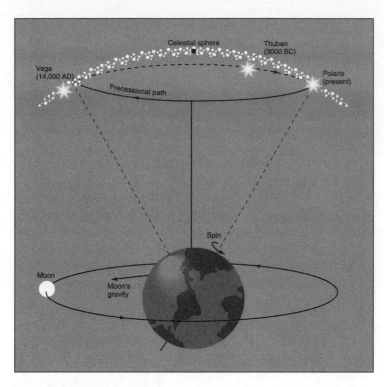

The precessional motion of the Earth.

Is it true that Pluto is not always the **outermost planet** in the solar system?

Pluto's very eccentric orbit carried it inside Neptune's orbit on January 23, 1979. It will remain there until March 15, 1999. During this time, Neptune is the outermost planet in the solar system. However, because they are so far apart, the planets are in no danger of colliding with one another.

Pluto, discovered in 1930 by American astronomer Clyde Tombaugh (b. 1906), is the smallest planet in the solar system. It is composed of rock and ice, with methane ice on the surface and a thin methane atmosphere. Pluto's single moon, Charon, discovered by James Christy in 1978, has a diameter of 741 miles (1,192 kilometers). This makes Charon, at half the size of Pluto, a very large moon relative to the planet. Some astronomers consider Pluto and Charon to be a double planet system.

What is **Planet X**?

Astronomers have observed perturbations, or disturbances, in the orbits of Uranus and Neptune since the discoveries of both planets. They speculated that Uranus and Neptune were being influenced by the gravity of another celestial body. Pluto, discovered in 1930, does not appear to be large enough to cause these disturbances. The existence of another planet, known as Planet X, orbiting beyond Pluto, has been proposed. As yet there have been no sightings of this tenth planet, but the search continues. There is a possibility that the unmanned space probes *Pioneer 10 & 11* and *Voyager 1 & 2*, now heading out of the solar system, will be able to locate this elusive object.

What does it mean when a **planet** is said to be in **opposition**?

A body in the solar system is in opposition when its longitude differs from the sun by 180°. In that position, it is exactly opposite the sun in the sky and it crosses the meridian at midnight.

How can an observer distinguish **planets** from **stars**?

In general, planets emit a constant light or shine, whereas stars appear to twinkle. The twinkling effect is caused by the combination of the distance between the stars and Earth and the refractive effect Earth's atmosphere has on a star's light. Planets are relatively closer to Earth than stars and their disk-like shapes average out the twinkling effect, except when they're observed near the Earth's horizon.

How many **moons** does each planet have?

Planet	Number of moons	Names of moons
Mercury	0	
Venus	0	
Earth	1	The Moon (sometimes called Luna)
Mars	2	Phobos, Deimos
Jupiter	16*	Metis, Adrastea, Amalthea, Thebe, Io, Europa, Ganymede, Callisto, Leda, Himalia, Lysithia, Elara, Ananke, Carme, Pasiphae, Sinope

Planet	Number of moons	Names of moons
Saturn	18*	Atlas, 1981S13 (unnamed as yet), Prometheus, Pandora, Epimetheus, Janus, Mimas, Enceladus, Tethys, Telesto, Calypso, Dione, Helene, Rhea, Titan, Hyperion, Iapetus, Phoebe
Uranus	15	Cordelia, Ophelia, Bianca, Cressida, Desdemona, Juliet, Portia, Rosalind, Belinda, Puck, Miranda, Ariel, Umbriel, Titania, Oberon
Neptune	8	Naiad, Thalassa, Despina, Galatea, Larissa, Proteus, Triton, Nereid
Pluto	1	Charon

*Several other satellites have been reported but not confirmed.

How far is the moon from the Earth?

Since the moon's orbit is elliptical, its distance varies from about 221,463 miles (356,334 kilometers) at perigee (closest approach to Earth), to 251,968 miles (405,503 kilometers) at apogee (farthest point), with the average distance being 238,857 miles (384,392 kilometers).

What are the diameter and circumference of the moon?

The moon's diameter is 2,159 miles (3,475 kilometers) and its circumference is 6,790 miles (10,864 kilometers). The moon is 27% the size of the Earth.

Why does the moon always keep the same face toward the Earth?

Only one side of the moon is seen because it always rotates in exactly the same length of time that it takes to revolve about the Earth. This combination of motions (called "captured rotation") means that it always keeps the same side toward the Earth.

What are the phases of the moon?

The phases of the moon are changes in the moon's appearance during the month, which are caused by the moon's turning different portions of its illuminated hemisphere towards the Earth. When the moon is between the Earth and the sun, its daylight side is turned away from the Earth, so it is not seen. This is called the new moon. As the moon continues its revolution around the Earth, more and more of its surface becomes visible. This is called the waxing crescent phase. About a week after the new moon, half the moon is visible—the first quarter phase. During the next week, more than half of the moon is seen; this is called the waxing gibbous phase. Finally, about two weeks after the new moon, the moon and sun are on opposite sides of the Earth. The side of the moon facing the sun is also facing the Earth, and all the moon's illuminated side is seen as a full moon. In the next two weeks the moon goes through the same phases, but in reverse from a waning gibbous to third or last quarter to waning crescent phase. Gradually, less and less of the moon is visible until a new moon occurs again.

Is the moon really blue during a **blue moon**?

The term "blue moon," the second full moon in a single month, does not refer to the color of the moon. A blue moon occurs, on average, every 2.72 years. Since 29.53 days pass between full moons (a synodial month), there is never a blue moon in February. On rare occasions, a blue moon can be seen twice in one year, but only in certain parts of the world. The next pair of blue moons will occur in 1999, during the months of January and March.

A bluish-looking moon can result from effects of the Earth's atmosphere. For example, the phenomenon was widely observed in North America on September 26, 1950, due to Canadian forest fires that had scattered high-altitude dust.

What is the difference between a **hunter's moon** and a **harvest moon**?

The harvest moon is the full moon nearest the autumnal equinox (on or about September 23). It is followed by a period of several successive days when the moon rises soon after sunset. In the southern hemisphere the harvest moon is the full moon closest to the vernal equinox (on or about March 21). This gives farmers extra hours of light for harvesting crops. The next full moon after the harvest moon is called the hunter's moon.

Why do **lunar eclipses** happen?

A lunar eclipse occurs only during a full moon when the moon is on one side of the Earth, the sun is on the opposite side, and all three bodies are aligned in the same plane. In this alignment the Earth blocks the sun's rays to cast a shadow on the moon. In a total lunar eclipse the moon seems to disappear from the sky when the whole moon passes through the umbra, or total shadow, created by the Earth. A total lunar eclipse may last up to one hour and 40 minutes. If only part of the moon enters the umbra, a partial eclipse occurs. A penumbral eclipse takes place if all or part of the moon passes through the penumbra (partial shadow or "shade") without touching the umbra. It is difficult to detect this type of eclipse from Earth. From the moon one could see that the Earth blocked only part of the sun.

What is the **moon's tail** that astronomers have discovered?

A glowing 15,000 mile (24,000 kilometer) long tail of sodium atoms streams from the moon. The faint, orange glow of sodium cannot be seen by the naked eye but it is detectable by instruments. Astronomers are not certain of the source of these sodium atoms.

What are the **craters** on the moon that are named for the famous Curie family?

Curie—named for Pierre Curie (1859–1906), French chemist and Nobel prize winner.

Sklodowska—the maiden name of Marie Curie (1867–1934), French physical chemist and Nobel prize winner.

Joliot—named for physicist Frederic Joliot-Curie (1900–1958), Pierre and Marie's son-in-law and Nobel prize winner.

What is the **Genesis rock**?

The Genesis rock is a lunar rock brought to Earth by *Apollo 15*. It is approximately 4.15 billion years old, which is only 0.5 billion years younger than the generally accepted age of the moon.

COMETS, METEORITES, ETC.

Where are **asteroids** found?

The asteroids, also called the minor planets, are smaller than any of the nine major planets in the solar system and are not satellites of any major planet. The term asteroid means "starlike" because asteroids appear to be points of light when seen through a telescope.

Most asteroids are located between Mars and Jupiter, between 2.1 and 3.3 AUs (astronomical units) from the sun. Ceres, the largest and first to be discovered, was found by Giuseppe Piazzi on January 1, 1801, and has a diameter of 582 miles (936 kilometers). A second asteroid, Pallas, was discovered in 1802. Since then, astronomers have identified more than 18,000 asteroids and have established orbits for about 5,000 of them. Some of these have diameters of only 0.62 mile (one kilometer). Originally, astronomers thought the asteroids were remnants of a planet that had been destroyed; now they believe asteroids to be material that never became a planet, possibly because it was affected by Jupiter's strong gravity.

Not all asteroids are in this main asteroid belt. Three groups reside in the inner solar system. The Aten asteroids have orbits that lie primarily inside Earth's orbit. However, at their farthest point from the sun, these asteroids may cross Earth's orbit. The Apollo asteroids cross Earth's orbit; some come even closer than the moon. The Amor asteroids cross the orbit of Mars, and some come close to Earth's orbit. The Trojan asteroids move in virtually the same orbit as Jupiter but at points 60° ahead or 60° behind the planet. In 1977 Charles Kowal discovered an object now known as Chiron orbiting between Saturn and Uranus. Originally cataloged as an asteroid, Chiron was later observed to have a coma (a gaseous halo), and it may be reclassified as a comet.

An **asteroid** came close to hitting the Earth sometime in 1989. How much **damage** might it have done?

Asteroid 1989 FC passed within 434,000 miles (700,000 kilometers) of the Earth on March 22, 1989. The impact, had it hit the Earth, would have delivered the energy equivalent of more than one million tons of exploding TNT and created a crater up to 4.3 miles (seven kilometers) across.

What was the **Tunguska Event**?

On June 30, 1908, a violent explosion occurred in the atmosphere over the Podkamennaya Tunguska River, in a remote part of central Siberia. The blast's consequences were similar to an H-bomb going off, leveling thousands of square miles of forest. The shock of the explosion was heard more than 600 miles (960 kilometers) away. A number of theories have been proposed to account for this event.

Some people thought that a large meteorite or a piece of anti-matter had fallen to Earth. But a meteorite, composed of rock and metal, would have created a crater and none was found at the impact site. There are no high radiation levels in the area that would have resulted from the collision of anti-matter and matter. Two other theories include a mini–black hole striking the Earth or the crash of an extraterrestrial spaceship. However, a mini–black hole would have passed through the Earth and there is no record of a corresponding explosion on the other side of the world. As for the spaceship, no wreckage of such a craft was ever found.

The most likely cause of the explosion was the entry into the atmosphere of a piece of a comet, which would have produced a large fireball and blast wave. Since a comet is composed primarily of ice, the fragment would have melted during its passage through the Earth's atmosphere, leaving no impact crater and no debris. Since the Tunguska Event coincided with the Earth's passage through the orbit of Comet Encke, the explosion could have been caused by a piece of that comet.

From where do **comets** originate?

According to a theory developed by Dutch astronomer Jan Oort, there is a large cloud of gas, dust, and comets orbiting beyond Pluto out to perhaps 100,000 astronomical units (AU). Occasional stars passing close to this cloud disturb some of the comets from their orbits. Some fall inwards towards the sun.

Comets, sometimes called "dirty snowballs," are made up mostly of ice, with some dust mixed in. When a comet moves closer to the sun, the dust and ice of the core, or nucleus, heats up, producing a tail of material that trails along behind it. The tail is pushed out by the solar wind and almost always points away from the sun.

Most comets have highly elliptical orbits that carry them around the sun and then fling them back out to the outer reaches of the solar system, never to return. Occasionally, however, a close passage by a comet near one of the planets can alter a comet's orbit, making it stay in the middle or inner solar system. Such a comet is called a short-period comet because it passes close to the sun at regular intervals. The most famous short-period comet is Comet Halley, which reaches perihelion (the point in its orbit that is closest to the sun) about every 76 years. Comet Encke, with an orbital period of 3.3 years, is another short-period comet.

When will **Halley's comet** return?

Halley's comet returns about every 76 years. It was most recently seen in 1985/1986 and is predicted to appear again in 2061, then in 2134. Every appearance of what is now known as Comet Halley has been noted by astronomers since the year 239 B.C.

Edmund Halley.

The comet is named for Edmund Halley (1656–1742), England's second Astronomer Royal. In 1682 he observed a bright comet and noted that it was moving in an orbit similar to comets seen in 1531 and 1607. He concluded that the three comets were actually one and the same and that the comet had an orbit of 76 years. In 1705 Halley published *A Synopsis of the Astronomy of Comets*, in which he predicted that the comet seen in 1531, 1607, and 1682 would return in 1758. On Christmas night, 1758, a German farmer and amateur astronomer named Johann Palitzsch spotted the comet in just the area of the sky that Halley had foretold.

Prior to Halley, comets appeared at irregular intervals and were often thought to

53

be harbingers of disaster and signs of divine wrath. Halley proved that they are natural objects subject to the laws of gravity.

What is **comet Hale-Bopp**?

Named after Alan Hale and Thomas Bopp, Hale-Bopp was discovered on July 23, 1995. It will be visible by August 1996, and will be at its brightest during March and April of 1997.

When do **meteor showers** occur?

There are a number of groups of meteoroids orbiting the sun just as the Earth is. When Earth's orbit intercepts the path of one of these swarms of meteoroids, some of them enter Earth's atmosphere. When friction with the air causes a meteoroid to burn up, the streak, or shooting star, that is produced is called a meteor. Large numbers of meteors can produce a spectacular shower of light in the night sky. Meteor showers are named for the constellation that occupies the area of the sky from which they originate. Listed below are 10 meteor showers and the dates during the year during which they can be seen.

Name of Shower	Dates
Quadrantids	January 1–6
Lyrids	April 19–24
Eta Aquarids	May 1–8
Perseids	July 25–August 18
Orionids	October 16–26
Taurids	October 20–November 20
Leonids	November 13–17
Phoenicids	December 4–5
Geminids	December 7–15
Ursids	December 17–24

How does a **meteorite** differ from a **meteoroid**?

A meteorite is a natural object of extraterrestrial origin that survives passage through the Earth's atmosphere and hits the Earth's surface. A meteorite is often confused with a meteoroid or a meteor. A meteoroid is a small object in outer space, generally less than 30 feet (10 meters) in diameter. A meteor (sometimes called a shooting star) is the flash of light seen when an object passes through Earth's atmosphere and burns as a result of heating caused by friction. A meteoroid becomes a meteor when it enters the Earth's atmosphere; if any portion of a meteoroid lands on Earth, it is a meteorite.

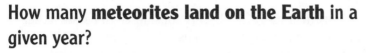

There are three kinds of meteorites. Irons contain 85% to 95% iron; the rest of their mass is mostly nickel. Stony irons are relatively rare meteorites composed of about 50% iron and 50% silicates. Stones are made up mostly of silicates and other stony materials.

How many **meteorites land on the Earth** in a given year?

Approximately 26,000 meteorites, each weighing over 3.5 ounces (99.2 grams) land on the Earth during a given year. This figure is compiled from the number of fireballs visually observed by the Canadian Camera Network. Of that number, only five or six falls are witnessed or cause property damage. The majority fall in the oceans, covering over 70% of the Earth's surface.

What are the **largest meteorites** that have been found in the world?

The famous Willamette (Oregon) iron, displayed at the American Museum of Natural History in New York, is the largest specimen found in the United States. It is 10 feet (3.048 meters) long and five feet (1.524 meters) high.

Name	Location	Weight	
		Tons	Tonnes
Hoba West	Namibia	66.1	60
Ahnighito (The Tent)	Greenland	33.5	30.4
Bacuberito	Mexico	29.8	27
Mbosi	Tanzania	28.7	26
Agpalik	Greenland	22.2	20.1
Armanty	Outer Mongolia	22	20
Willamette	Oregon, USA	15.4	14
Chupaderos	Mexico	15.4	14
Campo del Cielo	Argentina	14.3	13
Mundrabilla	Western Australia	13.2	12
Morito	Mexico	12.1	11

How do scientists know that some **meteorites** that were found in Antarctica came **from the Moon**?

Because of the high-quality reference collection of lunar rocks collected during space-flights to the moon, the original 1979 meteorite find in Antarctica and the 10 subsequent findings were varified as lunar in origin.

OBSERVATION AND MEASUREMENT

Who is considered the founder of systematic astronomy?

The Greek scientist Hipparchus (fl. 146–127 B.C.E.) is considered to be the father of systematic astronomy. He measured as accurately as possible the directions of objects in the sky. He compiled the first catalog of stars, containing about 850 entries, and designated each star's celestial coordinates, indicating its position in the sky. Hipparchus also divided the stars according to their apparent brightness or magnitudes.

What is a light year?

A light year is a measure of distance, not time. It is the distance that light, which travels in a vacuum at the rate of 186,282 miles (299,792 kilometers) per second, can travel in a year (365.25 days). This is equal to 5.87 trillion miles (9.46 trillion kilometers).

Besides the light year, what other units are used to measure distances in astronomy?

The astronomical unit (AU) is often used to measure distances within the solar system. One AU is equal to the average distance between the Earth and the sun, or 92,955,630 miles (149,597,870 kilometers). The parsec is equal to 3.26 light years, or about 19.18 trillion miles (30.82 trillion kilometers).

How are new celestial objects named?

Many stars and planets have names that date back to antiquity. The International Astronomical Union (IAU), the professional astronomers organization, has attempted, in this century, to standardize names given to newly discovered celestial objects and their surface features.

Stars are generally called by their traditional names, most of which are of Greek, Roman, or Arabic origin. They are also identified by the constellation in which they appear, designated in order of brightness by Greek letters. Thus Sirius is also called alpha Canis Majoris, which means it is the brightest star in the constellation Canis Major. Other stars are called by catalog numbers, which include the star's coordinates. To the horror of many astronomers, several commercial star registries exist, and for a fee, you can submit a star name to them. These names are not officially recognized by the IAU.

The IAU has made some recommendations for naming the surface features of the planets and their satellites. For example, features on Mercury are named for com-

SPACE

> ## What is widely considered to be one of the earliest celestial observatories?
>
> **B**uilt in England over a period of years between 2500 and 1700 B.C.E., Stonehenge is one of the earliest observatories or observatory-temples. It is widely believed that its primary function was to observe the mid-summer and mid-winter solstices.

posers, poets, and writers; features of Venus for women; and features on Saturn's moon Mimas for people and places in Arthurian legend.

Comets are named for their discoverers. Newly discovered asteroids are first given a temporary designation consisting of the year of discovery plus two letters. The first letter indicates the half month of discovery and the second the order of discovery in that half month. Thus asteroid 1991BA was the first asteroid (A) discovered in the second half of January (B) in 1991. After an asteroid's orbit is determined it is given a permanent number and its discoverer is given the honor of naming it. Asteroids have been named after such diverse things as mythological figures (Ceres, Vesta), an airline (Swissair), and the Beatles (Lennon, McCartney, Harrison, Starr).

What is an **astrolabe**?

Invented by the Greeks or Alexandrians in about 100 B.C.E. or before, an astrolabe is a two-dimensional working model of the heavens, with sights for observations. It consists of two concentric flat disks, one fixed, representing the observer on Earth, the other moving, which can be rotated to represent the appearance of the celestial sphere at a given moment. Given latitude, date, and time, the observer can read off the altitude and azimuth of the sun, the brightest stars, and the planets. By measuring the altitude of a particular body, one can find the time. The astrolabe can also be used to find times of sunrise, sunset, twilight, or the height of a tower or depth of a well. It was replaced by the sextant and other more accurate instruments.

Who invented the **telescope**?

Hans Lippershey (ca. 1570–1619), a German-Dutch lens grinder and spectacle maker, is generally credited with inventing the telescope in 1608 because he was the first scientist to apply for a patent. Two other inventors, Zacharias Janssen and Jacob Metius, also developed telescopes. Modern historians consider Lippershey and Janssen as the two likely candidates for the title of inventor of the telescope, with Lippershey possess-

57

ing the strongest claim. Lippershey used his telescope for observing grounded objects from a distance.

In 1609, Galileo also developed his own refractor telescope for astronomical studies. Although small by today's standards, the telescope enabled Galileo to observe the Milky Way and to identify blemishes on the moon's surface as craters.

Who is the **Hubble** for whom the **space telescope** is named?

Edwin Powell Hubble (1889–1953) was an American astronomer known for his studies of galaxies. His study of nebulae, or clouds—the faint, unresolved luminous patches in the sky—showed that some of them were large groups of many stars. Hubble classified galaxies by their shapes as being spiral, elliptical, or irregular.

Hubble's Law establishes a relationship between the velocity of recession of a galaxy and its distance. The speed at which a galaxy is moving away from our solar system (measured by its redshift, the shift of its light to longer wavelengths, presumed to be caused by the Doppler effect) is directly proportional to the galaxy's distance from it.

The Hubble Space Telescope was deployed by the space shuttle *Discovery* on April 25, 1990. The telescope, which would be free of distortions caused by the Earth's atmosphere, was designed to see deeper into space than any telescope on land. However, on June 27, 1990, the National Aeronautics and Space Administration announced that the telescope had a defect in one of its mirrors that prevented it from properly focusing. Although other instruments, including one designed to make observations in ultraviolet light, were still operating, nearly 40% of the telescope's experiments had to be postponed until repairs were made. On December 2, 1993, astronauts were able to make the necessary repairs. Four of Hubble's six gyroscopes were replaced as well as two solar panels. Hubble's primary camera, which had a flawed mirror, was also replaced.

EXPLORATION

How probable is it that **intelligent life** exists on other planets?

The possibility of intelligent life depends on several factors. An estimation can be calculated by using an equation developed originally by American astronomer Frank Drake (b. 1930). Drake's equation reads $N = N_* f_p n_e f_l f_i f_c f_L$. This means that the number of advanced civilizations (N) is equal to

Is anyone looking for extraterrestrial life?

A program called SETI (the Search for Extraterrestrial Intelligence) began in 1960, when American astronomer Frank Drake (b. 1930) spent three months at the National Radio Astronomy Observatory in Green Bank, West Virginia, searching for radio signals coming from the nearby stars Tau Ceti and Epsilon Eridani. Although no signals were detected and scientists interested in SETI have often been ridiculed, support for the idea of seeking out intelligent life in the universe has grown.

Project Sentinel, which used a radio dish at Harvard University's Oak Ridge Observatory in Massachusetts, could monitor 128,000 channels at a time. This project was upgraded in 1985 to META (Megachannel Extraterrestrial Assay), thanks in part to a donation by filmmaker Steven Spielberg. Project META is capable of receiving 8.4 million channels. NASA began a 10-year search in 1992 using radio telescopes in Arecibo, Puerto Rico, and Barstow, California.

Scientists are searching for radio signals that stand out from the random noises caused by natural objects. Such signals might repeat at regular intervals or contain mathematical sequences. There are millions of radio channels and a lot of sky to be examined and, as of October 1995, Project BETA (Billion-channel Extraterrestrial Assay) has been scanning a quarter of a billion channels. This new design improves upon Project META 300-fold, making the challenge of scanning millions of radio channels seem less daunting.

N_*, the number of stars in the Milky Way galaxy, times

f_p, the fraction of those stars that have planets, times

n_e, the number of planets capable of supporting life, times

f_l, the fraction of planets suitable for life on which life actually arises, times

f_i, the fraction of planets where intelligent life evolves, times

f_c, the fraction of planets with intelligent life that develops a technically advanced civilization, times

f_L, the fraction of time that a technical civilization lasts.

The equation is obviously subjective and the answer depends on whether optimistic or pessimistic numbers are assigned to the various factors. However, the galaxy is so large that the possibility of life elsewhere cannot be ruled out.

What is meant by the phrase "greening of the galaxy"?

The expression means the spreading of human life, technology, and culture through interstellar space and eventually across the entire Milky Way galaxy, the Earth's home galaxy.

When was the **Outer Space Treaty** signed?

The United Nations Outer Space Treaty was signed on January 23, 1967. The treaty provides a framework for the exploration and sharing of outer space. It governs the outer space activities of nations that wish to exploit and make use of space, the moon, and other celestial bodies. It is based on a humanist and pacifist philosophy and on the principle of the nonappropriation of space and the freedom that all nations have to explore and use space. A very large number of countries have signed this agreement, including those from the Western alliance, the former Eastern bloc, and non-aligned countries.

Space law, or those rules governing the space activities of various countries, international organizations, and private industries, has been evolving since 1957 when the General Assembly of the United Nations created the Committee on the Peaceful Uses of Outer Space (COPUOS). One of its subcommittees was instrumental in drawing up the 1967 Outer Space Treaty.

What is a "close encounter of the third kind"?

UFO expert J. Allen Hynek (1910–1986) developed the following scale to describe encounters with extraterrestrial beings or vessels:

Close Encounter of the First Kind—sighting of a UFO at close range with no other physical evidence.

Close Encounter of the Second Kind—sighting of a UFO at close range, but with some kind of proof, such as a photograph, or an artifact from a UFO.

Close Encounter of the Third Kind—sighting of an actual extraterrestrial being.

Close Encounter of the Fourth Kind—abduction by an extraterrestrial spacecraft.

Who was the **first man in space**?

Yuri Gagarin (1934–1968), a Soviet cosmonaut, became the first man in space when he made a full orbit of the Earth in *Vostok I* on April 12, 1961. Gagarin's flight lasted only one hour and 48 minutes, but as the first man in space, he became an international hero. Partly because of this Soviet success, U.S. President John F. Kennedy (1917–1963) announced on May 25, 1961, that the United States would land a man on the moon before the end of the decade. The United States took its first step toward that goal when it launched the first American into orbit on February 20, 1962. Astronaut John H. Glenn Jr. (b. 1921) completed three orbits in *Friendship 7* and traveled about 81,000 miles (130,329 kilometers). Prior to this, on May 5, 1961, Alan B. Shepard Jr. (b. 1923) became the first American to pilot a spaceflight, aboard *Freedom 7*. This suborbital flight reached an altitude of 116.5 miles (187.45 kilometers).

What did NASA mean when it said *Voyager 1* and *2* would take a "grand tour" of the planets?

Once every 176 years the giant outer planets—Jupiter, Saturn, Uranus, and Neptune—align themselves in such a pattern that a spacecraft launched from Earth to Jupiter at just the right time might be able to visit the other three planets on the same mission. A technique called "gravity assist" used each planet's gravity as a power boost to point *Voyager* toward the next planet. 1977 was the opportune year for the "grand tour."

What is the **message** attached to the *Voyager* spacecraft?

Voyager 1 (launched September 5, 1977) and *Voyager 2* (launched August 20, 1977) were unmanned space probes designed to explore the outer planets and then travel out of the solar system. A gold-coated copper phonograph record containing a message to any possible extraterrestrial civilization that they may encounter is attached to each spacecraft. The record contains both video and audio images of Earth and the civilization that sent this message to the stars.

The record begins with 118 pictures. These show the Earth's position in the galaxy; a key to the mathematical notation used in other pictures; the sun; other planets in the solar system; human anatomy and reproduction; various types of terrain (seashore, desert, mountains); examples of vegetation and animal life; people of both sexes and of all ages and ethnic types engaged in a number of activities; structures (from grass huts to the Taj Mahal to the Sydney Opera House) showing diverse architectural styles; and means of transportation, including roads, bridges, cars, planes, and space vehicles.

The pictures are followed by greetings from Jimmy Carter, then president of the United States, and Kurt Waldheim, then Secretary General of the United Nations. Brief messages in 54 languages, ranging from ancient Sumerian to English, are included, as is a "song" of the humpback whales.

The next section is a series of sounds common to the Earth. These include thunder, rain, wind, fire, barking dogs, footsteps, laughter, human speech, the cry of an infant, and the sounds of a human heartbeat and human brainwaves.

The record concludes with approximately 90 minutes of music, "Earth's Greatest Hits." These musical selections were drawn from a broad spectrum of cultures and include such diverse pieces as a Pygmy girl's initiation song; bagpipe music from Azerbaijan; the Fifth Symphony, First Movement by Ludwig von Beethoven; and "Johnny B. Goode" by Chuck Berry.

It will be tens, or even hundreds of thousands of years before either *Voyager* comes close to another star, and perhaps the message will never be heard; but it is a sign of humanity's hope to encounter life elsewhere in the universe.

Which astronauts have **walked on the moon**?

Twelve astronauts have walked on the moon. Each Apollo flight had a crew of three. One crew member remained in orbit in the command service module (CSM) while the other two actually landed on the moon.

Apollo 11, July 16–24, 1969
> Neil A. Armstrong
> Edwin E. Aldrin, Jr.
> Michael Collins (CSM pilot, did not walk on the moon)

Apollo 12, November 14–24, 1969
> Charles P. Conrad
> Alan L. Bean
> Richard F. Gordon, Jr. (CSM pilot, did not walk on the moon)

Apollo 14, January 31–February 9, 1971
> Alan B. Shepard, Jr.
> Edgar D. Mitchell
> Stuart A. Roosa (CSM pilot, did not walk on the moon)

Apollo 15, July 26–August 7, 1971
> David R. Scott
> James B. Irwin
> Alfred M. Worden (CSM pilot, did not walk on the moon)

Apollo 16, April 16–27, 1972
> John W. Young
> Charles M. Duke, Jr.
> Thomas K. Mattingly, II (CSM pilot, did not walk on the moon)

Apollo 17, December 7–19, 1972
> Eugene A. Cernan
> Harrison H. Schmitt
> Ronald E. Evans (CSM pilot, did not walk on the moon)

Who made the first golf shot on the moon?

Alan B. Shepard Jr. (b. 1923), commander of *Apollo 14*, launched on January 31, 1971, made the first golf shot. He attached a six iron to the handle of the contingency sample return container, dropped a golf ball on the moon, and took a couple of one-handed swings. He missed with the first, but connected with the second. The ball, he reported, sailed for miles and miles.

Which **manned space flight** was the longest?

Dr. Valerij Polyakov manned a flight to the space station *Mir* on January 8, 1994. He returned aboard *Soyuz TM-20* on March 22, 1995, making the total time in space equal 438 days and 18 hours.

When and what was the **first animal** sent into orbit?

A dog named Laika, aboard the Soviet *Sputnik 2*, launched November 3, 1957, was the first animal sent into orbit. This event followed the successful Soviet launch on October 4, 1957, of *Sputnik 1*, the first man-made satellite ever placed in orbit. Laika was a very small female dog and became the first living creature to go into orbit. She was placed in a pressurized compartment within a capsule that weighed 1,103 pounds (500 kilograms). After a few days in orbit, she died, and *Sputnik 2* reentered the Earth's atmosphere on April 14, 1958. Some sources list the dog as a Russian samoyed laika named "Kudyavka" or "Limonchik."

What were the **first monkeys** and **chimpanzees** in space?

On a United States *Jupiter* flight on December 12, 1958, a squirrel monkey named Old Reliable was sent into space, but not into orbit. The monkey drowned during recovery.

On another *Jupiter* flight, on May 28, 1959, two female monkeys were sent 300 miles (482.7 kilometers) high. Able was a six-pound (2.7-kilogram) rhesus monkey and Baker was an 11-ounce (0.3-kilogram) squirrel monkey. Both were recovered alive.

A chimpanzee named Ham was used on a *Mercury* flight on January 31, 1961. Ham was launched to a height of 157 miles (253 kilometers) into space but did not go into orbit. His capsule reached a maximum speed of 5,857 miles (9,426 kilometers) per hour and landed 422 miles (679 kilometers) downrange in the Atlantic Ocean where he was recovered unharmed.

On November 29, 1961, the United States placed a chimpanzee named Enos into orbit and recovered him alive after two complete orbits around the Earth. Like the Soviets, who usually used dogs, the United States had to obtain information on the effects of space flight on living beings before they could actually launch a human into space.

Who were the first man and woman to **walk in space**?

On March 18, 1965, the Soviet cosmonaut Alexei Leonov (b. 1934) became the first person to walk in space when he spent 10 minutes outside his *Voskhod 2* spacecraft. The first woman to walk in space was Soviet cosmonaut Svetlana Savitskaya (b. 1947) who, during her second flight aboard the *Soyuz T-12* (July 17, 1984), performed 3½ hours of extravehicular activity.

The first American to walk in space was Edward White II (1930–1967) from the spacecraft *Gemini 4* on June 3, 1965. Kathryn D. Sullivan (b. 1951) became the first American woman to walk in space when she spent 3.5 hours outside the *Challenger* orbiter during the space shuttle mission 41G on October 11, 1984.

American astronaut Bruce McCandless II (b. 1937) performed the first untethered space walk from the space shuttle *Challenger* on February 7, 1984, using an MMU (manual maneuvering unit) backpack.

What were the **first words spoken** by an astronaut after touchdown of the lunar module on the *Apollo 11* flight, and by an astronaut standing on the moon?

On July 20, 1969, at 4:17:43 p.m. Eastern Daylight Time (20:17:43 Greenwich Mean Time), Neil A. Armstrong (b. 1930) and Edwin E. Aldrin Jr. (b. 1930) landed the lunar module *Eagle* in the moon's Sea of Tranquility, and Armstrong radioed: "Houston, Tranquility Base here. The *Eagle* has landed." Several hours later, when Armstrong descended the lunar module ladder and made the small jump between the *Eagle* and the lunar surface, he announced: "That's one small step for man, one giant leap for mankind." The article "a" was missing in the live voice transmission, and was later inserted in the record to amend the message to "one small step for *a* man."

What material was used in the **United States flag** planted on the moon by astronauts Neil Armstrong and Edwin Aldrin Jr.?

The astronauts erected a three-by-five foot nylon U.S. flag, its top edge braced by a spring wire to keep it extended.

What was the **first meal on the moon**?

American astronauts Neil A. Armstrong (b. 1930) and Edwin E. Aldrin, Jr. (b. 1930) ate four bacon squares, three sugar cookies, peaches, pineapple-grapefruit drink, and coffee before their historic moonwalk on July 20, 1969.

Who was the first **woman in space**?

Valentina V. Tereshkova-Nikolaeva (b. 1937), a Soviet cosmonaut, was the first woman in space. She was aboard the *Vostok 6*, launched June 16, 1963. She spent three days circling the Earth, completing 48 orbits. Although she had little cosmonaut training, she was an accomplished parachutist and was especially fit for the rigors of space travel.

The United States space program did not put a woman in space until 20 years later when, on June 18, 1983, Sally K. Ride (b. 1951) flew aboard the space shuttle *Challenger* mission STS-7. In 1987, she moved to the administrative side of NASA and was instrumental in issuing the "Ride Report," which recommended future missions and direction for NASA. She retired from NASA in August 1987 to become a research fellow at Stanford University after serving on the Presidential Commission that investigated the *Challenger* disaster. At present, she is the director of the California Space Institute at the University of California San Diego.

Sally Ride with fellow crewmembers.

What are some of the accomplishments of female astronauts?

First American woman in space: Sally K. Ride—June 18, 1983, aboard *Challenger* STS-7.

First American woman to walk in space: Kathryn D. Sullivan—October 11, 1984, aboard *Challenger* STS 41G.

First woman to make three spaceflights: Shannoin W. Lucid—June 17, 1985; October 18, 1989; and August 2, 1991.

First African American woman in space: Mae Carol Jemison—September 12, 1992, aboard *Endeavour*.

First American woman space shuttle pilot: Eileen M. Collins—February 3, 1995, aboard *Discovery*.

Who was the first **African American in space?**

Guion S. Bluford, Jr. (b. 1942), became the first African American to fly in space during the Space Shuttle *Challenger* mission STS-8 (August 30–September 5, 1983). Astronaut Bluford, who holds a Ph.D. in aerospace engineering, made a second shuttle flight aboard *Challenger* mission STS-61-A/Spacelab D1 (October 30–November 6, 1985). The first black man to fly in space was Cuban cosmonaut Arnaldo Tamayo-Mendez, who was aboard *Soyuz 38* and spent eight days aboard the Soviet space station *Salyut 6* during September 1980. Dr. Mae C. Jemison became the first African American woman in space on September 12, 1992 aboard the Space Shuttle *Endeavour* mission Spacelab-J.

Who were the first **married couple** to go into space together?

Astronauts Jan Davis and Mark Lee were the first married couple in space. They flew aboard the space shuttle *Endeavor* on an eight-day mission that began on September 12, 1992. Ordinarily NASA bars married couples from flying together. An exception was made for Davis and Lee because they had no children and had begun training for the mission long before they got married.

Who has spent the **most time in space?**

As of December 31, 1994, cosmonaut Musa H. Manarov had accumulated the most time in space. During two spaceflights—from December 21, 1987 to December 21, 1988, and from December 2, 1990 to May 26, 1991—Manarov clocked a total of 541 days in space.

How many successful space flights were **launched in 1991,** and by what countries?

A total of 88 flights that achieved Earth orbit or beyond were made in 1991:

Country or Organization	Number of Launches
U.S.S.R.	59
United States	18
European Space Agency	8
Japan	2
Peoples' Republic of China	1

In 1990, there were 116 such launches, with 75 by the former U.S.S.R.; 27 (including seven commercial launches) by the United States; five by the European Space Agency; five by the People's Republic of China; and one by Israel.

When was the first United States **satellite** launched?

Explorer 1, launched January 31, 1958, by the U.S. Army, was the first United States satellite launched into orbit. This 31-pound (14.06-kilogram) satellite carried instrumentation that led to the discovery of the Earth's radiation belts, which would be named after University of Iowa scientist James A. Van Allen. It followed four months after the launching of the world's first satellite, the Soviet Union's *Sputnik 1*. On October 3, 1957, the Soviet Union placed the large 184-pound (83.5-kilogram) satellite into low Earth orbit. It carried instrumentation to study the density and temperature of the upper atmosphere, and its launch was the event that opened the age of space.

What is the mission of the *Galileo* spacecraft?

Galileo, launched October 18, 1989, required almost six years to reach Jupiter after looping past Venus once and the Earth twice. The *Galileo* spacecraft was designed to make a detailed study of Jupiter and its rings and moons over a period of years. On December 7, 1995, it released a probe to analyze the different layers of Jupiter's atmosphere. *Galileo* will record a multitude of measurements of the planet, its four largest moons, and its mammoth magnetic field. The mission is scheduled to continue until the end of 1997.

Who was the founder of the **Soviet space program**?

Sergei P. Korolev (1907–1966) made enormous contributions to the development of Soviet manned space flight, and his name is linked with their most significant space achievements. Trained as an aeronautical engineer, he directed the Moscow group studying the principles of rocket propulsion, and in 1946 took over the Soviet program to develop long-range ballistic rockets. Under Korolev, the Soviets used these rockets for space projects and launched the world's first satellite in October 4, 1957. Besides a vigorous unmanned interplanetary research program, Korolev's goal was to place men in space, and following tests with animals his manned space flight program was initiated when Yuri Gagarin (1934–1968) was successfully launched into Earth's orbit.

How many **fatalities** have occurred during space-related missions?

The 14 astronauts and cosmonauts listed below died in space-related accidents.

Date	Astronaut/Cosmonaut	Mission
January 27, 1967	Roger Chaffee (U.S.)	Apollo 1
January 27, 1967	Edward White II (U.S.)	Apollo 1
January 27, 1967	Virgil "Gus" Grissom (U.S.)	Apollo 1
April 24, 1967	Vladimir Komarov (U.S.S.R.)	Soyuz 1
June 29, 1971	Viktor Patsayev (U.S.S.R.)	Soyuz 11
June 29, 1971	Vladislav Volkov (U.S.S.R.)	Soyuz 11
June 29, 1971	Georgi Dobrovolsky (U.S.S.R.)	Soyuz 11
January 28, 1986	Gregory Jarvis (U.S.)	STS 51L
January 28, 1986	Christa McAuliffe (U.S.)	STS 51L
January 28, 1986	Ronald McNair (U.S.)	STS 51L
January 28, 1986	Ellison Onizuka (U.S.)	STS 51L
January 28, 1986	Judith Resnik (U.S.)	STS 51L
January 28, 1986	Francis Scobee (U.S.)	STS 51L
January 28, 1986	Michael Smith (U.S.)	STS 51L

Chaffee, Grissom, and White died in a cabin fire during a test firing of the *Apollo 1* rocket. Komarov was killed in *Soyuz 1* when the capsule's parachute failed. Dobrovolsky, Patsayev, and Volkov were killed during the *Soyuz II*'s re-entry when a valve accidently opened and released their capsule's atmosphere. Jarvis, McAuliffe, McNair, Onizuka, Resnik, Scobee, and Smith died when the space shuttle *Challenger* STS 51L exploded 73 seconds after lift-off.

In addition, 19 other astronauts and cosmonauts have died of non-space related causes. Fourteen of these died in air crashes, four died of natural causes, and one died in an auto crash.

What was the **worst disaster** in the U.S. space program and what caused it?

Challenger mission STS 51L was launched on January 28, 1986, but exploded 73 seconds after lift-off. The entire crew of seven was killed and the *Challenger* was completely destroyed. The investigation of the *Challenger* tragedy was performed by the Rogers Commission, established and named for its chairman, former Secretary of State William Rogers.

The consensus of the Rogers Commission (which studied the accident for several months) and participating investigative agencies is that the accident was caused by a failure in the joint between the two lower segments of the right solid rocket motor. The specific failure was the destruction of the seals that are intended to prevent hot gases from leaking through the joint during the propellant burn of the rocket motor. The evidence assembled by the commission indicated that no other element of the space shuttle system contributed to this failure.

Although the commission did not affix blame to any individuals, the public record made clear that the launch should not have been made that day. The weather was unusually cold at Cape Canaveral and temperatures had dipped below freezing during the night. Test data had suggested that the seals (called O-rings) around the solid rocket booster joints lost much of their effectiveness in very cold weather.

What were some of the accomplishments of the **first nine *Challenger* spaceflights**?

First American woman in space—Sally Ride

First African American man in space—Guion S. Bluford Jr.

First American woman to spacewalk—Kathryn Sullivan

First shuttle spacewalk—Donald Peterson and Story Musgrave

First untethered spacewalk—Robert Stewart and Bruce McCandless

First satellite repair in orbit—Pinky Nelson and Ox Van Hoften

First Coke and Pepsi in orbit—1985

What is the composition of the **tiles** on the **underside of the space shuttle** and how hot do they get?

The 20,000 tiles are composed of a low-density, high purity silica fiber insulator hardened by ceramic bonding. Bonded to a Nomex fiber felt pad, each tile is directly bonded to the shuttle exterior. The maximum surface temperature can reach up to 922K to 978K (649°C to 704°C or 1,200°F to 1,300°F).

EARTH

AIR

See also: Climate and Weather

What is the **composition** of the **Earth's atmosphere**?

The Earth's atmosphere, apart from water vapor and pollutants, is composed of 78% nitrogen, 21% oxygen, and less than 1% each of argon and carbon dioxide. There are also traces of hydrogen, neon, helium, krypton, xenon, methane, and ozone. The Earth's original atmosphere was probably composed of ammonia and methane; 20 million years ago the air started to contain a broader variety of elements.

How many **layers** does the **Earth's atmosphere** contain?

The atmosphere, the "skin" of gas that surrounds the Earth, consists of five layers that are differentiated by temperature:

The troposphere is the lowest level; it averages about seven miles (11 kilometers) in thickness, varying from five miles (eight kilometers) at the poles to 10 miles (16 kilometers) at the equator. Most clouds and weather form in this layer. Temperature decreases with altitude in the troposphere.

The stratosphere ranges between seven and 30 miles (11 to 48 kilometers) above the Earth's surface. The ozone layer, important because it absorbs most of the sun's harmful ultraviolet radiation, is located in this band. Temperatures rise slightly with altitude to a maximum of about 32°F (0°C).

The mesosphere (above the stratosphere) extends from 30 to 55 miles (48 to 85 kilometers) above the Earth. Temperatures decrease with altitude to -130°F (-90°C).

The thermosphere (also known as the hetereosphere) is between 55 to 435 miles (85 to 700 kilometers). Temperatures in this layer range to 2696°F (1475°C).

The exosphere beyond the thermosphere, applies to anything above 435 miles (700 kilometers). In this layer, temperature no longer has any meaning.

The ionosphere is a region of the atmosphere that overlaps the others, reaching from 30 to 250 miles (48 to 402 kilometers). In this region, the air becomes ionized (electrified) from the sun's ultraviolet rays, etc. This area affects the transmission and reflection of radio waves. It is divided into three regions: the D region (at 35 to 55 miles [56 to 88 kilometers]), the E Region (Heaviside-Kennelly Layer, 55 to 95 miles [56 to 153 kilometers]), and the F Region (Appleton Layer, 95 to 250 miles [153 to 402 kilometers]).

What are the **Van Allen belts**?

The Van Allen belts (or zones) are two regions of highly charged particles above the Earth's equator trapped by the magnetic field that surrounds the Earth. Also called the magnetosphere, the first belt extends from a few hundred to about 2,000 miles (3,200 kilometers) above the Earth's surface and the second is between 9,000 and 12,000 miles (14,500 to 19,000 kilometers). The particles, mainly protons and electrons, come from the solar wind and cosmic rays. The belts are named in honor of James Van Allen (b. 1914), the American physicist who discovered them in 1958 and 1959, with the aid of radiation counters carried aboard the artificial satellites, *Explorer I* (1958) and *Pioneer 3* (1959).

Why is the **sky blue**?

The sunlight interacting with the Earth's atmosphere makes the sky blue. In outer space the astronauts see blackness because outer space has no atmosphere. Sunlight consists of light waves of varying wavelengths, each of which is seen as a different color. The minute particles of matter and molecules of air in the atmosphere intercept and scatter the white light of the sun. A larger portion of the blue color in white light is scattered, more so than any other color because the blue wavelengths are the shortest. When the size of atmospheric particles are smaller than the wavelengths of the colors, selective scattering occurs—the particles only scatter one color and the atmosphere will appear to be that color. Blue wavelengths especially are affected, bouncing off the air particles to become visible. This is why the sun looks yellow (yellow equals white minus blue). At sunset, the sky changes color because as the sun drops to the horizon, sunlight has more atmosphere to pass through and loses more of its blue wavelengths (the shortest of all the colors). The orange and red, having the longer wavelengths and making up more of sunlight at this distance, are most likely to be scattered by the air particles.

PHYSICAL CHARACTERISTICS, ETC.

See also: Space—Planets and Moons

What is the **mass** of the **Earth?**

The mass of the Earth is estimated to be 6 sextillion, 588 quintillion short tons (6.6 sextillion short tons) or 5.97×10^{24} kilograms, with the Earth's mean density being 5.515 times that of water (the standard). This is calculated from using the parameters of an ellipsoid adopted by the International Astronomical Union in 1964 and recognized by the International Union of Geodesty and Geophysics in 1967.

What is the **interior of the Earth** like?

The Earth is divided into a number of layers. The topmost layer is the crust, which contains about 0.6% of the Earth's volume. The depth of the crust varies from 3.5 to five miles (five to nine kilometers) beneath the oceans to 50 miles (80 kilometers) beneath some mountain ranges. The crust is formed primarily of rocks such as granite and basalt.

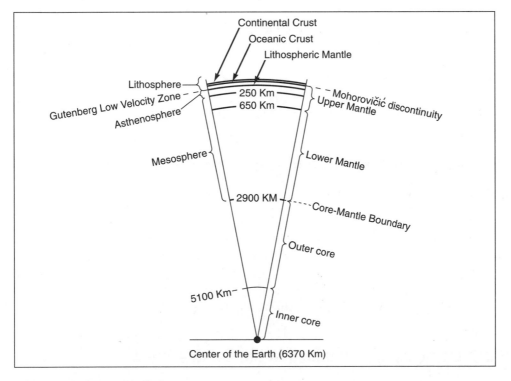

A diagram of the interior of the Earth.

What causes sinkholes?

A sinkhole is a depression shaped like a well or funnel that occurs in a land surface. Most common in limestone regions, sinkholes are usually formed by the dissolving action of groundwater or the seepage of above-ground streams into the limestone below, causing cracks or fractures in subterranean rock. The collapse of cave roofs can also cause large sinkholes. The resulting depression may be several miles in diameter.

Between the crust and the mantle is a boundary known as the Mohorovičič discontinuity (or Moho for short), named for the Croatian seismologist, Andrija Mohorovičič (1857–1936), who discovered it in 1909. Below the Moho is the mantle, extending down about 1,800 miles (2,900 kilometers). The mantle is composed mostly of oxygen, iron, silicon, and magnesium, and accounts for about 82% of the Earth's volume. Although mostly solid, the upper part of the mantle, called the asthenosphere, is partially liquid.

The core-mantle boundary, also called the Gutenberg discontinuity for the German-American seismologist, Beno Gutenberg (1889–1960), separates the mantle from the core. Made up primarily of nickel and iron, the core contains about 17% of the Earth's volume. The outer core is liquid and extends from the base of the mantle to a depth of about 3,200 miles (5,155 kilometers). The solid inner core reaches from the bottom of the outer core to the center of the Earth, about 3,956 miles (6,371 kilometers) deep. The temperature of the inner core is estimated to be about 7,000°F (3,850°C).

How does the **temperature of the Earth** change as one goes deeper underground?

The Earth's temperature increases with depth. Measurements made in deep mines and drill-holes indicate that the rate of temperature increase varies from place to place in the world, ranging from 59° to 167°F (15 to 75°C) per kilometer in depth. Actual temperature measurements cannot be made beyond the deepest drill-holes, which are a little more than 6.2 miles (10 kilometers) deep. Estimates suggest that the temperatures at the Earth's center can reach values of 5,000°F (2,760°C) or higher.

Which elements are contained in the **Earth's crust**?

The most abundant elements in the Earth's crust are listed in the table below. In addi-

tion, nickel, copper, lead, zinc, tin, and silver account for less than 0.02% with all other elements comprising 0.48%.

Element	Percentage
Oxygen	47.0
Silicon	28.0
Aluminum	8.0
Iron	4.5
Calcium	3.5
Magnesium	2.5
Sodium	2.5
Potassium	2.5
Titanium	0.4
Hydrogen	0.2
Carbon	0.2
Phosphorous	0.1
Sulfur	0.1

What are the **highest and lowest** points on **Earth**?

The highest point on land is the top of Mt. Everest (in the Himalayas on the Nepal-Tibet border) at 29,028 feet (8,848 meters) above sea level, plus or minus 10 feet (three meters) because of snow. This height was established by the Surveyor General of India in 1954 and accepted by the National Geographic Society. Prior to that the height was taken to be 29,002 feet (8,840 meters). Satellite measurements taken in 1987 indicate that Mt. Everest is 29,864 feet (9,102 meters) high but this measurement has not been adopted by the National Geographic Society.

The lowest point on land is the Dead Sea between Israel and Jordan, which is 1,312 feet (399 meters) below sea level. The lowest point on the Earth's surface is thought to be in the Marianas Trench in the western Pacific Ocean extending from southeast of Guam to northwest of the Marianas Islands. It has been measured as 36,198 feet (11,034 meters) below sea level.

What are the **highest and lowest** elevations in the **United States**?

Named in honor of U.S. president William McKinley (1843–1901), Mt. McKinley, Alaska, at 20,320 feet (6,194 meters), is the highest point in the United States and North America. Located in central Alaska, it belongs to the Alaska Range. Its south peak measures 20,320 feet (6,194 meters) high and the north peak is 19,470 feet (5,931 meters) high. It boasts one of the world's largest unbroken precipices and is the main scenic attraction at Denali National Park. Denali means the "high one" or the "great one" and is a native American name sometimes used for Mt. McKinley. Mt. Whitney, California, at 14,494 feet (4,421 meters), is the highest point in the continental United States. Death Valley, California, at 282 feet (86 meters) below sea level, is the lowest point in the United States and in the western hemisphere.

How much of the **Earth's surface** is land and how much is water?

Approximately 30% of the Earth's surface is land. This is about 57,259,000 square miles (148,300,000 square kilometers). The area of the Earth's water surface is approximately 139,692,000 square miles (361,800,000 square kilometers), or 70% of the total surface area.

WATER

If the Earth were a uniform sphere, **how much water** would cover the surface?

It is estimated that 97% of all water in the world or over one quadrillion acre-feet ($1,234 \times 10^{15}$ cubic meters) is contained within the oceans. If the Earth were a uniform sphere, this volume of water would cover the Earth to a depth of 800 feet (244 meters).

If you **melted all the ice** in the world, how high would the oceans rise?

If you melted all the ice in the world, some 23 million cubic kilometers in all, the oceans would rise 1.7% or about 180 feet (60 meters), enough for example, for 20 stories of the Empire State Building to be underwater.

What fraction of an **iceberg** shows above water?

Only one seventh to one-tenth of an iceberg's mass shows above water.

What is an **aquifer**?

Some rocks of the upper part of the Earth's crust contain many small holes, or pores. When these holes are large or are joined together so that water can flow through them easily, the rock is considered to be permeable. A large body of permeable rock in which water is stored and flows through is called an aquifer (from the Latin for "water" and "to bear"). Sandstones and gravels are excellent examples of permeable rock.

As water reservoirs, aquifers provide about 60% of American drinking water. The huge Ogallala Aquifer, underlying about two million acres of the Great Plains, is a major source of water for the central United States. It has been estimated that after oceans (containing 850 million cubic miles [1,370 million cubic kilometers] of water), aquifers, with an estimated 31 million cubic miles (50 million cubic kilometers), are the second largest store of water. Water is purified as it is filtered through the rock, but it can be polluted by spills, dumps, acid rain, and other causes. In addition, recharging of water by rainfall often cannot keep up with the volume removed by heavy pumping. The Ogallala Aquifer's supply of water could be depleted by 25% in the year 2020.

What is the **chemical composition** of the **ocean**?

The ocean contains every known naturally occurring element plus various gases, chemical compounds, and minerals. Below is a sampling of the most abundant chemicals.

Constituent	Concentration (parts per million)
Chloride	18,980
Sodium	10,560
Sulfate	2,560
Magnesium	1,272
Calcium	400
Potassium	380
Bicarbonate	142
Bromide	65
Strontium	13
Boron	4.6
Fluoride	1.4

Why is the **sea blue**?

There is no single cause for the colors of the sea. What is seen depends in part on when and from where the sea is observed. Eminent authority can be found to support almost any explanation. Some explanations include absorption and scattering of light by pure water; suspended matter in sea water; the atmosphere; and color and brightness variations of the sky. For example, one theory is that when sunlight hits seawater, part of the white light, composed of different wavelengths of various colors, is absorbed, and some of the wavelengths are scattered after colliding with the water molecules. In clear water, red and infrared light are greatly absorbed but blue is least absorbed, so that the blue wavelengths are reflected out of the water. The blue effect requires a minimum depth of 10 feet (three meters) of water.

How far can **sunlight penetrate** into the ocean?

Because seawater is relatively transparent, approximately 5% of sunlight can penetrate clean ocean water to a depth of 262 feet (80 meters). When the water is turbid (cloudy) due to currents, mixing of silt, increased growth of algae, or other factors, the depth of penetration is reduced to less than 164 feet (50 meters).

How **deep** is the ocean?

The average depth of the ocean floor is 13,124 feet (4,000 meters). The average depth of the four major oceans is given below:

Ocean	Average depth Feet	Meters
Pacific	13,740	4,188
Atlantic	12,254	3,735
Indian	12,740	3,872
Arctic	3,407	1,038
Average overall	13,124	4,000

There are great variations in depth because the ocean floor is often very rugged. The greatest depth variations occur in deep, narrow depressions known as trenches along the margins of the continental plates. The deepest measurements made—36,198 feet (11,034 meters), deeper than the height of the world's tallest mountains—was taken in Mariana Trench east of the Mariana Islands. In January 1960, the French oceanographer Jacques Piccard, together with the United States Navy Lieutenant David Walsh, took the bathyscaphe *Trieste* to the bottom of the Mariana Trench.

Ocean	Deepest point	Depth Feet	Meters
Pacific	Mariana Trench	36,200	11,033
Atlantic	Puerto Rico Trench	28,374	8,648
Indian	Java Trench	25,344	7,725
Arctic	Eurasia Basin	17,881	5,450

What causes **waves** in the ocean?

The most common cause of surface waves is air movement (the wind). Waves within

the ocean can be caused by tides, interactions among waves, submarine earthquakes or volcanic activity, and atmospheric disturbances. Wave size depends on wind speed, wind duration, and the distance of water over which the wind blows. The longer the distance the wind travels over water, or the harder it blows, the higher the waves. As the wind blows over water it tries to drag the surface of the water with it. The surface cannot move as fast as air, so it rises. When it rises, gravity pulls the water back, carrying the falling water's momentum below the surface. Water pressure from below pushes this swell back up again. The tug of war between gravity and water pressure constitutes wave motion. Capillary waves are caused by breezes of less than two knots. At 13 knots the waves grow taller and faster than they grow longer, and their steepness cause them to break, forming whitecaps. For a whitecap to form, the wave height must be one-seventh the distance between wave crests.

What is a **tidal bore**?

A tidal bore is a large, turbulent, wall-like wave of water that moves inland or upriver as an incoming tidal current surges against the flow of a more narrow and shallow river, bay, or estuary. It can be 10 to 16 feet (three to five meters) high and move rapidly (10 to 15 knots) upstream with and faster than the rising tide.

Where are the world's **highest tides**?

The Bay of Fundy (New Brunswick, Canada) has the world's highest tides. They average about 45 feet (14 meters) high in the northern part of the bay, far surpassing the world average of 2.5 feet (0.8 meter).

What is the difference between an **ocean** and a **sea**?

There is no neatly defined distinction between ocean and sea. One definition says the ocean is a great body of interconnecting salt water that covers 71% of the Earth's surface. There are four major oceans—the Arctic, Atlantic, Indian, and Pacific—but some sources do not include the Arctic Ocean, calling it a marginal sea. The terms "ocean" and "sea" are often used interchangeably but a sea is generally considered to be smaller than an ocean. The name is often given to saltwater areas on the margins of an ocean, such as the Mediterranean Sea.

How **salty** is seawater?

Sea water is, on average, 3.3 to 3.7% salt. The amount of salt varies from place to place. In areas where large quantities of fresh water are supplied by melting ice, rivers,

What are rip tides and why are they so dangerous?

At points along a coast where waves are high, a substantial buildup of water is created near the shore. This mass of water moves along the shore until it reaches an area of lower waves. At this point, it may burst through the low waves and move out from shore as a strong surface current moving at an abnormally rapid speed known as a rip current. Swimmers who become exhausted in a rip current may drown unless they swim parallel to the shore. Rip currents are sometimes incorrectly called rip tides.

or rainfall, such as the Arctic or Antarctic, the level of salinity is lower. Areas such as the Persian Gulf and the Red Sea have salt contents over 4.2%. If all the salt in the ocean were dried, it would form a mass of solid salt the size of Africa. Most of the ocean salt comes from processes of dissolving and leaking from the solid Earth over hundreds of millions of years. Some is the result of salty volcanic rock that flows up from a giant rift that runs through all the ocean's basins.

Is the **Dead Sea** really dead?

Because the Dead Sea, on the boundary between Israel and Jordan, is the lowest body of water on the Earth's surface, any water that flows into it has no outflow. It is called "dead" because its extreme salinity makes impossible any animal or vegetable life except bacteria. Fish introduced into the sea by the Jordan River or by smaller streams die instantly. The only plant life consists primarily of halophytes (plants that grow in salty or alkaline soil). The concentration of salt increases toward the bottom of the lake. The water also has a high density so bathers float on the surface easily.

How much salt is in **brackish water**?

Brackish water has a saline (salt) content between that of fresh water and sea water. It is neither fresh nor salty, but somewhere in between. Brackish waters are usually regarded as those containing 0.5 to 30 parts per thousand salt, while the average saltiness of seawater is 35 parts per thousand.

What is the **bearing capacity of ice** on a lake?

The following chart indicates the maximum safe load. It applies only to clear lake ice that has not been heavily traveled. For early winter slush ice, ice thickness should be doubled for safety.

| Ice thickness | | Examples | Maximum safe load | |
Inches	Centimeters		Tons	Kilograms
2	5	One person on foot		
3	7.6	Group in single file		
7.5	19	Car or snowmobiles	2	907.2
8	20.3	Light truck	2½	1,361
10	25.4	Medium truck	3½	1,814.4
12	30.5	Heavy truck	9	7,257.6
15	38		10	9,072
20	50.8		25	22,680

Where is the world's **deepest lake**?

Lake Baikal, located in southeast Siberia, Russia, is approximately 5,371 feet (1,638 meters) deep at its maximum depth, Olkhon Crevice, making it the deepest lake in the world. Lake Tanganyika in Tanzania and Zaire is the second deepest lake, with a depth of 4,708 feet (1,435 meters).

Where are the **five largest lakes** in the world located?

| Location | Area | | Length | | Depth | |
	Square miles	Square km[a]	Miles	Km[a]	Feet	Meters
Caspian Sea[b], Asia-Europe	143,244	370,922	760	1,225	3,363	1,025
Superior, North America	31,700	82,103	350	560	1,330	406
Victoria, Africa	26,828	69,464	250	360	270	85
Aralb, Asia	24,904	64,501	280	450	220	67
Huron, North America	23,010	59,600	206	330	750	229

[a]-Kilometers — [b]-Salt water lake

Which of the **Great Lakes** is the largest?

| Lake | Surface area | | Maximum depth | |
	Square miles	Square kilometers	Feet	Meters
Superior	31,700	82,103	1,333	406
Huron	23,010	59,600	750	229

Lake	Surface area		Maximum depth	
	Square miles	Square kilometers	Feet	Meters
Michigan	22,300	57,757	923	281
Erie	9,910	25,667	210	64
Ontario	7,540	19,529	802	244

The North American Great Lakes form a single watershed with one common outlet to the sea—the St. Lawrence Seaway. The total volume of all five basins is 6,000 trillion gallons (22.7 trillion liters). Only Lake Michigan lies wholly within the United States borders; the others share their boundaries with Canada. Some believe that Lake Huron and Lake Michigan are two lobes of one lake, since they are the same elevation and are connected by the 120-foot (36.5-meter) deep Strait of Mackinac, which is 3.6 to five miles (six to eight kilometers) wide. Gage records indicate that they both have similar water level regimes and mean long term behavior, so that hydrologically thay act as one lake. Historically they were considered two by the explorers who named them, but this is considered a misnomer by some.

What is an **oxbow lake**?

An oxbow lake is a crescent-shaped lake lying alongside a winding river, formed when a meander (a bend or loop in the river) becomes separated from the main stream. Erosion and deposition tend to accentuate the meander, with the faster-flowing water on the outside edges of the curves eroding the banks, while the slower-moving water on the inside edges deposits silt on the opposite banks. Over time, this process widens the loop of the meander, while narrowing the neck of land dividing the straight path of the river, until the neck vanishes and the river runs past the isolated meander. Without a current to keep it clear, the narrow horseshoe-shaped lake silts up. During the comparatively brief period after the meander is cut off and before it fills with silt, it is an oxbow lake.

A different explanation for the mechanics involved in cutting off a meander has been suggested by laboratory experiments. A stream needs a minimum slope or gradient (horizontal distance divided by height change) to be able to flow and to transport sediment; a meander decreases the gradient of a stream by increasing the distance that it must cover before dropping to a lower height. If a stream's gradient falls below the minimum required, it will tend to cut across the meanders in order to continue flowing.

What is a **yazoo**?

A yazoo is a tributary of a river that runs parallel to the river, being prevented from joining the river because the river has built up high banks. The name is derived from the Yazoo River, a tributary of the Mississippi River, which demonstrates this effect.

What are the **longest rivers** in the world?

The two longest rivers in the world are the Nile in Africa and the Amazon in South America. However, which is the longest is a matter of some debate. The Amazon has several mouths that widen toward the South Atlantic, so the exact point where the river ends is uncertain. If the Pará estuary (the most distant mouth) is counted, its length is approximately 4,195 miles (6,750 kilometers). The length of the Nile as surveyed before the loss of a few miles of meanders due to the formation of Lake Nasser behind the Aswan Dam was 4,145 miles (6,670 kilometers). The table below lists the five longest river systems in the world.

River	Length Miles	Length Kilometers
Nile (Africa)	4,145	6,670
*Amazon (South America)	4,000	6,404
Chang jiang-Yangtze (Asia)	3,964	6,378
Mississippi-Missouri river system (North America)	3,740	6,021
Yenisei-Angara river system (Asia)	3,442	5,540

*excluding Pará estuary

What is the world's **highest waterfall**?

Angel Falls, named after the explorer and bush pilot, Jimmy Angel, on the Carrao tributary in Venezuela is the highest waterfall in the world. It has a total height of 3,212 feet (979 meters) with its longest unbroken drop being 2,648 feet (807 meters).

It is difficult to determine the height of a waterfall because many are composed of several sections rather than one straight drop. The highest waterfall in the United States is Yosemite Falls on a tributary of the Merced River in Yosemite National Park, California, with a total drop of 2,425 feet (739 meters). There are three sections to the Yosemite Falls: Upper Yosemite is 1,430 feet (435 meters); Cascades (middle portion), 675 feet (205 meters); and Lower Yosemite, 320 feet (97 meters).

Why was **Niagara Falls shut down** for thirty hours in 1848?

The volume of Niagara waters depends on the height of Lake Erie at Buffalo, a factor that varies with the direction and intensity of the wind. Changes of as much as eight feet (2.5 meters) in the level of Lake Erie at the Niagara River source have been recorded. On March 29, 1848, a gale drove the floating ice in Lake Erie to the lake outlet, quickly blocking that narrow channel and shutting off a large proportion of the river's flow. Eyewitness accounts stated that the American falls were passable on foot, but for that day only.

When will Niagara Falls disappear?

The water dropping over Niagara Falls digs great plunge pools at the base, undermining the shale cliff and causing the hard limestone cap to cave in. Niagara has eaten itself seven miles (11 kilometers) upstream since it was formed 10,000 years ago. At this rate, it will disappear into Lake Erie in 22,800 years. The Niagara River connects Lake Erie with Lake Ontario, and marks the U.S.–Canada boundary (New York–Ontario).

LAND

See also: Space—Planets and Moons

Are there **tides in the solid part of the Earth** as well as in its waters?

The solid Earth is distorted about 4.5 to 14 inches (11.4 to 35.6 centimeters) by the gravitational pull of the sun and moon. It is the same gravitational pull that creates the tides of the waters. When the moon's gravity pulls water on the side of the Earth near to it, it pulls the solid body of the Earth on the opposite side away from the water to create bulges on both sides, and causing high tides. These occur every 12.5 hours. Low tides occur in those places from which the water is drained to flow into the two high-tide bulges. The sun causes tides on the Earth that are about 33 to 46% as high as those due to the moon. During a new moon or a full moon when the sun and moon are in a straight line, the tides of the moon and the sun reinforce each other to make high tides higher; these are called spring tides. At the quarter moons, the sun and moon are out of step (at right angles), the tides are less extreme than usual; these are called neap tides. Smaller bodies of water, such as lakes, have no tides because the whole body of water is raised all at once, along with the land beneath it.

Do the **continents move?**

In 1912, a German geologist, Alfred Lothar Wegener (1880–1930), theorized that the continents had drifted or floated apart to their present locations and that once all the continents had been a single land mass near Antarctica, which is called *Pangaea* (from the Greek word meaning *all-earth*). Pangaea then broke apart some 200 million years ago into two major continents called Laurasia and Gondwanaland. These two conti-

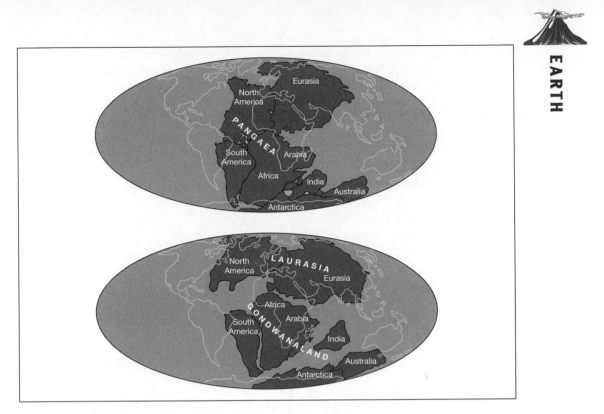

The Pangaea supercontinent (top) and its break up into Laurasia and Gondwanaland.

nents continued drifting and separating until the continents evolved their present shapes and positions. Wegener's theory was discounted but it has since been found that the continents do move sideways (not drift) at an estimated 0.75 inch (19 millimeters) annually because of the action of plate tectonics. American geologist William Maurice Ewing (1906–1974) and Harry Hammond Hess (1906–1969) proposed that the Earth's crust is not a solid mass, but composed of eight major and seven minor plates that can move apart, slide by each other, collide, or override each other. Where these plates meet are major areas of mountain-building, earthquakes, and volcanoes.

How much of the Earth's surface is **covered with ice**?

About 10.4% of the world's land surface is glaciated, or permanently covered with ice. Approximately 6,020,000 square miles (15,600,000 square kilometers) are covered by ice in the form of ice sheets, ice caps, or glaciers. An ice sheet is a body of ice that blankets an area of land, completely covering its mountains and valleys. Ice sheets have an area of over 19,000 square miles (50,000 square kilometers); ice caps are smaller. Glaciers are larger masses of ice that flow, under the force of gravity, at a rate of between 10 and 1,000 feet (three to 300 meters) per year. Glaciers on steep slopes

85

flow faster. For example, the Quarayoq Glacier in Greenland averages 65 to 80 feet (20 to 24 meters) per day. The areas of glaciation in some parts of the world are:

Place	Area	
	Square miles	Square kilometers
Antarctica	5,250,000	12,588,000
North Polar Regions (Greenland, Northern Canada, Arctic Ocean islands)	799,000	2,070,000
Asia	44,000	115,800
Alaska & Rocky Mountains	29,700	76,900
South America	10,200	26,500
Iceland	4,699	12,170
Alpine Europe	3,580	9,280
New Zealand	391	1,015
Africa	5	12

How much of the Earth's surface is **permanently frozen**?

About one-fifth of the Earth's land is permafrost, or ground that is permanently frozen. This classification is based entirely on temperature and disregards the composition of the land. It can include bedrock, sod, ice, sand, gravel, or any other type of material in which the temperature has been below freezing for over two years. Nearly all permafrost is thousands of years old.

Where are the **northernmost** and **southernmost** points of land?

The most northern point of land is Cape Morris K. Jesup on the northeastern extremity of Greenland. It is at 83 degrees, 39 minutes north latitude and is 440 miles (708 kilometers) from the North Pole. However, the *Guinness Book of Records* reports that an islet of 100 feet (30 meters) across, called Oodaq, is more northerly at 83 degrees, 40 minutes north latitude and 438.9 miles (706 kilometers) from the North Pole. The southernmost point of land is the South Pole (since the South Pole, unlike the North Pole, is on land).

In the United States, the northernmost point of land is Point Barrow, Alaska (71 degrees, 23 minutes north latitude), and the southernmost point of land is Ka Lae or South Cape (18 degrees, 55 minutes north latitude) on the island of Hawaii. In the 48 contiguous states, the northernmost point is Northwest Angle, Minnesota (49 degrees, 23 minutes north latitude); the southernmost point is Key West, Florida (24 degrees, 33 minutes north latitude).

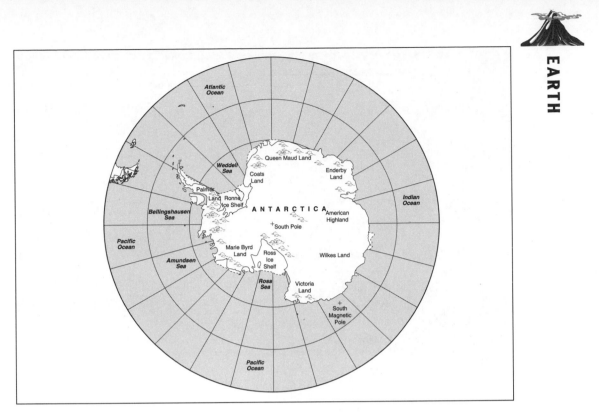

Antarctica.

How thick is the ice that covers **Antarctica**?

The ice that covers Antarctica is 15,700 feet (4,785 meters) in depth at its thickest point. This is about ten times taller than the Sears Tower in Chicago, the world's tallest building. However, the average thickness is 7,100 feet (2,164 meters).

Who was the **first person on Antarctica**?

Historians are unsure who first set foot on Antarctica, the fifth largest continent covering 10 percent of the Earth's surface with its area of 5.4 million square miles (14 million square kilometers). In 1773–1775 British Captain James Cook (1728–1779) circumnavigated the continent. American explorer Nathaniel Palmer (1799–1877) discovered Palmer Peninsula in 1820, without realizing that this was a continent. In this the same year Fabian Gottlieb von Bellingshausen (1779–1852) sighted the Antarctic continent. American sealer John Davis went ashore at Hughes Bay on February 7, 1821. In 1823, sealer James Weddell (1787–1834) traveled the farthest south (74 degrees south) that anyone had until that time and entered what is now called the Weddell Sea. In 1840, American Charles Wilkes (1798–1877), who followed the coast for 1,500 miles, announced the existence of Antarctica as a continent. In 1841, Sir

Hoodoos at Bryce Canyon, Utah.

James Clark Ross (1800–1862) discovered Victoria Land, Ross Island, Mount Erebus, and the Ross Ice Shelf. In 1895, the whaler Henryk Bull landed on the Antarctic continent. Norwegian explorer Roald Amundsen (1872–1928) was the first to reach the South Pole on December 14, 1911. Thirty-four days later, Amundsen's rival Robert Falcon Scott (1868–1912) stood at the South Pole, the second to do so, but he and his companions died upon their return trip.

When was the **Ice Age**?

Ice ages, or glacial periods, have occurred at irregular intervals for over 2.3 billion years. During an ice age, sheets of ice cover large portions of the continents. The exact reasons for the changes in the Earth's climate are not known, although some think they are caused by changes in the Earth's orbit around the sun.

The Great Ice Age occurred during the Pleistocene Epoch, which began about two million years ago and lasted until 11,000 years ago. At its height, about 27% of the world's present land area was covered by ice. In North America, the ice covered Canada and moved southward to New Jersey; in the Midwest, it reached as far south as St. Louis. Small glaciers and ice caps also covered the western mountains. Greenland was covered in ice as it is today. In Europe, ice moved down from Scandinavia into

Germany and Poland; the British Isles and the Alps also had ice caps. Glaciers also covered the northern plains of Russia, the plateaus of Central Asia, Siberia, and the Kamchetka Peninsula.

The glaciers' effect on the United States can still be seen. The drainage of the Ohio River and the position of the Great Lakes were influenced by the glaciers. The rich soil of the Midwest is mostly glacial in origin. Rainfall in areas south of the glaciers formed large lakes in Utah, Nevada, and California. The Great Salt Lake in Utah is a remnant of one of these lakes. The large ice sheets locked up a lot of water; sea level fell about 450 feet (137 meters) below what it is today. As a result, some states, such as Florida, were much larger during the ice age.

The glaciers of the last ice age retreated about 11,000 years ago. Some believe that the ice age is not over yet; the glaciers follow a cycle of advance and retreat many times. There are still areas of the Earth covered by ice and this may be a time in between glacial advances.

What is a **moraine**?

A moraine is a mound, ridge, or any other distinct accumulation of unsorted, unstratified material or drift, deposited chiefly by direct action of glacier ice.

What is a **hoodoo**?

A hoodoo is a fanciful name for a grotesque rock pinnacle or pedestal, usually of sandstone, that is the result of weathering in a semi-arid region. An outstanding example of hoodoos occurs in the Wasatch Formation at Bryce Canyon, Utah.

Where are the world's **largest deserts**?

A desert is an area that receives little precipitation and has little plant cover. Many deserts form a band north and south of the equator at about 20 degrees latitude because moisture-bearing winds do not release their rain over these areas. As the moisture-bearing winds from the higher latitudes approach the equator, their temperatures increase and they rise higher and higher in the atmosphere. When the winds arrive over the equatorial areas and come in contact with the colder parts of the Earth's atmosphere, they cool down and release all their water to create the tropical rain forests near the equator.

The Sahara desert is three times the size of the Mediterranean Sea. In the United States, the largest desert is the Mojave Desert in southern California with an area of 15,000 square miles (38,900 square kilometers).

Desert	Location	Area	
		Square miles	Square kilometers
Sahara	North Africa	3,500,000	9,065,000
Gobi	Mongolia-China	500,000	1,295,000
Kalahari	Southern Africa	225,000	582,800
Great Sandy	Australia	150,000	338,500
Great Victoria	Australia	150,000	338,500

Are all craters part of a volcano?

No, not all craters are of volcanic origin. A crater is a nearly circular area of deformed sedimentary rocks, with a central vent-like depression. Some craters are caused by the collapse of the surface when underground salt or limestone dissolves. The withdrawal of groundwater and the melting of glacial ice can also cause the surface to collapse, forming a crater.

Craters are also caused by large meteorites, comets, and asteroids that hit the Earth. A notable impact crater is Meteor Crater near Winslow, Arizona. It is 4,000 feet (1,219 meters) in diameter, 600 feet (183 meters) deep and is estimated to have been formed 30,000 to 50,000 years ago.

How is speleothem defined?

Speleothem is a term given to those cave features that form after a cave itself has formed. They are secondary mineral deposits that are created by the solidification of fluids or from chemical solutions. These mineral deposits usually contain calcium carbonate ($CaCO_3$) or limestone, but gypsum or silica may also be found. Stalactites, stalagmites, soda straws, cave coral, boxwork and cave pearls are all types of speleothems.

What is a tufa?

It is a general name for calcium carbonate ($CaCO_3$) deposits or spongy porous limestone found at springs in limestone areas, or in caves as massive stalactite or stalagmite deposits. *Tufa*, derived from the Italian word for "soft rock," is formed by the precipitation of calcite from the water of streams and springs.

What is the difference between spelunking and speleology?

Spelunking, or sport caving, is exploring caves as a hobby or for recreation. Speleology is the scientific study of caves and related phenomena, such as the world's deepest

How does a stalactite differ from a stalagmite?

A stalactite is a conical or cylindrical calcite ($CaCO_3$) formation hanging from a cave roof. It forms from the centuries-long buildup of mineral deposits resulting from the seepage of water from the limestone rock above the cave. This water containing calcium bicarbonate evaporates, losing some carbon dioxide, to deposit small quantities of calcium carbonate (carbonate of lime), which eventually forms a stalactite.

A stalagmite is a stone formation that develops upward from the cave floor and resembles an icicle upside down. Formed from water containing calcite that drips from the limestone walls and roof of the cave, it sometimes joins a stalactite to form a column.

cave, Réseau Jean Bernard, Haute Savoie, France with a depth of 5,256 feet (1,602 meters), or the world's longest cave system, Mammoth Cave in Kentucky, with a length of 348 miles (560 kilometers).

What and where is the **continental divide** of North America?

The Continental Divide, also known as the Great Divide, is a continuous ridge of peaks in the Rocky Mountains that marks the watershed separating easterly flowing waters from westerly flowing waters in North America. To the east of the Continental Divide, water drains into Hudson Bay or the Mississippi River before reaching the Atlantic Ocean. To the west, water generally flows through the Columbia River or the Colorado River on its way to the Pacific Ocean.

Which **natural attractions** in the United States are the most popular?

1. The Grand Canyon, Arizona
2. Yellowstone National Park, Wyoming
3. Niagara Falls, New York
4. Mount McKinley, Alaska
5. California's "Big Trees": the sequoias and redwoods
6. Hawaii's volcanoes
7. Florida's Everglades

How long is the Grand Canyon?

The Grand Canyon, cut out by the Colorado River over a period of 15 million years in the northwest corner of Arizona, is the largest land gorge in the world. It is four to 13 miles (6.4 to 21 kilometers) wide at its brim, 4,000 to 5,500 feet (1,219 to 1,676 meters) deep, and 217 miles (349 kilometers) long, extending from the mouth of the Little Colorado River to Grand Wash Cliffs (and 277 miles, 600 feet [445.88 kilometers] if Marble Canyon is included).

The Grand Canyon

However, it is not the deepest canyon in the United States; that distinction belongs to Kings Canyon, which runs through the Sierra and Sequoia National Forests near East Fresno, California, with its deepest point being 8,200 feet (2,500 meters). Hell's Canyon of the Snake River between Idaho and Oregon is the deepest United States canyon in low-relief territory. Also called the Grand Canyon of the Snake, it plunges 7,900 feet (2,408 meters) down from Devil Mountain to the Snake River.

What are the LaBrea tar pits?

The tar pits are located in an area of Los Angeles, California, formerly known as Rancho LaBrea. Heavy, sticky tar oozed out of the Earth, the scum from great petroleum reservoirs far underground. The pools were cruel traps for uncounted numbers of animals. Today the tar pits are a part of Hancock Park where many fossil remains are displayed along with life-sized reconstructions of these prehistoric species.

The tar pits were first recognized as a fossil site in 1875. However, scientists did not systematically excavate the area until 1901. By comparing Rancho La Brea's fossil specimens with their nearest living relatives, paleontologists have a greater understanding of the climate, vegetation and animal life in the area during the Ice Age. Perhaps the most impressive fossil bones recovered belong to such large extinct mammals as the imperial mammoth and the saber-toothed cat. Paleontologists have even found the remains of the western horse and the camel, which originated in North America, migrated to other parts of the world, and became extinct in North America at the end of the Ice Age.

From what type of stone was **Mount Rushmore** National Monument carved?

Granite. The monument, in the Black Hills of southwestern South Dakota, depicts the 60-foot high (18-meter high) faces of four United States presidents: George Washington, Thomas Jefferson, Abraham Lincoln, and Theodore Roosevelt. Sculptor Gutzon Borglum (1867–1941) designed the monument, but died before the completion of the project; his son, Lincoln, finished it. From 1927 to 1941, 360 people, mostly construction workers, drillers, and miners, "carved" the figures using dynamite.

What is the composition of the **Rock of Gibraltar**?

It is composed of gray limestone, with a dark shale overlay on parts of its western slopes. Located on a peninsula at the southern extremity of Spain, the Rock of Gibraltar is a mountain at the east end of the Strait of Gibraltar, the narrow passage between the Atlantic Ocean and the Mediterranean Sea. "The Rock" is 1,398 feet (425 meters) tall at its highest point.

VOLCANOES AND EARTHQUAKES

How many **kinds of volcanoes** are there?

Volcanoes are usually cone-shaped hills or mountains built around a vent connecting to reservoirs of molten rock, or magma, below the surface of the Earth. At times the molten rock is forced upwards by gas pressure until it breaks through weak spots in the Earth's crust. The magma erupts forth as lava flows or shoots into the air as clouds of lava fragments, ash, and dust. The accumulation of debris from eruptions cause the volcano to grow in size. There are four kinds of volcanoes:

Cinder cones are built of lava fragments. They have slopes of 30 degrees to 40 degrees and seldom exceed 1,640 feet (500 meters) in height. Sunset Crater in Arizona and Paricutin in Mexico are examples of cinder cones.

Composite cones are made of alternating layers of lava and ash. They are characterized by slopes of up to 30 degrees at the summit, tapering off to five degrees at the base. Mount Fuji in Japan and Mount St. Helens in Washington are composite cone volcanoes.

Shield volcanoes are built primarily of lava flows. Their slopes are seldom more than 10 degrees at the summit and two degrees at the base. The Hawaiian Islands are clusters of shield volcanoes. Mauna Loa is the world's largest active volcano, rising 13,653 feet (4,161 meters) above sea level.

Lava domes are made of viscous, pasty lava squeezed like toothpaste from a tube. Examples of lava domes are Lassen Peak and Mono Dome in California.

Where is the **Circle of Fire?**

The belt of volcanoes bordering the Pacific Ocean is often called the "Circle of Fire" or the "Ring of Fire." The Earth's crust is composed of 15 pieces, called plates, which "float" on the partially molten layer below them. Most volcanoes, earthquakes, and mountain building occur along the unstable plate boundaries. The Circle of Fire marks the boundary between the plate underlying the Pacific Ocean and the surrounding plates. It runs up the west coast of the Americas from Chile to Alaska (through the Andes Mountains, Central America, Mexico, California, the Cascade Mountains, and the Aleutian Islands) then down the east coast of Asia from Siberia to New Zealand (through Kamchatka, the Kurile Islands, Japan, the Philippines, Celebes, New Guinea, the Solomon Islands, New Caledonia, and New Zealand). Of the 850 active volcanoes in the world, over 75% of them are part of the Circle of Fire.

Which **volcanoes** have been the **most destructive?**

The five most destructive eruptions from volcanoes since 1700 are as follows:

Volcano	Date of eruption	Number killed	Lethal agent
Mt. Tambora, Indonesia	April 5, 1815	92,000	2,000 directly by the volcano, 80,000 from starvation afterwards
Karkatoa, Indonesia	Aug. 26, 1883	36,417	90% killed by a tsunami
Mt. Pelee, Martinque	Aug. 30, 1902	29,025	Pyroclastic flows
Nevada del Ruiz, Colombia	Nov. 13, 1985	23,000	Mud flow
Unzen, Japan	1792	14,300	70% killed by cone collapse; 30% by a tsunami

When did **Mount St. Helens** erupt?

Mount St. Helens, located in southwestern Washington state in the Cascades mountain range, erupted on May 18, 1980. Sixty-one people died as a result of the eruption. This was the first known eruption in the 48 contiguous United States to claim a human life. Geologists call Mount St. Helens a composite volcano (a steep-sided, often symmetrical cone constructed of alternating layers of lava flows, ash, and other volcanic debris). Composite volcanoes tend to erupt explosively. Mount St. Helens and the other active volcanoes in the Cascade Mountains are a part of the "Ring of Fire"— the Pacific zone having frequent and destructive volcanic activity.

Volcanoes have not only been active in Washington, but also in three other U.S. states: California, Alaska, and Hawaii. Lassen Peak is one of several volcanoes in the Cascade Range. It last erupted in 1921. Mount Katmai in Alaska had an eruption in 1912 in which the flood of hot ash formed the Valley of Ten Thousand Smokes 15 miles (24 kilometers) away. And Hawaii has its famed Mauna Loa, which is the world's largest volcano, being 60 miles (97 kilometers) in width at its base.

What is a **tsunami**?

A tsunami is a giant wave set in motion by a large earthquake occurring under or near the ocean that causes the ocean floor to shift vertically. This vertical shift pushes the water ahead of it, starting a tsunami. These are very long waves (100 to 200 miles [161 to 322 kilometers]) with high speeds (500 mph [805 kph]) that, when approaching shallow water, can grow into a 100-foot (30.5-meter) high wave as its wavelength is reduced abruptly. Ocean earthquakes below a magnitude of 6.5 on the Richter scale, and those that shift the sea floor only horizontally, do not produce these destructive waves.

How does a **seismograph** work?

A seismograph records earthquake waves. When an earthquake occurs, three types of waves are generated. The first two, the P and S waves, are propagated within the Earth, while the third, consisting of Love and Rayleigh waves, is propagated along the planet's surface. The P wave travels about 3.5 miles (5.6 kilometers) per second and is is the first wave to reach the surface. The S wave travels at a velocity of a little more than half of the P waves. If the velocities of the different modes of wave propagation are known, the distance between the earthquake and an observation station may be deduced by measuring the time interval between the arrival of the faster and slower waves.

When the ground shakes, the suspended weight of the seismograph, because of its inertia, scarcely moves, but the shaking motion is transmitted to the marker, which leaves a record on the drum.

What is the **Richter scale**?

On a machine called a seismograph, the Richter scale measures the magnitude of an earthquake, i.e., the size of the ground waves generated at the earthquake's source. The scale was devised by American geologist Charles W. Richter (1900–1985) in 1935. Every increase of one number means a tenfold increase in magnitude.

Richter Scale

Magnitude	Possible effects
1	Detectable only by instruments
2	Barely detectable, even near the epicenter
3	Felt indoors
4	Felt by most people; slight damage
5	Felt by all; damage minor to to moderate
6	Moderately destructive
7	Major damage
8	Total and major damage

What is the **modified Mercalli Scale**?

The modified Mercalli Scale is a means of measuring the intesity of an earthquake. Unlike the Richter Scale, which uses mathematical calculation to measure seismic waves, the modified Mercalli Scale uses the effects of an earthquake on the people and structures in a given area to determine its intensity. It was invented by Guiseppe Mercalli (1850–1914) in 1902 and modified by Harry Wood and Frank Neumann in the 1930s to take into consideration such modern inventions as the automobile and the skyscraper.

The Modified Mercalli Scale

I   Only felt by a few under especially favorable circumstances.

II Felt only by a few sleeping persons, particularly on upper floors of buildings. Some suspended objects may swing.

III Felt quite noticeably indoors, especially on upper floors of buildings, but may not be recognized as an earthquake. Standing automobiles may rock slightly. Vibration like passing of truck.

IV   During the day felt indoors by many, outdoors by few. At night some awakened. Dishes, windows, doors disturbed; walls make creaking sound. Sensation like heavy truck striking building. Standing automobiles rocked noticeably.

V   Felt by nearly everyone, many awakened. Some dishes, windows, and so on broken; cracked plaster in a few places; unstable objects overturned. Disturbances of trees, poles, and other tall objects sometimes noticed. Pendulum clocks may stop.

VI   Felt by all; many frightened and run outdoors. Some heavy furniture moved; a few instances of fallen plaster and damaged chimneys. Damage slight.

VII Everybody runs outdoors. Damage negligible in buildings of good design and construction; slight to moderate in well-built ordinary structures; considerable in poorly built or badly designed structures; some chimneys broken. Noticed by persons driving cars.

VIII Damage slight in specially designed structures; considerable in ordinary substantial buildings with partial collapse; great in poorly built structures. Panel walls thrown out of frame structures. Fall of chimneys, factory stacks, columns, monuments, walls. Heavy furniture overturned. Sand and mud ejected in small amounts. Changes in well water. Persons driving cars disturbed.

IX   Damage considerable in specially designed structures; well-designed frame structures thrown out of plumb; great in substantial buildings, with partial collapse. Building shifted off foundations. Ground cracked conspicuously. Underground pipes broken.

X   Some well-built wooden structures destroyed; most masonry and frame structures destroyed with foundations; ground badly cracked. Rails bent. Landslides considerable from river banks and steel slopes. Shifted sand and mud. Water splashed, slopped over banks.

XI   Few, if any, (masonry) structures remain standing. Bridges destroyed. Broad fissures in ground. Underground pipelines completely out of service. Earth slumps and landslips in soft ground. Rails bent greatly.

XII Damage total. Waves seen on ground surface. Lines of sight and level distorted. Objects thrown into the air.

When did the **most severe earthquake** in American history occur?

The New Madrid earthquakes (a series of quakes starting on December 16, 1811, and lasting until March 1812) is considered to be the most severe earthquake event in United States history. It shook more than two-thirds of the United States and was felt in Canada. It changed the level of land by as much as 20 feet (six meters), altered the course of the Mississippi River, and created new lakes, such as Lake St. Francis west of the Mississippi and Reelfoot Lake in Tennessee. Because the area was so sparsely populated, no known loss of life occurred. Scientists agree that at least three, and possibly five, of the quakes had surface wave magnitudes of 8.0 or greater. The largest was probably a magnitude of 8.8, which is larger than any quake yet experienced in California.

Of what magnitude was the **earthquake** that hit **San Francisco** on April 18, 1906?

The historic 1906 San Francisco earthquake took a mighty toll on the city and surrounding area. Over 700 people were killed; the newly constructed $6 million city hall was ruined; the Sonoma Wine Company collapsed, destroying 15 million gallons (57 million liters) of wine. The quake registered 8.3 on the Richter scale and lasted 75 seconds total. Many poorly constructed buildings built on landfills were flattened and the quake destroyed almost all of the gas and water mains. Fires broke out shortly after the quake, and when they were finally eliminated, 3,000 acres of the city, the equivalent of 520 blocks, were charred. Damage was estimated to be $500 million, and many insurance agencies went bankrupt after paying out the claims.

Again on October 17, 1989, an earthquake hit San Francisco, measuring 7.1 on the Richter scale, killing 67 people, and causing billions of dollars worth of damage.

OBSERVATION AND MEASUREMENT

What are the major eras, periods, and epochs in geologic time?

Modern dating techniques have given a range of dates as to when the various geologic time periods have started, as they are listed below:

Era	Period	Epoch	Beginning date (Est. millions of years)
Cenozoic	Quaternary	Holocene	10,000 years ago
		Pleistocene	1.9
	Tertiary	Pliocene	6
		Miocene	25
		Oligocene	38
		Eocene	55
		Paleocene	65

Era	Period	Epoch	Beginning date (Est. millions of years)
Mesozoic	Cretaceous		135
	Jurassic		200
	Triassic		250
Paleozoic	Permian		285
	Carboniferous (divided into Mississippian and Pennsylvanian periods by some in the U.S.)		350
	Devonian		410
	Silurian		425
	Ordovician		500
	Cambrian		570
Precambrian	Proterozoic		2500
	Archeozoic		3800
	Azoic		4600

What is **magnetic declination**?

It is the angle between magnetic north and true north at a given point on the Earth's surface. It varies at different points on the Earth's surface and at different times of the year.

Which direction does a **compass needle** point at the **north pole**?

At the north magnetic pole, the compass needle would be attracted by the ground and point straight down.

What is a **Foucault pendulum**?

An instrument devised by Jean Foucault (1819–1868) in 1851 to prove that the Earth rotates on an axis, the pendulum consisted of a heavy ball suspended by a very long fine wire. Sand beneath the pendulum recorded the plane of rotation of the pendulum over time.

A reconstruction of Foucault's experiment is located in Portland, Oregon at its Convention Center. It swings from a cable 90 feet (27.4 meters) long, making it the longest pendulum in the world.

What is the **prime meridian**?

The north-south lines on a map run from the North Pole to the South Pole and are called "meridians," a word that meant "noon," for when it is noon on one place on the line, it is noon at any other point as well. The lines are used to measure longitudes, or how far east or west a particular place might be, and they are 69 miles (111 kilometers) apart at the equator. The east-west lines are called parallels, and unlike meridians, are all parallel to each other. They measure latitude, or how far north or south a particular place might be. There are 180 lines circling the Earth, one for each degree of latitude. The degrees of both latitude and longitude are divided into 60 minutes, further divided into 60 seconds each.

The prime meridian is the meridian of 0 degrees longitude, used as the origin for measurement of longitude. The meridian of Greenwich, England, is used almost universally for this purpose.

What is **Mercator's projection** for maps?

The Mercator projection is a modification of a standard cylindrical projection, a technique used by cartographers to transfer the spherical proportions of the Earth to the flat surface of a map. For correct proportions, the parallels, or lines of latitude, are spaced at increasing distances toward the poles, resulting in severe exaggeration of size in the polar regions. Greenland, for example, appears five times larger than it actually is. Created by Flemish cartographer Gerardus Mercator in 1569, this projection is useful primarily because compass directions appear as straight lines, making it ideal for navigation.

Who is regarded as the founder of American **geology**?

Born in Scotland, the American William Maclure (1763–1840) was a member of a commission set up to settle claims between the United States and France from 1803 through 1807. In 1809 he made a geographical chart of the United States in which the land areas were divided by rock types. In 1817 he revised and enlarged this map. Maclure wrote the first English language articles and books on United States geology.

When were **relief maps** first used?

The Chinese were the first to use relief maps, in which the contours of the terrain were represented in models. Relief maps in China go back at least to the third century B.C.E. Some early maps were modeled in rice or carved in wood. It is likely that the idea of making relief maps was transmitted from the Chinese to the Arabs and then to Europe. The earliest known relief map in Europe was a map showing part of Austria, made in 1510 by Paul Dox.

What is the Piri Re'is map?

In 1929, a map was found in Constantinople that caused great excitement. Painted on parchment and dated in the Moslem year 919 (1541 according to the Christian calendar), it was signed by an admiral of the Turkish navy known as Piri Re'is. This map appears to be one of the earliest maps of America, and it shows South America and Africa in their correct relative longitudes. The mapmaker also indicated that he had used a map drawn by Columbus for the western part. It was an exciting statement because for several centuries geographers had been trying to find a "lost map of Columbus" supposedly drawn by him in the West Indies.

Who was the first person to map the **Gulf Stream**?

In his travels to and from France as a diplomat, Benjamin Franklin (1706–1790) noticed a difference in speed in the two directions of travel between France and America. He was the first to study ships' reports seriously to determine the cause of the speed variation. As a result, he found that there was a current of warm water coming from the Gulf of Mexico that crossed the North Atlantic Ocean in the direction of Europe. In 1770, Franklin mapped it.

Franklin thought the current started in the Gulf of Mexico. However, the Gulf Stream actually originates in the western Caribbean Sea and moves through the Gulf of Mexico, the Straits of Florida, then north along the east coast of the United States to Cape Hatteras in North Carolina where it becomes northeast. The Gulf Stream eventually breaks up near Newfoundland, Canada, to form smaller currents, or eddies. Some of these eddies blow toward the British Isles and Norway, causing the climate of these regions to be more mild than other areas of northwestern Europe.

What are **Landsat maps**?

They are images of the Earth taken at an altitude of 567 miles (912 kilometers) by an orbiting Landsat satellite, or ERTS (Earth Resources Technology Satellite). The Landsats were originally launched in the 1970s. Rather than cameras, the Landsats use multispectral scanners, which detect visible green and blue wavelengths, and four infrared and near-infrared wavelengths. These scanners can detect differences between soil, rock, water, and vegetation; types of vegetation; states of vegetation (e.g., healthy/unhealthy or underwatered/well-watered); and mineral content. The differences are especially accurate when multiple wavelengths are compared using multi-

101

spectral scanners. Even visible light images have proved useful—some of the earliest Landsat images showed that some small Pacific islands were up to 10 miles (16 kilometers) away from their charted positions.

The results are displayed in "false-color" maps, where the scanner data is represented in shades of easily distinguishable colors—usually, infrared is shown as red, red as green, and green as blue. The maps are used by farmers, oil companies, geologists, foresters, foreign governments, and others interested in land management. Each image covers an area approximately 115 square miles (185 square kilometers). Maps are offered for sale by the United States Geological Survey.

Other systems that produce similar images include the French SPOT satellites, the Russian Salyut and Mir manned space stations, and NASA's Airborne Imaging Spectrometer, which senses 128 infrared bands. NASA's Jet Propulsion Laboratories are developing instruments that will sense 224 bands in infrared, which will be able to detect specific minerals absorbed by plants.

From what distance are **satellite photographs** taken?

U.S. Department of Defense satellites orbit at various distances above the Earth. Some satellites are in low orbit, 100 to 300 miles (160 to 483 kilometers) above the surface, while others are positioned at intermediate altitudes from 500 to 1,000 miles (804 to 1,609 kilometers) high. Some have an altitude of 22,300 miles (35,880 kilometers).

CLIMATE AND WEATHER

TEMPERATURE

Is the **world** actually **getting warmer**?

The year 1990 was the warmest year since 1880, with an average global temperature of 59.8°F (15.45°C). Six of the seven warmest years of the 20th century have occurred during the 1980s. The average annual temperature for the contiguous United States (during the time period 1895–1990) is 52.5°F (11.4°C). The United States began the century with cool temperatures; the 1920s through 1950s were warm; the 1960s and 1970s were cool; and the 1980s were warm.

What are the **highest** and **lowest recorded** temperatures on Earth?

The highest temperature in the world was recorded as 136°F (58°C) at Al Aziziyah (el-Aziia), Libya on September 13, 1922; the highest temperature recorded in the United States was 134°F (56.7°C) in Death Valley, California on July 10, 1913. The temperatures of 140°F (60°C) at Delta, Mexico in August 1953 and 136.4°F (58°C) at San Luis, Mexico on August 11, 1933 are not internationally accepted. The lowest temperature was -128.6°F (-89.6°C) at Vostok Station in Antarctica on July 21, 1983. The record cold temperature for an inhabited area was -90.4°F (-68°C) at Oymyakon, Siberia (population 4,000) on February 6, 1933. This temperature tied with the readings at Verkhoyansk, Siberia, on January 3, 1885, and February 5 and 7, 1892. The lowest temperature reading in the United States was -79.8°F (-62.1°C) on January 23, 1971 in **103**

Prospect Creek, Alaska; for the contiguous 48 states, the coldest temperature was -69.7°F (-56.5°C) at Rogers Pass, Montana, on January 20, 1954.

What is the **heat index**?

The index is a measure of what hot weather feels like to the average person for various temperatures and relative humidities. Heat exhaustion and sunstroke are inclined to happen when the heat index reaches 105°F (40°C). The chart below provides the heat index for some temperatures and relative humidities.

	Air Temperature (°F)										
	70	75	80	85	90	95	100	105	110	115	120
Relative Humidity					Feels like (°F)						
0%	64	69	73	78	83	87	91	95	99	103	107
10%	65	70	75	80	85	90	95	100	105	111	116
20%	66	72	77	82	87	93	99	105	112	120	130
30%	67	73	78	84	90	96	104	113	123	13 5	148
40%	68	74	79	86	93	101	110	123	137	151	
50%	69	75	81	88	96	107	120	135	150		
60%	70	76	82	90	100	114	132	149			
70%	70	77	85	93	106	124	144				
80%	71	78	86	97	113	136					
90%	71	79	88	102	122						
100%	72	80	91	108							

Which place has the **maximum amount of sunshine** in the United States?

Yuma, Arizona, has an annual average of 90% of sunny days or over 4,000 sunny hours per year. St. Petersburg, Florida, had 768 consecutive sunny days from February 9, 1967, to March 17, 1969. On the other extreme, the South Pole has no sunshine for 182 days annually, and the North Pole has none for 176 days.

Why was 1816 known as the **year without a summer**?

The eruption of Mount Tambora, a volcano in Indonesia, in 1815 threw billions of cubic yards of dust over 15 miles (24 kilometers) into the atmosphere. Because the dust penetrated the stratosphere, wind currents spread it throughout the world. As a consequence of this volcanic activity, in 1816 normal weather patterns were greatly

Why are the hot, humid days of summer called "dog days"?

This period of extremely hot, humid, sultry weather that traditionally occurs in the northern hemisphere in July and August received its name from the dog star Sirius of the constellation *Canis Major*. At this time of year, Sirius, the brightest visible star, rises in the east at the same time as the sun. Ancient Egyptians believed that the heat of this brilliant star added to the sun's heat to create this hot weather. Sirius was blamed for the withering droughts, sickness, and discomfort that occurred during this time. Traditional dog days start on July 3 and end on August 11.

altered. Some parts of Europe and the British Isles experienced average temperatures 2.9 to 5.8°F (1.6 to 3.2°C) below normal. In New England heavy snow fell between June 6 and June 11 and frost occurred every month of 1816. Crop failures were experienced in Western Europe and Canada as well as in New England. In 1817, the excess dust had settled and the climate returned to more normal conditions.

How can the temperature be determined from the frequency of **cricket chirps**?

Listen for the chirping of either katydids or crickets, then count the number of chirps you hear in one minute. For the following equations "C" equals the number of chirps per minute.

For katydids, Fahrenheit temperature = $60 + (C-19)/3$

For crickets, Fahrenheit temperature = $50 + (C-50)/4$

AIR PHENOMENA

What is a **bishop's ring**?

It is a ring around the sun, usually with a reddish outer edge. It is probably due to dust particles in the air, since it is seen after all great volcanic eruptions.

When does the **green flash** phenomenon occur?

On rare occasions, the sun may look bright green for a moment, as the last tip of the sun is setting. This green flash occurs because the red rays of light are hidden below the horizon and the blue are scattered in the atmosphere. The green rays are seldom seen because of dust and pollution in the lower atmosphere. It may best be seen when the air is cloudless and when a distant, well-defined horizon exists, as on an ocean.

How often does an **aurora** appear?

Because it depends on solar winds (electrical particles generated by the sun) and sunspot activity, the frequency of an aurora cannot be determined. Auroras usually appear two days after a solar flare (a violent eruption of particles on the sun's surface) and reach their peak two years into the 11-year sunspot cycle. The auroras, occurring in the polar regions, are broad displays of usually colored light at night. The northern polar aurora is called Aurora Borealis or Northern Lights and the southern polar aurora is called the Aurora Australis.

When and by whom were **clouds** first classified?

The French naturalist Jean Lamarck (1744–1829) proposed the first system for classifying clouds in 1802. His work, however, did not receive wide acclaim. A year later the Englishman Luke Howard (1772–1864) developed a cloud classification system that has been generally accepted and is still used today. Clouds are distinguished by their general appearance ("heap clouds" and "layer clouds") and by their height above the ground. Latin names and prefixes are used to describe these characteristics. The shape names are *cirrus* (curly or fibrous), *stratus* (layered), and *cumulus* (lumpy or piled). The prefixes denoting height are *cirro* (high clouds with bases above 20,000 feet [6,067 meters]) and *alto* (mid-level clouds from 6,000 to 20,000 feet [1,820 to 6,067 meters]). There is no prefix for low clouds. *Nimbo* or *nimbus* is also added as a name or prefix to indicate that the cloud produces precipitation.

What are the four major **cloud groups** and their types?

1. High Clouds—composed almost entirely of ice crystals. The bases of these clouds start at 16,500 feet (5,000 meters) and reach 45,000 feet (13,650 meters).

   Cirrus (from Latin, "lock of hair")—are thin feather-like crystal clouds in patches or narrow bands. The large ice crystals that often trail downward in well-defined wisps are called "mares tails."

   Cirrostratus—is a thin, white cloud layer that resembles a veil or sheet. This layer can be striated or fibrous. Because of the ice content, these clouds are associated with the halos that surround the sun or moon.

Cirrocumulus—are thin clouds that appear as small white flakes or cotton patches and may contain super-cooled water.

2. Middle Clouds—composed primarily of water. The height of the cloud bases range from 6,500 to 23,000 feet (2,000 to 7,000 meters).

Altostratus—appears as a bluish or grayish veil or layer of clouds that can gradually merge into altocumulus clouds. The sun may be dimly visible through it, but flat, thick sheets of this cloud type can obscure the sun.

Altocumulus—is a white or gray layer or patches of solid clouds with rounded shapes.

3. Low Clouds—composed almost entirely of water that may at times be super-cooled; at subfreezing temperatures, snow and ice crystals may be present as well. The bases of these clouds start near the Earth's surface and climb to 6,500 feet (2,000 meters) in the middle latitudes.

Stratus—are gray uniform sheet-like clouds with a relatively low base or they can be patchy, shapeless, low gray clouds. Thin enough for the sun to shine through, these clouds bring drizzle and snow.

Stratocumulus—are globular rounded masses that form at the top of the layer.

Nimbostratus—are seen as a gray or dark relatively shapeless massive cloud layer containing rain, snow, and ice pellets.

4. Clouds with Vertical Development—contain super-cooled water above the freezing level and grow to great heights. The cloud bases range from 1,000 feet (300 meters) to 10,000 feet (3,000 meters).

Cumulus—are detached, fair weather clouds with relatively flat bases and dome-shaped tops. These usually do not have extensive vertical development and do not produce precipitation.

Cumulonimbus—are unstable large vertical clouds with dense boiling tops that bring showers, hail, thunder, and lightning.

How **hot** is **lightning**?

The temperature of the air around a bolt of lightning is about 54,000°F (30,000°C), which is six times hotter than the surface of the sun, yet many times people survive a bolt of lightning. American park ranger Roy Sullivan was hit by lightning seven times between 1942 and 1977. In cloud-to-ground lightning, its energy seeks the shortest route to Earth, which could be through a person's shoulder, down the side of the body through the leg to the ground. As long as the lightning does not pass across the heart or spinal column, the victim usually does not die.

Does lightning ever **strike twice in the same place**?

It is not true that lightning does not strike twice in the same place. In fact, tall buildings, such as the Empire State Building in New York, can be struck several times during the same storm. During one storm, lightning struck the Empire State Building 12 times.

How **long** is a **lightning stroke**?

The visible length of the streak of lightning depends on the terrain and can vary greatly. In mountainous areas where clouds are low, the flash can be as short as 300 yards (273 meters); whereas in flat terrain, where clouds are high, the bolt can measure as long as four miles (6.5 kilometers). The usual length is about one mile (1.6 kilometers), but streaks of lightning up to 20 miles (32 kilometers) have been recorded. The stroke channel is very narrow—perhaps as little as half an inch (1.27 centimeters). It is surrounded by a "corona envelope" or a glowing discharge that can be as wide as 10 to 20 feet (three to six meters) in diameter. The speed of lightning can vary from 100 to 1,000 miles (161 to 1,610 kilometers) per second for the downward leader track; the return stroke is 87,000 miles (140,070 kilometers) per second (almost half the speed of light).

How many **volts** are in lightning?

A stroke of lightning discharges from 10 to 100 million volts of electricity. An average lightning stroke has 30,000 amperes.

How is the **distance of a lightning flash** calculated?

Count the number of seconds between seeing a flash of lightning and hearing the sound of the thunder. Divide the number by five to determine the number of miles away that the lightning flashed.

What is **ball lightning**?

Ball lightning is a rare form of lightning in which a persistent and moving luminous white or colored sphere is seen. It can last from a few seconds to several minutes, and travels at about a walking pace. Spheres have been reported to vanish harmlessly, or to pass into or out of rooms—leaving, in some cases, sign of their passage such as a hole in a window pane. Sphere dimensions vary but are most commonly from four to eight inches (10 to 20 centimeters).

Other types of lightning include the common streak lightning (a single or multiple zigzagging line from cloud to ground); forked lightning (lightning that forms two branches simultaneously); sheet lightning (a shapeless flash covering a broad area); ribbon lightning (streak lightning blown sideways by the wind to make it appear like parallel successive strokes); bead or chain lightning (a stroke interrupted or broken into evenly spaced segments or beads); and heat lightning (lightning seen along the horizon during hot weather and believed to be a reflection of lightning occurring beyond the horizon).

What are **fulgurites**?

Fulgurites (from the Latin word *fulgur*, meaning lightning) are petrified lightning, created when lightning strikes an area of dry sand. The intense heat of the lightning melts the sand surrounding the stroke into a rough glassy tube forming a fused record of its path. These tubes may be one-half to two inches (1.5 to five centimeters) in diameter, and up to 10 feet (three meters) in length. They are extremely brittle and break easily. The inside walls of the tube are glassy and lustrous while the outside is rough, with sand particles adhering to it. Fulgurites are usually tan or black in color, but translucent white ones have been found.

What is **Saint Elmo's fire**?

Saint Elmo's fire has been described as a corona from electric discharge produced on high grounded metal objects, chimney tops, and ship masts. Since it often occurs during thunderstorms, the electrical source may be lightning. Another description refers to this phenomenon as weak static electricity formed when an electrified cloud touches a high exposed point. Molecules of gas in the air around this point become ionized and glow. The name originated with sailors who were among the first to witness the display of spearlike or tufted flames on the tops of their ships' masts. Saint Elmo (which is a corruption of Saint Ermo) is the patron saint of sailors, so they named the fire after him.

What is the order of **colors in a rainbow**?

Red, orange, yellow, green, blue, indigo, and violet are the colors of the rainbow, but these are not necessarily the sequence of colors that an observer might see. Rainbows are formed when raindrops reflect sunlight. As sunlight enters the drops, the different wavelengths of the colors that compose sunlight are refracted at different lengths to produce a spectrum of color. Each observer sees a different set of raindrops at a slightly different angle. Drops at different angles from the observer send different wave lengths (i.e., different color) to the observer's eyes. Since the color sequence of the rainbow is the result of refraction, the color order depends on how the viewer sees this refraction from the viewer's angle of perception.

109

What is the origin of the **Brown Mountain Lights** of North Carolina?

For a period of some 30 years the "lights" seen at Brown Mountain could not be explained. In 1922, the United States Geological Survey studied the mystery. The area has extraordinary atmospheric conditions, and automobile, locomotive, and fixed lights from miles away are reflected in the atmosphere.

WIND

What is the **Coriolis effect**?

The 19th-century French engineer Gaspard C. Coriolis (1792–1843) discovered that the rotation of the Earth deflects streams of air. Because the Earth spins to the east, all moving objects in the Northern Hemisphere tend to turn somewhat to the right of a straight path, while those in the Southern Hemisphere turn slightly left. The Coriolis effect explains the lack of northerly and southerly winds in the tropics and polar regions; the northeast and southeast trade winds and the polar easterlies all owe their westward deflection to the Coriolis effect.

When was the **jet stream** discovered?

A jet stream is a flat and narrow tube of air that moves more rapidly than the surrounding air. Discovered by World War II bomber pilots flying over Japan and the Mediterranean Sea, jet streams have become important with the advent of airplanes capable of cruising at over 30,000 feet (9,144 meters). The currents of air flow from west to east and are usually a few miles deep, up to 100 miles (160 kilometers) wide, and well over 1,000 miles (1,600 kilometers) in length. The air current must flow at over 57.5 miles (92 kilometers) per hour.

There are two polar jet streams, one in each hemisphere. They meander between 30 and 70 degrees latitude, occur at altitudes of 25,000 to 35,000 feet (7,620 to 10,668 meters), and achieve maximum speeds of over 230 miles (368 kilometers) per hour. The subtropical jet stream (again one per hemisphere) wander between 20 and 50 degrees latitude. They are found at altitudes of 30,000 to 45,000 feet (9,144 to 13,715 meters) and have speeds of over 345 miles (552 kilometers) per hour.

Why are the **horse latitudes** called by that name?

The horse latitudes are two high pressure belts characterized by low winds about 30 degrees north and south of the equator. Dreaded by early sailors, these areas have undependable winds with periods of calm. In the northern hemisphere, particularly near Bermuda, sailing ships carrying horses from Spain to the New World were often becalmed. When water supplies ran low, these animals were the first to be rationed water. Dying from thirst or tossed overboard, the animals were sacrificed to conserve water for the men. Explorers and sailors reported that the seas were "strewn with bodies of horses," which may be why the areas are called the horse latitudes. The term might also be rooted in complaints by sailors who were paid in advance and received no overtime when the ships slowly transversed this area. During this time they were said to be "working off a dead horse."

What are **halcyon days**?

This term is often used to refer to a time of peace or prosperity. Among sailors, it is the two-week period of calm weather before and after the shortest day of the year, approximately December 21. The phrase is taken from halcyon, the name the ancient Greeks gave to the kingfisher. According to legend, the halcyon built its nest on the surface of the ocean and was able to quiet the winds while its eggs were hatching.

What is a **Siberian express**?

This term describes storms that are severely cold and cyclonic; they descend from northern Canada and Alaska to other parts of the United States.

What is an **Alberta clipper**?

An Alberta Clipper is a little gyrating storm that develops on the Pacific front, usually over the Rocky Mountains of Alberta, Canada. This quick-moving storm moves southeast into the Great Plains, leaving a trail of cold air.

What is a **Chinook**?

It is a wind that is generally warm and originates from the eastern slope of the Rocky Mountains. It often moves from the southwest in a downslope manner, causing a noticeable rise in temperature that helps to warm the plains just east of the Rocky Mountains.

The Chinook is classified as a katabatic wind; a katabatic wind develops because of cold, heavy air spilling down sloping terrain, moving the lighter, warmer air in front of it. The air is dried and heated as it streams down the slope. At times the falling air becomes warmer than the air it restores. Some katabatic winds have been interestingly named, like Taku, a frigid wind in Alaska, or Santa Ana, a warmer wind from the Sierras.

111

Is Chicago the **windiest city**?

In 1990 Chicago ranked 21st in the list of 68 windy cities with an average wind speed of 10.3 miles (16.6 kilometers) per hour. Cheyenne, Wyoming, with an average wind speed of 12.9 miles (20.8 kilometers) per hour, ranks number one, closely followed by Great Falls, Montana, with an average wind speed of 12.8 miles (20.6 kilometers) per hour. The highest surface wind ever recorded was on Mount Washington, New Hampshire, at an elevation of 6,288 feet (1.9 kilometers). On April 12, 1934, its wind was 231 miles (371.7 kilometers) per hour and its average wind speed was 35 miles (56.3 kilometers) per hour.

What is meant by the **wind chill factor**?

The wind chill factor or wind chill index is a number that expresses the cooling effect of moving air at different temperatures. It indicates in a general way how many calories of heat are carried away from the surface of the body.

Scientists have devised an equivalent temperature scale that makes it easy to determine the wind chill factor. The accompanying chart is used for that purpose. Find the wind speed in the column on the left and find the temperature reading in the horizontal row at the top. The intersection of these two points gives the corresponding wind chill factor. For example, a temperature of 10°F (-12°C) along with a wind speed of 29 to 32 miles per hour (46 to 51 kilometers per hour) corresponds to a wind chill factor of -35°F (-37°C).

WIND CHILL EQUIVALENT TEMPERATURE TABLE
DRY BULB TEMPERATURE (°F)

WIND VELOCITY (MPH)	45	40	35	30	25	20	15	10	5	0	−5	−10	−15	−20	−25	−30	−35	−40	−45	WIND VELOCITY (MPH)
4	45	40	35	30	25	20	15	10	5	0	−5	−10	−15	−20	−25	−30	−35	−40	−45	4
5	43	37	32	27	22	16	11	6	0	−5	−10	−15	−21	−26	−31	−36	−42	−47	−52	5
10	34	28	22	16	10	3	−3	−9	−15	−22	−27	−34	−40	−46	−52	−58	−64	−71	−77	10
15	29	23	16	9	2	−5	−11	−18	−25	−31	−38	−45	−51	−58	−65	−72	−78	−85	−92	15
20	26	19	12	4	−3	−10	−17	−24	−31	−39	−46	−53	−60	−67	−74	−81	−88	−95	−103	20
25	23	16	8	1	−7	−15	−22	−29	−36	−44	−51	−59	−66	−74	−81	−88	−96	−103	−110	25
30	21	13	6	−2	−10	−18	−25	−33	−41	−49	−56	−64	−71	−79	−86	−93	−107	−109	−116	30
35	20	12	4	−4	−12	−20	−27	−35	−43	−52	−58	−67	−74	−82	−89	−97	−105	−113	−120	35
40	19	11	3	−5	−13	−21	−29	−37	−45	−53	−60	−68	−76	−84	−92	−100	−107	−115	−123	40
45	18	10	2	−6	−14	−22	−30	−38	−46	−54	−62	−70	−78	−85	−93	−102	−109	−117	−125	45

VERY COLD
BITTER COLD
EXTREME COLD

Is there a **formula** for computing the **wind chill**?

The formula is $T_e = 33 - \dfrac{(10.45 + V - V(33 - T)}{22.04}$

T_e = Wind chill equivalent temperature in degrees Celsius
V = Wind speed in meters per second
T = Air temperature in degrees Celsius

Who is associated with developing the **concept of wind chill**?

The Antarctic explorer Paul A. Siple coined the term in his 1939 dissertation "Adaptation of the Explorer to the Climate of Antarctica." Siple was the youngest member of Admiral Byrd's Antarctica expedition in 1928–1930, and later made other trips to the Antarctic as part of Byrd's staff and for the United States Department of the Interior assigned to the United States Antarctic Expedition. He also served in many other endeavors related to the study of cold climates.

How does a **cyclone** differ from a **hurricane** or a **tornado**?

All three wind phenomena are rotating winds that spiral in toward a low-pressure center as well as upward. Their differences lie in their size, wind velocity, rate of travel, and duration. Generally, the faster the winds spin, the shorter (in time) and smaller (in size) the event becomes.

A cyclone has rotating winds from 10 to 60 miles per hour (16 to 97 kilometers per hour); can be up to 1,000 miles (1,600 kilometers) in diameter, travels about 25 miles per hour (40 kilometers per hour), and lasts from one to several weeks. A hurricane (or typhoon, as it is called in the Pacific Ocean area) has winds that vary from 75 to 200 miles per hour (120 to 320 kilometers per hour), moves between 10 to 20 miles per hour (16 to 32 kilometers per hour), can have a diameter up to 600 miles (960 kilometers), and can exist from several days to more than a week. A tornado can reach a rotating speed of 300 miles per hour (400 kilometers per hour), travels between 25 to 40 miles per hour (40 to 64 kilometers per hour), and generally lasts only minutes, although some have lasted for five to six hours. Its diameter can range from 300 yards (274 meters) to one mile (1.6 kilometers) and its average path length is 16 miles (26 kilometers), with a maximum of 300 miles (483 kilometers).

Typhoons, hurricanes, and cyclones tend to breed in low-altitude belts over the oceans generally from five degrees to fifteen degrees latitude north or south. A tornado generally forms several thousand feet above the Earth's surface, usually during warm, humid weather; many times it is in conjunction with a thunderstorm. **113**

A computer-enhanced image of Hurricane Diana, which reached wind speeds of 130 miles per hour (209 kilometers per hour).

Although a tornado can occur in many places, they mostly appear on the continental plains of North America (i.e., from the Plains States eastward to western New York and the southeastern Atlantic states). Eighty-two percent of tornadoes materialize during the warmest hours of the day (noon to midnight), while 23% of all tornado activity occurs between 4 p.m. and 6 p.m.

What is the **Fujita and Pearson Tornado Scale**?

The Fujita and Pearson Tornado Scale, developed by T. Theodore Fujita and Allen Pearson, ranks tornadoes by their wind speed, path, length, and width. Sometimes known simply as the Fujita scale, the ranking ranges from F0 (very weak) to F6 (inconceivable).

F0—Light damage: damage to trees, billboards, and chimneys.

F1—Moderate damage: mobile homes pushed off their foundations and cars pushed off roads.

F2—Considerable damage: roofs torn off, mobile homes demolished, and large trees uprooted.

F3—Severe damage: even well-constructed homes torn apart, trees uprooted, and cars lifted off the ground.

F4—Devastating damage: houses leveled, cars thrown, and objects become flying missiles.

F5—Incredible damage: structures lifted off foundations and carried away; cars become missiles. Less than 2% of tornadoes are in this category.

F6—Maximum tornado winds not expected to exceed 318 mph (511 kph).

Fujita and Pearson Tornado Scale

Scale	Speed miles per hour	Path length in miles	Path width
0	≤72	≤1.0	≤17 yards
1	73–112	1.0–3.1	18–55 yards
2	113–157	3.2–9.9	56–175 yards
3	158–206	10.0–31.0	176–556 yards
4	207–260	32.0–99.0	0.34–0.9 miles
5	261–318	100–315	1.0–3.1 miles
6	319–380	316–999	3.2–9.9 miles

What is the **Beaufort scale**?

The Beaufort scale was devised in 1805 by a British Admiral, Sir Francis Beaufort (1774–1857), to help mariners in handling ships. It uses a series of numbers from 0 to 17 to indicate wind speeds and applies to both land and sea.

Beaufort number	Name	Wind speed Miles per hour	Kilometers per hour
0	Calm	less than 1	less than 1.5
1	Light air	1–3	1.5–4.8
2	Light breeze	4–7	6.4–11.3
3	Gentle breeze	8–12	12.9–19.3
4	Moderate breeze	13–18	21–29
5	Fresh breeze	19–24	30.6–38.6
6	Strong breeze	25–31	40.2–50
7	Moderate gale	32–38	51.5–61.1
8	Fresh gale	39–46	62.8–74
9	Strong gale	47–54	75.6–86.9
10	Whole gale	55–63	88.5–101.4
11	Storm	64–73	103–117.5
12–17	Hurricane	74 and above	119.1 and above

Which **year** had the **most tornadoes**?

From the period 1916 (when records started to be kept) to 1989, more tornadoes occurred in 1973 than in any other year. That year 1,102 tornadoes struck in 46 states, **115** killing 87 persons. From 1980 to 1989, an average of 820 tornadoes occurred each year. The largest outbreak of tornadoes occurred on April 3 and 4, 1974. 127 tornadoes were recorded in this "Super Outbreak" in the Plains and Midwestern states. Six of these tornadoes had winds greater than 260 miles (420 kilometers) per hour and some of them were the strongest ever recorded. In the 1990s, even greater numbers of tornadoes per year have been reported:

Year	Number of Tornados
1990	1140
1991	1138
1992	1303
1993	1179

Which **month** is the most **dangerous for tornadoes** in the United States?

According to one study, May is the most dangerous month for tornadoes in the United States, with an average of 329, while February's average is the safest with only three. In another study the months December and January were usually the safest, and the months having the greatest number of tornadoes were April, May, and June. In February, tornado frequency begins to increase. February tornadoes tend to occur in the central Gulf states; in March the center of activity moves eastward to the southeastern Atlantic states, where tornado activity peaks in April. In May the center of activity is in the southern Plains states; in June this moves to the northern Plains and Great Lakes area (into western New York).

How are **hurricanes classified**?

The Saffir/Simpson Hurricane Damage–Potential scale assigns numbers 1 through 5 to measure the disaster potential of a hurricane's winds and its accompanying storm surge. The purpose of the scale, developed in 1971 by Herbert Saffir and Robert Simpson, is to help disaster agencies gauge the potential significance of these storms in terms of assistance.

Saffir/Simpson Hurricane Scale Ranges

Scale number (category)	Barometric pressure (in inches)	Winds (miles per hour)	Surge (in feet)	Damage
1	≥28.94	74–95	4–5	Minimal
2	28.50–28.91	96–110	6–8	Moderate
3	27.91–28.47	111–130	9–12	Extensive
4	27.17–27.88	131–155	13–18	Extreme
5	<27.17	>155	>18	Catastrophic

Damage categories:

Minimal—No real damage to building structures. Some tree, shrubbery, and mobile home damage. Coastal road flooding and minor pier damage.

Moderate—Some roof, window, and door damage. Considerable damage to vegetation, mobile homes, and piers. Coastal and low-lying escape routes flood two to four hours before center of storm arrives. Small craft can break moorings in unprotected areas.

Extensive—Some structural damage to small or residential buildings. Mobile homes destroyed. Flooding near coast destroys structures and floods of homes five feet (1.5 meters) above sea level as far inland as six miles (9.5 kilometers).

Extreme—Extensive roof, window, and door damage. Major damage to lower floors of structures near the shore, and some roof failure on small residences. Complete beach erosion. Flooding of terrain 10 feet (three meters) above sea level as far as six miles (9.5 kilometers) inland requiring massive residential evacuation.

Catastrophic—Complete roof failure to many buildings; some complete building failure, with small utility buildings blown away. Major damage to lower floors of all structures 19 feet (5.75 meters) above sea level located within 500 yards (547 meters) of the shoreline. Massive evacuation of residential areas on low ground five to 10 miles (eight to 16 kilometers) from shoreline may be required.

How do **hurricanes** get their **names**?

Since 1950, hurricane names have been officially selected from library sources and are decided on during the international meetings of the World Meteorological Organization (WMO). The names are chosen to reflect the cultures and languages found in the Atlantic, Caribbean, and Hawaiian regions. When a tropical storm with rotary action and wind speeds above 39 miles (63 kilometers) per hour develops, the National Hurricane Center near Miami, Florida, selects a name from one of the six listings for Region 4 (Atlantic and Caribbean area). Letters Q, U, X, Y, and Z are not included because of the scarcity of names beginning with those letters. Once a storm has done great damage, its name is retired from the six-year list cycle.

1996	1997	1998	1999	2000
Arthur	Ana	Alex	Arlene	Alberto
Bertha	Bill	Bonnie	Bret	Beryl
Cesar	Claudette	Charley	Cindy	Chris
Diana	Danny	Danielle	Dennis	Debbie
Edouard	Erika	Earl	Emily	Ernesto
Fran	Fabian	Frances	Floyd	Florence
Gustav	Grace	Georges	Gert	Gordon
Hortense	Henri	Hermine	Harvey	Helene

1996	1997	1998	1999	2000
Isidore	Isabel	Ivan	Irene	Isaac
Josephine	Juan	Jeanne	Jose	Joyce
Klaus	Kate	Karl	Katrina	Keith
Lili	Larry	Lisa	Lenny	Leslie
Marco	Mindy	Mitch	Maria	Michael
Nana	Nicholas	Nicole	Nate	Nadine
Omar	Odette	Otto	Ophelia	Oscar
Paloma	Peter	Paula	Philippe	Patty
Rene	Rose	Richard	Rita	Rafael
Sally	Sam	Shary	Stan	Sandy
Teddy	Teresa	Tomas	Tammy	Tony
Vicky	Victor	Virginie	Vince	Valerie
Wilfred	Wanda	Walter	Wilma	William

Which United States **hurricanes** have caused the **most deaths**?

The ten deadliest United States hurricanes are listed below.

Hurricane	Year	Deaths
1. Texas (Galveston)	1900	6,000
2. Florida (Lake Okeechobee)	1928	1,836
3. Florida (Keys/S. Texas)	1919	600–900+
4. New England	1938	600
5. Florida (Keys)	1935	408
6. Louisiana/Texas	1957	390
7. Northeast U.S.	1944	390
8. Louisiana (Grand Isle)	1909	350
9. Louisiana (New Orleans)	1915	275
10. Texas (Galveston)	1915	275

What was the **greatest natural disaster** in United States history?

The greatest natural disaster occurred when a hurricane struck Galveston, Texas, on September 8, 1900, and killed over 6,000 people. However, the costliest national disaster to date was Hurricane Andrew, which hit Florida on August 31, 1992, and Louisiana on September 1, 1992. Early warning kept the death toll low, but property damage is estimated at $20 billion.

PRECIPITATION

What is the **dew point**?

The dew point is the temperature at which air is full of moisture and cannot store any more. When the relative humidity is 100%, the dew point is either the same as or lower than the air temperature. If a fine film of air contacts a surface and is chilled to below the dew point, then actual dew is formed. This is why dew often forms at night or early morning: as the temperature of the air falls, the amount of water vapor the air can hold also decreases. Excess water vapor then condenses as very small drops on whatever it touches. Fog and clouds develop when sizable volumes of air are cooled to temperatures below the dew point.

How **fast** does **rain** fall?

The speed of rainfall varies with drop size and wind speed. A typical raindrop in still air falls about 600 feet (182 meters) per minute or about seven miles (11 kilometers) per hour.

Where is the **rainiest place** on Earth?

The wettest place in the world is Tutunendo, Colombia, with an average annual rainfall of 463.4 inches (1,177 centimeters) per year. The place that has the most rainy

What is the shape of a raindrop?

Although a raindrop has been illustrated as being pear-shaped or tear-shaped, high-speed photographs reveal that a large raindrop has a spherical shape with a hole not quite through it (giving it a doughnut-like appearance). Water surface tension pulls the drop into this shape. As a drop larger than 0.08 inch (two millimeters) in diameter falls, it will become distorted. Air pressure flattens its bottom and its sides bulge. If it becomes larger than one-quarter inch (6.4 millimeters) across, it will keep spreading crosswise as it falls and will bulge more at its sides, while at the same time, its middle will thin into a bow-tie shape. Eventually in its path downward, it will divide into two smaller spherical drops.

119

days per year is Mount Wai-'ale'ale on Kauai, Hawaii. It has up to 350 rainy days annually.

In contrast, the longest rainless period in the world was from October 1903 to January 1918 at Arica, Chile—a period of 14 years. In the United States the longest dry spell was 767 days at Bagdad, California, from October 3, 1912, to November 8, 1914.

What is the **greatest amount of rainfall** ever measured?

Time duration	Amount		Place
	Inches	Centimeters	
1 minute	1.5	3.8	Barst, Guadeloupe, West Indies, November 26, 1970
24 hours	73.62	187	Cilaos, La Réunion, Indian Ocean, March 15–16, 1952
24 hours in the United States	19.0	48.3	Alvin, Texas, July 25–26, 1979
calendar month	366.14	930	Cherrapunji, Meghalaya, India, July 1861
12 months	1,041.78	2646	Cherrapunji, Meghalaya, India, between August 1, 1860 and July 31, 1861
12 months in the United States	739	1877	Kukui, Maui, Hawaii, December 1981–December 1982

When do **thunderstorms** occur?

In the United States thunderstorms usually occur in the summertime, especially from May through August. Thunderstorms tend to occur in late spring and summer when large amounts of tropical maritime air move across the United States. Storms usually develop when the surface air is heated the most from the sun (2 to 4 p.m.). Thunderstorms are relatively rare in the New England area, North Dakota, Montana, and other northern states (latitude 60 degrees) where the air is often too cold. These storms are also rare along the Pacific Ocean because the summers there are too dry for these storms to occur. Florida, the Gulf states, and the southeastern states tend to have the most storms, averaging 70 to 90 annually. The mountainous southwest averages 50 to 70 storms annually. In the world, thunderstorms are most plentiful in the areas between latitude 35 degrees north and 35 degrees south; in these areas there can be as many as 3,200 storms within a 12-hour nighttime period. As many as 1,800 storms can occur at once throughout the world.

Lightning does perform a vital function; it returns to the Earth much of the negative charge the Earth loses by leakage into the atmosphere. The annual death toll in

What would cause frogs and toads to fall from the sky like a rain shower?

Documented cases of showers of frogs have been recorded since 1794, usually during heavy summer rainstorms. Whirlwinds, waterspouts, and tornadoes are given as the conventional explanation. Extensive falls of fish, birds, and other animals have also been reported.

the United States from lightning is greater than the annual death toll from tornadoes or hurricanes—150 Americans die annually from lightning and 250 are injured.

How far away can **thunder** be heard?

Thunder is the crash and rumble associated with lightning. It is caused by the explosive expansion and contraction of air heated by the stroke of lightning. This results in sound waves that can be heard easily six to seven miles (9.7 to 11.3 kilometers) away. Occasionally such rumbles can be heard as far away as 20 miles (32.2 kilometers). The sound of great claps of thunder are produced when intense heat and the ionizing effect of repeated lightning occurs in a previously heated air path. This creates a shock wave that moves at the speed of sound.

How large can **hailstones** become?

The average hailstone is about one-quarter inch (0.64 centimeter) in diameter. However, hailstones weighing up to 7.5 pounds (3.4 kilograms) are reported to have fallen in Hyderabad state in India in 1939, although scientists think these huge hailstones may be several stones that partly melted and stuck together. On April 14, 1986, hailstones weighing 2.5 pounds (one kilogram) were reported to have fallen in the Gopalgang district of Bangladesh.

The largest hailstone ever recorded in the United States fell in Coffeyville, Kansas, on September 3, 1970. It measured 5.57 inches (14.15 centimeters) in diameter and weighed 1.67 pounds (0.75 kilogram).

Hail is precipitation consisting of balls of ice. Hailstones usually are made of concentric, or onion-like, layers of ice alternating with partially melted and refrozen snow, structured around a tiny central core. It is formed in cumulonimbus or thunderclouds when freezing water and ice cling to small particles in the air, such as dust. The winds in the cloud blow the particles through zones of different temperatures, causing them to accumulate additional layers of ice and melting snow and to increase in size.

What is the difference between **freezing rain** and **sleet**?

Freezing rain is rain that falls as a liquid but turns to ice on contact with a freezing object to form a smooth ice coating called *glaze*. Usually freezing rain only lasts a short time, because it either turns to rain or to snow. Sleet is frozen or partially frozen rain in the form of ice pellets. Sleet forms when rain falls from a warm layer of air, passes through a freezing air layer near the Earth's surface, and forms hard, clear, tiny ice pellets that can hit the ground so fast that they bounce off with a sharp click.

How does **snow** form?

Snow is not frozen rain. Snow forms by sublimation of water vapor—the turning of water vapor directly into ice, without going through the liquid stage. High above the ground, chilled water vapor turns to ice when its temperature reaches the dew point. The result of this sublimation is a crystal of ice, usually hexagonal. Snow begins in the form of these tiny hexagonal ice crystals in the high clouds; the young crystals are the seeds from which snowflakes will grow. As water vapor is pumped up into the air by updrafts, more water is deposited on the ice crystals, causing them to grow. Soon some of the larger crystals fall to the ground as snowflakes.

How much **water** is in an **inch of snow**?

An average figure is 10 inches (25 centimeters) of snow is equal to one inch (2.5 centimeters) of water. Heavy, wet snow has a high water content; four to five inches (10 to 12 centimeters) may contain one inch (2.5 centimeters) of water. A dry, powdery snow might require 15 inches (38 centimeters) of snow to equal one inch (2.5 centimeters) of water.

Are all **snowflakes shaped** alike?

Some snowflakes may have strikingly similar shapes, but these twins are probably not molecularly identical. In 1986, cloud physicist Nancy Knight believed she found a uniquely cloned pair of crystals on an oil coated slide that had been hanging from an airplane. This pair may have been the result of breaking off from a star crystal, or were attached side by side thereby experiencing the same weather conditions simultaneously. Unfortunately the smaller aspects of each of the snow crystals could not be studied because the photograph was unable to capture possible molecular differences. So, even if the human eye may see twins flakes, on a minuscule level these flakes are

different.

What is the record for the **greatest snowfall** in the United States?

The record for the most snow in a single storm is 189 inches (480 centimeters) at Mount Shasta Ski Bowl in California from February 13–19, 1959. For the most snow in a 24-hour day, the record goes to Silver Lake, Colorado on April 14–15, 1921, with 76 inches (193 centimeters) of snow. The year record goes to Paradise, Mount Rainier, in Washington with 1,224.5 inches (3,110 centimeters) from February 19, 1971 to February 18, 1972. The highest average annual snowfall was 241 inches (612 centimeters) for Blue Canyon, California. In March 1911, Tamarack, California, had the deepest snow accumulation—over 37.5 feet (11.4 meters).

Is it ever **too cold** to snow?

No matter how cold the air gets, it still contains some moisture, and this can fall out of the air in the form of very small snow crystals. Very cold air is associated with no snow because these invasions of air from northerly latitudes are associated with clearing conditions behind cold fronts. Heavy snowfalls are associated with relatively mild air in advance of a warm front. The fact that snow piles up, year after year, in Arctic regions illustrates that it is never too cold to snow.

When does **frost** form?

A frost is a crystalline deposit of small thin ice crystals formed on objects that are at freezing or below freezing temperatures. This phenomenon occurs when atmospheric water vapor condenses directly into ice without first becoming a liquid; this process is called sublimation. Usually frost appears on clear, calm nights, especially during early autumn when the air above the Earth is quite moist. Permafrost is ground permanently frozen that never thaws out completely.

WEATHER PREDICTION

When did modern **weather forecasting** begin?

On May 14, 1692, a weekly newspaper, *A Collection for the Improvement of Husbandry and Trade*, gave a seven-day table with pressure and wind readings for the comparable dates of the previous year. Readers were expected to make up their own forecasts from the data. Other journals soon followed with their own weather features. In 1771, a new journal called the *Monthly Weather Paper* was completely devoted to weather prediction. In 1861, the British Meteorological Office began issuing daily weather forecasts. The first broadcast of weather forecasts was done by the University of Wisconsin's station 9XM at Madison, Wisconsin, on January 3, 1921.

What is nowcasting?

Nowcasting is a form of very short-range weather forecasting. The term is sometimes used loosely to refer to any area-specific forecast for the period up to 12 hours ahead that is based on very detailed observational data. However, nowcasting should probably be defined more restrictively as the detailed description of the current weather along with forecasts obtained by extrapolation up to about two hours ahead.

What is barometric pressure and what does it mean?

Barometric, or atmospheric, pressure is the force exerted on a surface by the weight of the air above that surface, as measured by an instrument called a barometer. Pressure is greater at lower levels because the air's molecules are squeezed under the weight of the air above. So while the average air pressure at sea level is 14.7 pounds per square inch, at 1,000 feet (304 meters) above sea level, the pressure drops to 14.1 pounds per square inch, and at 18,000 feet (5,486 meters) the pressure is 7.3 pounds, about half of the figure at sea level. Changes in air pressure bring weather changes. High pressure areas bring clear skies and fair weather; low pressure areas bring wet or stormy weather. Areas of very low pressure have serious storms, such as hurricanes.

Can groundhogs accurately predict the weather?

Over a 60-year period, groundhogs have accurately predicted the weather (i.e., when spring will start) only 28% of the time on Groundhog Day, February 2. Groundhog Day was first celebrated in Germany, where farmers would watch for a badger to emerge from winter hibernation. If the day was sunny, the sleepy badger would be frightened by his shadow and duck back for another six weeks' nap; if it was cloudy he would stay out, knowing that spring had arrived. German farmers who emigrated to Pennsylvania brought the celebration to America. Finding no badgers in Pennsylvania, they chose the groundhog as a substitute.

Can weather be predicted from the stripes on a wooly-bear caterpillar?

It is an old superstition that the severity of the coming winter can be predicted by the width of the brown bands or stripes around the wooly-bear caterpillar in the autumn.

If the brown bands are wide, says the superstition, the winter will be mild, but if the

Are there trees that predict the weather and tell time?

Observing the leaves of a tree may be an old-fashioned method of predicting the weather, but farmers have noted that when maple leaves curl and turn bottom up in a blowing wind, rain is sure to follow. Woodsmen claim they can tell how rough a winter is going to be by the density of lichens on a nut tree. Before the katydid awakes, a black gum tree is able to indicate the oncoming winter. Trees can also be extraordinary timekeepers: *Griffonia*, in tropical west Africa, has two-inch (five-centimeter) inflated pods that burst with a hearty noise, indicating that it is time for farmers of the Accra Plains to plant crops; *Trichilia* is a 60-foot (18-meter) tree that flowers in February and again in August, signaling that it is time, just before the second rains arrive, for the second planting of corn. In the Fiji Islands, planting yams is cued by the flowering of the coral tree.

brown bands are narrow, a rough winter is foretold. Studies at the American Museum of Natural History in New York failed to show any connection between the weather and the caterpillar's stripes. This belief is only a superstition; it has no basis in scientific fact.

Is a **halo** around the **sun or moon** a sign of rain or snow approaching?

The presence of a ring around the sun or, more commonly, the moon in the night sky, betrays very high ice crystals composing cirrostratus clouds. The brighter the ring, the greater the odds of precipitation and the sooner it may be expected. Rain or snow will not *always* fall, but two times out of three, precipitation will start to fall within twelve to eighteen hours. These cirroform clouds are a forerunner of an approaching warm front and an associated low pressure system.

MINERALS AND OTHER MATERIALS

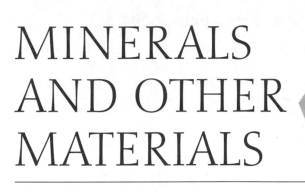

ROCKS AND MINERALS

See also: Energy

How do **rocks** differ?

Rocks can be conveniently placed into one of three groups—igneous, sedimentary, and metamorphic.

Igneous rocks, such as granite, pegmatite, rhyolite, obsidian, gabbro, and basalt, are formed by the solidification of molten magma that emerges through the Earth's crust via volcanic activity. The nature and properties of the crystals vary greatly, depending in part on the composition of the original magma and partly on the conditions under which the magma solidified. There are thousands of different igneous rock types. For example, granite is formed by slow cooling of molten material (within the Earth). It has large crystals of quartz, feldspars, and mica.

Sedimentary rocks, such as brecchia, sandstone, shale, limestone, chert, and coals, are produced by the accumulation of sediments. These are fine rock particles or fragments, skeletons of microscopic organisms, or minerals leached from rocks that have accumulated from weathering. These sediments are then redeposited under water and later compressed in layers over time. The most common sedimentary rock is sandstone, which is predominantly quartz crystals.

Metamorphic rocks, such as marble, slate, schist, gneiss, quartzite, and hornsfel, are formed by the alteration of igneous and sedimentary rocks through heat and/or pressure. One example of these physical and chemical changes is the formation of marble from thermal changes in limestone.

What is **petrology** and what does a **petrologist** do?

Petrology is the science of rocks. A petrologist is a person who studies the mineralogy of rocks and the record of the geological past contained within rocks. From rocks, a petrologist can learn about past climates and geography, past and present composition of the Earth, and the conditions that prevail within the interior of the Earth.

How are **fossils formed**?

Fossils are the remains of animals or plants that were preserved in rock before the beginning of recorded history. It is unusual for complete organisms to be preserved; fossils usually represent the hard parts such as bones or shells of animals and leaves, seeds, or woody parts of plants.

Some fossils are simply the bones, teeth, or shells themselves, which can be preserved for a relatively short period of time. Another type of fossil is the imprint of a buried plant or animal that decomposes, leaving a film of carbon that retains the form of the organism.

Some buried material is replaced by silica and other materials that permeate the organism and replace the original material in a process called petrification. Some woods are replaced by agate or opal so completely that even the cellular structure is duplicated. The best examples of this can be found in the Petrified Forest National Park in Arizona.

Molds and casts are other very common fossils. A mold is made from an imprint, such as a dinosaur footprint, in soft mud or silt. This impression may harden, then be covered with other materials. The original footprint will have formed a mold and the sediments filling it will be a cast of the footprint.

How **old** are **fossils**?

The oldest known fossils are of single-celled organisms, blue-green algae, found in 3.2 billion-year-old cherts, shales, and sandstone from the Transvaal of South Africa. Multicellular fossils dating from about 700 million years ago are also known. The largest number of fossils come from the Cambrian period of 590 million years ago, when living organisms began to develop skeletons and hard parts. Since these parts tended to last longer than ordinary tissue, they were more likely to be preserved in clay and become fossilized.

What are **Indian Dollars**?

They are six-sided disk-shaped twin crystals of aragonite ($CaCO_3$), which have altered to calcite but retained their outer form. They occur in large numbers in northern Colorado, where they are known as "Indian Dollars." In New Mexico they are called "Aztec Money" and in western Kansas they are called "Pioneer Dollars."

How does a **rock** differ from a **mineral**?

Mineralogists use the term "mineral" for a substance that has all four of the following features: it must be found in nature; it must be made up of substances that were never alive (organic); it has the same chemical makeup wherever it is found; and its atoms are arranged in a regular pattern and form solid crystals.

While "rocks" are sometimes described as an aggregate or combination of one or more minerals, geologists extend the definition to include clay and loose sand and certain limestones.

Who was the first person to attempt a **color standardization** scheme for minerals?

The German mineralogist Abraham Gottlob Werner (1750–1817) devised a method of describing minerals by their external characteristics, including color. He worked out an arrangement of colors and color names, illustrated by an actual set of minerals.

What is the **Mohs scale**?

The Mohs scale is a standard of 10 minerals by which the hardness of a mineral is rated. It was introduced in 1812 by the German mineralogist Friedrich Mohs (1773–1839). The minerals are arranged from softest to hardest.

Hardness	Mineral	Comment
1	Talc	Hardness 1–2 can be scratched by a fingernail
2	Gypsum	Hardness 2–3 can be scratched by a copper coin
3	Calcite	Hardness 3–6 can be scratched by a steel pocket knife
4	Fluorite	
5	Apatite	
6	Orthoclase	Hardness 6–7 will not scratch glass
7	Quartz	
8	Topaz	Hardness 8–10 will scratch glass
9	Corundum	
10	Diamond	

What is meant by the term **strategic minerals**?

Strategic minerals are minerals essential to national defense—the supply of which a country uses but cannot produce itself. 33% to 50% of the 80 minerals used by industry could be classed as strategic minerals. Wealthy countries, such as the United States, stockpile these minerals to avoid any crippling effect on their economy or military strength if political circumstances were to cut off their supplies. The United States, for instance, stockpiles bauxite (14.5 million tons), manganese (2.2 million tons), chromium (1.8 million tons), tin (185,000 tons), cobalt (19,000 tons), tantalum (635 tons), palladium (1.25 million troy ounces), and platinum (453,000 troy ounces).

What is **pitchblende**?

Pitchblende is a massive variety of uraninite or uranium oxide found in metallic veins. It is radioactive material and the most important ore of uranium. It is the original source of radium.

What is **galena**?

Galena is a lead sulphide (PbS) and the most common ore of lead, containing 86.6% lead. Lead-gray in color, with a brilliant metallic luster, galena has a specific gravity of 7.5 and a hardness of 2.5 on the Mohs scale, and usually occurs as cubes or a modification of an octahedral form. Mined in Australia, it is also found in Missouri, Kansas, Oklahoma, Colorado, Montana, and Idaho.

What is **stibnite**?

Stibnite is a lead-gray mineral (Sb_2S_3) with a metallic luster. It is the most important ore of antimony, and is also known as antimony glance. One of the few minerals that fuse easily in a match flame (977°F or 525°C), stibnite has a hardness of two on the Mohs scale and a specific gravity of 4.5 to 4.6. It is commonly found in hydrothermal veins or hot springs deposits. Stibnite is mined in Germany, Romania, France, Bolivia, Peru, and Mexico. The Yellow Pine mine at Stibnite, Idaho, is the largest producer in the United States, but California and Nevada also have deposits.

What are **Cape May diamonds**?

They are quartz pebbles, found in the vicinity of the Coast Guard station in Cape May, New Jersey. The pebbles are polished, faceted, and sold to tourists as "Cape May diamonds."

Are there any **diamond mines** in the United States?

The only significant diamond deposit in North America is at Murfreesboro, Arkansas. It is on government-owned land and has never been systematically developed. For a small fee, tourists can dig there and try to find diamonds. The largest crystal found there weighed 40.23 carats and was named the "Uncle Sam" diamond.

What is fool's gold?

Iron pyrite (FeS_2) is a mineral popularly known as "fool's gold." Because of its metallic luster and pale brass yellow color it is often mistaken for gold. Real gold is much heavier, softer, not brittle, and not grooved.

Diamonds crystallize directly from rock melts rich in magnesium and saturated with carbon dioxide gas that has been subjected to high pressures and temperatures exceeding 2559°F (1400°C). These rock melts originally came from deep in the Earth's mantle at depths of 93 miles (150 kilometers).

Diamonds are minerals composed entirely of the element carbon, with an isometric crystalline structure. The hardest natural substance, gem diamonds have a density of 3.53, though black diamonds (black carbon cokelike aggregates of microscopic crystals) may have a density as low as 3.15. Diamonds have the highest thermal conductivity of any known substance. This property enables diamonds to be used in cutting tools, because they do not become hot.

How can a **genuine diamond** be identified?

There are several tests that can be performed without the aid of tools. A knowledgeable person can recognize the surface lustre, straightness and flatness of facets, and high light reflectivity. Diamonds become warm in a warm room and cool if the surroundings are cool. A simple test that can be done is exposing the stones to warmth and cold and then touching them to one's lips to determine their appropriate temperature. This is especially effective when the results of this test are compared to the results of the test done on a diamond known to be genuine. Another test is to pick up the stone with a moistened fingertip. If this can be done, then the stone is likely to be a diamond. The majority of other stones cannot be picked up in this way.

The water test is another simple test. A drop of water is placed on a table. A perfectly clean diamond has the ability to almost "magnetize" water and will keep the water from spreading. An instrument called a diamond probe can detect even the most sophisticated fakes. Gemologists always use this as part of their inspection.

How is the **value of a diamond** determined?

Demand, beauty, durability, rarity, freedom from defects, and perfection of cutting determine the value of a gemstone. But the major factor in establishing the price of gem diamonds is the control over output and price as exercised by the Central Selling

Organization's (CSO) Diamond Trading Company Ltd. The CSO is a subsidiary of DeBeers Consolidated Mines Ltd.

How are **diamonds weighed**?

The basic unit is a carat, which is 200 milligrams or 1/142 of an avoirdupois ounce. A well-cut round diamond of one carat measures almost exactly 0.25 inch (6.3 millimeters) in diameter. Another unit commonly used is the point, which is one hundredth of a carat. A stone of one carat weighs 100 points.

Which **diamond** is the **world's largest**?

The Cullinan Diamond, weighing 3,106 carats, is the world's largest. It was discovered on January 25, 1905, at the Premier Diamond Mine, Transvaal, South Africa. Named for Sir Thomas M. Cullinan, chairman of the Premier Diamond Company, it was cut into nine major stones and 96 smaller brilliants. The total weight of the cut stones was 1,063 carats, only 35% of the original weight.

Cullinan I, also known as the "Greater Star of Africa" or the "First Star of Africa," is a pear-shaped diamond weighing 530.2 carats. It is 2.12 inches (5.4 centimeters) long, 1.75 inches (4.4 centimeters) wide, and one inch (2.5 centimeters) thick at its deepest point. It was presented to Britain's King Edward VII in 1907, and was set in the British monarch's sceptre with the cross. It is still the largest cut diamond in the world.

Cullinan II, also know as the "Second Star of Africa," is an oblong stone that weighs 317.4 carats. It is set in the British Imperial State Crown.

Besides the Cullinan diamonds, what are the **largest precious stones**?

The largest ruby is a 8,500 carat stone that is 5.5 inches (14 centimeters) tall, carved to resemble the Liberty Bell. The largest star ruby is the 6,465 carat "Eminent Star" from India that has a six-line star. The largest cut emerald was found in Carnaiba, Brazil, in August 1974. It is 86,136 carats. A 2,302 carat sapphire from Anakie, Queensland, Australia, was carved into a 1,318 carat head of Abraham Lincoln, making it the largest carved sapphire. "The Lone Star," at 9,719.5 carats, is the largest star sapphire. The largest natural pearl is the "Pearl of Lao-tze," also called the "Pearl of Allah." Found in May 1934 in the shell of a giant clam at Palawan, Philippines, the pearl weighs 14 pounds, 1 ounce (6.4 kilograms).

How does the **emerald** get its color?

Emerald is a variety of green beryl ($Be_3Al_2Si_6O_{18}$) that is colored by a trace of chromium

(Cr), which replaces the aluminum (Al) in the beryl structure. Other green beryls exist; but if no chromium is present, they are, technically speaking, not emeralds.

How is the star in **star sapphires** produced?

Sapphires are composed of blue gem-quality corundum (Al_2O_3). When cut in the unfaceted cabochon (dome or convex) form, a sapphire with a trace of titanium dioxide will display a rayed (star) figure that usually has six rays. The same effect produces the star in star rubies as well.

What is a **tiger's eye**?

Tiger's eye is a semiprecious quartz gem that has a vertical luminescent band like that of a cat's eye. To achieve the effect of a cat's eye, veins of parallel blue asbestos fibers are first altered to iron oxides and then replaced by silica. The gem has a rich yellow to yellow-brown or brown color.

METALS

Which **metallic element** is the **most abundant**?

Aluminum is the most abundant metallic element on the surface of the Earth and moon; it comprises more than 8% of the Earth's crust. It is never free in nature, combining with oxygen, sand, iron, titanium, etc.; its ores are mainly bauxites (aluminum hydroxide). Nearly all rocks, particularly igneous rocks, contain aluminum as aluminosilicate minerals. Napoleon III (1808–1883) recognized that the physical characteristic of its lightness could revolutionize the arms industry, so he granted a large subsidy to French chemist Sainte-Claire Deville (1818–1881) to develop a method to make its commercial use feasible. In 1854, Deville obtained the first pure aluminum metal through the process of reduction of aluminum chloride. In 1886, the American Charles Martin Hall (1863–1914) and the Frenchman Paul Heroult (1863–1914) independently discovered an electrolytic process to produce aluminum from bauxite. Because of aluminum's resistance to corrosion, low density, and excellent heat-conducting property, it is used in cookware manufacturing and can-making industries. It is a good conductor of electricity and is widely used in overhead cables. Aluminum alloys, such as duralumin, have high tensile strengths and are of considerable industrial importance, especially in the aerospace industry.

Why are **alchemical symbols for metals** and **astrological symbols for planets** identical?

The ancient Greeks and Romans knew seven metals and also knew seven "planets" (the five nearer planets plus the sun and the moon). They related each planet to a specific metal. Alchemy, originating in about the third century B.C.E., focused on changing base metals, such as lead, into gold. Although at times alchemy bordered on mysticism, it contained centuries of chemical experience, which provided the foundation for the development of modern chemistry.

English name	Chemical symbol	Latin name	Alchemical symbol
Gold	Au	*aurum*	☉(Sun)
Silver	Ag	*argentum*	☽ (Moon)
Copper	Cu	*cuprum*	♀ (Venus)
Iron	Fe	*ferrum*	♂ (Mars)
Mercury	Hg	*hydrargyrum*	☿(Mercury)
Tin	Sn	*stannum*	♃(Jupiter)
Lead	Pb	*plumbum*	♄(Saturn)

What are the **noble metals**?

The noble metals are gold, silver, mercury, and the platinum group (including palladium, iridium, rhodium, ruthenium, and osmium). The term refers to those metals highly resistant to chemical reaction or corrosion and is contrasted with "base" metals, which are not so resistant. The term has its origins in ancient alchemy whose goals of transformation and perfection were pursued through the different properties of metals and chemicals. The term is not synonomous with "precious metals," although a metal, like platinium, may be both.

What are the **precious metals**?

This is a general term for expensive metals that are used for making coins, jewelry, and ornaments. The name is limited to gold, silver, and platinum. Expense or rarity does not make a metal precious, but rather, it is a value set by law that states that the object made of these metals has a certain intrinsic value. The term is not synonymous with "noble metals," although a metal (such as platinum) may be both noble and precious.

What is **24 karat gold**?

The term "karat" refers to the percentage of gold versus the percentage of an alloy in an object. Gold is too soft to be usable in its purest form; it has to be mixed with other
metals.

Karatage	Percentage of fine gold
24	100
22	91.75
18	75
14	58.5
12	50.25
10	42
9	37.8
8	33.75

Is white gold really gold?

White gold is the name of a class of jeweler's white alloys used as substitutes for platinum. Different grades vary widely in composition, but usual alloys consist of from 20% to 50% nickel, with the balance gold. A superior class of white gold is made of 90% gold and 10% palladium. Other elements used include copper and zinc. The main use of these alloys is to give the gold a white color.

How thick is **gold leaf**?

Gold leaf is pure gold that is hammered so thin that it can take 300,000 units to make a stack one inch high. The thickness of a single gold leaf is typically 0.0000035 inch (3.5 millionths of an inch), although this may vary widely according to which manufacturer makes it. Also called gold foil, it is used for architectural coverings and for hot-embossed printing on leather.

Gold leaf.

What are the chief **gold-producing countries**?

The Republic of South Africa is by far the leading producer of gold. Since the breakup of the former Soviet Union, the United States has become the second largest gold producing nation. Commercial usage in 1993 was estimated as follows: jewelry and arts, 71%; industrial (mainly electronic), 22%; and dental, 7%. In the United States, Nevada is the leading gold producer, with California a distant second, followed by South Dakota.

World production of the top six countries in 1993 was:

Country	Gold production
South Africa	1,365,338 lbs (619,201 kg)
United States	729,884 lbs (331,013 kg)
Australia	545,067 lbs (247,196 kg)
China	352,800 lbs (160,000 kg)
Canada	337,208 lbs (152,929 kg)
Russia	329,648 lbs (149,500 kg)

What is **sterling silver**?

Sterling silver is a high-grade alloy that contains a minimum of 925 parts in 1,000 of silver. It is used for fine tableware, jewelry, and electrical contacts.

What is **German silver**?

Nickel silver, sometimes known as German silver, is a silver-white alloy composed of 52% to 80% copper, 10% to 35% zinc, and 5% to 35% nickel. It may also contain a small percent of lead and tin. There are other forms of nickel silver, but the term "German silver" is the name used in the silverware trade.

Which metal is the main component of **pewter**?

Tin. Roman pewter has about 70% tin. The best pewter used for expensive articles today contains 100 parts tin, eight parts antimony, two parts bismuth, and two parts copper. This alloy is easy to work with, does not become brittle when repeatedly beaten, and can be worked cold. However, it is too soft to use for heavy tools or weapons, so its use is confined to domestic utensils.

Where were the first successful **ironworks** in America?

Although iron ore in this country was first discovered in North Carolina in 1585, and the manufacture of iron was first undertaken (but never accomplished) in Virginia in 1619, the first successful ironworks in America was established by Thomas Dexter and Robert Bridges near the Saugus River in Lynn, Massachusetts. As the original promoters of the enterprise, they hired John Winthrop, Jr. from England to begin production. By 1645, a blast furnace had begun operations and, by 1648 a forge was working there.

What is the Q-BOP process for **steelmaking**?

A variation of the basic oxygen process (BOP), it involves blowing high-purity oxygen
through a bath of molten pig iron. This is called the Q-BOP process and is used in the

production of low-alloy steel, which is defined as steel that has no more than 5% total combined alloying elements. It has mainly a surface hardness. The depth of hardness depends on the alloy content. There are five types of processes currently employed in the production of low-alloy steels: oxygen top-blowing, known as LD (Linz-Donawitz) process; BOF (basic oxygen furnace), or BOP; oxygen and lime bottom blowing, known as OBM or Q-BOP; top and bottom mixed blowing; open-hearth furnace; and electric-arc furnace.

What is **high speed steel**?

High speed steel is a general name for high alloy steels that retain their hardness at very high temperatures and are used for metal-cutting tools. All high speed steels are based on either tungsten or molybdenum (or both) as the primary heat-resisting alloying element. These steels require a special heat so that their unique properties can be fully realized. The manufacturing process consists of heating the steel to a temperature of 2150°F to 2400°F (1175°C to 1315°C) to obtain solution of a substantial percentage of the alloy carbides, quenching to room temperature, tempering at 1000°F to 1150°F (535°C to 620°C), and again cooling to room temperature.

Who invented **stainless steel**?

Metallurgists in several countries developed stainless steel between 1903 and 1912. An American, Elwood Haynes, developed several alloy steels and in 1911 produced stainless steel. Harry Brearly of Great Britain receives most of the credit for its development. Frederick Beckett, a Canadian-American metallurgist and German scientists P. Monnartz and W. Borchers were among the early developers.

What material is used to make a **tuning fork**?

A tuning fork, an instrument that when struck emits a fixed pitch, is made of steel.

Which countries have **uranium** deposits?

Uranium, a radioactive metallic element, is the only natural material capable of sustaining nuclear fission. But only one isotope, uranium-235, which occurs in one molecule out of 40 of natural uranium, can undergo fission under neutron bombardment. Mined in various parts of the world, it must then be converted during purification to uranium dioxide (UO_2). Uranium deposits occur throughout the world. The United States (especially Arizona, Colorado, New Mexico, North Carolina, and Utah), Canada, France, South Africa, Zaire, Australia, and the former Soviet Union have significant uranium resources. Canada and Zaire provide the best sources.

What is **technetium**?

Technetium (Tc, element 43) is a radioactive metallic element that does not occur naturally either in its pure form or as compounds; it is produced during nuclear fission. A fission product of molybdenum (Mo, element 42), Tc can also occur as a fission product of uranium (U, element 92). It was the first element to be made artificially in 1937 when it was isolated and extracted by C. Perrier and Emilio Segre (1905–1989).

Tc has found some application in diagnostic medicine. Ingested soluble technetium compounds tend to concentrate in the liver and are valuable in labeling and in radiological examination of that organ. Also, by technetium labeling of blood serum components, diseases involving the circulatory system can be explored.

NATURAL SUBSTANCES
See also: Energy

Is **lodestone** a magnet?

Lodestone is a magnetic variety of natural iron oxide. It was used by early mariners to find magnetic north. Lodestone is frequently called a natural magnet.

What is **red dog**?

Red dog is the residue from burned coal dumps. The dumps are composed of waste products incidental to coal mining. Under pressure in these waste dumps, the waste frequently ignites from spontaneous combustion, producing a red-colored ash, which is used for driveways, parking lots, and roads.

In coal mining what is meant by **damp**?

Damp is a poisonous or explosive gas in a mine. Carbon monoxide is known as white damp, and methane is known as firedamp. Blackdamp is formed by mine fires and explosion of firedamp in mines. It extinguishes fire and suffocates its victims. The average blackdamp contains 10% to 15% carbon dioxide and 85% to 90% nitrogen.

What is **diatomite**?

Diatomite (also called diatomaceous earth) is a white or cream-colored, friable, porous rock composed of the fossil remains of diatoms (small water plants with silica cell walls). These fossils build up on the ocean bottoms to form diatomite, and in some places, these areas have become dry land or diatomaceous earth. Chemically inert and having a rough texture and other unusual physical properties, it is suitable for many scientific and industrial purposes, including use as a filtering agent; building material; heat, cold, and sound insulator; catalyst carrier; filler absorbent; abrasive; and ingredient in pharmaceutical preparations. Dynamite is made from it by soaking it in the liquid explosive nitroglycerin.

What is **fuller's earth**?

It is a naturally occurring white or brown clay containing aluminum magnesium silicate. Once used to clean wool and cloth (known as fulling), it is currently used for decolorizing oils and fats, as a pigment extender, a filter, and an absorbent, and in floor sweeping compounds.

How much wood is used to make a ton of **paper**?

In the United States, the wood used for the manufacture of paper is mainly from small diameter bolts and pulpwood. It is usually measured by the cord or by weight. Although the fiber used in making paper is overwhelmingly wood fiber, a large percentage of other ingredients is needed. One ton of a typical paper requires two cords of wood, but also requires 55,000 gallons (208,000 liters) of water, 102 pounds (46 kilograms) of sulfur, 350 pounds (159 kilograms) of lime, 289 pounds (131 kilograms) of clay, 1.2 tons of coal, 112 kilowatt hours of power, 20 pounds (9 kilograms) of dye and pigments, and 108 pounds (49 kilograms) of starch, as well as other ingredients.

Which woods are used for **telephone poles**?

The principal woods used for telephone poles are southern pine, Douglas fir, western red cedar, and lodgepole pine. Ponderosa pine, red pine, jack pine, northern white cedar, other cedars, and western larch are also used.

Which woods are used for **railroad ties**?

Many species of wood are used for ties. The more common are oaks, gums, Douglas fir, mixed hardwoods, hemlock, southern pine, and mixed softwoods.

What products come from **tropical forests**?

Products from Tropical Forests

Woods	Houseplants	Spices	Foods
Balsa	*Anthurium*	Allspice	Avocado

Mahogany
Rosewood
Sandalwood
Teak

Fibers
Bamboo
Jute/Kenaf
Kapok
Raffia
Ramie
Rattan

Gums, resins
Chicle latex
Copaiba
Copal
Gutta percha
Rubber latex
Tung oil

Croton
Dieffenbachia
Dracaena
Fiddle-leaf fig
Mother-in-law's tongue
Parlor ivy
Philodendron
Rubber tree plant
Schefflera
Silver vase bromeliad
Spathiphyllum
Swiss cheese plant
Zebra plant

Oils, etc.
Camphor oil
Cascarilla oil
Coconut oil
Eucalyptus oil
Oil of star anise
Palm oil
Patchouli oil
Rosewood oil
Tolu balsam oil
Annatto
Curare
Diosgenin
Quinine
Reserpine
Strophanthus
Strychnine
Yang-Yang

Black pepper
Cardamom
Cayenne
Chili
Cinnamon
Cloves
Ginger
Mace
Nutmeg
Paprika
Sesame seeds
Turmeric
Vanilla bean

Banana
Coconut
Grapefruit
Lemon
Lime
Mango
Orange
Papaya
Passion fruit
Pineapple
Plantain
Tangerine
Brazil nuts
Cane sugar
Cashew nuts
Chocolate
Coffee
Cucumber
Hearts of palm
Macadamia nuts
Manioc/tapioca
Okra
Peanuts
Peppers
Cola beans
Tea

What wood is the favorite for **butcher's blocks**?

The preferred wood for butcher's blocks is the American sycamore (*Platanus occidentalis*), also known as American planetree, buttonball, buttonwood, plane-tree and water beech, because of its toughness. It is also used as a veneer for decorative surfaces as well as for railroad ties, fence posts and fuel.

Does any type of **wood sink** in water?

Ironwood is a name applied to many hard, heavy woods. Some ironwoods are so dense that their specific gravity exceeds 1.0 and they are therefore unable to float in water.

How is petrified wood formed?

Petrified wood is formed when water containing dissolved minerals such as calcium carbonate ($CaCO_3$) and silicate infiltrates wood or other structures. The process takes thousands of years. The foreign material either replaces or encloses the organic matter and often retains all the structural details of the original plant material. Botanists find these types of fossils to be very important since they allow for the study of the internal structure of extinct plants. After a time, wood seems to have turned to stone because the original form and structure are retained. The wood itself does not turn to stone.

North American ironwoods include the American hornbeam, the mesquite, the desert ironwood, and leadwood (*Krugiodendron ferreum*), which has a specific gravity of 1.34–1.42, making it the heaviest in the United States.

The heaviest wood is black ironwood (*Olea laurifolia*), also called South African ironwood. Found in the West Indies, it has a specific gravity of 1.49 and weighs up to 93 pounds (42.18 kilograms) per foot. The lightest wood is *Aeschynomene hispida*, found in Cuba, with a specific gravity of 0.044 and a weight of 2.5 pounds (1.13 kilograms) per foot. Balsa wood (*Ochroma pyramidale*) varies between 2.5 and 24 pounds (one to 10 kilograms) per foot.

What is rosin?

Rosin is the resin produced after the distillation of turpentine, obtained from several varieties of pine trees, especially the longleaf pine (*Pinus palustris*) and the slash pine (*Pinus caribaea*). Rosin is used in varnishes, paint driers, soluble oils, paper-sizing, belt dressings, and for producing many chemicals.

What are naval stores?

Naval stores are products of such coniferous trees as pine and spruce. These products include pitch, tar, resin, turpentine, pine oil, and terpenes. The term "naval stores" originated in the seventeenth century when these materials were used for building and maintaining wooden sailing ships.

141

Why are **essential oils** called "essential"?

Called essential oils because of their ease of solubility in alcohol to form essences, essential oils are used in flavorings, perfumes, disinfectants, medicine, and other products. They are naturally occurring volatile aromatic oils found in uncombined forms within various parts of plants (leaves, pods, etc.). These oils contain as one of their main ingredients a substance belonging to the terpene group. Examples of essential oils include bergamot, eucalyptus, ginger, pine, spearmint, and wintergreen oils. Extracted by distillation or enfleurage (extraction using fat) and mechanical pressing, these oils can now be made synthetically.

What is **gutta percha**?

Gutta percha is a rubberlike gum obtained from the milky sap of trees of the Sapotaceae family, found in Indonesia and Malaysia. Once of great economic value, gutta percha is now being replaced by plastics in many items, although it is still used in some electrical insulation and dental work. The English natural historian John Tradescant (c. 1570–1638) introduced gutta percha to Europe in the 1620s, and its inherent qualities gave it a slow but growing place in world trade. By the end of World War II, however, many manufacturers switched from gutta percha to plastics, which are more versatile and cheaper to produce.

What is **excelsior**?

Excelsior is a trade name dating from the mid-nineteenth century for the curly, fine wood shavings used as packing material when shipping breakable items. It is also used as a cushioning and stuffing material. Poplar, aspen, basswood or cottonwood are woods that are often made into excelsior.

What is **ambergris**?

Ambergris, a highly odorous waxy substance found floating in tropical seas, is a secretion from the sperm whale (*Physeter catodon*). The whale secretes ambergris to protect its stomach from the sharp bone of the cuttlefish, a squid-like sea mollusk, which it ingests. Ambergris is used in perfumery as a fixature to extend the life of a perfume and as a flavoring for food and beverages. Today ambergris is synthesized and used by the perfume trade, which has voluntarily refused to purchase ambergris to protect

sperm whales from exploitation.

Where does **isinglass** come from?

Isinglass is the purest form of animal gelatin. It is manufactured from the swimming bladder of the sturgeon. It is used in the clarification of wine and beer as well as in the making of some cements, jams, jellies, and soups.

What products are made from **horsehair**?

Products made from horsehair include baskets, belts, bird nests, hair and industrial brushes, buttons, carpet, curlers, fishing lines, furniture padding, hats, lariats, fishing nets, plumes for military hats or horse bridles, surgical sutures (during the Civil War), upholstery cloth, bows (for violin, cello, and viola), whips, and wigs.

From where do **frankincense and myrrh** originate?

Frankincense is an aromatic resin obtained by tapping the trunks of trees belonging to the genus *Boswellia*. The milky resin hardens when exposed to the air and forms irregular lumps—the form in which it is usually marketed.

Myrrh comes from a tree of the genus *Commiphora*, a native of Arabia and Northeast Africa. It too is a resin obtained from the tree trunk.

Where does a **luffa sponge** come from?

Luffas are nonwoody vines of the cucumber family. The interior fibrous skeletons of the fruit are used as sponges. The common name is sometimes spelled loofah. Dishcloth gourd, rag gourd, and vegetable sponge are other popular names for this sponge.

MAN–MADE PRODUCTS

How is **dry ice** made?

Dry ice is composed of carbon dioxide, which at normal temperatures is a gas. The carbon dioxide is stored and shipped as a liquid in tanks that are pressurized at 1,073 pounds per square inch. To make dry ice, the carbon dioxide liquid is withdrawn from the tank and allowed to evaporate at a normal pressure in a porous bag. This rapid evaporation consumes so much heat that part of the liquid CO_2 freezes to a temperature of -109°F (-78°C). The frozen liquid is then compressed by machines into blocks of "dry ice," which will melt into a gas again when set out at room temperature.

It was first made commercially in 1925 by the Prest-Air Devices Company of Long Island City, New York, through the efforts of Thomas Benton Slate. It was used by Schrafft's of New York in July 1925 to keep ice cream from melting. The first large sale of dry ice was made later in that year to Breyer Ice Cream Company of New York.

Why is **sulfuric acid** important?

Sometimes called "oil of vitriol," sulfuric acid (H_2SO_4) has become one of the most important of all chemicals. It was little used until it became essential for the manufacture of soda in the eighteenth century. It is prepared industrially by the reaction of water with sulfur trioxide, which in turn is made by chemical combination of sulfur dioxide and oxygen by one of two processes (the contact process or the chamber process). Many manufactured articles in common use depend in some way on sulfuric acid for their production. Its greatest use is in the production of fertilizers, but it is also used in the refining of petroleum, and production of automobile batteries, explosives, pigments, iron and other metals, and paper pulp.

What is **aqua regia**?

"Aqua regia," also known as nitrohydrochloric acid, is a mixture of one part concentrated nitric acid and three parts concentrated hydrochloric acid. The chemical reaction between the acids makes it possible to dissolve all metals except silver. The reaction of metals with nitrohydrochloric acid typically involves oxidation of the metals to a metallic ion and the reduction of the nitric acid to nitric oxide. The term comes from Latin and means royal water. It was named by the alchemists for its ability to dissolve gold, sometimes called the "royal metal."

Who developed the process for making **ammonia**?

Known since ancient times, ammonia (NH_3) has been commercially important for more than 100 years. The first breakthrough in the large-scale synthesis of ammonia resulted from the work of Fritz Haber (1863–1934). In 1913, Haber found that ammonia could be produced by combining nitrogen and hydrogen ($N_2+3H_2 \rightleftarrows 2NH_3$) with a catalyst (iron oxide with small quantities of cerium and chromium) at 131°F (55°C) under a pressure of about 200 atmospheres. The process was adapted for industrial-quality production by Karl Bosch (1874–1940). Thereafter, many improved ammonia-synthesis systems, based on the Haber-Bosch process, were commercialized using various operating conditions and synthesis loop-designs. One of the five top inorganic chemicals produced in the United States, it is used in refrigerants, detergents and other cleaning preparations, explosives, fabrics, and fertilizers. A little over 75% of ammonia production in the United States is used for fertilizers. It has been shown to produce cancer of the skin in humans, in doses of 1,000 milligram per kilogram (2.2 pounds) of body weight.

What does the symbol H₂O₂ stand for?

Hydrogen peroxide, a syrupy liquid used as a strong bleaching, oxidizing, and disinfecting agent, is the compound. It is made from barium peroxide and diluted phosphoric acid. A 3% solution of hydrogen peroxide is used medicinally as an antiseptic and germicide. Undiluted, it can cause burns to human skin and mucous membranes, is a fire and explosion risk, and can be highly toxic.

Who discovered **deuterium**?

American chemist Harold C. Urey (1893–1981), 1934 winner of the Nobel Prize for Chemistry, discovered deuterium (heavy hydrogen, symbol D) in 1931 with F.G. Brickwedde and G.M. Murphy. This isotope (a form of an element that differs in the number of neutrons and atomic weight) has twice the weight of hydrogen, while all the other isotopes differed slightly in their atomic weights. Deuterium and its oxide make heavy water (D_2O), which is used to slow down the neutrons in atomic piles of nuclear reactors.

What is the **lightest solid material**?

The lightest substance is silica aerogels, made of tiny spheres of bonded silicon and oxygen atoms linked together into long strands separated with air pockets. They appear almost like frozen wisps of smoke. In February 1990, the lightest of these aerosols, having a density of only five ounces per cubic foot, was produced at the Lawrence Livermore Laboratory in California. It will be used in window insulation, as traps for sampling cosmic dust in space, and in liquid rocket fuel storage.

What is **buckminsterfullerene**?

It is a large molecule in the shape of a soccer ball, containing 60 carbon atoms, whose structure is the shape of a truncated icosahedron (a hollow, spherical object with 32 faces, 12 of them pentagons and the rest hexagons). This molecule was named buckminsterfullerene because of the structure's resemblance to the geodesic domes designed by American architect R. Buckminster Fuller (1895–1983). The molecule was formed by vaporizing material from a graphite surface with a laser. Large molecules containing only carbon atoms have been known to exist around certain types of carbon-rich stars. Similar molecules are also thought to be present in soot formed during the incomplete combustion of organic materials. Chemist Richard Smalley identified buckminsterfullerene in 1985 and speculated that it may be fairly common throughout the universe. Since that time, other stable, large, even-numbered carbon clusters have been produced. This new class of molecules has been called "fullerenes" since they all seem to have the structure of a geodesic dome. They are also popularly known as "bucky balls." Buckministerfullerene (C_{60}) seems to function as an insulator, conductor, semi-conductor, and superconductor in various compounds; however, no practical application has yet to be developed for it or the other fullerenes.

Is **glass** a solid or a liquid?

Even at room temperature, glass appears to be a solid in the ordinary sense of the word. However, it actually is a fluid with an extremely high *viscosity,* which refers to the internal friction of fluids. Viscosity is a property of fluids by which the flow motion is gradually damped (slowed) and dissipated by heat. Viscosity is a familiar phenomenon in daily life. An opened bottle of wine can be poured: the wine flows easily under the influence of gravity. Maple syrup, on the other hand, cannot be poured so easily; under the action of gravity, it flows sluggishly. The syrup has a higher viscosity than the wine. It has been documented that century-old windows show signs of flow.

Glass is usually composed of mixed oxides based around the silicon dioxide (SiO_2) unit. A very good electrical insulator, and generally inert to chemicals, commercial glass is manufactured by the fusing of sand (silica, SiO_2), limestone ($CaCO_2$), and soda (sodium carbonate, Na_2CO_3) at temperatures around 2552°F to 2732°F (1400°C to 1500°C). On cooling, the melt becomes very viscous and at about 932°F (500°C, known as glass transition temperature), the melt "solidifies" to form soda glass. Small amounts of metal oxides are used to color glass, and its physical properties can be changed by the addition of substances like lead oxide (to increase softness, density, and refractive ability for cutglass and lead crystal), and borax (to significantly lower thermal expansion for cookware and laboratory equipment). Other materials can be used to form glasses if rapidly cooled from the liquid or gaseous phase to prevent an ordered crystalline structure from forming.

Glass objects might have been made as early as 2500 B.C.E. in Egypt and Mesopotamia, and glass blowing developed about 100 B.C.E. in Phoenicia.

What is **crown glass**?

In the early 1800s, window glass was called crown glass. It was made by blowing a bubble, then spinning it until flat. This left a sheet of glass with a bump, or crown, in the center. This blowing method of window-pane making required great skill and was very costly. Still, the finished crown glass produced a distortion through which everything looked curiously wavy, and the glass itself was also faulty and uneven. By the end of the nineteenth century, flat glass was mass-produced and was a common material. The cylinder method replaced the old method, and used compressed air to produce glass that could be slit lengthwise, reheated, and allowed to flatten on an iron

How is bulletproof glass made?

Bulletproof glass is composed of two sheets of plate glass with a sheet of transparent resin in between, molded together under heat and pressure. When subjected to a severe blow, it will crack without shattering. Today's bulletproof glass is a development of laminated or safety glass, invented by the French chemist Edouard Benedictus. It is basically a multiple lamination of glass and plastic layers.

table under its own weight. New furnaces and better polishing machines made the production of plate-glass a real industry. Today, glass is produced by a float-glass process, which reheats the newly formed ribbon and glass and allows it to cool without touching a solid surface. This produces inexpensive glass that is flat and free from distortion.

When were glass blocks invented?

Glass building bricks were introduced in 1931. They were invented in Europe in the early 1900s as thin blocks of glass supported by a grid. They have been in and out of favor since they were introduced. They are small, the largest being 12 × 12 inches (30 × 30 centimeters). They offer the following advantages: they allow natural light to filter through, but their patterns can afford privacy; they have the insulating value of a 12 inch (30 centimeter) thick concrete wall; they absorb outside noise; and they are much more secure than ordinary flat glass.

Who invented thermopane glass?

Thermopane insulated window glass was invented by C. D. Haven in the United States in 1930. It is two sheets of glass that are bonded together in such a manner that they enclose a captive air space in between. Often this space is filled with an inert gas that increases the insulating quality of the window. Glass is also one of the best transparent materials because it allows the short wavelengths of solar radiation to pass through it, but prohibits nearly all of the long waves of reflected radiation from passing back through it.

What is the float glass process?

Manufacture of high-quality flat glass, needed for large areas and industrial uses, depends on the float glass process, invented by Alistair Pilkington in 1952. The float **147** process departs from all other glass processes where the molten glass flows from the melting chamber into the float chamber, which is a molten tin pool approximately 160 feet (49 meters) long and 12 feet (3.5 meters) wide. During its passage over this molten tin, the hot glass assumes the perfect flatness of the tin surface and develops excellent thickness uniformity. The finished product is as flat and smooth as plate glass without having been ground and polished.

How is the **glass used in movie stunts** made?

The "glass" might be made of candy (sugar boiled down to a translucent pane) or plastic. This looks like glass and will shatter like glass, but will not cut a performer.

Who developed **fiberglass**?

Coarse glass fibers were used for decoration by the ancient Egyptians. Other developments were made in Roman times. Parisian craftsman Dubus-Bonnel was granted a patent for the spinning and weaving of drawn glass strands in 1836. In 1893, the Libbey Glass Company exhibited lampshades at the World's Columbian Exposition in Chicago that were made of coarse glass thread woven together with silk. However, this was not a true woven glass. Between 1931 and 1939, the Owens Illinois Glass Company and the Corning Glass Works developed practical methods of making fiberglass commercially. Once the technical problem of drawing out the glass threads to a fraction of their original thinness was solved—basically an endless strand of continuous glass filament as thin as 1/5000 of an inch—the industry began to produce glass fiber for thermal insulation and air filters, among other uses. When glass fibers were combined with plastics during World War II, a new material was formed. Glass fibers did for plastics what steel did for concrete—gave strength and flexibility. Glass-fiber-reinforced plastics (GFRP) became very important in modern engineering. Fiberglass combined with epoxy resins and thermosetting polyesters are now used extensively in boat and ship construction, sporting goods, automobile bodies, and circuit boards in electronics.

When was **cement** first used?

Cements are finely ground powders that, when mixed with water, set to a hard mass. The cement used by the Egyptians was calcined gypsum, and both the Greeks and Romans used a cement of calcined limestone. Roman concrete (a mixture of cement, sand, and some other fine aggregate) was made of broken brick embedded in a pozzolanic lime mortar. This mortar consisted of lime putty mixed with brick dust or volcanic ash. Hardening was produced by a prolonged chemical reaction between these components in the presence of moisture. With the decline of the Roman empire, concrete fell into disuse. The first step toward its reintroduction was about 1790, when the English engineer, John Smeaton (1724–1792), found that when lime containing a certain amount of clay was burned, it would set under water. This cement resembled what had been made by the Romans. Further investigations by James Parker in the same decade led to the commercial production of natural hydraulic cement. In 1824, Englishman Joseph Aspdin (1799–1855) obtained a patent for what he called "portland cement," a material produced from a synthetic mixture of limestone and clay. He called it "portland" because it resembled a building stone that was quarried on the Isle of Portland off the coast of Dorset. The manufacture of this cement spread rapidly to Europe and the United States by 1870. Today, concrete is often reinforced or pre-stressed, increasing its load-bearing capabilities.

How was early **macadam** different from modern paved roads?

Macadam roads developed originally in England and France and are named after the Scottish road builder and engineer, John Louden MacAdam (1756–1836). The term "macadam" originally designated road surface or base in which clean, broken, or crushed ledge stone was mechanically locked together by rolling with a heavy weight and bonded together by stone dust screenings that were worked into the spaces and then "set" with water. With the beginning of the use of bituminous material (tar or asphalt), the terms "plain macadam," "ordinary macadam," or "waterbound macadam" were used to distinquish the original type from the newer bituminous macadam. Waterbound macadam surfaces are almost never built now in the United States, mainly because they are expensive and the vacuum effect of vehicles loosens them. Many miles of bituminous macadam roads are still in service, but their principal disadvantages are their high crowns and narrowness. Today's roads that carry very heavy traffic are usually surfaced with very durable portland cement.

What is **Belgian block?**

Belgian block is a road-building material, first used in Brussels, Belgium, and introduced into New York about 1850. Its shape is a truncated pyramid with a base of about five to six inches (13 to 15 centimeters) square and a depth of seven to eight inches (18 to 20.5 centimeters). The bottom of the block is not more than one inch (2.5 centimeters) different from the top. The original blocks were cut from trap-rock from the Palisades of New Jersey.

Belgian blocks replaced cobblestones mainly because their regular shape allowed them to remain in place better than cobblestones. They were not universally adopted, however, because they would wear round and create joints or openings that would then form ruts and hollows. Although they provided a smooth surface compared to the uneven cobblestones, they still made for a rough and noisy ride.

What is slag?

Slag is a non-metallic by-product of iron production that is drawn from the surface of pig iron in the blast furnace. Consisting primarily of silica and lime, slag is used in cements, concrete, and roofing materials as well as a ballast for roads and railways. Slag can also be produced in smelting copper, lead, and other metals.

What is solder?

Solder is an alloy of two or more metals used for joining other metals together. The most common solder is called half-and-half, or "plumber's" solder, and is composed of equal parts of lead and tin. Other metals used in solder are aluminum, cadmium, zinc, nickel, gold, silver, palladium, bismuth, copper, and antimony. Various melting points to suit the work are obtained by varying the proportions of the metals.

Solder is an ancient joining method, mentioned in the Bible (Isaiah 41:7). There is evidence of its use in Mesopotamia some 5,000 years ago, and later in Egypt, Greece, and Rome. For the near future, it appears that as long as a combination of conductors, semiconductors, and insulators is used to build circuitry, based on electrical and magnetic impulses, solder will remain indispensable.

What is creosote?

Creosote is a yellowish poisonous oily liquid obtained from the distillation of coal tar. Coal tar constitutes the major part of the liquid condensate obtained from the "dry" distillation or carbonization of coal to coke. Crude creosote oil, also called dead oil or pitch oil, is used as a wood preservative. Railroad ties, poles, fence posts, marine pilings, and lumber for outdoor use are impregnated with creosote in large cylindrical vessels. This treatment can greatly extend the useful life of wood that is exposed to the weather.

What is neatsfoot oil?

Neastfoot oil is a pale yellow, inedible oil that is rendered from the feet and shin bones of cattle by boiling them in water. It was once prized as a leather dressing and as a lubricating oil for delicate machinery.

What is carbon black?

Carbon black is finely divided carbon produced by incomplete combustion of methane or other hydrocarbon gases (by letting the flame impinge on a cool surface). This forms a very fine pigment containing up to 95% carbon, which gives a very intense black color that is widely used in paints, inks, and protective coatings and as a colorant for paper and plastics.

What is the name of the chemical used in watches to make them glow in the dark?

Generally, radioactive paints are used to make watch surfaces visible in the dark. These paints, which do not require activation by an outside light source, will glow for several years. In the past, radium was often the active substance used in luminescent paints for watch faces. However, the practice was discontinued when it was found to emit dangerous gamma rays. The radioactive materials used today give off much lower emmissions, which are easily blocked by the glass or plastic covering the watch face. These substances include tritium, krypton 85, promethium 147, and thallium 204.

How is **sandpaper** made?

Sandpaper is a coated abrasive that consists of a flexible-type backing (paper) upon which a film of adhesive holds and supports a coating of abrasive grains. Various types of resins and hide glues are used as adhesives. The first record of a coated abrasive is in thirteenth century China, when crushed seashells were bound to parchment using natural gums. The first known article on coated abrasives was published in 1808 and described how calcined, ground pumice was mixed with varnish and spread on paper with a brush. Most abrasive papers are now made with aluminum oxide or silicon carbide, although the term sandpapering is still used. Quartz grains are also used for wood polishing. The paper used is heavy, tough, and flexible, and the grains are bonded with a strong glue.

Why is **titanium dioxide** the most widely used white pigment?

Titanium dioxide has become the predominant white pigment in the world because of its high refractive index, lack of absorption of visible light, ability to be produced in the right size range, and its stability. It is the whitest known pigment, unrivalled for color, opacity, stain resistance, and durability; it is also non-toxic. The main consuming industries are paint, printing inks, plastics, and ceramics, which together account for 60% to 70% of the total demand.

When and where was **gunpowder** invented?

The explosive mixture of saltpeter (potassium nitrate), sulfur, and charcoal called gun-   **151** powder was known in China at least by 850 C.E., and probably was discovered by Chinese alchemists searching for components to make artificial gold. Early mixtures had too little saltpeter (50%) to be truly explosive; 75% minimum is needed to get a detonation. The first use of the mixture was in making fireworks. Later, the Chinese used it in incendiary-like weapons. Eventually it is thought that the Chinese found the correct proportions to utilize its explosive effects in rockets and "bamboo bullets." However, some authorities still maintain that the "Chinese gunpowder" really had only pyrotechnic qualities, and "true" gunpowder was an European invention. Roger Bacon (1214–1292) had a formula for it and so might have the German monk Berthold Schwartz (1353). Its first European use depended on the development of firearms in the fourteenth century. Not until the seventeenth century was gunpowder used in peacetime, for mining and civil engineering applications.

How are colored fireworks made?

Fireworks existed in ancient China in the ninth century where saltpeter (potassium nitrate), sulfur, and charcoal were mixed to produce the dazzling effects. Magnesium burns with a brilliant white light and is widely used in making flares and fireworks. Various other colors can be produced by adding certain substances to the flame. Strontium compounds color the flame scarlet and barium compounds produce a yellowish-green color; borax produces a green color, and lithium a purple color.

What is the chemical formula for TNT?

TNT is the abbreviation for 2,4,6–$trinitro$toluene ($C_7H_5N_3O_6$). TNT is a powerful, highly explosive compound widely used in conventional bombs. Discovered by J. Wilbrand in 1863, it is made by treating toluene with nitric acid and sulfuric acid. This yellow crystalline solid with a low melting point has low shock sensitivity and even burns without exploding. This makes it safe to handle and cast; but once detonated, it explodes violently.

Who invented dynamite?

Alfred Nobel.

Dynamite was not an accidental discovery but the result of a methodical search by the Swedish technologist Alfred Nobel (1833–1896). Nitroglycerine had been discovered in 1849 by the Italian organic chemist Ascanio Sobriero (1812–1888), but it was so sensitive and difficult to con-

152

trol that it was useless. Nobel sought to turn nitroglycerine into a manageable solid by absorbing it into a porous substance. In 1866–1867, he tried an unusual mineral, kieselguhr, and created a doughlike explosive that was controllable. He also invented a detonating cap incorporating mercury fulminate with which nitroglycerine could be detonated at will. Nobel made a great fortune and bequeathed it to a foundation for awarding prizes for contributions to science, literature, and the promotion of peace.

When was **plastic** first invented?

Around the year 1850, Alexander Parkes (1813–1890) experimented with nitrocellulose (or guncotton). Mixed with camphor, it made a hard but flexible transparent material, which he called "Parkesine." He teamed up with a manufacturer to produce it, but there was no demand for it, and the firm went bankrupt. An American, John Wesley Hyatt (1837–1920), acquired the patent in 1868 with the idea of producing artificial ivory for billiard-balls. Improving the formula and with an efficient manufacturing process, he marketed the material, intended for use in making a few household articles, under the name "celluloid." It soon found use in the manufacture of novelty and fancy goods—buttons, letter openers, boxes, hatpins, combs and the like were products often made of celluloid. The material also became the medium for cinematography: celluloid strips coated with a light-sensitive "film" were ideal for shooting and showing movie pictures.

Celluloid was the only plastic material until 1904, when a Belgian scientist, Leo Hendrik Baekeland (1863–1944), succeeded in producing a synthetic shellac from formaldehyde and phenol. Called "bakelite," it was the first of the thermosetting plastics (i.e., synthetic materials that, having once been subjected to heat and pressure, became extremely hard and resistant to high temperatures). Bakelite and other, more versatile plastics, eventually eclipsed celluloid, and by the 1940s, celluloid's markets had shrunk so that it was no longer of commercial importance.

How can **plastics** be made **biodegradable**?

Plastic does not rust nor rot. This is an advantage in its usage, but when it comes to disposal of plastic, the advantage turns into a liability. Degradable plastic has starch in it so that it can be attacked by starch-eating bacteria to eventually disintegrate the plastic into bits. Chemically degradable plastic can be broken up with a chemical solution that dissolves it. Used in surgery, biodegradable plastic stitches slowly dissolve in the body fluids. Photodegradable plastic contains chemicals that disintegrate over a period of one to three years when exposed to light. 25% of the plastic yokes used to package beverages are made from a plastic called Ecolyte®, which is photodegradable.

Who invented teflon?

In 1938, the American engineer Roy J. Plunkett (b. 1910) at DuPont de Nemours discovered the polymer of tetraluorethylene (PTFE) by accident. This fluorocarbon is marketed under the name of Fluon in Great Britain and Teflon® in the United States. Patented in 1939 and first exploited commercially in 1954, PTFE is resistant to all acids and has exceptional stability and excellent electrical insulating properties. It is used in making piping for corrosive materials, in insulating devices for radio transmitters, in pump gaskets, and in computer microchips. In addition, its non-stick properties make PTFE an ideal material for surface coatings. In 1956, French engineer Marc Gregoire discovered a process whereby he could fix a thin layer of teflon on an aluminum surface. He then patented the process of applying it to cookware, and the no-stick frying pan was created.

Who made the first successful synthetic gemstone?

In 1902, Auguste Victor Louis Verneuil (1856–1913) synthesized the first man-made gemstone—a ruby. Verneuil perfected a "flame-fusion" method of producing crystals of ruby and other corundums within a short time period.

ENERGY

NON–NUCLEAR FUELS

What are the three types of **primary energy** that flow continuously on or to the surface of the Earth?

Geothermal energy is heat contained beneath the Earth's crust, and brought to the surface in the form of steam or hot water. The five main sources of this geothermal reservoir are dry, super-heated steam from steam fields below the Earth's surface, mixed hot water, wet steam, etc., from geysers, etc., dry rocks (into which cold water is pumped to create steam), pressurized water fields of hot water and natural gas beneath ocean beds, and magma (molten rock in or near volcanoes and five to 30 miles (eight to 48 kilometers) below the Earth's crust). Most Iceland buildings are heated by geothermal energy, a few communities in the United States, such as Boise, Idaho, use geothermal home heating. Electric power production, industrial processing, space heating, etc., are fed from geothermal sources. The California Geysers project is the world's largest geothermal electric generating complex with 200 steam wells that provide some 1,300 megawatts of power. The first geothermal power station was built in 1904 at Larderello, Italy.

Solar radiation utilization depends on the weather, number of cloudy days, and the ability to store energy for night use. The process of collecting and storing is difficult and expensive. A solar thermal facility (LUZ International Solar Thermal Plant), in the Mojave Desert, currently produces 274 megawatts and is used to supplement power needs of the Los Angeles utilities companies. Japan has four million solar panels on roofs and two-thirds of the houses in Israel have them; 90% of Cyprus homes do as well. Solar photo voltaic cells can generate electric

155

current when exposed to the sun. Virtually every spacecraft and satellite since 1958 utilizes this kind of resource.

Tidal and wave energy contain enormous amounts of energy to be harnessed. The first tidal-powered mill was built in England in 1100; another in Woodbridge, England, built in 1170, has functioned for over 800 years. The Rance River Power Station in France, in operation since 1966, was the first large tidal electric generator plant, producing 160 megawatts. A tidal station works like a hydropower dam, with its turbines spinning as the tide flows through them. Unfortunately the tidal period of 13.5 hours causes problems of integrating the peak use with the peak generation ability. Ocean wave energy can also be made to drive electrical generators.

What is the difference between passive **solar energy systems** and active solar energy systems?

Passive solar energy systems use the architectural design, the natural materials or absorptive structures of the building as an energy saving system. The building itself serves as a solar collector and storage device. An example would be thick-walled stone and adobe dwellings that slowly collect heat during the day and gradually release it at night. Passive systems require little or no investment of external equipment.

Active solar energy systems require a separate collector, a storage device, and controls linked to pumps or fans that draw heat from storage when it is available. Active solar systems generally pump a heat-absorbing fluid medium (air, water, or an antifreeze solution) through a collector. Collectors, such as insulated water tanks, vary in size, depending on the number of sunless days in a locale. Another heat storage system uses eutectic (phase-changing) chemicals to store a large amount of energy in a small volume.

What is **biomass energy**?

The catch-all term biomass includes all the living organisms in an area. Wood, crops and crop waste, and wastes of plant, mineral, and animal matter are part of the biomass. Much of it is in garbage, which can be burned for heat energy, or allowed to decay and produce methane gas. However, some crops are grown specifically for energy, including sugar cane, sorghum, ocean kelp, water hyacinth, and various species of trees. It has been estimated that 90% of United States waste products could be burned to provide as much energy as 100 million tons of coal (20% will not burn, but can be recycled). In Western Europe, there are over 200 power plants that burn rubbish to produce electricity. Biomass can be converted into biofuels such as biogas or methane, methanol, ethanol, etc. However, the process has been more costly than the conventional fossil fuel processes. Rubbish buried in the ground can provide methane gas through an aerobic decomposition. One ton of refuse can produce 8,000 cubic feet (227 cubic meters) of methane. Worldwide there are 140 such schemes that tap into the underground rubbish "tips."

Which woods have the best heating quality in a **wood-burning stove**?

Woods that have high heat value, meaning that one cord equals 200 to 250 gallons (757 to 946 liters) of fuel oil or 250 to 300 cubic feet (7 to 8.5 cubic meters) of natural gas, are hickory, beech, oak, yellow birch, ash, hornbeam, sugar maple, and apple.

Woods that have medium heat value, meaning that one cord equals 150 to 200 gallons (567 to 757 liters) of fuel oil or 200 to 250 cubic feet (5.5 to 7 cubic meters) of natural gas, are white birch, douglas fir, red maple, eastern larch, big leaf maple, and elm.

Woods that have a low heat value, meaning that one cord equals 100 to 150 gallons (378 to 567 liters) of fuel oil or 150 to 200 cubic feet (4 to 5.5 cubic meters) of natural gas, are aspen, red alder, white pine, redwood, western hemlock, eastern hemlock, sitka spruce, cottonwood, western red cedar, and lodgepole pine.

Which **plant** has been investigated as a **source of petroleum**?

A number of plant species have been investigated as potential sources of petroleum. The shrub called the gopher plant (*Euphorbia lathyrus*) produces significant quantities of a milk-like sap—called latex—that is an emulsion of hydrocarbons in water. Another candidate is *Pittosporum resiniferum,* a native of the Phillippines. The fruit of this plant, called a petroleum nut, is quite large and the oil harvested from it is frequently used for illumination. Various experiments are under way to use vegetable and seed oils as diesel substitutes, particularly in farm machinery.

Why are coal, oil, and natural gas called **fossil fuels**?

They are composed of the remains of organisms that lived as long ago as 500 million years. These organisms (such as phytoplankton) became incorporated into the bottom sediments and then were converted, with time, to oil and gas. Coal is the remains of plants and trees that were buried and subjected to pressure, temperature, and chemical processes (changing into peat and then lignite) for millions of years.

How and when was **coal formed**?

Coal is formed from the remains of plants that have undergone a series of far-reaching changes, turning into a substance called peat, which subsequently was buried. Through millions of years, the Earth's crust buckled and folded, subjecting the peat deposits to very high pressure and changing the deposits into coal. The Carboniferous, or coal-bearing period, occurred about 250 million years ago. Geologists in the United States sometimes divide this period into the Mississippian and the Pennsylvanian periods. Most of the high-grade coal deposits are to be found in the strata of the Pennsylvanian period.

What types of coal are there?

The first stage in the formation of coal converts peat into lignite, a dark brown type of coal. Lignite is then converted into subbituminous coal as pressure from overlying materials increases. Under still greater pressure, a harder coal called bituminous, or soft, coal is produced. Intense pressure changes bituminous coal into anthracite, the hardest of all coals.

What is cannel coal?

Cannel coal is a type of coal that possesses some of the properties of petroleum. Valued primarily for its quick-firing qualities, it burns with a long, luminous flame. It is made up of coal-like material mixed with clay and shale, and it may also look like black shale, being compact and dull black in color.

How is underground coal mined?

There are two basic types of underground mining methods: room and pillar and longwall. In room and pillar mines, coal is removed by cutting rooms, or large tunnels, in the solid coal, leaving pillars of coal for roof support. Longwall mining takes successive slices over the entire length of a long working face. In the United States, almost all of the coal recovered by underground mining is by room and pillar method. Coal seams in the United States range in thickness from a thin film to 50 feet (15 meters) or more. The thickest coalbeds are in the western states, ranging from 10 feet (three meters) in Utah and New Mexico to 50 feet (15 meters) in Wyoming. Other places, such as Great Britian, use the longwall method.

What is a miner's canary?

"Miner's canary" refers to the birds used by miners to test the purity of the air in the mines. At least three birds were taken by exploring parties and the distress of any one bird was taken as an indication of carbon monoxide danger. Some miners used mice rather than birds. This method of safety was used prior to the more sophisticated equipment used today.

Miners in a coal shaft.

Where are the largest **oil and gas fields** in the world and in the United States?

The Ghawar field, discovered in 1948 in Saudi Arabia, is the largest in the world; it measures 150 × 22 miles (241 × 35 kilometers). The largest oil field in the United States is the Permian Basin, which covers approximately 100,000 square miles in southeast New Mexico and western and northwestern Texas.

When was the first **oil well** in the United States drilled?

The Drake well at Titusville, Pennsylvania was completed on August 28, 1859 (some sources list the date as August 27). The driller, William "Uncle Billy" Smith, went down 69.5 feet (21 meters) to find oil for Edwin L. Drake (1819–1880), the well's operator. Within 15 years, Pennsylvania oil field production reached over 10 million 360-pound (163-kilogram) barrels a year.

When was **offshore drilling** for oil first done?

The first successful offshore oil well was built off the coast at Summerland, Santa Barbara County, California, in 1896.

159

Why is **Pennsylvania crude oil** so highly valued?

The waxy, sweet paraffinic oils found in Pennsylvania first became prominent because high quality lubricating oils and greases could be made from them. Similar grade crude oil is also found in West Virginia, eastern Ohio, and southern New York. Different types of crude oil vary in thickness and color, ranging from a thin, clear oil to a thick, tar-like substance.

What is the process known as **hydrocarbon cracking**?

Cracking is a process that uses heat to decompose complex substances. Hydrocarbon cracking is the decomposition by heat, with or without catalysts, of petroleum or heavy petroleum fractions (groupings) to give materials of lower boiling points. Thermal cracking, developed by William Burton in 1913, uses heat and pressure to break some of the large heavy hydrocarbon molecules into smaller gasoline-grade ones. The cracked hydrocarbons are then sent to a flash chamber where the various fractions (groupings) are separated. Thermal cracking not only doubles the gasoline yield, but has improved gasoline quality, producing gasoline components with good anti-knock characteristics.

What kinds of **additives** are **in gasoline** and why?

Additive	Function
Antiknock compounds	Increase octane number
Scavengers	Remove combustion products of antiknock compounds
Combustion chamber	Suppress surface ignition and spark plug deposit modifiers fouling
Antioxidants	Provide storage stability
Metal deactivators	Supplement storage stability
Antirust agents	Prevent rusting in gasoline-handling systems
Anti-icing agents	Suppress carburetor and fuel system freezing
Detergents	Control carburetor and induction system cleanliness
Upper cylinder lubricants	Lubricate upper cylinder areas and control intake system deposits
Dyes	Indicate presence of antiknock compounds and identify makes and grades of gasoline

Why is **lead added to gasoline** and why is **lead-free gasoline** used in new cars?

Tetraethyl lead has been used for more than 40 years to improve the combustion characteristics of gasoline. It reduces or eliminates "knocking" (pinging caused by premature ignition) in high performance large engines and in smaller high compression engines. It provides lubrication to the extremely close fitting engine parts where oil has a tendency to wash away or burn off. However, lead will ruin and effectively destroy the catalyst presently used in emission control devices installed in new cars. So lead-free gasoline must be used.

What is a **reformulated gasoline**?

Oil companies are being required to offer new gasolines that burn more cleanly and have less impact on the environment. Typically, reformulated gasolines contain lower concentrations of benzene, aromatics, and olefins; less sulfur; a lower Reid vapor pressure (RVP); and some percentage of an oxygenate (non-aromatic component) such as methyl tertiary butyl ether (MTBE). MTBE is a high-octane gasoline blending components produced by the reaction of isobutylene and methanol. The Clean Air Act calls for reformulated gasoline to be sold in the nine worst ozone nonattainment areas as of January 1, 1995. One company estimated a price increase of 10¢ to 15¢ per gallon in the manufacturing cost to produce reformulated gasoline.

What do the **octane numbers** of gasoline mean?

The octane number is a measure of the gasoline's ability to resist engine knock (pinging caused by premature ignition). Two test fuels, normal heptane and isooctane, are blended for test results to determine octane number. Normal heptane has an octane number of zero and isooctane a value of 100. Gasolines are then compared with these test blends to find one that makes the same knock as the test fuel. The octane rating of the gasoline under testing is the percentage by volume of isooctane required to produce the same knock. For example, if the test blend has 85% isooctane, the gasoline has an octane rating of 85. The octane rating that appears on gasoline pumps is an average of research octane determined in laboratory tests with engines running at low speeds, and motor octane, determined at higher speeds.

When did **gasoline stations** open?

The first service station (or garage) was opened in Bordeaux, France, in December 1895 by A. Barol. It provided overnight parking, repair service, and refills of oil and "motor spirit." In April 1897 a parking and refueling establishment—Brighton Cycle and Motor Co.—opened in Brighton, England.

The pump that would be used to eventually dispense gasoline was devised by Sylanus Bowser of Fort Wayne, Indiana, but in September 1885, it dispensed kerosene. Twenty years later Bowser manufactured the first self-regulating gasoline pump. In 1912, a Standard Oil of Louisiana superstation opened in Memphis, Tennessee, featuring 13 pumps, a ladies' rest room, and a maid who served ice water to waiting customers. On December 1, 1913, in Pittsburgh, Pennsylvania the Gulf Refining Company opened the first drive-in station as a 24-hour-a-day operation. Only 30 gallons (114 liters) of gasoline were sold the first day.

What are the advantages and disadvantages of the alternatives to gasoline to power automobiles?

Because the emissions of gasoline is a major air pollution problem in most U.S. urban areas, alternatives are being worked on. Currently none of the alternatives deliver as much energy content as gasoline so more of each of these fuels must be consumed to equal the distance that the energy of gasoline propels the automobile. The most viable alternative is flexible fuel, a combination of methanol and gasoline, which would add at least $300 to car prices for an expensive fuel sensor and a longer fuel tank.

Alternative	Advantages	Disadvantages
Electricity from batteries	No vehicle emissions, good for stop-and-go driving	Short-lived bulky batteries; limited trip range
Ethanol from corn, biomass, etc.	Relatively clean fuel	Costs, corrosive damage
Hydrogen from electrolysis; etc.	Plentiful supply; non-toxic emissions	High cost; highly flammable
Methanol from methanol gas, coal, biomass, wood	Cleaner combustion; less volatile	Corrosive; some irritant emissions
Natural gas from hydrocarbons and petroleum deposits	Cheaper on energy basis; relatively clean	Cost to adapt vehicle bulky storage; sluggish performance

How is gasohol made?

Gasohol, a mixture of 90% unleaded gasoline and 10% ethyl alcohol (ethanol), has gained some acceptance as a fuel for motor vehicles. It is comparable in performance to 100% unleaded gasoline with the added benefit of superior antiknock properties (no premature fuel ignition). No engine modifications are needed for the use of gasohol.

Since corn is the most abundant United States grain crop, it is predominantly used in producing ethanol. However, the fuel can be made from other organic raw materials, such as oats, barley, wheat, milo, sugar beets, or sugar cane. Potatoes, cassava (a starchy plant), and cellulose (if broken up into fermentable sugars) are possible other sources. The corn starch is processed through grinding and cooking. The process requires the conversion of a starch into a sugar, which in turn is converted into alcohol by reaction with yeast. The alcohol is distilled and any water is removed until it is 200 proof (100% alcohol).

One acre of corn yields 250 gallons (946 liters) of ethanol; an acre of sugar beets yields 350 gallons (1,325 liters), while an acre of sugar can produce 630 gallons (2,385 liters). In the future motor fuel could conceivably be produced almost exclusively from garbage, but currently its conversion remains an expensive process.

What are the main components found in motor vehicle **exhaust**?

The main components of exhaust gas are nitrogen, carbon dioxide and water. Smaller amounts of nitrogen oxides, carbon monoxide, hydrocarbons, aldehydes and other products of incomplete combustion are also present. The most important air pollutants, in order of amount produced, are carbon monoxide, nitrogen oxides, and hydrocarbons.

What is **cogeneration**?

Cogeneration is an energy production process involving the simultaneous generation of thermal (steam or hot water) and electric energy by using a single primary heat source. By producing two kinds of useful fuels in the same facility the net energy yield from the primary fuel increases from 30–35% to 80–90%. Cogeneration can result in significant cost savings and can reduce any possible environmental effects conventional energy production may produce. Cogeneration facilities have been installed at a variety of sites, including oil refineries, chemical plants, paper mills, utility complexes, and mining operations.

NUCLEAR POWER

What is the **life of a nuclear power plant**?

The working life of a nuclear power plant is approximately 40 years, which is about the same as that of other types of power stations.

Where is the **oldest operational nuclear power plant** in the United States?

The Big Rock Point plant at Charlevoix, Michigan, started in 1962 and initially put into commercial operation in November 1965 is the oldest nuclear power plant still operational in the United States. The Yankee Plant at Rowe, Massachusetts, which was **163** constructed in 1960 and closed in 1991, was the first commercially used nuclear power plant to be built in the U.S.

How many nuclear power plants are there worldwide?

As of 1994, 432 reactors were operational with 48 more under construction.

Country	Number of Units
Argentina	2
Belgium	7
Brazil	1
Bulgaria	6
Canada	22
China	3
Czech Republic	4
Finland	4
France	56
Germany	21
Hungary	4
India	9
Japan	49
Kazakhstan	1
Korea, South	10
Lithuania	2
Mexico	2
Netherlands	2
Pakistan	1
Russia	29
South Africa	2
Slovakia	4
Slovenia	1
Spain	9
Sweden	12
Switzerland	5
Taiwan	6
Ukraine	15
United Kingdom	34
United States	109

As of May 1995, the United States had 109 reactors in operation, with one under construction. The plants generated 640,440 million net kilowatt hours or 22% of domestic electricity in 1994.

What is the **Rasmussen report**?

Professor Rasmussen of the Massachusetts Institute of Technology (MIT) conducted a study of nuclear reactor safety for the United States Atomic Energy Commission. The study cost four million dollars and took three years to complete. It concluded that the odds against a worst-case accident occurring were astronomically large—ten million to one. The worse case accident projected about three thousand early deaths and 14 billion dollars in property damage due to contamination. Cancers occurring later due to the event might number 1,500 per year. The study concluded that the safety features engineered into a plant are very likely to prevent serious consequences from a meltdown. Other groups criticized the Rasmussen report and in particular declared that the estimates of risk were too low. After the Chernobyl disaster in 1986, some scientists estimated that a major nuclear accident might in fact happen every decade.

Which **nuclear reactors** have had accidents?

Incidents with core damage in nuclear reactors

Description of incident	Site	Date	Adult thyroid dose (in rems)
Minor core damage (no release of radiologic material)	Chalk River, Ontario, Canada	1952	not applicable
	Breeder Reactor Idaho	1955	not applicable
	Westinghouse Test Reactor	1960	not applicable
	Detroit Edison Fermi, Michigan	1966	not applicable
Major core damage (radioiodine released)			
Noncommercial	Windscale, England	1957	16
	Idaho Falls SL-1, Idaho	1961	0.035
Commercial	Three Mile Island, Pennsylvania	1979	0.005
	Chernobyl, Soviet Union	1986	100 (estimated)

What actually happened at **Three Mile Island**?

The Three Mile Island nuclear power plant in Pennsylvania experienced a partial meltdown of its reactor core and radiation leakage. On March 28, 1979, just after 4:00 a.m., a water pump in the secondary cooling system of the Unit 2 pressurized water reactor failed. A relief valve jammed open, flooding the containment vessel with radioactive water. A backup system for pumping water was down for maintenance. Temperatures **165**

What is a meltdown, and what does it have to do with the "China Syndrome"?

A meltdown is a type of accident in a nuclear reactor in which the fuel core melts, resulting in the release of dangerous amounts of radiation. In most cases the large containment structure that houses a reactor would prevent the radioactivity from escaping. However, there is a small possibility that the molten core could become hot enough to burn through the floor of the containment structure and go deep into the Earth. Nuclear engineers call this type of situation the "China Syndrome." The phrase derives from a discussion on the theoretical problems that could result from a meltdown, when a scientist commented that the molten core could bore a hole through the Earth, coming out—if one happened to be standing in North America—in China. Although the scientist was grossly exaggerating, some took him seriously. In fact, the core would only bore a hole about 30 feet (10 meters) into the Earth, but even this distance would have grave repercussions. All reactors are equipped with emergency systems to prevent such an accident from occurring.

inside the reactor core rose, fuel rods ruptured, and a partial (52%) meltdown occurred, because the radioactive uranium core was almost entirely uncovered by coolant for 40 minutes. The thick steel-reinforced containment building prevented nearly all the radiation from escaping—the amount of radiation released into the atmosphere was one-millionth of that at Chernobyl. However, if the coolant had not been replaced, the molten fuel would have penetrated the reactor containment vessel, where it would have come into contact with the water, causing a steam explosion, breaching the reactor dome, and leading to radioactive contamination of the area similar to the Chernobyl accident.

What caused the **Chernobyl** accident?

Site of the worst nuclear power accident in history, the Chernobyl nuclear power plant in the Ukraine will affect, in one form or another, 20% of the republic's population (2.2 million people). On April 26, 1986 at 1:23:40 a.m., during unauthorized experiments by the operators, in which safety systems were deliberately circumvented in order to learn more about the plant's operation, one of the four reactors rapidly overheated and its water coolant "flashed" into steam. The hydrogen formed from the steam reacted with the graphite moderator to cause two major explosions and a fire. The explosions blew apart the 1,000 ton (907 metric ton) lid of the reactor, and released radioactive debris high into the atmosphere. It is estimated that 3.5% of the reactor's fuel and 10% of the graphite reactor itself was emitted into the atmosphere. Human error and design features (positive void coefficient type of reactor, use of graphite in construction, and lack of a containment building) are generally cited as the causes of the accident. Thirty-one people initially died from trying to stop the fires. More than 240 others sustained severe radiation sickness. Eventually 150,000 people living near the reactor were relocated; some of whom may never be allowed to return home. Fallout from the explosions, containing radioactive isotope cesium—137, was carried by the winds westward across Europe.

The problems created by the Chernobyl disaster are overwhelming and continue today. Particularly troubling is the fact that by 1990–1991, a five-fold increase has occurred in the rate of thyroid cancers in children in Belarus. A significant rise in general morbidity has also taken place among children in the heaviest hit areas of Gomel and Mogilev.

MEASURES AND MEASUREMENT

What is the **weight** per gallon of common **fuels**?

One gallon of fuel	Weight in pounds
Butane	4.86
Propane	4.23
Kerosene	6.75
Gasoline	6.00
Aviation gasoline	6.46–6.99

How much does a **barrel of oil weigh**?

A barrel of oil weighs about 306 pounds (139 kilograms).

How many **gallons** are in a **barrel of oil**?

The barrel, a common measure of crude oil, contains 42 U.S. gallons and 34.97 imperial gallons.

How do various energy sources compare?

Below is listed some comparisons (approximate equivalents) for the energy sources as of 1990:

Energy unit	Equivalent
1 BTU of energy	1 match tip
	250 calories (International Steam Table)
	0.25 kilocalories (food calories)
1,000 BTU of energy	2 5-ounce glasses of wine
	250 kilocalories (food calories)
	0.8 peanut butter and jelly sandwiches
1 million BTU of energy	90 pounds of coal
	120 pounds of oven-dried hardwood
	8 gallons of motor gasoline
	10 therms of dry natural gas
	11 gallons of propane
	2 months of the dietary intake of a laborer
1 quadrillion BTU of energy	45 million short tons of coal
	60 million short tons of oven-dried hardwood
	1 trillion cubic feet of dry natural gas
	170 million barrels of crude oil
	470 thousand barrels of crude oil per day for 1 year
	28 days of U.S. petroleum imports
	26 days of U.S. motor gasoline
	26 hours of world energy use (1989)
1 barrel of crude oil	5.6 thousand cubic feet of dry natural gas
	0.26 short tons (520 pounds) of coal
	1,700 kilowatt-hours of electricity
1 short ton of coal	3.8 barrels of crude oil
	21 thousand cubic feet of dry natural gas
	6,500 kilowatt-hours of electricity
1,000 cubic feet of natural gas	0.18 barrels (7.4 gallons) of crude oil
	0.05 short tons (93 pounds) of coal
	300 kilowatt-hours of electricity
1,000 kilowatt-hours of electricity	0.59 barrels of crude oil
	0.15 short tons (310 pounds) of coal
	3,300 cubic feet of dry natural gas

Notes: One quadrillion equals 1,000,000,000,000,000.

Because of energy losses associated with the generation of electricity, about three times as much fossil fuel is required to generate 1,000 kilowatt-hours: 1.8 barrels of oil, 0.47 short tons of coal, or 10,000 cubic feet (283 cubic meters) of dry natural gas.

What are the **fuel equivalents** to produce one quad of energy?

One quad (meaning one quadrillion) is equivalent to:

1×10^{15} BTU

252×10^{15} calories or 252×10^{12} K calories

In fossil fuels, one quad is equivalent to:

180 million gallons (681 million liters) of crude oil

0.98 trillion cubic feet (0.028 trillion cubic meters) of natural gas

37.88 million tons of anthracite coal

38.46 million tons of bituminous coal

In nuclear fuels, one quad is equivalent to 2,500 tons of U_3O_8 if only U_{235} is used.

In electrical output, one quad is equivalent to 2.93×10^{11} kilowatt-hours electric.

What are the approximate **heating values** of fuels?

Fuel	BTU	Unit of measure
Oil	141,000	gallon
Coal	31,000	pound
Natural gas	1,000	cubic feet
Steam	1,000	cubic feet
Electricity	3,413	kilowatt hour
Gasoline	124,000	gallon

A BTU (British thermal unit), a common energy measurement, is defined as the amount of energy required to raise the temperature of one pound of water by 1°F.

How much heat will 100 cubic feet of **natural gas** provide?

One hundred cubic feet of natural gas can provide about 100,000 BTUs (British thermal units) of heat. A British thermal unit, a common energy measurement, is defined as the amount of energy required to raise one pound of water by 1°F.

How is a **heating degree day** defined?

Early this century engineers developed the concept of heating degree days as a useful index of heating fuel requirements. They found that when the daily mean temperature **169** is lower than 65°F (18°C), most buildings require heat to maintain a 70°F (21°C) temperature. Each degree of mean temperature below 65°F (18°C) is counted as "one heating degree day." For every additional heating degree day, more fuel is needed to maintain a 70°F (21°C) indoor temperature. For example, a day with a mean temperature of 35°F (1.5°C) would be rated as 30 heating degree days and would require twice as much fuel as a day with a mean temperature of 50°F (10°C; 15 heating degree days). The heating degree concept has become a valuable tool for fuel companies for evaluation of fuel use rates and efficient scheduling of deliveries. Detailed daily, monthly, and seasonal totals are routinely computed for the stations of the National Weather Service.

What does the term cooling degree day mean?

It is a unit for estimating the energy needed for cooling a building. One unit is given for each degree Fahrenheit above the daily mean temperature when the mean temperature exceeds 75°F (24°C).

How many BTUs are equivalent to one ton of cooling capacity?

1 ton = 288,000 BTUs/24 hours or 12,000 BTUs/hour.

How are utility meters read?

Older electric and gas meters have a series of four or five dials, which indicate the amount of energy being consumed. The dials are read from left to right, and if the pointer falls between two numbers, the lower number is recorded. Gas meters are set to read hundred of cubic feet. New meter models have digital displays.

How much wood is in a cord?

A cord of wood is a pile of logs four feet (1.2 meters) wide and four feet (1.2 meters) high and eight feet (2.4 meters) long. It may contain from 77 to 96 cubic feet of wood. The larger the unsplit logs the larger the gaps, with fewer cubic feet of wood actually in the cord.

CONSUMPTION AND CONSERVATION

Does the United States currently produce enough energy to meet its consumption needs?

No. From 1958 forward, the United States consumed more energy than it produced, and the difference was met by energy imports. In 1990, 67.59 quadrillion BTUs was the total United States energy production with coal being 22.6 quadrillion BTUs; natural gas being 18 quadrillion BTUs; crude oil and natural plant liquids, 17.6; hydroelectric, 2.9; nuclear, 6.2; and geothermal, biomass, photovoltaic, wind, and solar energy, 0.2. In that year the United States imported 13.83 quadrillion BTUs in petroleum to make up the deficit since its 1990 energy consumption was 81.44 quadrillion BTUs (29.2 in residential and commercial; 30.2 in industrial; and 22 in transportation).

Which countries **consume the most energy?**

Top Energy-Consuming Countries (1987)

Country	World total %	Oil %	Coal %	Gas %
United States	24.6	41.1	23.4	22.4
U.S.S.R.	18.0	32.3	22.6	38.3
China	7.8	18.4	75.5	2.3
Japan	4.9	55.9	18.0	9.9
West Germany	3.6	42.2	27.5	17.1
Canada	3.2	31.5	10.7	19.8
United Kingdom	2.7	36.2	32.9	23.8
France	2.7	42.6	9.6	12.4
India	2.0	32.1	55.8	4.2
Italy	2.0	59.3	9.9	21.9

One study projected that in the year 2010, the largest consumers are expected to be the United States, the former Soviet Union, and China. China is projected to increase its annual energy consumption, on average, twice as fast as energy consumption grows worldwide between 1990 and 2012.

What is the current **per capita energy consumption** in the United States?

In 1994 in the United States, per capita consumption was about 260 million BTUs (British Thermal Units). A BTU, a common energy measurement, is defined as the amount of energy required to raise one pound of water by 1°F. Below is listed per capita consumption for representative years:

Year	Quantity (End-Use) (Million BTU)
1950	194
1960	212

Year	Quantity (End-Use) (Million BTU)
1970	270
1980	259
1990	256
1994	260

(End use energy consumption is total energy consumption less losses incurred in the generation, transmission and distribution of electricity, etc.)

How long, at the present rate of consumption, will U.S. current major energy reserves last?

The best estimates indicate there will be enough oil to provide energy to the world for another 50 years. Recoverable reserves of coal and natural gas have expanded too. The current supply of natural gas, at gradually increased rates of consumption, will last almost 60 years. Known coal supplies should last until about the year 2225. All in all, taking into account the likely discovery of new deposits of fossil fuels and the development of new technologies to get it out of the ground or from under the sea, the total energy supply may soon reach 600 times current world consumption levels.

How much money can be saved by lowering the setting on a home furnace thermostat?

Tests have shown that a 5°F reduction in the home thermostat setting for approximately eight hours will save up to 10% in fuel costs.

How much energy is saved by raising the setting for a house air conditioner?

For every 1°F the inside temperature is increased the energy needed for air conditioning is reduced by 3%. If all consumers raised the settings on their air conditioners by 6°F, for example, 190,000 barrels of oil could be saved each day.

How are fireplace logs made from newspaper?

In a large tub, make a neat stack of old newspapers. Cover the pile with water and let them soak until all the layers are saturated. Pick up the layers of the paper and roll them tightly into logs. Make thin ones for kindling. Stand on end to dry.

How much energy is required to use various electrical appliances?

The table below indicates the annual estimated energy consumption for various household electrical products.

Appliance	Estimated kilowatt-hours
Air conditioner (room)	1,389
Blender	15
Broiler	100
Clock	17
Clothes dryer	993
Clothes washer	103
Coffee maker	106
Computer	25–400
Dehumidifier	377
Dishwasher	165–363
Fan (circulating)	43
Fan (attic)	291
Food mixer	13
Freezer (frost-free)	1,820
Frying pan	186
Garbage disposal	30
Hair dryer	14
Iron	144
Microwave oven	300
Radio	86
Range (self-cleaning oven)	1,205
Refrigerator-freezer (frost-free)	1,591–1,829
Television (black-and-white)	362
Television (color)	502
Toaster	39
Vacuum cleaner	46
Video cassette recorder (VCR)	10–70
Water heater (standard)	4,219

What is the advantage of switching from incandescent to fluorescent light bulbs?

One 18-watt fluorescent bulb provides the light of a 75-watt incandescent bulb and lasts ten times as long. Even though the purchase price is higher, over its useful life, an 18-watt fluorescent light bulb saves 80 pounds (36 kilograms) of coal used to pro-

How much energy is saved by recycling one aluminum can?

Some sources indicate that one recycled aluminum can saves as much energy as it takes to run a TV set for four hours or the energy equivalent of half a gallon (1.9 liters) of gasoline. To manufacture one ton of aluminum, nearly 9,000 pounds (4,086 kilograms) of bauxite and 1,020 pounds (463 kilograms) of petroleum coke are needed. Recycling aluminum cans reduces the need for raw material by 95% and reduces the energy needed to produce aluminum by 90%.

duce electricity. This translates into 250 pounds (113 kilograms) less of carbon dioxide released into the Earth's atmosphere.

When should a **fluorescent light** be turned off to save energy?

Fluorescent lights use a lot of electric current getting started, and frequently switching the light on and off will shorten the lamp's life and efficiency. It is energy-efficient to turn off a fluorescent light only if it will not be used again within an hour or more.

How does **driving speed** affect **gas mileage** for most automobiles?

Most automobiles get about 28% more miles per gallon of fuel at 50 miles (80.5 kilometers) per hour than at 70 miles (112 kilometers) per hour, and about 21% more at 55 miles (88.5 kilometers) per hour than at 70 miles (112 kilometers) per hour.

Is it more economical to run an automobile with its **windows open** rather than using its **air conditioner**?

At speeds greater than 40 miles (64 kilometers) per hour, less fuel is used in driving an automobile with the air conditioner on and the windows up than with the windows rolled down. This is due to the air drag effect—the resistance that a vehicle encounters as it moves through a fluid medium, such as air. In automobiles, the amount of engine power required to overcome this drag force increases with the cube of the vehicle's speed—twice the speed requires eight times the power. For example, it takes five horsepower for the engine to overcome the air resistance at 40 miles (64 kilometers) per hour; but at 60 miles (97 kilometers) per hour, it takes 18 horsepower; at 80 miles (128 kilometers) per hour, it takes 42 horsepower. Improved aerodynamics, in which the drag coefficient (measure of air drag effect) is reduced, significantly increases fuel efficiency. The average automobile in 1990 has a drag coefficient of about 0.4. In the early 1960s it was 0.5, on the average, to 0.47 in the 1970s. The lowest maximum level possible for wheeled vehicles is 0.15.

When is it more economical to **restart an automobile** rather than let it idle?

Tests by the Environmental Protection Agency have shown that it is more economical to turn the engine off rather than let it idle if the idle time would exceed 60 seconds.

How much gasoline do **underinflated tires** waste?

Underinflated tires waste as much as one gallon (4.5 liters) out of every 20 gallons (91 liters) of gasoline. To save fuel, follow the automaker's guidelines regarding recommended air pressure levels for the tires. However, greater fuel economy can be achieved by inflating tires to the maximum air pressure listed on the sidewall of the tire, resulting in less rolling resistance.

What is a **pedicar**?

As a response to the concern of energy conservation, the pedicar was introduced in 1973. It was a pedal-powered, all-weather one passenger vehicle with straight-line pedal action, disc brakes, five forward speeds plus neutral and reverse. Costing about $550 in 1973, the vehicle was conceived as an alternative to the automobile. It had a speed of eight to 15 miles (13 to 24 kilometers) per hour and was developed mainly for fun use around parks, resorts, college campuses, country clubs and similar protected areas.

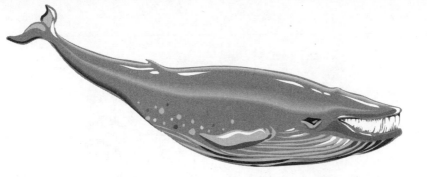

ENVIRONMENT

ECOLOGY, RESOURCES, ETC.

What is a **biome**?

It is a plant and animal community that covers a large geographical area. Complex interactions of climate, geology, soil types, water resources, and latitude all determine the kinds of plants and animals that thrive in different places. Fourteen major ecological zones, called "biomes," exist over five major climatic regions and eight zoogeographical regions. Important land biomes include tundra, coniferous forests, deciduous forests, grasslands, savannas, deserts, chaparral, and tropical rainforests.

How does the process work in a **food chain**?

A food chain is the transfer of food energy from the source in plants through a series of organisms with repeated eating and being eaten. The number of steps or "links" in a sequence is usually four to five. The first trophic level (group of organisms that get their energy the same way) is plants; the animals that eat plants (called herbivores) form the second trophic level. The third level consists of primary carnivores (animal-eating animals like wolves) who eat herbivores, and the fourth level are animals (like killer whales) that eat primary carnivores. Food chains overlap because many organisms eat more than one type of food, so that these chains can look more like food webs. In 1891 German zoologist Karl Semper introduced the food chain concept.

What is a **food web**?

A food web consists of interconnecting food chains. Many animals feed on different **177**

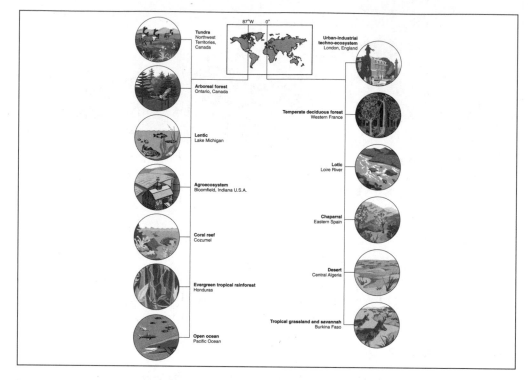

Biomes along 87 degrees west longitude and along 0 degrees longitude.

foods rather than exclusively on one single species of prey or one type of plant. Animals that use a variety of food sources have a greater chance of survival than those with a single food source. Complex food webs provide greater stability to a living community.

What is **eutrophication**?

Eutrophication is a process in which the supply of plant nutrients in a lake or pond is increased. In time, the result of natural eutrophication may be dry land where water once flowed, caused by plant overgrowth.

Natural fertilizers, washed from the soil, result in an accelerated growth of plants, producing overcrowding. As the plants die off, the dead and decaying vegetation depletes the lake's oxygen supply, causing fish to die. The accumulated dead plant and animal material eventually changes a deep lake to a shallow one, then to a swamp, and finally it becomes dry land.

While the process of eutrophication is a natural one, it has been accelerated enormously by human activities. Fertilizers from farms, sewage, industrial wastes, and some detergents all contribute to the problem.

The structure of a eutrophic lake.

How does **ozone** benefit life on Earth?

Ozone in the upper atmosphere (stratosphere) is a major factor in making life on Earth possible. The ozone belt shields the Earth from excessive ultraviolet radiation generated by the sun. Scientists predict that depletion of this layer could lead to increased health problems for humans and disruption of sensitive terrestrial and aquatic ecosystems. Ozone, a form of oxygen with three atoms instead of the normal two, is highly toxic; less than one part per million of this blue-tinged gas is poisonous to humans. While beneficial in the stratosphere, near ground level it is a pollutant that helps form photochemical smog and acid rain.

What is the **greenhouse effect**?

The greenhouse effect is a warming near the Earth's surface that results when the Earth's atmosphere traps the sun's heat. The atmosphere acts much like the glass walls and roof of a greenhouse. The effect was described by John Tyndall (1820–1893) in 1861. It was given the greenhouse analogy much later in 1896 by the Swedish chemist Svante Arrhenius (1859–1927). The greenhouse effect is what makes the

An atmosphere with natural levels of greenhouse gases (left) compared with an atmosphere of increased greenhouse effect (right).

Earth habitable. Without the presence of water vapor, carbon dioxide, and other gases in the atmosphere, too much heat would escape and the Earth would be too cold to sustain life. Carbon dioxide, methane, nitrous oxide, and other "greenhouse gases" absorb the infrared radiation rising from the Earth and holds this heat in the atmosphere instead of reflecting it back into space.

In the 20th century, the increased build-up of carbon dioxide, caused by the burning of fossil fuels, has been a matter of concern. There is some controversy concerning whether the increase noted in the Earth's average temperature is due to the increased amount of carbon dioxide and other gases, or is due to other causes. Volcanic activity, destruction of the rainforests, use of aerosols, and increased agricultural activity may also be contributing factors.

Why is El Niño harmful?

Along the west coast of South America, near the end of each calendar year, a warm current of nutrient-poor tropical water moves southward, replacing the cold, nutrient-rich surface water. Because this condition frequently occurs around Christmas,

What is red tide and what causes it?

Red tide is a term used for a brownish or reddish discoloration occurring in ocean, river, or lake water. It is caused by the rapid reproduction of a variety of toxic organisms, especially the toxic red dinoflagellates that are members of the genera *Gymnodidium* and *Gonyaulax*. Some red tides are harmless, but millions of fish may be killed during a "bloom," as the build-up is called. Other red tides can poison shellfish and the birds or humans who eat the contaminated food. Scientists do not fully understand why the "bloom" occurs.

local residents call it *El Niño* (Spanish for child), referring to the Christ child. In most years the warming lasts for only a few weeks. However, when El Niño conditions last for many months, the economic results can be catastrophic. It is this extended episode of extremely warm water that scientists now refer to as El Niño. During a severe El Niño, large numbers of fish and marine plants may die. Decomposition of the dead material depletes the water's oxygen supply, which leads to the bacterial production of huge amounts of smelly hydrogen sulfide. A greatly reduced fish (especially anchovy) harvest affects the world's fishmeal supply, leading to higher prices for poultry and other animals that normally are fed fishmeal.

Studies reveal that El Niño is not an isolated occurrence, but is instead part of a pattern of change in the global circulation of the oceans and atmosphere. The 1982–1983 El Niño was one of the most severe climate events of the twentieth century in both its geographical extent as well as in the degree of warming (14°F or 8°C). The 1986–1987 El Niño might have been responsible in part for record global warmth in 1987—the warmest year in the last 100 years.

How many acres of tropical forest does the world lose annually?

Using data from satellite observations, it is estimated that 16.4 to 20.4 million hectares are being destroyed each year (a hectare equals 107,639 square feet [10,000 square meters]). Only 50% of the mature tropical forests remain, with 750 to 800 million hectares of the original 1.5 to 1.6 billion hectares destroyed. Of the two types of tropical forests, wet and dry, the wet or "rain" forests have been incurring the most losses. Latin America has lost 37% of them; Asia, 42%; and Africa, 52%. Logging, fuelwood gathering, and conversion of forests to agriculture are the main causes. Yet tropical forests have been called "green deserts," because their soils are poor in nutrients. The forest vegetation, seemingly lush, has survived through ingenious life-support systems. When the trees are stripped away, the exposed soil deteriorates rapidly, **181** eroded by torrential rains. After the rain ceases, the sun bakes the earth into a hard mass, rendering the soil incapable of vegetative growth.

How rapidly is **deforestation** occurring?

In the 1990 figures given below, the annual deforestation rate is given in percent of forests eradication as well as amount in square kilometers.

Country	Deforestation (square kilometers)	Percent
Brazil	13,820	0.4
Colombia	6,000	1.3
Mexico	7,000	1.5
Indonesia	10,000	0.9
Peru	2,700	0.4
Malaysia	3,100	1.5
Ecuador	3,400	2.4
India	10,000	2.7
Zaire	4,000	0.4
Madagascar	1,500	1.5

How long will it be before all **tropical forests** have been destroyed, if present **rates of destruction** continue?

If present deforestation rates continue, all tropical forests will be cleared in 177 years. These forests contain 155,000 of the 250,000 known plant species and innumerable insect and animal species. Half of all medicines prescribed worldwide are originally derived from wild products, and the United States National Cancer Institute has identified more than two thousand tropical rainforest plants with the potential to fight cancer. Rubber, timber, gums, resins and waxes, pesticides, lubricants, nuts and fruits, flavorings and dyestuffs, steroids, latexes, essential and edible oils, and bamboo are among the forest's products that would be drastically affected by the depletion of the tropical forests.

When did the symbol of **Smokey the Bear** begin to be used for forest fire prevention?

The origin of Smokey Bear can be traced to World War II when the U.S. Forest Service, concerned about maintaining a steady lumber supply for the war effort, wished to educate the public about the dangers of forest fires. They sought volunteer advertising support from the War Advertising Council, and on August 9, 1944, Albert Staehle, a noted illustrator of animals, created Smokey Bear. In 1947, a Los Angeles advertising

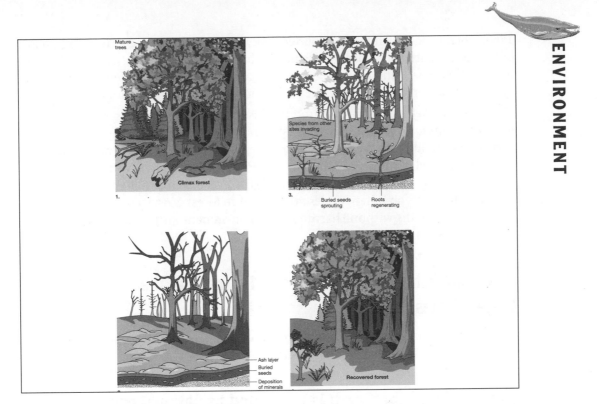

A forest (1) destroyed by wildfire (2) and its recovery (3,4).

agency coined the slogan "Only you can prevent forest fires." The campaign gained a living mascot in 1950 when a firefighting crew rescued a male bear cub from a forest fire in the Capital Mountains of New Mexico. Sent to the National Zoo in Washington, D.C. to become Smokey Bear, the animal was a living symbol of forest fire protection until his death in 1976. His remains are buried at the Smokey Bear State Historical Park in Capitan, New Mexico.

What causes the most **forest fires** in the western United States?

Lightning is the single largest cause of forest fires in the western states.

How many acres in the United States are infested by the **gypsy moth**?

In 1990, the total acreage of U.S. land infested by the gypsy moth was reported to be more than seven million acres, four million of which were in Pennsylvania. Since **183**

1869, when Leopold Trouvelot imported gypsy moths from France to Boston in hopes of breeding a better silkworm, these insects have spread across the continent. In one of their record breaking years, 1981, they defoliated almost 13 million acres; in 1993, due to several control measures, the destruction decreased to 1.8 million acres.

Several methods of controlling the insect have been investigated. The *Entomophaga maimaiga* fungus, a natural enemy of the gypsy moth, has been used. A biological insecticide, Gypchek, is registered for use against the gypsy moth and is the only one deemed harmless to other insects. *Bacillus thuringiensis* (Bt), another biological pesticide, and diflubenzuron (Dimilin) are also being studied. However, their undesirable effects on other species are a threat to forest ecosystems. Finding ways of killing gypsy moths without harming the environment still presents a formidable challenge to entomologists.

Who established the first **botanical garden** in the United States?

John Bartram planned and laid out a botanic garden of five to six acres (two to 2.5 hectare) in 1728. It is located in Philadelphia, PA.

How much of the Earth is protected as national parks and similar sites?

Below is a table of protected areas by country for the year 1990.

Country	Percent of total land area
Venezuela	22.2
Bhutan	19.8
Chile	18.2
Botswana	17.4
Panama	16.9
Czechoslovakia	15.4
Namibia	12.7
United States	10.5
Indonesia	9.3
Australia	5.9
Canada	5.0
Mexico	4.8
Brazil	2.4
Madagascar	1.8
Former Soviet Union	1.1
WORLD	4.9

What was the United States' **first national park**?

The U.S. government authorized Yellowstone National Park on March 1, 1872.

What are some of the **largest National Parks**?

The largest National Parks are in Alaska:

Park	Area (acres)
Wrangell-St. Elias	8,331,604
Gates of the Arctic	7,523,888
Denali	4,716,726
Katmai	3,716,000
Glacier Bay	3,225,284
Lake Clark	2,636,839
Kobuk Valley	1,750,421

The five largest parks in the 48 contiguous states are:

Park	Location	Area (acres)
Yellowstone	Idaho, Montana, Wyoming	2,219,791
Everglades	Florida	1,506,599
Grand Canyon	Arizona	1,218,375
Glacier	Montana	1,013,572
Olympic	Washington	922,651

Where is **Hawk Mountain Sanctuary**?

Hawk Mountain Sanctuary, founded in 1934 as the first sanctuary in the world to offer protection to migrating hawks and eagles, is near Harrisburg, Pennsylvania, on the Kittatinny Ridge. Each year between the months of August and December, over 15,000 migrating birds pass by. Rare species such as golden eagles may be seen there.

When was the **first zoo** in the United States established?

The Philadelphia Zoological Garden, chartered in 1859, was the first zoo in the United States. The zoo was delayed by the Civil War, financial difficulties, and restrictions on transporting wild animals. It opened in 1874 on 33 acres, and 282 animals were exhibited.

Who is considered the founder of modern **conservation**?

American naturalist John Muir (1838–1914) was the father of conservation and the founder of the Sierra Club. He fought for the preservation of the Sierra Nevada Mountains in California, and the creation of Yosemite National Park. He directed most of the Sierra Club's conservation efforts and was a lobbyist for the Antiquities Act.

John Muir.

Another prominent influence was George Perkins Marsh (1801–1882), a Vermont lawyer and scholar. His outstanding book *Man and Nature* emphasized the mistakes of past civilizations that resulted in destruction of natural resources. As the conservation movement swept through the country in the last three decades of the 19th century, a number of prominent citizens joined the efforts to conserve natural resources and to preserve wilderness areas. Writer John Burroughs, forester Gifford Pinchot, botanist Charles Sprague Sargent, and editor Robert Underwood Johnson were early advocates of conservation.

Who coined the term **"Spaceship Earth"**?

American inventor and environmentalist Buckminster Fuller (1895–1983) coined the term "Spaceship Earth" as an analogy of the need for technology to be self-contained and to avoid waste.

When was the **Environmental Protection Agency** created?

In 1970, President Richard M. Nixon created the Environmental Protection Agency (EPA) as an independent agency of the U.S. government by executive order. The creation of a federal agency by executive order rather than by an act of the legislative branch is somewhat of an exception to the rule. The EPA was originally designed to consolidate a variety of activities, including environmental research, monitoring, and enforcement activities into one agency.

What is a **"green product"**?

Green products are environmentally safe products that contain no chlorofluorocarbons, are degradable (can decompose), and are made from recycled materials. "Deep-

Who started Earth Day?

The first Earth Day, April 22, 1970, was coordinated by Denis Hayes at the request of Gaylord Nelson, United States Senator from Wisconsin. Nelson is sometimes called the father of Earth Day. His main objective was to organize a nationwide public demonstration so large it would get the attention of politicians and force the environmental issue into the political dialogue of the nation. Important official actions that began soon after the celebration of the first Earth Day were: the establishment of the Environmental Protection Agency (EPA); the creation of the President's Council on Environmental Quality; and the passage of the Clean Air Act, establishing national air quality standards.

green" products are those from small suppliers who build their identities around their claimed environmental virtues. "Greened-up" products come from the industry giants and are environmentally improved versions of established brands.

EXTINCT AND ENDANGERED PLANTS AND ANIMALS

Did **dinosaurs and humans** ever coexist?

No. Dinosaurs first appeared in the Triassic Period (about 220 million years ago) and disappeared at the end of the Cretaceous Period (about 65 million years ago). Modern humans (*Homo sapiens*) appeared only about 25,000 years ago. Movies that show humans and dinosaurs existing together are only Hollywood fantasies.

What were the **smallest** and **largest** dinosaurs?

Compsognathus, a carnivore from the late Jurassic period (131 million years ago), was about the size of a chicken and measured, at most, 35 inches (89 centimeters) from the tip of its snout to the tip of its tail. It probably weighed up to 15 pounds (6.8 kilograms).

The largest species for which a whole skeleton is known is *Brachiosaurus*. A specimen in the Humboldt Museum in Berlin measures 72.75 feet (22.2 meters) long and 46 feet (14 meters) high. It weighed an estimated 34.7 tons (31,480 kilograms). **187**

Brachiosaurus was a four-footed plant-eating dinosaur with a long neck and a long tail and lived from about 155 to 121 million years ago.

How long did dinosaurs live?

The lifespan has been estimated at 75 to 300 years. Such estimates are educated guesses. From examination of the microstructure of dinosaur bones, scientists have inferred that they matured slowly and probably had proportionately long lifespans.

How does a mastodon differ from a mammoth?

Although the words are sometimes used interchangeably, the mammoth and the mastodon were two different animals. The mastodon seems to have appeared first and a side branch may have led to the mammoth.

The *mastodon* lived in Africa, Europe, Asia, and North and South America. It appears in the Oligocene (25 to 38 million years ago) and survived until less than one million years ago. It stood a maximum of 10 feet (three meters) tall and was covered with dense woolly hair. Its tusks were straight forward and nearly parallel to each other.

The *mammoth* evolved less than two million years ago and died out about 10 thousand years ago. It lived in North America, Europe, and Asia. Like the mastodon, the mammoth was covered with dense, woolly hair, with a long, coarse layer of outer hair to protect it from the cold. It was somewhat larger than the mastodon, standing 9 to 15 feet (2.7 to 4.5 meters). The mammoth's tusks tended to spiral outward, then up.

The gradual warming of the Earth's climate and the change in environment were probably primary factors in the animals' extinction. But early man killed many of them as well, perhaps hastening the process.

Why did dinosaurs become extinct?

There are many theories as to why dinosaurs disappeared from the Earth about 65 million years ago. Scientists argue over whether the dinosaurs became extinct gradually or all at once. The gradualists believe that the dinosaur population steadily declined at the end of Cretaceous Period. Numerous reasons have been proposed for this. Some claim the dinosaurs' extinction was caused by biological changes that made them less competitive with other organisms, especially the mammals who were just beginning to appear. Overpopulation has been argued, as has the theory that mammals ate too many dinosaur eggs for the animals to reproduce themselves. Others

believe that disease—everything from rickets to constipation—wiped them out.

Changes in climate, continental drift, volcanic eruptions, and shifts in the Earth's axis, orbit, and/or magnetic field have also been held responsible.

The catastrophists argue that a single disasterous event caused the extinction, not only of the dinosaurs, but also of a large number of other species that coexisted with them. In 1980, American physicist Luis Alvarez (1911–1988) and his geologist son, Walter Alvarez (b. 1940), proposed that a large comet or meteoroid struck the Earth 65 million years ago. They pointed out that there is a high concentration of the element iridium in the sediments at the boundary between the Cretaceous and Tertiary Periods. Iridium is rare on Earth, so the only source of such a large amount of it had to be outer space. This iridium anamoly has since been discovered at over 50 sites around the world. In 1990, tiny glass fragments, which could have been caused by the extreme heat of an impact, were identified in Haiti. A 110-mile (177-kilometer) wide crater in the Yucatan Peninsula, long covered by sediments, has been dated to 64.98 million years ago, making it a leading candidate for the site of this impact.

A hit by a large extraterrestrial object, perhaps as much as six miles (9.3 kilometers) wide, would have had a catastrophic effect upon the world's climate. Huge amounts of dust and debris would have been thrown into the atmosphere, reducing the amount of sunlight reaching the surface. Heat from the blast may also have caused large forest fires, which would have added smoke and ash to the air. Lack of sunlight would kill off plants and have a domino-like effect on other organisms in the food chain, including the dinosaurs.

It is possible that the reason for the dinosaurs' extinction may have been a combination of both theories. The dinosaurs may have been gradually declining, for whatever reason. The impact of a large object from space merely delivered the coup de grâce.

The fact that dinosaurs became extinct has been cited as proof of their inferiority and that they were evolutionary failures. However, these animals flourished for 150 million years. By comparison, the earliest ancestors of humanity appeared only about three million years ago. Humans have a long way to go before they can claim the same sort of success as the dinosaurs.

How did the **dodo** become extinct?

The dodo became extinct around 1800. Thousands were slaughtered for meat, but pigs and monkeys, which destroyed dodo eggs, were probably most responsible for the dodo's extinction. Dodos were native to the Mascarene Islands in the Central Indian Ocean. They became extinct on Mauritius soon after 1680 and on Réunion about 1750. They remained on Rodriguez until 1800.

What is a **quagga**?

The quagga, a native of South Africa, was basically a brown, rather than striped, zebra with white legs and tail. In the early 19th century, it lived in the wild in great herds **189** and was tamed to become a harness animal or was killed for its skin. The species became extinct in 1883.

Under what conditions is a species considered "endangered"?

This determination is a complex process that has no set of fixed criteria that can be applied consistently to all species. The known number of living members in a species is not the sole factor. A species with a million members known to be alive but living in only one small area could be considered endangered, whereas another species having a smaller number of members, but spread out in a broad area, would not be considered so threatened. Reproduction data—the frequency of reproduction, the average number of offspring born, the survival rate, etc.—enter into such determinations. In the United States, the director of the U.S. Fish and Wildlife Service (within the Department of the Interior) determines which species are to be considered endangered, based on research and field data from specialists, biologists, botanists, and naturalists.

According to the Endangered Species Act of 1973, a species can be listed if it is threatened by any of the following:

1. The present or threatened destruction, modification, or curtailment of its habitat or range.

2. Utilization for commercial, sporting, scientific, or educational purposes at levels that detrimentally affect it.

3. Disease or predation.

4. Absence of regulatory mechanisms adequate to prevent the decline of a species or degradation of its habitat.

5. Other natural or man-made factors affecting its continued existence.

If the species is so threatened, the director then determines the "critical habitat," that is the species' inhabitation areas that contain the essential physical or biological features necessary for the species' preservation. The critical habitat can include non-habitation areas, which are deemed necessary for the protection of the species.

Which animal species have **become extinct** since the Endangered Species Act was passed in 1973, and which have subsequently **been removed from the list**?

Seven domestic species have been declared extinct: Florida's dusky seaside sparrow, the Santa Barbara song sparrow, the blue pike, the Tecopa pupfish, Sampson's pearly mussel, and the fishes the longjaw cisco and the Amistad gambusic.

Six species have been removed from the federal endangered and threatened species list since 1973 because they have recovered. Seven species have been removed from the federal list because they have become extinct.

How many species of **plants and animals** are **threatened** in the United States?

There are 206 threatened species (114 animals and 92 plants) in the United States; and 754 endangered species (320 animals and 434 plants).

Category	Threatened	Endangered	Threatened & Endangered
Mammals	9	55	64
Birds	16	74	90
Reptiles	19	14	33
Amphibians	5	7	12
Fishes	40	65	105
Snails	7	15	22
Clams	6	51	57
Crustaceans	3	14	17
Insects	9	20	29
Arachnids	0	5	5
Plants	92	434	526
TOTAL	206	754	960

What is the status of the **elephant** in Africa?

From 1979 to 1989, Africa lost half of its elephants from poaching and illegal ivory trade, with the population decreasing from an estimated 1.3 million to 600,000. This **191** led to the transfer of the African elephant from threatened to endangered status in October 1989 by CITES (the Convention on International Trade in Endangered Species). An ivory ban took effect on January 18, 1990; but six African countries (South Africa, Zimbabwe, Botswana, Namibia, Malawi, and Zambia) are trying to downlist this mammal to threatened status to allow them to trade in ivory again.

Altogether there are 35 African nations that have elephants, and all want to conserve this resource for their countries' benefit. Kenya now values a living elephant at $14,375 in tourism income for every year of its life, giving it a potential life-time value of $900,000. The ivory from an average elephant killed for its tusk would only be worth $1,000 (the price paid before the ban on ivory.

Are turtles endangered?

Worldwide turtle populations have declined due to several reasons, including habitat destruction; exploitation of species by humans for their eggs, leather, and meat; and their becoming accidently caught in the nets of fishermen. In particular danger are sea turtles, such as Kemp's ridley sea turtle (*Lepidochelys kempii*), which is believed to have a population of only a few hundred.

The endangered Kemp's ridley sea turtle.

What is the current population and status of the great whales?

Species	Latin Name	Original Population (thousands)	Current Population (thousands)	Status
Sperm	*Physeter macro cephalas*	2400	1974	Insufficient
Blue	*Balenoptera musculus*	226	13	Endangered
Finback	*Balenoptera physalus*	543	123	Vulnerable
Humpback	*Megaptera novaeangliae*	146	4	Vulnerable
Right	*Eubalaena glacialis*	120	3	Endangered
	Eubalaena australis			Vulnerable
Sei	*Balaenoptera borealis*	254	51	Vulnerable
Gray	*Eschrichtius robustus*	20	11	Unlisted
Bowhead	*Balaena mysticetus*	20	2	Vulnerable
Bryde's	*Balaenoptera edeni*	92	92	Insufficient
Minke	*Balaenoptera acutorostrata*	295	280	Insufficient

What is a **dolphin-safe tuna?**

The order Cetacea, composed of whales, dolphins, and porpoises, were spared from the extinction of large mammals at the end of the Pleistocene about 10,000 years ago. But from 1000 B.C.E. on they, especially the whale, have been relentlessly hunted by man for their valuable products. The twentieth century, with its many technological improvements, has become the most destructive period for the Cetacea. In 1972, the United States Congress passed the Marine Mammal Protection Act; one of its goals was to reduce the number of small cetaceans (notably *Stenalla* and *Delphinus*) killed and injured during commercial fishing operations, such as the incidental catch of dolphins in tuna purse-seines (nets that close up to form a huge ball to be hoisted aboard ship). Dolphins are often found swimming with schools of yellowfin tuna and are caught along with the tuna by fisherman who use purse-seine nets. The dolphins are drowned by this fishing method because they must be able to breathe air to survive. The number of incidental deaths and injuries in 1972 was estimated at 368,000 for United States fishing vessels and 55,078 for non–United States vessels. In 1979 the figures were reduced to 17,938 and 6,837 respectively. But in the 1980s, the dolphins killed by foreign vessels rose dramatically to over 100,000 a year. Most of the slaughter occurs in the eastern Pacific Ocean from Chile to Southern California.

To further reduce the numbers of dolphins killed during tuna catches, the three largest sellers of canned tuna in the United States, spearheaded by the Starkist company, decided that they would not sell tuna that has been caught by these methods harmful to dolphins. Only dolphin-safe tuna would be sold by them.

POLLUTION
See also: Health and Medicine—Health Hazards, Risks, Etc.

What is the **Pollutant Standard Index?**

The U.S. Environmental Protection Agency and the South Coast Air Quality Management District of El Monte, California, devised the Pollutant Standard Index to monitor concentrations of pollutants in the air and inform the public concerning related health effects. The scale measures the amount of pollution in parts per million, and has been in use nationwide since 1978.

PSI Index	Health Effects	Cautionary Status
0	Good	
50	Moderate	
100	Unhealthful	

PSI Index	Health Effects	Cautionary Status
200	Very unhealthful	Alert: elderly or ill should stay indoors and reduce physical activity.
300	Hazardous	Warning: General population should stay indoors and reduce physical activity.
400	Extremely hazardous	Emergency: all people remain indoors windows shut, no physical exertion.
500	Toxic	Significant harm; same as above.

What is the **Toxic Release Inventory** (TRI)?

TRI is a government mandated, publicly available compilation of information on the release of over 300 individual toxic chemicals and 20 categories of chemical compounds by manufacturing facilities in the United States. The law requires manufacturers to state the amounts of chemicals they release directly to air, land, or water, or that they transfer to off-site facilities that treat or dispose of wastes. The U.S. Environmental Protection Agency compiles these reports into an annual inventory and makes the information available in a computerized database. In 1992, 23,630 facilities released 3.2 billion pounds (1.5 billion kilograms) of toxic chemicals into the environment. Over 272 million pounds (124 million kilograms) of this total were released into surface water; 1.8 billion pounds (818 million kilograms) were emitted into the air; over 337 million pounds (153 million kilograms) were released to land; and over 725 million pounds (330 million kilograms) were injected into underground wells. The total amount of toxic chemicals released in 1992 was 6.6% lower than the amount released in 1991.

What are **PCBs**?

Polychlorinated biphenyls (PCBs) are a group of chemicals that were widely used before 1970 in the electrical industry, as a coolant for transformers and in capacitors and other electrical devices. They caused environmental problems because they do not break down, and can spread through the water, soil, and air. They have been linked by some scientists to cancer and reproductive disorders and have been shown to cause liver function abnormalities. Government action has resulted in the control of the use, disposal, and production of PCBs in nearly all areas of the world, including the United States.

What was the distribution of **radioactive fallout** after the 1986 Chernobyl accident?

Radioactive fallout, containing the isotope cesium 137, and nuclear contamination covered an enormous area, including Byelorussia, Latvia, Lithuania, the central portion of the then Soviet Union, the Scandinavian countries, the Ukraine, Poland, Austria, Czechoslovakia, Germany, Switzerland, northern Italy, eastern France, Romania, Bulgaria, Greece, Yugoslavia, the Netherlands, and the United Kingdom. The fallout, extremely uneven because of the shifting wind patterns, extended 1,200 to 1,300 miles (1,930 to 2,090 kilometers) from the point of the accident. Roughly 5% of the reactor fuel or seven tons of fuel containing 50 to 100 million curies were released. Estimates of the effects of this fallout range from 28,000 to 100,000 deaths from cancer and genetic defects within the next 50 years. In particular, livestock in high rainfall areas received unacceptable dosages of radiation.

How do **chlorofluorocarbons** affect the Earth's ozone layer?

Chlorofluorocarbons (CFCs) are hydrocarbons, such as freon, in which part or all of the hydrogen atoms have been replaced by fluorine atoms. These can be liquids or gases, are non-flammable and heat-stable, and are used as refrigerants, aerosol propellants, and solvents. When released into the air, they slowly rise into the Earth's upper atmosphere, where they are broken apart by ultraviolet rays from the sun. Some of the resultant molecular fragments react with the ozone in the atmosphere, reducing the amount of ozone. The CFC molecules' chlorine atoms act as catalysts in a complex set of reactions that convert two molecules of ozone into three molecules of ordinary hydrogen. This is depleting the beneficial ozone layer faster than it can be recharged by natural processes. The resultant "hole" lets through more ultraviolet light to the Earth's surface and creates health problems for humans, such as cataracts and skin cancer, and disturbs delicate ecosystems (for example, making plants produce less seed). In 1978 the United States government banned the use of fluorocarbon aerosols, and currently aerosol propellants have been changed from fluorocarbons to hydrocarbons, such as butane. Chemical industries must cut CFC manufacture to 50% by the year 2000; they have mounted a massive research effort to find a safer chemical substitute.

Since 1988 a substantial slowdown has taken place in the atmospheric buildup of two prime ozone-destroying compounds, CFC 11 and CFC 12. Based upon these measurements, experts suggest that concentrations of these CFCs will peak before the turn of the century, allowing the ozone layer to begin the slow process of repairing itself. It is believed that it will take 50 to 100 years for reactions in the atmosphere to reduce the concentrations of ozone-destroying chlorine and bromine back to natural levels. Until then, these chemicals will continue to erode the global ozone layer.

What are the components of **smog**?

Photochemical air pollution, commonly known as smog, is the result of a number of complex chemical reactions. The hydrocarbons, hydrocarbon derivations, and nitric oxides emitted from such sources as automobiles are the raw materials for photo- **195** chemical reactions. In the presence of oxygen and sunlight, the nitric oxides combine with organic compounds, such as the hydrocarbons from unburned gasoline, to produce a whitish haze, sometimes tinged with a yellow-brown color. In the process, a large number of new hydrocarbons and oxyhydrocarbons are produced. These secondary hydrocarbon products may compose as much as 95% of the total organics in a severe smog episode.

What are **flue gas "scrubbers"**?

The scrubbing of flue gases refers to the removal of sulfur dioxide (SO_2) and nitric oxide (NO), which are major components of air pollution. Wet scrubbers use a chemical solvent or lime, limestone, sodium alkali, or diluted sulfuric acid to remove the SO_2 formed during combustion. Dry scrubbing uses either a lime/limestone slurry or ammonia sprayed into the flue gases.

What is **acid rain**?

The term "acid rain" was coined by British chemist Robert Angus Smith (1817–1884) who, in 1872, published *Air & Rain: The Beginnings of a Chemical Climatology*. Since then, acid rain has unfortunately become an increasingly used term for rain, snow, sleet, or other precipitation that has been polluted by acids such as sulfuric and nitric acids.

When gasoline, coal, or oil are burned, their waste products of sulfur dioxide and nitrogen dioxide combine in complex chemical reactions with water vapor in clouds to form acids. The United States alone discharges 40 million metric tons of sulfur and nitrogen oxides into the atmosphere. This, combined with natural emissions of sulfur and nitrogen compounds, has resulted in severe ecological damage. Hundreds of lakes in North America (especially northeastern Canada and United States) and in Scandinavia are so acidic that they cannot support fish life. Crops, forests, and building materials, such as marble, limestone, sandstone, and bronze, have been affected as well, but the extent is not as well documented. However, in Europe, where so many living trees are stunted or killed, a new word *Waldsterben* (forest death) has been coined to describe this new phenomenon.

In 1990, amendments to the U.S. Clean Air Act contained provisions to control emissions that cause acid rain. It included the reductions of sulfur dioxide emissions from 19 million tons to 9.1 million tons annually and the reduction of industrial nitrogen oxide emissions from six to four million tons annually, both by the year 2000. Also the elimination of 90% of industrial benzene, mercury, and dioxin emissions, the reduction of automotive nitrogen oxide by 60%, and hydrocarbons by 40% by year 1997 were specified.

How **acidic** is acid rain?

Acidity or alkalinity is measured by a scale known as the pH (potential for Hydrogen) scale. It runs from zero to 14. Since it is logarithmic, a change in one unit equals a tenfold increase or decrease. So a solution at pH 2 is 10 times more acidic than one at pH 3 and 100 times as acidic as a solution at pH 4. Zero is extremely acid, 7 is neutral, and 14 is very alkaline. Any rain below 5.0 is considered acid rain; some scientists use the value of 5.6 or less. Normal rain and snow containing dissolved carbon dioxide (a weak acid) measure about pH 5.6. Actual values vary according to geographical area. Eastern Europe and parts of Scandinavia have 4.3 to 4.5; the rest of Europe is 4.5 to 5.1; eastern United States and Canada ranges from 4.2 to 4.6, and Mississippi Valley has a range of 4.6 to 4.8. The worst North American area, having 4.2, is centered around Lake Erie and Lake Ontario. For comparison, some common items and their pH values are listed below:

Concentrated sulfuric acid	1.0
Lemon juice	2.3
Vinegar	3.3
Acid rain	4.3
Normal rain	5.0 to 5.6
Normal lakes and rivers	5.6 to 8.0
Distilled water	7.0
Human blood	7.35 to 7.45
Seawater	7.6 to 8.4

How much **oil** is **dumped into the oceans**?

Every year well over three million metric tons of oil contaminate the sea. A half comes from ships, but the rest come from land-based pollution, with only 33% of it spilled by accident. More than 1.1 million metric tons of oil are deliberately discharged from tankers washing out their tanks.

Source of oil	% of total
Tankers operational discharge	22%
Municipal wastes	22%
Tanker accidents	12.5%
Atmospheric rainout (oil released by industry and cars)	9.5%
Bilge and fuel oils	9%
Natural seeps	7.5%
Non-refining industrial waste	6%
Urban runoff	3.5%
Coastal oil refineries	3%
Offshore production	1.5%
River runoff	1%
Others	2.5%

Where did the **first major oil spill** occur?

The first major commercial oil spill occurred on March 18, 1967, when the tanker *Torrey Canyon* grounded on the Seven Stones Shoal off the coast of Cornwall, England, spilling 830,000 barrels (119,000 tons) of Kuwaiti oil into the sea. This was the first major tanker accident. However during World War II, German U-boat attacks on tankers, between January and June of 1942, off the United States East Coast, spilled 590,000 tons of oil. Although the *Exxon Valdez* was widely publicized as a major spill of 35,000 tons in 1989, it is dwarfed by the deliberate dumping of oil from Sea Island into the Persian Gulf on January 25, 1991. It is estimated that the spill equaled almost 1.5 million tons of oil. A major spill also occurred in Russia in October 1994 in the Komi region of the Arctic. The size of the spill was reported to be as much as two million barrels (286,000 tons).

In addition to the large disasters, day-to-day pollution occurs from drilling platforms where waste generated from platform life, including human waste, and oils, chemicals, mud and rock from drilling are discharged into the water.

Date	Cause	Thousands tons spilled
1/42-6/42	German U-boat attacks on tankers off the East Coast of U.S. during World War II	590
3/18/67	Tanker Torrey Canyon grounds off Land's End in the English Channel	119
3/20/70	Tanker Othello collides with another ship in Tralhavet Bay, Sweden	60–100
12/19/72	Tanker Sea Star collides with another ship in Gulf of Oman	115
5/12/76	Urquiola grounds at La Coruna, Spain	100
3/16/78	Tanker Amoco Cadiz grounds off Northwest France	223
6/3/79	Itox I oil well blows in Southern Gulf of Mexico	600
7/79	Tankers Atlantic Express and Aegean Captain collide off Trinidad and Tobago	300
2/19/83	Blowout in Norwuz oil field in the Persian Gulf	600
8/6/83	Fire aboard Castillo de Beliver off Cape Town, South Africa	250
1/25/91	Iraq begins deliberately dumping oil into Persian Gulf from Sea Island, Kuwait	1,450

How harmful are balloon releases?

Both latex and metallic balloons can be harmful. A latex balloon can land in water, lose its color, and resemble a jellyfish, which if eaten by sea animals can cause their death because they cannot digest it. A metal balloon can get caught in electric wires and cause power outages.

What are **Operation Ranch Hand** and **Agent Orange**?

Operation Ranch Hand was the tactical military project for the aerial spraying of herbicides in South Vietnam during the Vietnam Conflict (1961–1975). In these operations Agent Orange, the collective name for the herbicides 2,4-D and 2,4,5-T, was used for the defoliation. The name derives from the color-coded drums in which the herbicides were stored. In all, U.S. troops sprayed approximately 19 million gallons (72 million liters) of herbicides over four million acres (1.6 million hectare).

Concerns about the health effects of Agent Orange were initially voiced in 1970, and since then the issue has been complicated by scientific and political debate. In 1993, a 16-member panel of experts reviewed the existing scientific evidence and found strong evidence of a statistical association between herbicides and soft-tissue sarcoma, non-Hodgkin's lymphoma, Hodgkin's disease and chloracne. On the other hand, they concluded that no connection appeared to exist between exposure to Agent Orange and skin cancer, bladder cancer, brain tumors, or stomach cancer.

What causes **formaldehyde contamination** in homes?

Formaldehyde contamination is related to the widespread construction use of wood products bonded with urea-formaldehyde resins and products containing formaldehyde. Major formaldehyde sources include subflooring of particle board; wall paneling made from hardwood plywood or particle board; and cabinets and furniture made from particle board, medium density fiberboard, hardwood plywood, or solid wood. Urea-formaldehyde foam insulation (UFFI) has received the most media notoriety and regulatory attention. Formaldehyde is also used in drapes, upholstery, carpeting, and wallpaper adhesives, milk cartons, car bodies, household disinfectants, permanent-press clothing, and paper towels. In particular, mobile homes seem to have higher formaldehyde levels than houses do. Six billion pounds (2.7 billion kilograms) of formaldehyde are used in the United States each year.

The release of formaldehyde into the air by these products (called outgassing) can develop poisoning symptoms in humans. The EPA classifies formaldehyde as a potential human carcinogen (cancer-causing agent).

199

Which pollutants lead to **indoor air pollution**?

Indoor air pollution, also known as "tight building syndrome," results from conditions in modern, high energy efficiency buildings, which have reduced outside air exchange, or have inadequate ventilation, chemical contamination, and microbial contamination. Indoor air pollution can produce various symptoms, such as headache, nausea, and eye, nose, and throat irritation. In addition houses are affected by indoor air pollution emanating from consumer and building products and from tobacco smoke. Below are listed some pollutants found in houses:

Pollutant	Sources	Effects
Asbestos	Old or damaged insulation, fireproofing, or acoustical tiles	Many years later, chest and abdominal cancers and lung diseases
Biological pollutants	Bacteria, mold and mildew, viruses, animal dander and cat saliva, mites, cockroaches, and pollen	Eye, nose, and throat irritation; shortness of breath; dizziness; lethargy; fever; digestive problems; asthma; influenza and other infectious diseases
Carbon monoxide	Unvented kerosene and gas heaters; leaking chimneys and furnaces; wood stoves and fireplaces; gas stoves; automobile exhaust from attached garages; tobacco smoke	At low levels, fatigue; at higher levels, impaired vision and coordination; headaches; dizziness; confusion; nausea. Fatal at very high concentrations
Formaldehyde	Plywood, wall paneling, particle board, fiber-board; foam insulation; fire and tobacco smoke; textiles, and glues	Eye, nose, and throat irritations; wheezing and coughing; fatigue; skin rash; severe allergic reactions; may cause cancer
Lead	Automobile exhaust; sanding or burning of lead paint; soldering	Impaired mental and physical development in children; decreased coordination and mental abilities; kidneys, nervous system, and red blood cells damage

Pollutant	Sources	Effects
Mercury	Some latex paints	Vapors can cause kidney damage; long–term exposure can cause brain damage
Nitrogen dioxide	Kerosene heaters, unvented gas stoves and heaters; tobacco smoke	Eye, nose, and throat irritation; may impair lung function and increase respiratory infections in young children
Organic Gases	Paints, paint strippers, solvents, wood preservatives; aerosol sprays; cleansers and disinfectants; moth repellents; air fresheners; stored fuels; hobby supplies; dry-cleaned clothing.	Eye, nose and throat irritation; headaches; loss of coordination; nausea; damage to liver, kidney, and nervous system; some organics cause cancer in animals and are suspected of causing cancer in humans.
Pesticides	Products used to kill household pests and products used on lawns or gardens that drift or are tracked inside the house.	Irritation to eye, nose, and throat; damage to nervous system and kidneys; cancer.
Radon	Earth and rock beneath the home; well water, building materials.	No immediate symptoms; estimated to cause about 10% of lung cancer deaths; smokers at higher risk.

RECYCLING, CONSERVATION, AND WASTE

See also: Energy—Consumption and Conservation

What is the **NIMBY** syndrome?

NIMBY is the acronym for "Not In My Back Yard," referring to major community resistance to new incinerator sitings, landfills, prisons, roads, etc. NIMFY is "Not In My Front Yard."

Which states have the greatest number of hazardous waste sites?

The top five are:

New Jersey	107
Pennsylvania	102
New York	81
California	96
Michigan	77

A total of 1,276 sites were recorded.

Where are the six nuclear dump sites in the United States?

As of 1991, the six nuclear waste dump sites are in West Valley, New York; Sheffield, Illinois; Maxey Flats, Kentucky; Barnwell, South Carolina; Beatty, Nevada; and Richland, Washington.

How is nuclear waste stored?

Nuclear wastes consist either of fission products formed from atom splitting of uranium, cesium, strontium, or krypton, or from transuranic elements formed when uranium atoms absorb free neutrons. Wastes from transuranic elements are less radioactive than fission products; however, these elements remain radioactive far longer— hundreds of thousands of years. The types of waste are irradiated fuel (spent fuel) in the form of 12-foot (4-meter) long rods, high-level radioactive waste in the form of liquid or sludge, and low-level waste (non-transuranic or legally high-level) in the form of reactor hardware, piping, toxic resins, water from fuel pool, etc.

In the United States most of the spent fuel has been left for 10 years or more in water-filled pools at the individual plant sites. They are waiting permanent disposal that is set for 1998 by a mandate in the Nuclear Waste Policy Act (1982). Most low-level radioactive waste has been stored in steel drums in shallow landfills at the six nuclear dump sites and at the Hanford Nuclear Reservation in the state of Washington. Most high-level nuclear waste has been stored in double-walled stainless-steel tanks surrounded by three feet (one meter) of concrete. The current best storage method, developed by the French in 1978, is to incorporate the waste into a special molten glass mixture, then enclose it in a steel container and bury it in a special pit.

How much garbage does the average American generate?

According to one study, Americans produce about 230 million tons of refuse a year— 5.1 pounds (2.3 kilograms) per person a day or about 1,900 pounds (863 kilograms) per year. Another survey reported that a typical suburban family of three generated 40 pounds (18 kilograms) of garbage weekly with the components of the content given in percentages below:

Type of solid waste	Percent
Aluminum	1%
Polystyrene meat trays, cups, egg cartons, and packing	3%
Disposable diapers	3%
Wood, textiles, old clothing	5%
Metal cans and nails	5%
Plastic soda bottles and bags	5%
Glass	8%
Miscellaneous	10%
Food	11%
Paper	21%
Yard waste and grass clippings	23%

An analysis by the U.S. Environmental Protection Agency, published in 1990, indicated not only an increase in the amount of garbage per person, but a change in the content of it as well:

Garbage in pounds per person per day

Waste materials	1960	1970	1980	1988
Total nonfood product wastes	1.65	2.26	2.57	2.94
Paper and paperboard	0.91	1.19	1.32	1.60
Glass	0.20	0.34	0.36	0.28
Metals	0.32	0.38	0.35	0.34
Plastics	0.01	0.08	0.19	0.32
Rubber and leather	0.06	0.09	0.10	0.10
Textiles	0.05	0.05	0.06	0.09
Wood	0.09	0.11	0.12	0.14
Other	0.00	0.02	0.07	0.07
Other Wastes				
Food wastes	0.37	0.34	0.32	0.29
Yard wastes	0.61	0.62	0.66	0.70
Miscellaneous inorganic waste	0.04	0.05	0.05	0.06
Total waste generated	2.66	3.27	3.61	4.00

How much **solid waste** is generated annually in the United States?

The United States produces 4.543 million tons of solid waste annually.

Type of waste	Million tons	Percent
Agriculture	2,340	52
Mineral industries (mining and milling waste)	1,620	36
Industrial (nonhazardous)	225	5
Municipal (domestic)	180	4
Utility	90	2
Hazardous	45	2
Low-level radioactive	3	0.0007

Of the municipal solid wastes in 1988 of approximately 180 million tons in the above table, paper waste ranked the highest.

Municipal Solid Waste

Type of waste	Million tons
Paper	71.8
Yard wastes	31.6
Rubber, Textile, Wood, etc.	20.8
Metals	15.3
Plastics	14.4
Food wastes	13.2
Glass	12.5

How critical is the problem of **landfilling** in the United States?

According to one source, landfilling is currently over-used in the United States, but will continue to be an essential component of waste management. There are more than 9,000 landfills in the United States. In 1960, 62% of all garbage was sent to landfills; in 1980, the figure was 81%; and in 1990 it decreased to 67%. After as much waste as possible has been reduced, recovered, reused, or converted to energy, there will still be some waste that cannot be disposed of in any other way except in landfills. However, landfill capacity is already dwindling severely in the most populous regions of the country. In 1995, a study reported that the number of landfills accepting municipal solid waste had declined from 4,482 to 3,558.

How much does **packaging** contribute to municipal solid waste?

Packaging accounted for 30.3% of municipal solid waste in 1990. The material components of this figure are paper (47.7%), glass (24.5%), plastic (14.5%), steel (6.5%), wood (4.5%), and aluminum (2.3%).

How much space does a **recycled ton of paper** save in a landfill?

Each ton (907 kilograms) saves more than three cubic yards of landfill space.

What **natural resources** are saved by **recycling paper**?

One ton (907 kilograms) of recycled waste paper would save an average of 7,000 gallons (26,460 liters) of water, 3.3 cubic yards (2.5 cubic meters) of landfill space, three barrels of oil, 17 trees, and 4,000 kilowatt-hours of electricity, or energy to power the average home for six months.

How much **newspaper** must be recycled to **save one tree**?

One 35 to 40 foot (10.6 to 12 meter) tree produces a stack of newspapers four feet (1.2 meters) thick; this much newspaper must be recycled to save a tree.

How much **waste paper** does a **newspaper** generate?

An average yearly newspaper subscription (for example *The San Francisco Chronicle*) received every day, produces 550 pounds (250 kilograms) of waste paper (per subscription per year). The average *New York Times* Sunday edition produces eight million pounds (3.6 million kilograms) of waste paper.

How many **paper mills** in the United States use waste paper to produce new products?

Of the approximately 600 mills in the United States producing pulp, paper, paperboard, or building products, 200 depend almost entirely on waste paper for their raw material. Another 300 mills use 10% to 50% waste paper in their manufacturing processes.

What problems may be encountered when **polyvinyl chloride (PVC) plastics** are burned?

Chlorinated plastics, such as PVC, contribute to the formation of hydrochloric acid gases. They also may be a part of a mix of substances containing chlorine that form a precursor to dioxin in the burning process. Polystyrene, polyethylene, and polyethylene terephthalate (PET) do not produce these pollutants.

What do the **numbers** inside the **recycling symbol** on plastic containers mean?

The Society of the Plastics Industry developed a voluntary coding system for plastic containers to assist recyclers in sorting plastic containers. The symbol is designed to be imprinted on the bottom of the plastic containers. The numerical code appears inside a three-sided triangular arrow. A guide to what the numbers mean is listed below. The most commonly recycled plastics are polyethylene terephthalate (PET) and high density polyethylene (HDPE).

Code	Material	Examples
1	Polyethylene terephthalate (PET)	Soft drink bottles
2	High-density polyethylene (HDPE)	Milk and water jugs
3	Vinyl	Shampoo bottles
4	Low-density polyethylene (LDPE)	Ketchup bottles
5	Polypropylene	Squeeze bottles
6	Polystyrene	Fast-food packaging
7	Other	

What products are made from **recycled plastic**?

Resin	Common Uses	Products Made From Recycled Resin
HDPE	Beverage bottles, milk jugs, milk and soft drink crates, pipe, cable, film	Motor oil bottles, detergent bottles, pipes and pails
LDPE	Film bags such as trash bags, coatings, and plastic bottles.	New trash bags, pallets
PET	Soft drink, detergent, and juice bottles	Carpets, fiberfill, non-food bottles/containers
PP	Auto battery cases, screw-on caps and lids; some yogurt and margarine tubs, plastic film	Auto parts, batteries, carpets
PS	Housewares, electronics, fast food carry-out packaging, plastic utensils	Insulation board, office equipment, reusable cafeteria trays
PVC	Sporting goods, luggage, pipes, auto parts. In packaging for shampoo bottles, blister packaging, and films	Drainage pipes, fencing, house siding

A new clothing fiber called Fortrel EcoSpun is made from recycled plastic soda bottles. The fiber is knit or woven into garments such as fleece for outerwear or long

Are cloth diapers or disposable diapers better for the environment?

This is a complex matter with both alternatives having an environmental impact. Disposable diapers make up 2% of the total solid waste while cloth diapers account for only 1% of the solid waste. In 1990, 16 to 17 billion disposable diapers were sold. However, cleaning cloth diapers requires the use of detergents (polluting-agent) and hot water (energy user). In addition, if a professional diaper service is used, then there is extra gasoline for delivery and the exhaust from trucks contributes to air pollution.

underwear. The processor estimates that every pound of Fortrel EcoSpun fiber results in 10 plastic bottles being kept out of landfills.

Is **washing dishes by hand** better for the environment than using an automatic **dishwasher**?

Dishwashers often save energy and water compared to hand washing. Depending on the brand, dishwashers typically consume 7.5 to 12 gallons (28 to 45 liters) of water per normal wash. Hand-washing a day's worth of dishes may use up to 15 gallons (57 liters) of water. One university study found that dishwashers consume about 37% less water than washing by hand.

Several steps can be taken for additional energy savings when using a dishwasher. The setting on a home's water heater can be turned down to 120°F (49°C) if the dishwasher has a booster heater. While some machines feature no-heat air-dry setting, simply opening the door after the final rinse to let the dishes air dry will save energy. Prewashing the dishes before loading generally wastes water since most machines can handle even heavily soiled plates.

How many **automobile tires** are scrapped each year and what can be done with them?

Approximately 242 million tires are discarded annually in the United States. Less than 7% are recycled, 11% are burned for their fuel value, and 5% are exported. The remaining 78% are sent to landfills, stockpiled, or illegally dumped.

A major use for discarded tires is in rubber modified asphalt and concrete. They can also be recycled into new products such as floor mats, blasting mats, and muffler hangers. Tires that have been ground into crumb can be used in a variety of molded or

207

die cut products such as traffic cone bases, mud flaps, and moisture barriers. Whole tires can be used in artificial reefs, for erosion control and to stabilize mine tailing ponds.

What is a **WOBO**?

A WOBO (world bottle) is the first mass-produced container designed for secondary use as a building product. It was conceived by Albert Heineken of the Heineken beer family. The beer bottles were designed in a special shape to be used, when empty, as glass bricks for building houses. The actual building carried out with WOBOs was only a small shed and a double garage built on the Heineken estate at Noordwijk, near Amsterdam. Although not implemented, WOBO was a sophisticated and intelligent design solution to what has emerged as a major environmental issue in recent years.

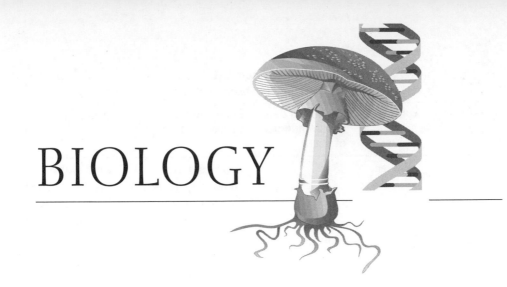

BIOLOGY

EVOLUTION AND GENETICS

Which **biological events** occurred during the **geologic time divisions**?

Cenozoic Era (Age of Mammals)				
Period	**Epoch**	**Beginning date in est. millions of years**	**Plants and microorganisms**	**Animals**
Quaternary	Holocene (Recent)	10,000 years ago	Decline of woody plants and rise of herbaceous plants	Age of *Homo sapiens*; humans dominate
	Pleistocene	1.9	Extinction of many species (from 4 ice ages)	Extinction of many large mammals (from 4 ice ages)
Tertiary	Pliocene	6.0	Development of grasslands; decline of forests; flowering plants	Large carnivores; many grazing mammals; first known human-like primates
	Miocene	25.0		Many modern mammals evolve

Cenozoic Era
(Age of Mammals)

Period	Epoch	Beginning date in est. millions of years	Plants and microorganisms	Animals
	Oligocene	38.0	Spread of forests; flowering plants, rise of monocotyledons	Apes evolve; all present mammal families evolve; saber-toothed cats
Tertiary	Eocene	55.0	Gymnosperms and angiosperms dominant	Beginning of age of mammals; modern birds
	Paleocene	65.0		Evolution of primate mammals

Mesozoic Era
(Age of Reptiles)

Period	Epoch	Beginning date in est. millions of years	Plants and microorganisms	Animals
Cretaceous		135.0	Rise of angiosperms; gymnosperms decline	Dinosaurs reach peak and then become extinct; toothed birds become extinct; first modern birds; primitive mammals
Jurassic		200.0	Ferns and gymnosperms common	Large, specialized dinosaurs; insectivorous marsupials
Triassic		250.0	Gymnosperms and ferns dominate	First dinosaurs; egg-laying mammals.

Paleozic Era
(Age of Ancient Life)

Period	Epoch	Beginning date in est. millions of years	Plants and microorganisms	Animals
Permian		285.0	Conifers evolve.	Modern insects appear; mammal-

Period	Epoch	Beginning date in est. millions of years	Plants and microorganisms	Animals
				like reptiles; extinction of many Paleozic invertebrates
Carboniferous (divided into Mississippian and Pennsylvanian periods by some in the U.S.)		350.0	Forests of ferns and gymnosperms; swamps; club mosses and horsetails	Ancient sharks abundant; many echinoderms, mollusks and insect forms; first reptiles; spread of ancient amphibians
Devonian		410.0	Terrestrial plants established; first forests; gymnosperms appear	Age of fish; amphibians; wingless insects and millipedes appear
Silurian		425.0	Vascular plants appear; algae dominant	Fish evolve; marine arachnids dominant; first insects; crustaceans
Ordovician		500.0	Marine algae dominant; terrestrial plants first appear	Invertebrates dominant; first fish appear
Cambrian		570.0	Algae dominant	Age of marine invertebrates

Precambrian Era

Period	Epoch	Beginning date in est. millions of years	Plants and microorganisms	Animals
Archeozoic and Proterozoic Eras		3800.0	Bacterial cells; then primitive algae and fungi; marine protozoans	Marine invertebrates at end of period
Azoic		4600.0	Origin of the Earth.	

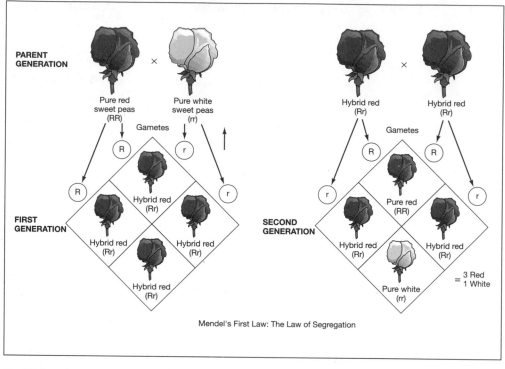

PARENT GENERATION

Pure red sweet peas (RR) × Pure white sweet peas (rr)

Gametes

R   r

R   r

FIRST GENERATION

Hybrid red (Rr)

Hybrid red (Rr)   Hybrid red (Rr)

Hybrid red (Rr)

Hybrid red (Rr) × Hybrid red (Rr)

Gametes

R   R

r   r

SECOND GENERATION

Pure red (RR)

Hybrid red (Rr)   Hybrid red (Rr)

Pure white (rr)

= 3 Red 1 White

Mendel's First Law: The Law of Segregation

Mendel's Law of Segregation.

How did **humans evolve**?

Evolution of the *Homo* lineage of modern humans (*Homo sapiens*) began with the hunter of nearly five feet tall, *Homo habilis*, who is widely presumed to have evolved from an australopithecine ancestor. Near the beginning of the Pleistocene (two million years ago), *Homo habilis* was transformed into *Homo erectus* (Java Man), who used fire and possessed culture. Middle Pleistocene populations of *Homo erectus* are said to show steady evolution toward the anatomy of *Homo sapiens* (Neanderthals, Cro-Magnons, and modern humans), 120,000 to 40,000 years ago. Pre-modern *Homo sapiens* built huts and made clothing.

What is meant by **Mendelian inheritance**?

Mendelian inheritance refers to genetic traits carried through heredity; the process was studied and described by Austrian monk Gregor Mendel (1822–1889). Mendel was the first to deduce correctly the basic principles of heredity. Mendelian traits are also called single gene or monogenic traits, because they are controlled by the action of a single gene or gene pair. More than 4,300 human disorders are known or suspected to be inherited as Mendelian traits, encompassing autosomal dominant (e.g., neurofibromatosis), autosomal recessive (e.g., cystic fibrosis), sex-linked dominant and recessive conditions (e.g., color-blindness and hemophilia).

Overall, incidence of Mendelian disorders in the human population is about 1%. Many non-anomalous characteristics that make up human variation are also inherited in Mendelian fashion.

Who is generally known as the **founder of genetics**?

Gregor Mendel (1822–1884), an Austrian monk and biologist, is considered the founder of genetics. Using his knowledge of statistics to analyze biological phenomena, Mendel discovered specific and regular ratios that he used to formulate the laws of heredity. It was the English biologist William Bateson (1861–1926), however, who brought Mendel's work to the attention of the scientific world and who coined the term "genetics."

What is the significance of *On the Origin of Species*?

Charles Darwin.

Charles Darwin (1809–1882) first proposed a theory of evolution based on natural selection in his treatise *On the Origin of Species*. The publication of *On the Origin of Species* ushered in a new era in our thinking about the nature of man. The intellectual revolution it caused and the impact it had on man's concept of himself and the world were greater than those caused by the works of Newton and others. The effect was immediate, the first edition being sold out on the day of publication (November 24, 1859). *Origin* has been referred to as "the book that shook the world." Every modern discussion of man's future, the population explosion, the struggle for existence, the purpose of man and the universe, and man's place in nature rests on Darwin.

The work was a product of his analyses and interpretations of his findings from his voyages on the H.M.S. *Beagle*, as a naturalist. In Darwin's day, the prevailing explanation for organic diversity was the story of creation in the book of Genesis in the Bible. *Origin* was the first publication to present scientifically sound, well-organized evidence for evolution. Darwin's theory of evolution was based on natural selection in which the best, the fittest, survive, and if there is a difference in genetic endowment **213** among individuals, the race will, by necessity, steadily improve. It is a two-step process: the first consists of the production of variation, and the second, of the sorting of this variability by natural selection in which the favorable variations tend to be preserved.

Did Charles Darwin have any nicknames?

Darwin had several nicknames. As a young naturalist on board the H.M.S. *Beagle*, he was called "Philos" because of his intellectual pursuits and "Flycatcher" when his shipmates tired of him filling the ship with his collections. Later in his life, when he became a leader in the scientific community, journalists refered to him as "The Sage of Down" or "The Saint of Science," but his friend Thomas Henry Huxley privately called him "The Czar of Down" and the "Pope of Science." His own favorite nickname was "Stultis the Fool" and he often signed letters to scientific friends with "Stultis." This name referred to his habit of trying experiments most people would prejudge to be fruitless or fool's experiments.

Who coined the phrase "survival of the fittest"?

Although frequently associated with Darwinism, this phrase was coined by Herbert Spencer (1820–1903), an English sociologist. It is the process by which organisms that are less well-adapted to their environment tend to perish and better-adapted organisms tend to survive.

What is Batesian mimicry?

In 1861, Henry Walter Bates (1825–1892), a British naturalist, proposed that a non-toxic species can evolve (especially in color and color pattern) to look like a toxic or unpalatable species, or to act like a toxic species, to avoid being eaten by a predator. The classic example is the viceroy butterfly, which resembles the unpalatable monarch butterfly. This is called Batesian mimicry. Subsequently, Fritz Müller (1821–1897), a German-born zoologist, discovered that all the species of similar appearance become distasteful to predators. This phenomenon is called Müllerian mimicry.

When was the Scopes (monkey) trial?

John T. Scopes (1900–1970), a high-school biology teacher, was brought to trial by the State of Tennessee in 1925 for teaching the theory of evolution. He challenged a recent law passed by the Tennessee legislature that made it unlawful to teach in any public school any theory that denies the divine creation of man. He was convicted and sentenced, but the decision was reversed later and the law repealed in 1967.

What is the Red Queen hypothesis?

This hypothesis, also called the law of constant extinction, is named after the Red Queen in Lewis Carroll's *Through the Looking Glass*, who said "now here, you see, it takes all the running you can do to keep in the same place." The idea is that an evolutionary advance by one species represents a deterioration of the environment for all remaining species. This places pressure on those species to advance just to keep up.

At the present, pressure against school boards still affects the teaching of evolution. Recent drives by anti-evolutionists either have tried to ban the teaching of evolution or have demanded "equal time" for "special creation" as described in the biblical book of Genesis. This has raised many questions about the separation of church and state, the teaching of controversial subjects in public schools, and the ability of scientists to communicate with the public. The gradual improvement of the fossil record, the result of comparative anatomy, and many other developments in biological science contributed toward making evolutionary thinking more palatable.

What is **genetic engineering**?

Genetic engineering is the deliberate alteration of the genetic make-up (genome) of an organism by manipulation of its DNA (deoxyribonucleic acid) molecule (a double helix chemical structure containing genetic information) to effect a change in heredity traits.

Genetic engineering techniques include cell fusion and the use of recombinant DNA (RNA) or gene-splicing. In cell fusion, the tough outer membranes of sperm and egg cells are stripped off by enzymes, and then the fragile cells are mixed and combined with the aid of chemicals or viruses. The result may be the creation of a new life form from two species. Recombinant DNA techniques transfer a specific genetic activity from one organism to the next through the use of bacterial plasmids (small circular pieces of DNA lying outside the main bacterial chromosome) and enzymes, such as restriction endonucleases (which cut the DNA strands); reverse transcriptase (which makes a DNA strand from an RNA strand); DNA ligase (which joins DNA strands together); and tag polymerase (which can make a double-stranded DNA molecule from a single stranded "primer" molecule). The process begins with the isolation of suitable DNA strands and fragmenting them. After these fragments are combined with vectors, they are carried into bacterial cells where the DNA fragments are "spliced" on to plasmid DNA that has been opened up. These hybrid plasmids are now mixed with host **215** cells to form transformed cells. Since only some of the transformed cells will exhibit the desired characteristic or gene activity, the transformed cells are separated and grown individually in cultures. This methodology has been successful in producing large quantities of hormones (such as insulin) for the biotechnology industry. However, it is more difficult to transform animal and plant cells. Yet the technique exists to make plants resistant to diseases and to make animals grow larger. Because genetic engineering interferes with the processes of heredity and can alter the genetic structure of our own species, there is much concern over the ethical ramifications of such power, as well as the possible health and ecological consequences of the creation of these bacterial forms. Some applications of genetic engineering in the various fields are listed below:

Agriculture—Crops having larger yields, disease- and drought-resistancy; bacterial sprays to prevent crop damage from freezing temperatures (1987); and livestock improvement through changes in animal traits (1982).

Industry—Use of bacteria to convert old newspaper and wood chips into sugar; oil- and toxin-absorbing bacteria for oil spill or toxic waste clean-ups (1991); and yeasts to accelerate wine fermentation.

Medicine—Alteration of human genes to eliminate disease (1990, experimental stage); faster and more economical production of vital human substances to alleviate deficiency and disease symptoms (but not to cure them) such as insulin (1982), interferon (cancer therapy), vitamins, human growth hormone ADA (1990), antibodies, vaccines, and antibiotics.

Research—Modification of gene structure in medical research (1989), especially cancer research (1990).

Food processing—Rennin (enzyme) in cheese aging (1989).

What is the **Genome Project**?

In late 1990, the biomedical community began work on a 15-year, $3 billion (government-financed) program to map the entire human *genome* (the complete genetic structure), which contains 50,000 to 100,000 genes. So far, 2,000 genes have been identified and mapped. The goal is not only to pinpoint these genes, but also to decode the biochemical information down to the so called "letters" of inheritance, the four basic constituents of all genes called *nucleotides*: A (adenine), C (cytosine), G (guanine), and T (thymine). Since these letters are linked in pairs of sequences in the double helix of DNA, this means that three billion pairs are involved in this process. The knowledge gained from the project would be a basis for studying human diseases, understanding evolution, and accelerating biomedical research. Although there is some controversy about spending such a large sum of money on one project, steady progress is being made in completing the program.

Can **human beings** be **cloned**?

In theory, yes. There are, however, many technical obstacles to human cloning, as well as moral, ethical, philosophical, religious, and economic issues to be resolved before a human being could be cloned.

A clone is a group of cells derived from the original cell by fission (one cell dividing into two cells) or by mitosis (cell nucleus division with each chromosome splitting into two). It perpetuates an existing organism's genetic make-up. Gardeners have been making clones (copies) of plants for centuries by taking cuttings of plants to make genetically identical copies. For plants that refuse to grow from cuttings, or for the animal world, modern scientific techniques have greatly extended the range of cloning. The technique for plants starts with taking a cutting of a plant, usually the "best" one in terms of reproductivity or decorativeness or other standard. Since all the plant's cells contain the genetic information from which the entire plant can be reconstructed, the cutting can be taken from any part of the plant. Placed in a culture medium having nutritious chemicals and a growth hormone, the cells in the cutting divide, doubling in size every six weeks until the mass of cells produces small white globular points called embryoids. These embryoids develop roots, or shoots, and begin to look like tiny plants. Transplanted into compost, these plants grow into exact copies of the parent plant. The whole process takes 18 months. This process, called tissue culture, has been used to make clones of oil palm, asparagus, pineapples, strawberries, brussels sprouts, cauliflower, bananas, carnations, ferns, etc. Besides making high productive copies of the best plant available, this method controls viral diseases that are passed through seed generations.

For animals, a technique called nuclear transfer enables up to 32 clones to be produced at one time. An embryo at the 32-cell stage of development is split up using tiny surgical tools. Each of the 32 cells then are combined with single cell embryos (from the same species) from which the nucleus has been removed. This method has been used on mice, frogs, sheep, and cattle. Ultimately, there seems to be no biological reason why human beings could not be cloned, sometime in the future.

Who originated the idea called **panspermia**?

Panspermia is the idea that microorganisms, spores, or bacteria attached to tiny particles of matter have traveled through space, eventually landing on a suitable planet and initiated the rise of life there. The word itself means "all-seeding." The British scientist Lord Kelvin (1824–1907) suggested, in the 19th century, that life may have arrived here from outer space, perhaps carried by meteorites. In 1903, the Swedish chemist Svante Arrhenius (1859–1927) put forward the more complex panspermia idea that life on Earth was "seeded" by means of extraterrestrial spores, bacteria, and microorganisms coming here on tiny bits of cosmic matter.

What is the difference between **DNA** and **RNA**?

DNA (deoxyribonucleic acid) is a nucleic acid formed from a repetition of simple building blocks called nucleotides. The nucleotides consist of phosphate (PO_4), sugar (deoxyribose) and a base that is either adenine (A), thymine (T), guanine (G), or cytosine (C). In a DNA molecule, this basic unit is repeated in a double helix structure made from two chains of nucleotides linked between the bases. The links are either between A and T or between G and C. The structure of the bases does not allow other kinds of links. The famous double helix structure resembles a twisted ladder. The 1962 Nobel Prize in physiology or medicine was awarded to James Watson (b. 1928), Francis Crick (b. 1916), and Maurice Wilkins (b. 1916) for determining the molecular structure of DNA.

RNA (ribonucleic acid) is also a nucleic acid, but it consists of a single chain and the sugar is ribose rather than deoxyribose. The bases are the same except that the thymine (T) which appears in DNA is replaced by another base called uracil (U), which links only to adenine (A).

How much **DNA** is in a typical human cell?

If the DNA in a single human cell were stretched out and laid end-to-end, it would measure approximately 6.5 feet (two meters). The average human body contains 10 to 20 billion miles (16 to 32 billion kilometers) of DNA distributed among trillions of cells.

What is **antisense**?

Antisense molecules, which are microscopic bits of DNA or RNA, are designed to bind to a cell's own DNA or RNA and interfere with its activity. It is hoped that antisense drugs can slow the progression of some types of cancer.

What is **p53**?

Discovered in 1979, *p53* is a gene that, when a cell's DNA is damaged, acts as an "emergency brake" to halt the resulting cycle of cell division that can lead to tumor growth and cancer. It also acts as an executioner, programming damaged cells to self-destruct before their altered DNA can be replicated. However, when it mutates, *p53* can lose its suppressive powers or have the devestating effect of actually promoting abnormal cell growth. Indeed, *p53* is the most commonly mutated gene found in human tumors. Currently, researchers are studying exactly how *p53* works and how its properties can be harnessed to treat cancer.

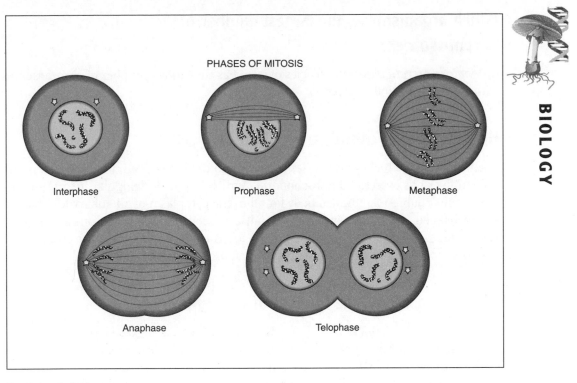

PHASES OF MITOSIS

Interphase

Prophase

Metaphase

Anaphase

Telophase

The phases of mitosis.

What are the stages in the type of cell division called **mitosis**?

Cell division in eukaryotes (higher organisms) consists of two stages: *mitosis*, the division of the nucleus, and *cytokinesis*, the division of the whole cell.

The first process in the actual division of the cell is mitosis. In mitosis, the replicated chromosomes are maneuvered so that each new cell gets a full complement of chromosomes—one of each. The process is divided into four phases: prophase, metaphase, anaphase, and telophase.

Nuclear division of sex cells is called meiosis. Sexual reproduction generally requires two parents and it always involves two events (meiosis and fertilization).

Do all cells have a **nucleus**?

Red blood cells are the only cells in the human body that do not have a nucleus. As a result, they cannot divide and so are are produced in bone marrow at the rate of 140,000 per minute. They exist in the body's circulatory system for about 120 days before being destroyed in the liver.

Which organism has the largest number of chromosomes?

Ophioglossum reticulatum, a species of fern, has the largest number of chromosomes with more than 1,260 (630 pairs).

How many mitochondria are there in a cell?

The number of mitochondria varies according to the type of cell, but each cell in the human liver has over 1,000 mitochondria. A mitochondrion (singular form) is a self-replicating double-membraned body found in the cytoplasm of all eukaryotic (having a nucleus) cells. The number of mitochondria per cell varies between one and 10,000, and averages about 200. The mitochondria are the sites for much of the metabolism necessary for the production of ATP, lipids, and protein synthesis.

Who is considered the founder of embryology?

Kaspar Friedrich Wolff (1733–1794), a German surgeon, is regarded as the founder of embryology. Wolff produced his revolutionary work *Theoria generationis* in 1759. Until that time it was generally believed that each living organism developed from an exact miniature of the adult within the seed or sperm. Wolff introduced the idea that cells in a plant or animal embryo are initially unspecified (undefined) but later differentiate to produce the separate organs and systems with distinct types of tissues.

What does "ontogeny recapitulates phylogeny" mean?

Ontogeny is the course of development of an organism from fertilized egg to adult; phylogeny is the evolutionary history of a group of organisms. So the phrase, originating in 19th century biology, means that as an embryo of an advanced organism grows, it will pass through stages that look very much like the adult phase of less advanced organisms. For example, at one point the human embryo has gills and resembles a tadpole.

LIFE PROCESSES, STRUCTURES, ETC.

What is a biological clock?

First recognized by the Chinese in the third century B.C.E., the biological clock is an intrinsic mechanism that controls the rhythm of various metabolic activities of plants

Is there any scientific basis for biorhythms?

There is little, if any, scientific support for this theory, which claims there are three precise cycles that control human behavior. These are: a physical cycle of 23 days; an emotional cycle of 28 days; and an intellectual cycle of 33 days. Hazardous critical days are proposed to occur when two or more cycles intersect.

In contrast, biological rhythms such as activity cycles, feeding cycles, and sleeping cycles, are well-known. They vary from individual to individual and most are tied to the 24 hour rotation period of the Earth. Biological rhythms are real; biorhythms are a hoax.

and animals. Some, such as mating, hibernation, and migration, have a yearly cycle; others, such as ovulation and menstrual cycles of women, follow a lunar month. The majority, however, have a 24-hour, day-night cycle called circadian rhythm. This day-night cycle, first recognized in plants over 250 years ago and existing in virtually all species of plants and animals, regulates these organisms' metabolic functions: plants opening and closing their petals or leaves, germination and flowering functions, changes in human body temperature, hormone secretion, blood sugar and blood pressure levels, and sleep cycles.

Research in chronobiology—the study of these daily rhythms—reveals that many accidents occur between 1 and 6 a.m., that most babies are born in the morning hours, that heart attacks tend to occur between 6 and 9 a.m., and that most Olympic records are broken in the late afternoon. The clock regulator may be the pineal gland located in the heads of animals (including humans).

Who was regarded as the founder of **biochemistry**?

Jan Baptista van Helmont (1577–1644) is called the father of biochemistry because he studied and expressed vital phenomena in chemical terms. The term "biochemistry," coined by F. Hoppe-Seyler in 1877, is the science dealing with the dynamics of living chemical processes or metabolism. It was formed from both the chemists' animal and vegetable chemistry, and the biologists' and doctors' physiological, zoological, or biological chemistry.

Helmont devoted his life to the study of chemistry as the true key to medicine and is considered as one of the founders of modern pathology because he studied the external agents of diseases as well as the anatomical changes caused by diseases.

What is the "Spiegelman monster"?

Sol Spiegelman, an American microbiologist, conducted an experiment to identify the smallest molecule capable of replicating itself. He began with a virus called Q_B, which consisted of a single molecule of ribonucleic acid (RNA) composed of 4,500 nucleotides (units of nucleic acid).

Usually this virus is able to make copies of itself only by invading a living cell because it requires a cellular enzyme called replicase. When Spiegelman added the replicase along with a supply of free nucleotides in a test tube to the virus, the virus replicated itself for several generations when a mutant appeared having fewer than 4,500 nucleotides. Being smaller, this mutant replicated faster than the original virus. Then another mutant appeared and displaced the first, and so it went. Finally, the virus degenerated into a little piece of ribonucleic acid with only 220 nucleotides, the smallest bit necessary for recognizing the replicase. This little test tube monster could continue to replicate at high speed, provided it had a source of building blocks.

Who is **Melvin Calvin**?

Calvin (b. 1911) is an American chemist who won the 1961 Nobel Prize for chemistry for his achievement of working out the chemical reaction cycles called biosynthetic pathways in photosynthesis. Photosynthesis is the process by which green plants use the energy of the sunlight to convert water and carbon dioxide into carbohydrates and oxygen. This cycle of reactions is now called the Calvin cycle. He also conducted research in organometallic chemistry, the chemical origin of life, and taught chemistry at the University of California at Berkeley.

Melvin Calvin.

In addition, Calvin pursued his interest in some unusual applications of chemistry, such as researching oil-bearing plants for their possible development as an alternative energy source. He also was interested in the search for other forms of life that may exist in the universe. During World War II, he developed a process for obtaining pure oxygen directly from the atmosphere. This process has been adapted for a number of applications, such as in machines that provide a continuous supply of oxygen for patients with breathing problems.

CLASSIFICATION, MEASUREMENTS, AND TERMS

What is **radiocarbon dating**?

Radiocarbon dating is a process for determining the age of a prehistoric object by measuring its radiocarbon content. The technique was developed by an American chemist, Dr. Willard F. Libby (1908–1980), in the late 1940s. All living things contain radiocarbon (carbon 14), an isotope that occurs in a small percentage of atmospheric carbon dioxide as a result of cosmic ray bombardment. After an animal or plant dies, it no longer absorbs radiocarbon and the radiocarbon present begins to decay (break down by releasing particles) at an exact and uniform rate. Its half-life of 5,730 years made it useful for measuring prehistory and events occurring within the past 35,000 to 50,000 years. A recent development, called the Accelerated Mass Spectrometer, which separates and detects atomic particles of different mass, can establish more accurate dates with a smaller sample. The remaining radiocarbon can be measured and compared to that of a living sample. In this way, the age of the 50,000 year old or less animal or plant (or more precisely the elapsed time since its death) can be determined.

Since Libby's work, other isotopes having longer half-lives have been used as "geologic clocks" to date very old rocks. The isotope uranium-238 (decaying to lead-206) has a half-life of 4.5 billion years, uranium-235 (decaying to lead-207) has a value of 704 million years, thorium-232 (decaying to lead-278) has a half-life of 14 billion years, rubidium-87 (decaying to strontium-87) has a half-life value of 48.8 billion years, potassium-40 (decaying to argon-40) has a value of 1.25 billion years and samarium-147 (decaying to neodymium-143) has a value of 106 billion years. These isotopes are used in dating techniques of gas formation light emission (called thermoluminescence). Other ways to date the past is dating by tree rings (counting its annual growth rings), and dating by thermoremanent magnetism (the magnetic field of the rock is compared to a date chart of changes in the Earth's magnetic field).

Who coined the term **biology**?

Biology was first used by Karl Burdach (1776–1847) to denote the study of man. Jean Baptiste Pierre Antoine de Monet Lamarck (1744–1829) gave the term a broader meaning in 1812. He believed in the integral character of science. For the special sciences, **223** chemistry, meteorology, geology, and botany-zoology, he coined the term "biology."

Lamarckism epitomizes the belief that changes acquired during an individual's lifetime as the result of active, quasi-purposive, functional adaptations can somehow be imprinted upon the genes, thereby becoming part of the heritage of succeeding generations. Today, very few professional biologists believe that anything of the kind occurs—or can occur.

Biology is the science that deals with living things (Greek *bios*, "life"). Formerly broadly divided into two areas, zoology (Greek *zoon*, "animal"), the study of animals, and botany (Greek *botanes*, "plant"), the study of plants, biology is now divided and sub-divided into hundreds of special fields involving the structure, function, and classification of the forms of life. These include anatomy, ecology, embryology, evolution, genetics, paleontology, and physiology.

Jean Baptiste Pierre Antoine de Monet Lamarck.

Where did the term **molecular biology** originate?

Warren Weaver, the director of the Rockefeller Foundation's Division of Natural Sciences originated the term molecular biology. Weaver used x-ray diffraction to investigate the molecular basis of inheritance and the structure of biological macromolecules. He called this relatively new field molecular biology in a 1938 report.

What is **gnotobiotics**?

Gnotobiotics is the scientific study of animals or other organisms that are raised in germ-free environments or ones that contain only specifically known germs. These animals are first removed from the womb and then are placed in sterilized cages called isolators. Scientists are able to use these animals to determine how specific agents, such as viruses, bacteria, and fungi, affect the body.

What are the **five kingdoms** presently used to categorize living things?

Carolus Linnaeus (1707–1778) in 1735 divided all living things into two kingdoms in his classification system that was based on similarities and differences of organisms.

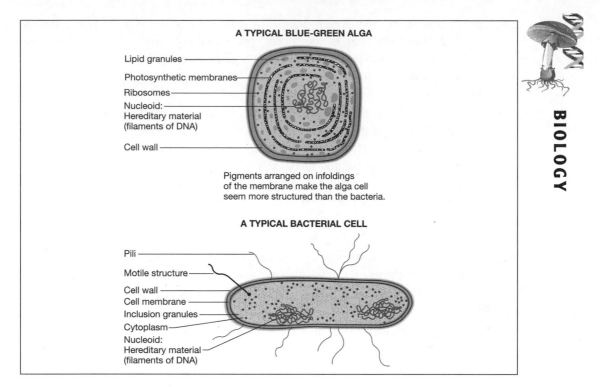

A TYPICAL BLUE-GREEN ALGA

Lipid granules

Photosynthetic membranes

Ribosomes

Nucleoid:
Hereditary material
(filaments of DNA)

Cell wall

Pigments arranged on infoldings
of the membrane make the alga cell
seem more structured than the bacteria.

A TYPICAL BACTERIAL CELL

Pili

Motile structure

Cell wall

Cell membrane

Inclusion granules

Cytoplasm

Nucleoid:
Hereditary material
(filaments of DNA)

Two typical prokaryotic cells: A blue-green algae and a bacteria.

However, since then, fungi seemed not to fit nicely into either kingdom. Although fungi were generally considered plants, they had no chlorophyll, roots, stems, or leaves, and hardly resemble any true plant. They also have several features found in the animal kingdom, as well as unique features characteristic of themselves alone. So fungi was considered the third kingdom. In 1959, R. H. Whittaker proposed the current five kingdom system, based on new evidence from biochemical techniques and electron microscope observations that revealed fundamental differences among organisms. Each kingdom is listed below.

Monera—One-celled organisms lacking a membrane around the cell's genetic matter. Prokaryote (or procaryote) is the term used for this condition where the genetic material lies free in the cytoplasm of the cell without a membrane to form the nucleus of the cell. The kingdom consists of bacteria and blue-green algae (also called blue-green bacteria or cyanobacteria). Bacteria do not produce their own food but blue-green algae do. Blue-green algae, the primary form of life 3.5 to 1.5 billion years ago, produce most of the world's oxygen through photosynthesis.

Protista—Mostly single-celled organisms with a membrane around the cell's genetic material called eukaryotes (or eucaryotes) because of the nuclear membrane and other organelles found in the cytoplasm of the cell. Protista consists of true algae, diatoms, slime molds, protozoa, and euglena. Protistans are diverse in their modes of nutrition, etc. They may be living examples of the kinds of ancient single cells that gave rise to the kingdoms of multicelled eukaryotes (fungi, plants, and animals).

Fungi—One-celled or multicelled eukaryotes (having a nuclear membrane or a membrane around the genetic material). The nuclei stream between cells giving the appearance that cells have multiple nuclei. This unique cellular structure, along with the unique sexual reproduction pattern, distinguish the fungi from all other organisms. Consisting of mushrooms, yeasts, molds, etc., the fungi do not produce their own food.

Plantae—Multicellular organisms having cell nuclei and cell walls, which directly or indirectly nourish all other forms of life. Most use photosynthesis (a process by which green plants, containing chlorophyll, utilize sunlight as an energy source to synthesize complex organic material, especially carbohydrates from carbon dioxide, water, and inorganic salts) and most are autotrophs (produce their own food from inorganic matter).

Animalia—Multicellular organisms whose eukaryotic cells (without cell walls) form tissues (and from tissues form organs). Most get their food by ingestion of other organisms; they are heterotrophs (cannot produce their food from inorganic elements). Most are able to move from place to place (mobile) at least during part of the life cycle.

Who devised the current **animal and plant classification** system?

The naming and organizing of the millions of species of plants and animals is frequently called taxonomy; such classifications provide a basis for comparisons and generalizations. A common classification format is an hierarchical arrangement in which a group is classified within a group, and the level of the group is denoted in a ranking.

Carolus Linnaeus (1707–1778) composed a hierarchical classification system for plants (1753) and animals (1758) using a system of nomenclature (naming) that continues to be used today. Every plant and animal was given two scientific names (binomial method) in Latin, one

Carolus Linnaeus.

for the species and the other for the group or genus within the species. He categorized the organisms by perceived physical differences and similarities. Although Linnaeus started with only two kingdoms, contemporary classifiers have expanded them into five kingdoms. Each kingdom is divided into two or more phyla (major groupings; phylum is the singular form). Members within one phylum are more closely related to one another than they are to members of another phylum. These phyla are subdivided into parts again and again; members of each descending level have a closer relationship to each other than those of the level above. Generally the ranking of the system, going from general to specific, are Kingdom, Phylum (plant world uses the term, division), Class, Order, Family, Genus, and Species. In addition, intermediate taxonomic levels can be created by adding the prefixes "sub" or "super" to the name of the level, for example, "subphylum" or "superfamily." Zoologists working on parts of the animal classification, many times are not uniform in their groupings. The system is still evolving and changing as new information emerges and new interpretations develop. Below is listed a comparison of hierarchy for four of the five kingdoms.

Taxonomic level	Human	Grasshopper	White Pine	Typhoid Bacterium
Kingdom	Animalia	Animalia	Plantae	Protista
Phylum	Chordata	Anthropoda	Tracheophyta	Schizomycophyta
Class	Mammalia	Insecta	Gymnospermae	Schizomycetes
Order	Primates	Orthoptera	Coniferales	Eubacteriales
Family	Hominidae	Arcridiidae	Pinaceae	Bacteriaceae
Genus	*Homo*	*Schistocerca*	*Pinus*	*Eberthella*
Species	*sapiens*	*americana*	*strobus*	*typhosa*

How many **different organisms** have been identified by biologists?

Almost 1.5 million different species of plants, animals, and microorganisms are currently known.

FUNGI, BACTERIA, ALGAE, ETC.

What are **diatoms**?

Diatoms are microscopic algae in the phylum *bacillarrophyte* of the protista kingdom. Yellow or brown in color, almost all diatoms are single-celled algae, dwelling in fresh and salt water, especially in the cold waters of the North Pacific Ocean and the Antarctic. Diatoms are an important food source for marine plankton (floating animal and plant life) and many small animals.

Diatoms have hard cell walls; these "shells" are made from silica that they extract from the water. It is unclear how they accomplish this. When they die, their glassy shells, called frustules, sink to the bottom of the sea, which hardens into rock called diatomite. One of the most famous and accessible diatomites is the Monterrey Formation along the coast of central and southern California.

What is the scientific study of fungi called?

Mycology is the science concerning fungi. In the past, fungi have been classified in other kingdoms, but currently they are recognized as a separate kingdom based on their unique cellular structure and their unique pattern of sexual reproduction.

Fungi are heterotrophs (cannot produce their own food from inorganic matter). They secrete enzymes that digest food outside their bodies and their fungal cells absorb the products. Their activities are essential in the decomposition of organic material and cycling of nutrients in nature.

Some fungi, called saprobes, obtain nutrients from non-living organic matter. Other fungi are parasites; they obtain nutrients from the tissues of living host organisms. The great majority of fungi are multicelled and filamentous. A mushroom is a modified reproductive structure in or upon which spores develop. Each spore dispersed from it may grow into a new mushroom.

What is a lichen?

Lichens are organisms that grow on rocks, tree branches, or bare ground. They are composed of a green algae and a colorless fungus living together symbiotically. They do not have roots, stems, flowers, or leaves. The fungus, having no chlorophyll, cannot manufacture its own food, but can absorb food from the algae that it enwraps completely, providing protection from the sun and moisture.

This relationship between the fungus and algae is called symbiosis (a close association of two organisms not necessarily to both their benefits). Lichens were the first recognized and are still the best examples of this phenomenon. An unique feature of lichen symbiosis is that it is so perfectly developed and balanced as to behave as a single organism.

Are there **stone-eating bacteria**?

Stone-eating bacteria belong to several families in the genus *Thiobacillus*. They can cause damage to monuments, tombs, buildings, and sculptures by converting marble into plaster. The principal danger seems to come from *Thiobacillus thioparus*. This microbe's metabolic system converts sulfur dioxide gas (found in the air) into sulfuric acid and uses it to transform calcium carbonate (marble) into calcium sulfate (plaster). The bacilli draw their nutrition from carbon dioxide formed in the transformation.

Nitrobacter and *Nitrosomonas* are other "stone-eating bacteria" that use ammonia from the air to generate nitric and nitrous acid. Still other kinds of bacteria and fungi can produce organic acids (formic, acetic, and oxalic acids) that attack the stone as well. The presence of these microbes was first observed by a French scientist, Henri Pochon at Angkor Wat, Cambodia, during the 1950s. The increase of these bacteria and other biological-damaging organisms that threaten tombs and buildings of antiquity are due to the sharp climb in the level of free sulfur dioxide gas in the atmosphere from automotive and industrial emissions.

Who was first to coin the word **virus**?

The English physician Edward Jenner (1749–1823), founder of virology and a pioneer in vaccination, first coined the word "virus". Using one virus to immunize against another one was precisely the strategy Jenner used when he inoculated someone with cowpox (a disease that attacks cows) to make them immune to smallpox. This procedure is called vaccination from *vaccine* (the Latin name for cowpox). Vaccines are usually a very mild dose of the disease-causing bacteria or virus (weakened or dead). These vaccines stimulate the creation of antibodies in the body that recognize and attack a particular infection. A virus is a minute parasitic organism that reproduces only inside the cell of its host. Viruses replicate by invading host cells and taking over the cell's "machinery" for DNA replication. Viral particles then can break out of the cells, causing disease.

Who were the founders of **modern bacteriology**?

The German bacteriologist, Robert Koch (1843–1910), and the French chemist, Louis Pasteur (1822–1895), are considered the founders. Pasteur devised a way to heat food or beverages at a temperature slow enough not to ruin them, but high enough to kill **229** most of the microorganisms that would cause spoilage and disease. This process is called pasteurization. By demonstrating that tuberculosis was an infectious disease caused by a specific *bacillus* and not by bad heredity, Koch laid the groundwork for public health measures that would significantly reduce such diseases. His working methodologies for isolating microorganisms, his laboratory procedures, and his four postulates for determination of disease agents gave medical investigators valuable insights into the control of bacterial infections.

Why are **Koch's postulates** significant?

The German bacteriologist, Robert Koch (1843–1910), developed four rules in his study of disease-producing organisms, which later investigators found useful. The following conditions must be met to prove that a bacterium causes a particular disease:

1. The microorganism must be found in large numbers in all diseased animals but not in healthy ones.

2. The organism must be isolated from a diseased animal and grown outside the body in a pure culture.

3. When the isolated microorganism is injected into other healthy animals, it must produce the same disease.

4. The suspected microorganism must be recovered from the experimental hosts, isolated, compared to the first microorganism, and found to be identical.

PLANT WORLD

PHYSICAL CHARACTERISTICS, FUNCTIONS, ETC.

What is the best type of **pollination**?

Effective pollination occurs when viable pollen is transferred to plant's stigmas, ovule-bearing organs, or ovules (seed precursors). Without pollination, there would be no fertilization. Since plants are immobile organisms, they usually need external agents to transport their pollen from where it is produced in the plant to where fertilization can occur. This situation produces cross-pollination, wherein one plant's pollen is moved by an agent to another plant's stigma. Some plants are able to self-pollinate—transfer their own pollen to their own stigmas. But of the two methods, cross-pollination seems the better, for it allows new genetic material to be introduced.

Cross-pollination agents include insects, wind, birds, mammals, and water. Many times flowers offer one or more "rewards" to attract these agents—sugary nectar, oil, solid food bodies, perfume, a place to sleep, or sometimes, the pollen itself. Other times the plant can "trap" the agent into transporting the pollen. Generally plants use color and fragrances as attractants to lure these agents. For example, a few orchids use a combination of smell and color to mimic the female of certain species of bees and wasps so successfully that the corresponding males will attempt to mate with them. Through this process (pseudocopulation) the orchids achieve pollination. While some plants cater to a variety of agents, other plants are very selective and are pollinated by a single species of insect only. This extreme pollinator specificity tends to maintain the purity of a plant species.

Plant structure can accommodate the type of agent used. For example, plants **231**

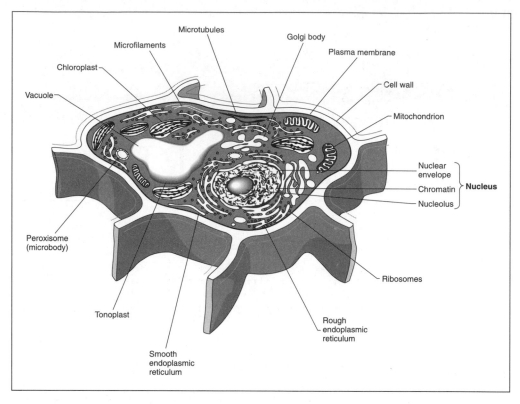

A plant cell.

such as grasses and conifers, whose pollen is carried by the wind, tend to have a simple structure lacking petals, with freely exposed and branched stigmas to catch airborne pollen and dangling anthers (pollen-producing parts) on long filaments. This type of anther allows the light round pollen to be easily caught by the wind. These plants are found in areas such as prairies and mountains, where insect agents are rare. In contrast, semi-enclosed, nonsymmetrical, long-lived flowers such as iris, rose, and snapdragon have a "landing platform" and nectar in the flower base to accommodate insect agents such as the bee. The sticky, abundant pollen can easily become attached to the insect to be borne away to another flower.

How many **chloroplasts** are in plant cells?

Chloroplasts are the functional units where photosynthesis takes place—the process whereby green plants use light energy for the synthesis of sugar from carbon dioxide and water, with oxygen released as a by-product. They contain the green pigments chlorophyll a and b, which trap light energy for photosynthesis. A unicellular plant may have only a single large chloroplast, whereas a plant leaf cell may have as many as 20 to 100.

What is **tropism**?

Tropism is the movement of a plant in response to a stimulus. The categories include:

Chemotropism—a response to chemicals by plants in which incurling of leaves may occur.

Geotropism or *gravitropism*—a response to gravity in which the plant moves in relation to gravity. Shoots of a plant are negatively geotropic (growing upward), while roots are positively geotropic (growing downward).

Hydrotropism—a response to water or moisture in which roots grow toward the water source.

Paraheliotropism—a response by the plant leaves to avoid exposure to the sun.

Phototropism—a response to light in which the plant may be positively phototropic (moving toward the light source) or negatively phototropic (moving away from the light source). Main axes of shoots are usually positively phototropic, whereas roots are generally insensitive to light.

Thermotropism—a response to temperature by plants.

Thigmotropism or *haptotropism*—a response to touch by the climbing organs of a plant. For example, the plant's tendrils may curl around a support in a spring-like manner.

In experiments done in the 1960s and 1970s, plants responded best to classical and Indian devotional music. In a controlled environment, plants exposed to these kinds of music had lush and abundant growth and good root development. Jazz music as well produced more abundant growth. Exposure to country music or silence brought about no abnormal growth reaction. With rock music, plants did poorly. Their roots were scrawny and sparse and they seemed to be in a dying stage. Plants exposed solely to white noise died quickly.

TREES AND SHRUBS

See also: Environment—Ecology, Resources, etc.; Minerals and Other Materials

What are the **longest-lived tree** species in the United States?

Of the 850 different species of tree in the United States, the oldest species is the bristlecone pine (*Pinus longaeva*), which grows in the deserts of Nevada and southern California (especially in the White Mountains). Some of these trees are believed to be over 4,600 years old. The potential life span of these pines is estimated to be 5,500 years. But these ages are very young when compared to the oldest surviving species in the world, which is the maiden-hair tree (*Ginkgo bibloba*) of Zhexiang, China. This tree first appeared during the Jurassic era some 160 million years ago. Also called icho, or the ginkyo ("silver apricot"), this species has been cultivated in Japan since 1100 B.C.E.

The longest lived tree species in the United States:

The Longest Lived Tree Species in the United States

Name of tree	Number of years
Bristlecone pine (*Pinus longaeva*)	3,000–4,700
Giant sequoia (*Sequoiadendron giganteum*)	2,500
Redwood (*Sequoia sempervirens*)	1,000–3,500
Douglas fir (*Pseudotsuga menziesii*)	750
Bald cypress (*Taxodium distichum*)	600

How are **tree rings** used to date historical events?

Tree fragments of unknown age and the rings of living trees can be compared in order to establish the date when the fragment was part of a living tree. Thus, tree rings can be used to establish the year in which an event took place as long as the event involved the maiming or killing of a tree. Precise dates can be established for the building of a medieval cathedral or an American Indian pueblo; the occurrence of an earthquake, landslide, volcanic eruption, or a fire; and even the date when a panel of wood was cut for a Dutch painting.

Every year, the tree produces an annular ring composed of one wide, light ring and one narrow, dark ring. During spring and early summer, tree stem cells grow rapidly and are larger; this produces the wide, light ring. In winter, growth is greatly reduced and cells are much smaller; this produces the narrow, dark ring. In the coldest part of winter or the dry heat of summer, no cells are produced.

Who first recorded that the **number of rings** in the cross-section of a tree trunk tell its **age**?

The painter Leonardo da Vinci (1452–1519) noticed this phenomenon. He also saw that the year's dampness can be determined by the space between the tree's rings. The farther apart the rings, the more moisture there was in the ground around the tree.

Why do tree **leaves turn color** in the fall?

The carotenoids (pigments in the photosynthesizing cells), which are responsible for the fall colors, are present in the leaves during the growing season. However, the colors are eclipsed by the green chlorophyll. Toward the end of summer, when the chlorophyll production ceases, the other colors of the carotenoids (such as yellow, orange, red, or purple) become visible. Listed below are the autumn leaf colors of some common trees.

Tree	Color
Sugar maple and sumac	Flame red and orange
Red maple, dogwood, sassafras, and scarlet oak	Dark red
Poplar, birch, tulip tree, willow	Yellow
Ash	Plum purple
Oak, beech, larch, elm, hickory, and sycamore	Tan or brown
Locust	Stays green until leaves drop
Black walnut and butternut	Drops leaves before they turn color

Why are fall leaves **bright red in some years** and **dull in others**?

Two factors are necessary in the production of red autumn leaves. There must be warm, bright, sunny days during which the leaves manufacture sugar. Warm days must be followed by cool nights with temperatures below 45°F. This weather combination traps the sugar and other materials in the leaves. This results in the manufacture of red anthocyanin. A warm cloudy day restricts the formation of bright colors. With decreased sunlight, sugar production is decreased and this small amount of sugar is transported back to the trunk and roots, where it has no color effect.

What is the **tallest tree**?

The tallest tree ever measured was the Australian eucalyptus (*Eucalyptus regnans*) at Watts River, Victoria, Australia. In 1872 it was reported to measure 435 feet (132 meters) tall and it was most likely over 500 feet (152 meters) originally. The tallest living tree is a coast redwood (*Sequoia sempervirens*) in Redwood National Park, California, named the National Geographic Society. In October 1991 it was measured at 365 feet (111 meters).

Which U.S. city has the greatest **number of trees**?

According to a survey of 20 cities, Houston, Texas, has the most trees with 956,700.

What is a **banyan tree**?

The banyan tree (*Ficus benghalensis*), a native of tropical Asia, is a member of the *Ficus* or fig genus. It is a magnificent evergreen, sometimes 100 feet (30.48 meters) in height. As the massive limbs spread horizontally, the tree sends down roots that **235** develop into secondary, pillar-like supporting trunks. Over a period of years a single tree may spread to occupy a tremendous area, as much as 2,000 feet (610 meters) around the periphery.

What are the distinguishing characteristics of **fir, pine, and spruce** trees?

The best way to tell the difference between the three trees is by their cones and leaves:

Pines

White Pine	Five needles in each bundle; needles soft and 3–5 inches long. Cones can be 4–8 inches long
Scotch Pine	Two needles in each bundle. Needles are stiff, yellow green, 1.5–3 inches long. Cones are 2–5 inches long.

Spruce

White Spruce	Dark green needles are rigid, but not prickly, grow from all sides of the twig and are less than an inch long. Cones are 1–2.5 inches long and hang downward.
Blue Spruce	Needles are about an inch long, silvery blue, very stiff and prickly; needles grow from all sides of the branch. Cones are 3.5 inches long.

Fir

Balsam Fir	Needles are flat, 1–1.5 inches long and arranged in pairs opposite each other. Cones are upright, cylindrical and 2–4 inches long.
Fraser Fir	Looks like a balsam but needles are smaller and more rounded.
Douglas Fir	Single needles, 1–1.5 inches long and very soft. Cone scales have bristles that stick out.

Which **conifers** in North America **lose their leaves in winter?**

Dawn redwood trees (*Metasequoia*) are deciduous. Their leaves are bright green in summer and turn coppery red in the fall before they drop. Previously known only as a fossil, the tree was found in China in 1941 and has been growing in the United States since the 1940s. The U.S. Department of Agriculture distributed seeds to experimental growers in the United States, and the dawn redwood tree now grows all over the country.

The only native conifers that shed all of their leaves in the fall are the bald cypress (*Taxodium distichum*) and the Tamarack (*Larix larcina*).

Does the **rose family** produce any trees?

The apple, pear, peach, cherry, plum, mountain ash, and hawthorn trees are members of the rose family (Rosaceae).

What is a **monkey ball tree**?

The osage orange (*Maclura pomifera*) produces large, green orange-like fruits. These are roughly spherical, 3.5 to 5 inches (8.8 to 12.7 centimeters) in diameter, and have a coarse, pebbly surface.

How much of a cut tree is sold as **timber**?

For the average hardwood tree cut down to make lumber, half the total wood volume is left in the woods as tops, limbs, and logging residue; about a quarter is lost as sawdust, slabs, and edgings in the sawmill; and one-eighth disappears as shavings and machining residues, leaving about one-eighth of the original volume to be sold as timber.

How is **glycerine** used to preserve leaves?

Glycerine and water are generally used to preserve coarser leaves, such as magnolia, rhododendron, beech, holly, heather, or Japanese maple. The leaves should be fresh. For autumn colors, the leaves should be picked just as they are turning color. The preserving solution is made by adding two parts boiling water to one part glycerine. Place the leaf stems, split if necessary, in the warm solution so they are covered about three to four inches (seven to 10 centimeters). When drops of glycerine form on the leaves, enough has been absorbed. Wipe off any excess oil. Entire branches may also be treated by using a container large enough to allow the solution to completely cover the leaves. The solution for this method is made with equal quantities of glycerine and water. The leaves are drained on thick sections of newspapers for a few days, then washed with a little soap and water and pegged on a line to dry.

Are there any natural **predators** of **gypsy moth caterpillars**?

About 45 kinds of birds, squirrels, chipmunks, and white-footed mice eat this serious insect pest. Among the 13 imported natural enemies of the moth, two flies, *Compislura concinnata* (a tachnid fly) and *Sturnia scutellata*, parasitize the caterpillar. Other parasites and various wasps have also been tried as controls, as well as spraying and male sterilization. Originally from Europe, this large moth (*Porthetria dispar*) lays its eggs on the leaves of oaks, birches, maples, and other hardwood trees. When the yellow hairy caterpillars hatch from the eggs, they devour the leaves in such quantities that the tree becomes temporarily defoliated. Sometimes this causes the tree to die. The

237

caterpillars grow from half an inch (three millimeters) to about two inches (5.1 centimeters) before they spin a pupa, in which they will metamorphose into adult moths.

Who introduced the gypsy moth into the United States?

In 1869, Professor Leopold Trouvelot brought gypsy moth egg masses from France to Medford, Massachusetts. His intention was to breed the gypsy moth with the silkworm to overcome a wilt disease of the silkworm. He placed the egg masses on a window ledge, and evidently the wind blew them away. About 10 years later these caterpillars were numerous on trees in that vicinity, and in 20 years, trees in eastern Massachusetts were being defoliated. In 1911, a contaminated plant shipment from Holland also introduced the gypsy moth to that area. These pests have now spread to 25 states, especially in the northeastern United States. Scattered locations in Michigan and Oregon have also reported occurrences of gypsy moth infestations.

FLOWERS AND OTHER PLANTS

See also: Environment—Extinct and Endangered Plants and Animals

Who is known as the founder of botany?

The ancient Greek, Theophrastus (ca. 372–ca. 287 B.C.), is known as the father of botany. His two large botanical works, *On the History of Plants* and *On the Causes of Plants*, were so comprehensive that 1,800 years went by before any new discovery in botany was made. He integrated the practice of agriculture into botany and established a theory of plant growth and the analysis of plant structure. He related plants to their natural environment and identified, classified, and described 550 different plants.

What are the parts of a flower?

Sepal—found on the outside of the bud or on the underside of the open flower. It serves to protect the flower bud from drying out. Some sepals ward off predators by their spines or chemicals.

Petals—serve to attract pollinators and are usually dropped shortly after pollination occurs.

Nectar—contains varying amounts of sugar and proteins that can be secreted by any of the floral organs. It usually collects inside the flower cup near the base of the cup formed by the flower parts.

Stamen—is the male part of a flower and consists of a filament and anther where pollen is produced.

Pistil—is the female part, which consists of the stigma, style, and ovary containing ovules. After fertilization the ovules mature into seeds.

What is meant by an "imperfect" flower?

An imperfect flower is one that is unisexual, having either stamens (male parts) or pistils (female parts) but not both.

How does a **bulb** differ from a **corm**, a **tuber**, and a **rhizome**?

Many times the term "bulb" is applied to any underground storage organ in which a plant stores energy for its dormant period. Dormancy is one of nature's devices a plant utilizes to get through difficult weather conditions (winter cold or summer drought).

A *true bulb*—consists of fleshy scales containing a small basal plate (a modified stem from which the roots emerge) and a shoot. The scales that surround the embryo are modified leaves that contain the nutrients for the bulb during dormancy and early growth. Some bulbs have a tunic (a paper-thin covering) around the scales. The basal plate can also hold the scales together. New bulbs form from the lateral buds on the basal plate. Tulips, daffodils, lilies, and hyacinths are examples of bulb flowers.

A *corm*—is actually a stem that has been modified into a mass of storage tissue. The eye(s) at the top of the corm is a growing point. The corm is covered by dry leaf bases similar to the tunic-covering of the bulb. Roots grow from the basal plate on the underside of the corm. New corms form on top of or beside the old one. Corm-type flowers include gladiolus, freesia, and crocus.

A *tuber*—is a solid underground mass of stem like a corm but it lacks both a basal plate and a tunic. Roots and shoots grow from "eyes" (growth buds) out of its sides, bottom, and sometimes its top. Some tubers are roundish. Others are flattened and lumpy. Some examples of tubers are gloxinia, caladium, ranunculuses, and anemone.

A *tuberous root*—is a swollen root that has taken in moisture and nutrients. It resembles a tuber. New growth occurs on the base of the old stem, where it joins the root. A tuberous root can be divided by cutting off a section with an eye-bearing portion from where the old stem was attached. Dahlias have tuberous roots.

A *rhizome or a rootstock*—is a thickened, branching storage stem that usually grows laterally along or slightly below the soil surface. Roots develop downward on the bottom surface, while buds and leaves sprout upwards from the top of the rhizome. It is propagated by cutting the parent plant into sections. Japanese, Siberian, and bearded irises; cannas; calla lilies; and trillium are rhizomes.

How are **carnivorous plants** categorized?

Carnivorous plants, numbering between 450 and 500 species and 12 genera, are classified according to the nature of their trapping mechanisms. Active traps display rapid motion in their capture of prey. The Venus fly trap (*Dionaea muscipula*) and the bladderwort (*Utricularia vulgaris*) are active traps. Semi-active traps employ a two-stage trap in which the prey is caught in the trap's adhesive fluid. As it struggles, the plant is triggered to slowly tighten its grip. The sundew (species *Drosera*) and butterwort (*Pinguicula vulgaris*) are semi-active traps. Passive traps entice insects by nectar. The insects fall into a reservoir of water and drown. An example of the passive trap is the pitcher plant (five genera).

The sundew is a carnivorous plant.

What are the symbolic meanings of herbs and plants?

Aloe—Healing, protection, affection
Angelica—Inspiration
Arbor vitae—Unchanging friendship
Bachelor's buttons—Single blessedness
Basil—Good wishes, love
Bay—Glory
Carnation—Alas for my poor heart
Chamomile—Patience
Chives—Usefulness
Clover, White—Think of me
Coriander—Hidden worth
Cumin—Fidelity
Fennel—Flattery
Fern—Sincerity
Geranium, Oak-leaved—True friendship
Goldenrod—Encouragement
Heliotrope—Eternal love
Holly—Hope
Hollyhock—Ambition
Honeysuckle—Bonds of love
Horehound—Health
Hyssop—Sacrifice, cleanliness

Ivy—Friendship, continuity

Lady's mantle—Comforting
Lavender—Devotion, virtue
Lemon balm—Sympathy
Marjoram—Joy, Happiness
Mints—Eternal refreshment
Morning glory—Affection
Nasturtium—Patriotism
Oak—Strength
Oregano—Substance
Pansy—Thoughts
Parsley—Festivity
Pine—Humility
Poppy, Red—Consolation
Rose—Love
Rosemary—Remembrance
Rudbeckia—Justice
Rue—Grace, clear vision
Sage—Wisdom, immortality
Salvia, Blue—I think of you
Salvia, Red—Forever mine
Savory—Spice, interest
Sorrel—Affection
Southernwood—Constancy, jest
Sweet-pea—Pleasures
Sweet woodruff—Humility
Tansy—Hostile thoughts
Tarragon—Lasting interest
Thyme—Courage, strength
Valerian—Readiness
Violet—Loyalty, devotion
Violet, Blue—Faithfulness
Violet, Yellow—Rural happiness
Willow—Sadness
Zinnia—Thoughts of absent friends

What flowers are designated as **symbolic of each month** of the year?

Month	Flower
January	Carnation
February	Violet

Month	Flower
March	Jonquil
April	Sweet Pea
May	Lily of the Valley
June	Rose
July	Larkspur
August	Gladiola
September	Aster
October	Calendula
November	Chrysanthemum
December	Narcissus

What do the different colors and varieties of roses symbolize?

Rose	Meaning
Yellow Rose	Jealousy; unfaithfulness
Red rosebud	Youth; beauty
White rose	Silence
Lancaster rose	Union
Burgundy rose	Unconscious beauty
Musk rose	Capricious beauty
Dog rose	Pleasure and pain
Cabbage rose	Ambassador of love
Bridal rose	Happy love
Carolina rose	Dangerous love
May rose	Precocity
Moss rose	Voluptuousness
Christmas rose	Tranquility
Pompon rose	Gentility

Is there a **national flower** for the United States?

The national flower of the United States is the rose, adopted on October 7, 1986.

What special significance does the **passionflower** have?

Spanish friars of the sixteenth century first gave the name to this flower. They saw in the form of the passionflower (*Passiflora*) a representation of the passion of Christ: the flowers have five petals and five sepals, which was thought to symbolize the 10 faithful apostles present at the crucifixion; the corona of five filaments was believed to resem-

> ## Does the familiar phrase "open sesame" have anything to do with sesame seeds?
>
> S esame seeds burst open when they ripen, so the phrase is probably inspired by that fact. Middle Easterners knew the plant, and sesame seeds and flour are still used in Near East cooking.

ble Christ's crown of thorns; the five stamens represented the five wounds in Christ's body, and the three stigmas stood for the nails driven into his hands and feet. Most species of passionflower are native to the tropical areas of the Western Hemisphere.

How was **anise** used in ancient times?

The Romans brought the licorice-flavored herb from Egypt to Europe, where they used it for payment of taxes. It became popular flavoring for cakes, cookies, bread, and candy.

What is the **first wildflower to bloom** in the spring in the northern United States?

The first flower of the northern spring is unusual and interesting, but rarely seen, because it blooms in the swamp. Commonly called skunk cabbage (*Spathyema foetidus*), it appears in February. The first spring flower that is generally known in New England and the Middle West is the *Hepatica*, or liverleaf, which blooms in March or early April.

What is **wormwood**?

Artemisia absinthium, known as wormwood, is a hardy, spreading, fragrant perennial, two to four feet (61 to 122 centimeters) tall. It is native to Europe but widely naturalized in North America. The liqueur absinthe is flavored from this plant.

What is the greatest number of leaves a **clover** can have?

A fourteen-leafed white clover (*Trifolium repens*) and a fourteen-leafed red clover (*Trifolium pratense*) have been found in the United States.

What is the origin of the name **Jimson weed**?

Jimson weed (*Datura stramonium*) is a corruption of the name Jamestown weed, given to a highly poisonous plant. The Jamestown, Virginia, colonists were familiar with this weed. It is also known as thorn apple, mad apple, stinkwort, angel's trumpet, devil's trumpet, stinkweed, dewtry, and white man's weed. Every part of this plant is potentially deadly if consumed in even moderate amounts. Even so, some of the alkaloids found in this plant are used by doctors as a preanesthetic.

Does **ivy cause damage** growing on a brick wall?

Experts at the New York Botanical Garden say it is possible for ivy to damage walls that are already in bad condition. Mortar that is in good shape is not normally subject to any damage.

A thick growth of ivy traps moisture against the walls. The adhesive disks that attach the ivy to the wall are subject to decay. This and other organic matter forms humic acid, which is capable of dissolving carbonate rock, like marble and lime mortar.

Why do cats like **catnip**?

Catnip (*Nepeta cataria*) is a hardy perennial herb attractive to cats. Also known as catmint or catnep, it belongs to the mint family. The whole cat family (*Felidae*) reacts to catnip. Mountain lions, lynx, tigers, and lions roll over, rub their face, extend their claws, and do a body twist when they smell catnip's pungent odor. The oil from the leaves of catnip probably excites cats because it contains a chemical called trans-neptalactone, which closely resembles an excretion in a female cat's urine.

What are **living stones**?

Various succulent plants from the stony deserts of South Africa that mimic their surroundings are given this name. Each shoot or plant is made up of two grossly swollen leaves virtually fused together and colored to resemble a pebble. Large daisy-like flowers are borne from between the leaf pair.

What is unique about the **water-lily** *Victoria amazonica*?

It is very big! Found only on the Amazon River, this water-lily has leaves that are up to six feet (1.8 meters) in diameter. The 12-inch (30-centimeter) flowers open at dusk on two successive nights.

GARDENING, FARMING, ETC.

What is the best **soil pH** for growing plants?

Nutrients such as phosphorous, calcium, potassium, and magnesium are most available to plants when the soil pH is between 6.0 and 7.5: Under highly acid (low pH) conditions, these nutrients become insoluble and relatively unavailable for uptake by plants. High soil pH can also decrease the availability of nutrients. If the soil is more alkaline than pH 8, phosphorous, iron, and many trace elements become insoluble and unavailable for plant uptake.

When is the best **time to work the soil**?

Although it is possible to prepare the soil at any time of year, fall digging is the best time. Dig in the fall and leave the ground rough. Freezing and thawing during winter breaks up clods and aerates the soil. Insects that otherwise survive the winter are mostly turned out. The soil settling during winter will lessen the likelihood of air pockets in the soil when planting the following spring. Fall preparation provides time for soil additives such as manure and compost to break down before planting time.

How can **garden soil** be used as **potting soil**?

The garden soil must be pasteurized and then mixed with coarse sand and peat moss. Soil may be pasteurized by putting the soil in a covered baking dish in the oven. When a meat thermometer stuck in the soil has registered 180°F (82°C) for 30 minutes, the soil is done.

What is the composition of **synthetic soil**?

Synthetic soil is composed of a variety of organic and inorganic materials. Inorganic substances used include pumice, calcinated clay, cinders, vermiculite, perlite, and sand. Organic materials used may be wood residues, manure, sphagnum moss, plant residues, and peat. Synthetic soil may also be referred to as growing medium, soil mixes, potting mixture, plant substrate, greenhouse soil, potting soil, and amended soil. Most synthetic soils are deficient in important mineral nutrients, which can be added during the mixing process or with water.

What is meant by the term **double-digging**?

Double-digging produces an excellent deep planting bed for perennials, especially if the area is composed of heavy clay. It involves removing the top 10 inches (25 cen-

What are the guidelines for gardening by the moon?

Guidelines for lunar gardening are simple. The waxing moon occurs between the new moon and full moon, and includes the first and second quarter phases. The waning moon occurs between the full moon and new moon, and includes the third and fourth quarters. Generally all activities for growth and increase, especially plants that produce above the ground, should take place during the waxing moon. Vegetables and fruits intended to be eaten immediately should be gathered at the waxing moon. Cutting, controlling, and harvesting for food to be conserved or preserved, as well as planting crops that yield below the ground, should take place during the waning moon.

timeters) of soil and moving it to a holding area, then spading the next 10 inches (25 centimeters) and amending this layer with organic matter and/or fertilizer. Then the soil from the "first" digging is amended as well, then replaced.

What is meant by **xeriscaping**?

A xeriscape, a landscape of low water–use plants, is the modern approach to gardening in areas that experience water shortages. Taken from the Greek word *xeros,* meaning dry, this type of gardening uses drought-resistant plants and low maintenance grasses, which require water only every two to three weeks. Drip irrigation, heavy mulching of plant beds, and organic soil improvements are other xeriscape techniques that allow better water absorption and retention, which in turn decrease garden watering time.

What does the term **hydroponics** mean?

This term refers to growing plants in some medium other than soil; the inorganic plant nutrients (such as potassium, sulphur, magnesium, and nitrogen) are continuously supplied to the plants in solution. Hydroponics is mostly used in areas where there is little soil or unsuitable soil. It is a much-used method of growing plants in research, but for the amateur, it has many limitations and may prove frustrating. Research plants have been grown in solution culture since the mid-1800s. William Gericke, a scientist at the University of California, defined the word hydroponics in 1937. In the 50 years that hydroponics has been used on a commercial basis, it has been adapted to many situations. NASA will be using hydroponics in the space station for crop production and to recycle carbon dioxide into oxygen.

What is meant by the phrase **rain shadow** in gardening?

The ground in the lee of a wall or solid fence receives less rainfall than the ground on the windward side. The wall or fence creates an area of rain shadow.

How many years can **seeds** be kept?

Seeds stored in an airtight container and kept in a cool, dry place are usable for a long time. The following table indicates how long commonly used seed can be kept for planting:

Vegetable	Years
Beans	3
Beets	3
Cabbage	4
Carrots	1
Cauliflower	4
Corn, sweet	2
Cucumbers	5
Eggplant	4
Kale	3
Lettuce	4
Melons	4
Onions	1
Peas	1
Peppers	2
Pumpkin	4
Radishes	3
Spinach	3
Squash	4
Swiss chard	3
Tomatoes	3
Turnips	5

How are **seedlings hardened off** before planting?

Hardening off is a gardening term for gradually acclimatizing seedlings raised indoors to the outdoor environment. Place the tray of seedlings outdoors for a few hours each

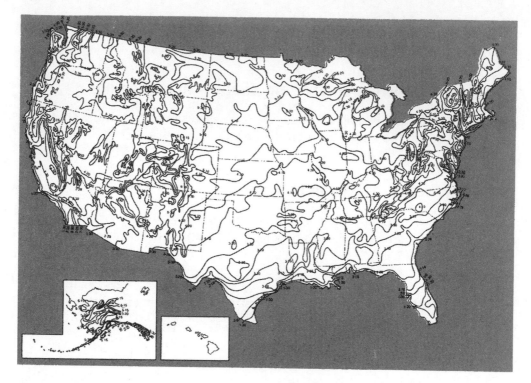

Average date of last killing frost.

day in a semi-protected spot. Lengthen the amount of time they stay out by an hour or so each day; at the end of the week, they will be ready for planting outdoors.

What are the average dates of the **last killing frost** in the spring in the eastern United States?

The map above indicates the usual spring date of the last killing frost in the eastern United States.

What are the average dates of the **first killing frost** in the autumn eastern United States?

The map below indicates the usual autumn date of the first killing frost in the eastern United States.

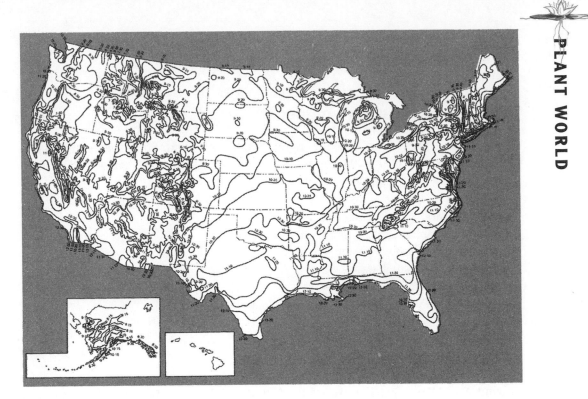

Average date of the first killing frost.

What is the difference between **container-grown, balled-and-burlapped,** and **bare-rooted** plants?

Container-grown plants have been grown in some kind of pot—usually peat, plastic, or clay—for most or all of their lives. Balled-and-burlapped plants have been dug up with the soil carefully maintained around their roots in burlap. Bare-rooted plants have also been dug from their growing place but without retaining the root ball. Typically plants from a mail-order nursery come bare-rooted with their roots protected with damp sphagnum moss. Bare-rooted plants are the most susceptible to damage.

Which plants are best for **container** gardening?

Most vegetables can be grown in a container—even large ones like pumpkins. Miniature varieties of vegetables are better because they require less space and develop earlier. Fluorescent lights help leaf crops to grow indoors even in winter. Most root crops are best grown outdoors. Fruit crops such as tomatoes can be grown indoors, but need warm temperatures and at least six hours of summer sunshine. Some of the plants

249

that may be grown are: bush beans, pole beans, beets, broccoli, cabbage, carrots, cucumbers, kale, lettuce, onions, peppers, summer squash, and tomatoes.

What is a **Shakespeare garden**?

A Shakespeare garden contains flowers referred to by William Shakespeare in his plays and poems. Not all of the 200 flowers Shakespeare mentions will grow in the United States. Here is a list of gardens you may visit:

Golden Gate Park, San Francisco, California
Huntington Botanical Gardens, San Marino, California
Northwestern University, Evanston, Illinois
Ellis Park, Cedar Rapids, Iowa
Vassar College, Poughkeepsie, New York
508 Alene Avenue North, Wessington Springs, South Dakota

What was a **victory garden**?

During World War I, patriots grew "liberty gardens." In World War II, U.S. Secretary of Agriculture Claude R. Wickard encouraged householders to plant vegetable gardens wherever they could find space. By 1945 there were said to be 20 million victory gardens producing about 40% of all American vegetables in many unused scraps of land. Such sites as the strip between a sidewalk and the street, town squares, and the land around Chicago's Cook County jail were used. The term "victory garden" derives from an English book by that title written by Richard Gardner in 1603.

What is a recommended size for a beginner's vegetable garden?

It really depends on the amount of space available, how much produce is desired from a garden, and how much work a person is willing to put into it. A modest-sized, 10 × 20 foot (3 × 6 meter) plot, laid out in traditional rows, is quite manageable in terms of weeding, cultivating, planting, and harvesting. Even a 10 × 10 foot (3 × 3 meter) plot will suffice for a salad or "kitchen" garden, with plenty of greens and herbs for salads and seasonings on a daily basis. "Intensive" gardening methods, where plants are arranged in blocks rather than rows, allow for increased yield in an even smaller space. One 4 × 4 foot (1 × 1 meter) block, with a vertical frame at one end, can provide salad vegetables for one person throughout the growing season, though two blocks would provide a wider variety of vegetables.

Is there a "best" time to weed in the vegetable garden?

Weeding is usually the most unpopular and the most time-consuming garden chore. Some studies (using weeding with peas and beans as examples) have shown that weeding done during the first three to four weeks of vegetable growth produced the best crops and that unabated weed growth after that time did not significantly reduce the vegetable yields.

What are the best annual and perennial plants to grow to attract butterflies?

Ageratum, cosmos, globe candytuft, heliotrope, lantana, marigold, mexican sunflower, torch flower, nasturtium, sweet alyssum, and zinnia attract butterflies.

Which flowers should be planted in the garden to attract hummingbirds?

Scarlet trumpet honeysuckle, weigela, butterfly bush, beardtongue, coralbells, red-hot-poker, foxglove, beebalm, nicotiana, petunia, summer phlox, and scarlet sage provide brightly colored (in shades of reds and orange), nectar-bearing attractants for hummingbirds.

Butterflies such as this monarch are attracted by a variety of flowers.

Why should lawn clippings be left on the grass after mowing?

The clippings are a valuable source of nutrients for the lawn. They provide nitrogen, potassium, and phosphorous to feed the new grass and reduce the need for fertilizer. Young, tender, short clippings decompose fast. Furthermore, when clippings are left on the lawn instead of being added to the trash collection, the amount of waste added to landfills is decreased.

What is snowmold and how do you treat it?

Snowmold is a lawn disease common in the northern United States, characterized by a white, cottony growth. The fungus *Fusarium nivale* often grows beneath the snow as it **251** melts in early spring. Avoiding late fall fertilizing in wet areas can prevent the spread of this disease. The lawn may be treated at the first sign of the disease with a fungicide and again in 10 to 14 days.

How can **daffodils** be encouraged to bloom the year after they are planted?

Try fertilizing daffodils (*Narcissus pseudonarcissus*) as soon as the new shoots appear. This helps the roots renew themselves and will also aid in leaf and flower development. If they don't bloom, the problem could be overcrowding, which hinders flower production. Try digging the bulbs up every third or fifth year, separating them, and re-spacing them.

How can **geraniums** be kept alive during the winter?

While they must be kept from freezing, geraniums can survive the winter happily in a cool sunny spot, such as a cool greenhouse, a bay window, or a sunny unheated basement. They need only occasional watering while in this semi-dormant state. Cuttings from these plants can be rooted in late winter or early spring for a new crop of geraniums (some sources suggest rooting in the fall). In homes without a suitable cool and sunny spot, the plants can be forced into dormancy by allowing the soil to dry completely, then gently knocking the soil off of the roots. While the plants can simply be hung from the rafters in a cool (45° to 50°F, or 7° to 10°C), slightly humid room, they will do better if put into individual paper bags, with the openings tied shut. The plants should be checked regularly. The leaves will dry and shrivel, but if the stems shrivel, the plants should be lightly misted with water. If any show mold or rot, cut off the affected sections, move the plants to a drier area, and leave the bags open for a day or two. In the early spring, prune the stems back to healthy green tissue and pot in fresh soil.

What is meant by the **chilling requirement** for fruit trees?

When a fruit tree's fruiting period has ended, a dormant period must follow, during which the plant rests and regains strength for another fruit set the following year. The length of this set is measured in hours between 32° and 45°F (0° to 7.2°C). A cherry tree requires about 700 hours of chilling time.

What is a **five-in-one tree**?

These very curious trees consist of a rootstock with five different varieties of the same fruit—usually apples—grafted to it. The blooming period is usually magnificent with various colors of blooms appearing on the same tree.

Did Johnny Appleseed really plant apple trees?

John Chapman (1774–1845), called Johnny Appleseed, did plant apple orchards in the midwest. He also encouraged the development of orchards farther west by giving pioneers free seedlings. His depiction as a barefoot tramp roaming the countryside scattering seeds at random from a bag slung over his shoulder, however, is more popular legend than fact. He was a curious figure who often preached from the Bible and from religious philosophy to passers-by. At his death in 1845 he was a successful businessman who owned thousands of acres of orchards and nurseries.

What is meant by **espaliering** a fruit tree and why is it done?

To espalier a fruit tree means to train it to grow flat against a surface. It can be grown in small places such as against a wall, and it will thrive even if its roots are underneath sidewalks or driveways. Since many fruit trees must be planted in pairs, espaliered fruit trees can be planted close together, providing pollen for each other, yet taking up little space.

How did the **navel orange** originate?

Every navel orange is derived from a mutant tree that appeared on a plantation in Brazil in the early nineteenth century. A bud from the mutant tree was grafted onto another tree, whose branches were then grafted onto another, and so forth.

How are **seedless grapes** grown?

Since seedless grapes cannot reproduce in the conventional way that grapes usually do (i.e., dropping seeds), growers have to take cuttings from other seedless grape plants and root them. Although the exact origin of seedless grapes is unknown, they might have been first cultivated in present-day Iran or Afghanistan thousands of years ago. Initially the first seedless grape was a genetic mutation in which the hard seed casing failed to develop—the mutation is called stenospermoscarpy. One modern seedless grape commonly bought today is the green Thompson seedless grape, from which 90% of all raisins are made.

What is pleaching?

Pleaching is a method of shearing closely planted trees or shrubs into a high wall of foliage. Many kinds of trees have been used—maples, sycamores, lindens, etc. Because of the time needed in caring for pleached allees, they are infrequently seen in American gardens, but are frequently observed in European ones.

What is the secret of bonsai, the Japanese art of growing dwarf trees?

These miniature trees with tiny leaves and twisted trunks can be centuries old. To inhibit growth of the plants, they have been carefully deprived of nutrients, pruned of their fastest-growing shoots and buds, and kept in small pots to reduce the root systems. Selective pruning, pinching out terminal buds, and wiring techniques are devices used to control the shape of the trees. Bonsai possibly started during the Chou dynasty (900–250 B.C.E.) in China, when emperors made miniature gardens that were dwarf representations of the provincial lands that they ruled.

What is a dwarf conifer?

The conifers are evergreen shrubs and trees with needle-shaped leaves, cones, and resinous wood, such as the pines, spruces, firs, and junipers. After 20 years, dwarf or slow-growing forms of these otherwise tall trees are typically about three feet (91 centimeters) tall.

Can a branch of the dogwood tree be forced into bloom?

Forcing dogwood (genus *Cornus*) into bloom is similar to forcing forsythia. Bring the dogwood branch indoors when the buds begin to swell. Put the branch in water and set it in a sunny window.

Is there a way to preserve a cut Christmas tree?

Soak the tree trunk in a solution containing:

> 1 gallon warm water
> 4 tablespoons chelated iron
> 4 tablespoons Karo syrup
> 4 tablespoons household bleach

254 Chelated iron is available at garden supply centers.

How can a Christmas tree be made fire-resistant?

Mix in a bucket:

> 2 cups corn syrup
> 2 ounces liquid chlorine bleach
> 2 pinches Epsom salts
> 1/2 teaspoon borax
> 1 teaspoon chelated iron
> 2 gallons hot water

Use the solution to water the tree every day. Chelated iron is available at garden supply centers.

What are chia seeds?

The minuscule black chia seeds are gathered from a type of wild sage that is found in the southwest United States and Mexico. Chia seeds have a very high protein content. They cannot be sprouted in the conventional manner because of their highly mucilaginous nature. However, if spread on hollow earthenware vessels (often in the shape of animals) that are made especially for the purpose, the seeds will soon produce a green blanket of protein-rich chia sprouts ready for plucking.

What is the difference between poison ivy, oak, and sumac?

These North American woody plants grow in almost any habitat and are quite similar in appearance. Each has alternating compound leaves of three leaflets each, berrylike fruits, and rusty brown stems. But poison ivy (*Rhus radicans*) acts more like a vine than a shrub at times and can grow high into trees. Its gray fruit is not hairy, and its leaves are slightly lobed. On the other hand, poison oak (*Rhus toxicodendron*) is often shrubby, but it can climb. Its leaflets are lobed and resemble oak leaves; its fruit is hairy. Poison sumac (*Rhus vernix*) grows only in North American wet acid swamps. This shrub can grow as high as 12 feet (3.6 meters). The fruit it produces hangs in a cluster and is grayish-brown in color. Poison sumac has sharply pointed, dark green, compound, alternating leaves; and greenish-yellow inconspicuous flowers. All parts of poison ivy, poison oak, and poison sumac can cause serious dermatitis.

What is a natural way to get rid of poison ivy?

Poison ivy can be killed by spraying or treating the plants with a saltwater solution. Large plants can be killed by cutting the vines at or below ground level and soaking the base with brine. A second application after two weeks may be needed. *Do not burn* the plants; smoke and ash may cause the rash on exposed parts of the body, eyes, nasal passages, and lungs.

What is the **railroad worm**?

The apple maggot (*Rhagoletis pomonella*), which becomes the apple fruit fly, is frequently called the railroad worm. Inhabiting orchards in Eastern United States and Canada, the larvae feed on the fruit pulp of apples, plums, cherries, etc., and cause damage to fruit crops.

Which **insects** are common problems in **strawberry** cultivation?

Earwigs, slugs, and snails are big problems in some areas. Strawberries (*Fragaria*) are also bothered by Japanese beetles, aphids, thrips, weevils, nematodes, and mites.

How can **fruit trees** be protected from being eaten by **field mice**?

Valuable trees, especially newly planted fruit trees, can be protected by wrappings or guards of wire, wood veneer, or plastic. Other controls, such as pieces of lava rocks soaked in garlic, are effective as repellents, and garlic sprays will repel most rodents.

Which type of **fence** protects a garden from **deer**?

A post and wire-mesh fence with a sharp-angled, narrow gate, which people and small animals can navigate, but deer cannot, plus the installation of a motion-sensing security light with a beeper helps keep deer away. Electric fences are also a good deterrent, but for smaller gardens snow fencing works well.

How can **squirrels** be kept away from vegetable and flower gardens?

Squirrels like to take a bite out of tomatoes, cucumbers, and melons, dig up bulbs, and ruin anything colorful in the flower garden. The traditional recommendation of spreading mothballs around is apparently not too successful. A better method is laying down one to two inch (2.5 to five centimeter) mesh sheets of chicken wire. Squirrels will avoid the mesh, apparently because they fear getting their toes stuck in it. Another method to try is sprinkling hot pepper around the plants, renewing it after it

How do you keep **cats** away from catnip growing in the garden?

Instead of transplanting plants, which can bruise the leaves and release the oil that attracts cats, grow catnip directly from seeds. Try not to disturb the leaves after the plant grows. Once the scent is released, it is difficult to keep cats away.

Who developed **DDT**?

Although DDT was synthesized as early as 1874 by Othmar Zeidler, it was the Swiss chemist Paul Müller (1899–1965) who recognized its insecticidal properties in 1939. He was awarded the 1948 Nobel Prize in medicine for his development of dichloro-diphenyl-trichloro-ethene, or DDT. Unlike the arsenic-based compounds then in use, DDT was effective in killing insects and seemed not to harm plants and animals. In the following 20 years it proved to be effective in controlling disease-carrying insects (mosquitoes that carry malaria and yellow fever, and lice that carry typhus), and in killing many plant crop destroyers. Increasingly DDT-resistant insect species and the accumulative hazardous effects of DDT on plant and animal life cycles led to its disuse in many countries during the 1970s.

What were some of the accomplishments of **Dr. George Washington Carver**?

Because of the work of Dr. George Washington Carver (1864–1943) in plant diseases, soil analysis, and crop management, many southern farmers who adopted his methods increased their crop yields and profits. Carver developed recipes using cowpeas, sweet potatoes, and peanuts. He eventually made 118 products from sweet potatoes, 325 from peanuts, and 75 from pecans. He promoted soil diversification and the adoption of peanuts, soybeans, and other soil-enriching crops. His other work included developing plastic material from soy beans, which Ford later used in part of his automobile. He extracted dyes and paints from the Alabama red clay and

George Washington Carver.

worked with hybrid cotton. Carver was a widely talented man who became an almost mythical American folk hero.

When was the first practical **greenhouse** built?

French botanist Jules Charles constructed one in 1599 in Leiden, Holland, which housed tropical plants grown for medicinal purposes. The most popular plant there was an Indian date called the tamarind, whose fruit was made into a curative drink.

When was the first **plant patent** issued?

Henry F. Bosenberg, a landscape gardener, received U.S. Plant Patent no. 1 on August 18, 1931, for a climbing or trailing rose.

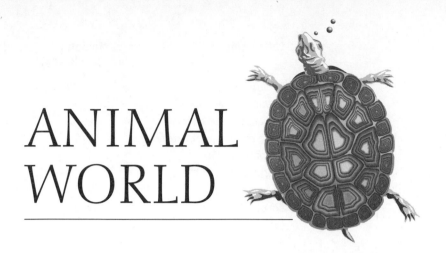

ANIMAL WORLD

PHYSICAL CHARACTERISTICS, ETC.

See Also: Environment—Extinct and Endangered Plants and Animals

Which animal has the **longest gestation** period?

The animal with the longest gestation period is not a mammal; it is the viviparous amphibian, the Alpine black salamander, which can have a gestation period of up to 38 months at altitudes above 4,600 feet (1,402 meters) in the Swiss alps; it bears two fully metamorphosed young.

How **long** do animals, in particular mammals, **live**?

Of the mammals, humans and fin whales live the longest. Below is the maximum life-span for several animal species.

Animal	Latin name	Maximum life span in years
Marion's tortoise	*Testudo sumeirii*	152+
Quahog	*Venus mercenaria*	ca. 150
Common box tortoise	*Terrapene carolina*	138
European pond tortoise	*Emys orbicularis*	120+
Spur-thighed tortoise	*Testudo graeca*	116+
Fin whale	*Balaenoptera physalus*	116
Human	*Homo sapiens*	116
Deep-sea clam	*Tindaria callistiformis*	ca. 100

Animal	Latin name	Maximum life span in years
Killer whale	*Orcinus orca*	ca. 90
European eel	*Anguilla anguilla*	88
Lake sturgeon	*Acipenser fulvescens*	82
Freshwater mussel	*Margaritana margaritifera*	80 to 70
Asiatic elephant	*Elephas maximus*	78
Andean condor	*Vultur gryphus*	72+
Whale shark	*Rhiniodon typus*	ca. 70
African elephant	*Loxodonta africana*	ca. 70
Great eagle-owl	*Bubo bubo*	68+
American alligator	*Alligator mississipiensis*	66
Blue macaw	*Ara macao*	64
Ostrich	*Struthio camelus*	62.5
Horse	*Equus caballus*	62
Orangutan	*Pongo pygmaeus*	ca. 59
Bataleur eagle	*Terathopius ecaudatus*	55
Hippopotamus	*Hippopotamus amphibius*	54.5
Chimpanzee	*Pan troglodytes*	51
White pelican	*Pelecanus onocrotalus*	51
Gorilla	*Gorilla gorilla*	50+
Domestic goose	*Anser a. domesticus*	49.75
Grey parrot	*Psittacus erythacus*	49
Indian rhinoceros	*Rhinoceros unicornis*	49
European brown bear	*Ursus arctos arctos*	47
Grey seal	*Halichoerus gryphus*	46+
Blue whale	*Balaenoptera musculus*	ca. 45
Goldfish	*Carassius auratus*	41
Common toad	*Bufo bufo*	40
Roundworm	*Tylenchus polyhyprus*	39
Giraffe	*Giraffa camelopardalis*	36.25
Bactrian camel	*Camelus ferus*	35+
Brazilian tapir	*Tapirus terrestris*	35
Domestic cat	*Felis catus*	34
Canary	*Serinus caneria*	34
American bison	*Bison bison*	33
Bobcat	*Felis rufus*	32.3
Sperm whale	*Physeter macrocephalus*	32+
American manatee	*Trichechus manatus*	30
Red kangaroo	*Macropus rufus*	ca. 30
African buffalo	*Syncerus caffer*	29.5
Domestic dog	*Canis familiaris*	29.5
Lion	*Panthera leo*	ca. 29

Animal	Latin name	Maximum life span in years
African civet	*Viverra civetta*	28
Theraphosid spider	*Mygalomorphae*	ca. 28
Red deer	*Cervus elaphus*	26.75
Tiger	*Panthera tigris*	26.25
Giant panda	*Ailuropoda melanoleuca*	26
American badger	*Taxidea taxus*	26
Common wombat	*Vombatus ursinus*	26
Bottle-nosed dolphin	*Tursiops truncatus*	25
Domestic chicken	*Gallus g. domesticus*	25
Grey squirrel	*Sciurus carolinensis*	23.5
Aardvark	*Orycteropus afer*	23
Domestic duck	*Anas platyrhynchos domesticus*	23
Coyote	*Canis latrans*	21+
Canadian otter	*Lutra canadensis*	21
Domestic goat	*Capra hircus domesticus*	20.75
Queen ant	*Myrmecina graminicola*	18+
Common rabbit	*Oryctolagus cuniculus*	18+
White or beluga whale	*Delphinapterus leucuas*	17.25
Platypus	*Ornithorhynchus anatinus*	17
Walrus	*Odobenus rosmarus*	16.75
Domestic turkey	*Melagris gallapave domesticus*	16
American beaver	*Castor canadensis*	15+
Land snail	*Helix spiriplana*	15
Guinea pig	*Cavia porcellus*	14.8
Hedgehog	*Erinaceus europaeus*	14
Burmeister's armadillo	*Calyptophractus retusus*	12
Capybara	*Hydrochoerus hydrochaeris*	12
Chinchilla	*Chinchilla laniger*	11.3
Giant centipede	*Scolopendra gigantea*	10
Golden hamster	*Mesocricetus auratus*	10
Segmented worm	*Allolobophora longa*	10
Purse-web spider	*Atypus affinis*	9+
Greater Egyptian gerbil	*Gerbillus pyramidum*	8+
Spiny starfish	*Marthasterias glacialis*	7+
Millipede	*Cylindroiulus landinensis*	7
Coypu	*Myocastor coypus*	6+
House mouse	*Mus musculus*	6
Malagasy brown-tailed mongoose	*Salanoia concolor*	4.75
Cane rat	*Thryonomys swinderianus*	4.3
Siberian flying squirrel	*Pteromys volans*	3.75
Common octopus	*Octopus vulgaris*	2 to 3

Animal	Latin name	Maximum life span in years
Pygmy white-toothed shrew	*Suncus etruscus*	2
Pocket gopher	*Thomomys talpoides*	1.6
Monarch butterfly	*Danaus plexippus*	1.13
Bedbug	*Cimex lectularius*	0.5 or 182 days
Black widow spider	*Latrodectus mactans*	0.27 or 100 days
Common housefly	*Musca domesticus*	0.04 or 17 days

What are the **largest** and **smallest** living animals?

Largest animals	Name	Length and weight
Sea mammal	Blue or sulphur-bottom whale (*Balaenoptera musculus*)	100–110 feet (30.5–33.5 meters) long; weighs 135–209 tons (122.4–189.6 tonnes)
Land mammal	African bush elephant (*Loxodonta africana*)	Bull is 10.5 feet (3.2 meters) tall at shoulder; weighs 5.25–6.2 tons (4.8–5.6 tonnes)
Living bird	North African ostrich (*Struthio c. camelus*)	8 to 9 feet (2.4–2.7 meters) tall; weighs 345 pounds (156.5 kilograms)
Fish	Whale shark (*Rhincodon typus*)	41 feet (12.5 meters) long; weighs 16.5 tons (15 tonnes)
Reptile	Salt-water crocodile (*Crocodylus porosus*)	14–16 feet (4.3–4.9 meters) long; weighs 900–1,500 pounds (408–680 kilograms)
Rodent	Capybara (*Hydrochoerus hydrochaeris*)	3.25–4.5 feet (1–1.4 meters) long; weighs 250 pounds (113.4 kilograms)

Smallest animals	Name	Length and weight
Sea mammal	Commerson's dolphin (*Cephalorhynchus commersonii*)	Weighs 50–70 pounds (236.7–31.8 kilograms)
Land mammal	Bumblebee or Kitti's hog-nosed bat (*Craseonycteris thong longyai*) or the pygmy shrew (*Suncus erruscus*)	1 inch (2.54 centimeters) long; weighs .062 to .07 ounces (1.6–2 grams) 1.5–2 inches (3.8–5 centimeters) long; weighs 0.052–.09 ounces (1.5–2.6 grams)
Bird	Bee hummingbird (*Mellisuga helenea*)	2.25 inches (5.7 centimeters) long; weighs 0.056 ounces (1.6 grams)
Fish	Dwarf pygmy goby (*Trimmatam nanus*)	0.35 inches (8.9 millimeters) long
Reptile	Gecko (*Spaerodactylus parthenopion*)	0.67 inches (1.7 centimeters) long
Rodent	Pygmy mouse (*Baiomys taylori*)	4.3 inches (10.9 centimeters) long; weighs 0.24–0.28 ounces (6.8–7.9 grams)

Do bears in zoos hibernate?

Bears do not hibernate in zoos because temperatures in cages and enclosures remain warm throughout the year and the bears are constantly fed by keepers. Hibernation occurs only with lack of food and temperatures below the freezing point.

Besides humans, which animals are the **most intelligent**?

According to Edward O. Wilson, a behavioral biologist, the ten most intelligent animals are the following:

1. Chimpanzee (two species)
2. Gorilla
3. Orangutan
4. Baboon (seven species, including drill and mandrill)
5. Gibbon (seven species)
6. Monkey (many species, especially macaques, the patas, and the Celebes black ape)
7. Smaller toothed whale (several species, especially killer whale)
8. Dolphin (many of the approximately 80 species)
9. Elephant (two species)
10. Pig

Bears in the wild will gorge themselves on food—sometimes from human sources—before entering hibernation.

Do animals have **color vision**?

Most birds appear to have a well-developed color sense. Most mammals are color-blind. Apes and monkeys have the ability to tell colors apart. Dogs and cats seem to be color-blind and only see shades of black, white, and gray.

Can animals **regenerate** parts of their bodies?

Regeneration does occur in animals; however, it progressively declines the more complex the animal species becomes. Among primitive invertebrates (lacking a backbone), regeneration frequently occurs. For example, a planarium (flatworm) can split symmetrically, each being a clone of the other. In higher invertebrates regeneration occurs in echinoderms (such as starfish) and arthropods (such as insects and crustaceans). Regeneration of appendages (limbs, wings, and antennae) occurs in insects (such as cockroaches, fruitflies, and locusts) and in crustaceans (such as lobsters, crabs, and crayfish). For example, regeneration of the crayfish's missing claw occurs at its next molt (shedding of its hard cuticle exterior shell/skin in order to grow and the subsequent hardening of a new cuticle exterior). However, sometimes the regenerated claw does not achieve the same size of the missing claw. But after every molt (occurring two to three times a year) it grows and will eventually become nearly as large as the original claw. On a very limited basis, some amphibians and reptiles can replace a lost leg or tail.

Do animals have **blood types**?

The number of recognized blood groups varies from species to species:

Species	Number of blood groups
Pig	16
Cow	12
Chicken	11
Horse	9
Sheep	7
Dog	7
Rhesus monkey	6
Mink	5
Rabbit	5
Mouse	4
Rat	4
Cat	2

Do all animals have **red blood**?

The color of blood is related to the compounds that transport oxygen. Hemoglobin, containing iron, is red and is found in all vertebrates (animals having a backbone) and a few invertebrates (animals lacking a backbone). Annelids (segmented worms) have either a green pigment, chlorocruorin, or a red pigment, hemerythrin. Some crustaceans (arthropods having divided bodies and generally having gills) have a blue pigment, hemocyanin, in their blood.

Which animals can **run faster than a human**?

The cheetah, the fastest mammal, can accelerate from zero to 45 miles (64 kilometers) per hour in two seconds; it has been timed at speeds of 70 miles (112 kilometers) per hour over short distances. In most chases, cheetahs average around 40 miles (63 kilometers) per hour. Humans can run very short distances at almost 28 miles (45 kilome-

Do any animals snore?

Many animals have been observed snoring occasionally, including dogs, cats, cows, oxen, sheep, buffaloes, elephants, camels, lions, leopards, tigers, gorillas, chimpanzees, horses, mules, zebras, and elands.

ters) per hour maximum. Most of the speeds given in the table below are for distances of one-quarter mile (0.4 kilometer).

Animal	Maximum speed	
	Miles per hour	Kilometers per hour
Cheetah	70	112.6
Pronghorn antelope	61	98.1
Wildebeest	50	80.5
Lion	50	80.5
Thomson's gazelle	50	80.5
Quarter horse	47.5	76.4
Elk	45	72.4
Cape hunting dog	45	72.4
Coyote	43	69.2
Gray fox	42	67.6
Hyena	40	64.4
Zebra	40	64.4
Mongolian wild ass	40	64.4
Greyhound	39.4	63.3
Whippet	35.5	57.1
Rabbit (domestic)	35	56.3
Mule deer	35	56.3
Jackal	35	56.3
Reindeer	32	51.3
Giraffe	32	51.3
White-tailed deer	30	48.3
Wart hog	30	48.3
Grizzly bear	30	48.3
Cat (domestic)	30	48.3
Human	27.9	44.9

NAMES

What names are used for **male** and **female animals**?

Animal	Male name	Female name
Alligator	Bull	
Ant		Queen
Ass	Jack, jackass	Jenny
Bear	Boar or he-bear	Sow or she-bear
Bee	Drone	Queen or queen bee
Camel	Bull	Cow
Caribou	Bull, stag, or hart	Cow or doe
Cat	Tom, tomcat, gib, gibeat, boarcat, or ramcat	Tabby, grimalkin, malkin, pussy, or queen
Chicken	Rooster, cock, stag, or chanticleer	Hen, partlet, or biddy
Cougar	Tom or lion	Lioness, she-lion, or pantheress
Coyote	Dog	Bitch
Deer	Buck or stag	Doe
Dog	Dog	Bitch
Duck	Drake or stag	Duck
Fox	Fox, dog-fox, stag, reynard, or renard	Vixen, bitch, or she-fox
Giraffe	Bull	Cow
Goat	Buck, billy, billie, billie-goat, or he-goat	She-goat, nanny, nannie, or nannie-goat
Goose	Gander or stag	Goose or dame
Guinea pig	Boar	
Horse	Stallion, stag, horse, stud, slot, stable horse, sire, or rig	Mare or dam
Impala	Ram	Ewe
Kangaroo	Buck	Doe
Leopard	Leopard	Leopardess
Lion	Lion or tom	Lioness or she-lion
Lobster	Cock	Hen
Manatee	Bull	Cow
Mink	Boar	Sow
Moose	Bull	Cow
Mule	Stallion or jackass	She-ass or mare
Ostrich	Cock	Hen
Otter	Dog	Bitch
Owl		Jenny or howlet

Animal	Male name	Female name
Ox	Ox, beef, steer, or bullock	Cow or beef
Partridge	Cock	Hen
Peacock	Peacock	Peahen
Pigeon	Cock	Hen
Quail	Cock	Hen
Rabbit	Buck	Doe
Reindeer	Buck	Doe
Robin	Cock	
Seal	Bull	Cow
Sheep	Buck, ram, male-sheep, or mutton	Ewe or dam
Skunk	Boar	
Swan	Cob	Pen
Termite	King	Queen
Tiger	Tiger	Tigress
Turkey	Gobbler or tom	Hen
Walrus	Bull	Cow
Whale	Bull	Cow
Woodchuck	He-chuck	She-chuck
Wren		Jenny or jennywren
Zebra	Stallion	Mare

What names are used for **juvenile animals**?

Animal	Name for young
Ant	Antling
Antelope	Calf, fawn, kid, or yearling
Bear	Cub
Beaver	Kit or kitten
Bird	Nestling
Bobcat	Kitten or cub
Buffalo	Calf, yearling, or spike-bull
Camel	Calf or colt
Canary	Chick
Caribou	Calf or fawn
Cat	Kit, kitling, kitty, or pussy
Cattle	Calf, stot, or yearling (m. bullcalf or f. heifer)
Chicken	Chick, chicken, poult, cockerel, or pullet
Chimpanzee	Infant
Cicada	Nymph
Clam	Littleneck

Animal	Name for young
Cod	Codling, scrod, or sprag
Condor	Chick
Cougar	Kitten or cub
Cow	Calf (m. bullcalf; f. heifer)
Coyote	Cub, pup, or puppy
Deer	Fawn
Dog	Whelp
Dove	Pigeon or squab
Duck	Duckling or flapper
Eagle	Eaglet
Eel	Fry or elver
Elephant	Calf
Elk	Calf
Fish	Fry, fingerling, minnow, or spawn
Fly	Grub or maggot
Frog	Polliwog or tadpole
Giraffe	Calf
Goat	Kid
Goose	Gosling
Grouse	Chick, poult, squealer, or cheeper
Horse	Colt, foal, stot, stag, filly, hog-colt, youngster, yearling, or hogget
Kangaroo	Joey
Leopard	Cub
Lion	Shelp, cub, or lionet
Louse	Nit
Mink	Kit or cub
Monkey	Suckling, yearling, or infant
Mosquito	Larva, flapper, wriggler, or wiggler
Muskrat	Kit
Ostrich	Chick
Otte	Pup, kitten, whelp, or cub
Owl	Owlet or howlet
Oyster	Set seed, spat, or brood
Partridge	Cheeper
Pelican	Chick or nestling
Penguin	Fledgling or chick
Pheasant	Chick or poult
Pigeon	Squab, nestling, or squealer
Quail	Cheeper, chick, or squealer
Rabbit	Kitten or bunny
Raccoon	Kit or cub

Animal	Name for young
Reindeer	Fawn
Rhinoceros	Calf
Sea Lion	Pup
Seal	Whelp, pup, cub, or bachelor
Shark	Cub
Sheep	Lamb, lambkin, shearling, or yearling
Skunk	Kitten
Squirrel	Dray
Swan	Cygnet
Swine	Shoat, trotter, pig, or piglet
Termite	Nymph
Tiger	Whelp or cub
Toad	Tadpole
Turkey	Chick or poult
Turtle	Chicken
Walrus	Cub
Weasel	Kit
Whale	Calf
Wolf	Cub or pup
Woodchuck	Kit or cub
Zebra	Colt or foal

What names are used for **groups of animals**?

Animal	Group name
Ants	Nest, army, colony, state, or swarm
Bees	Swarm, cluster, nest, hive, or erst
Caterpillars	Army
Eels	Swarm or bed
Fish	School, shoal, haul, draught, run, or catch
Flies	Business, hatch, grist, swarm, or cloud
Frogs	Arm
Gnats	Swarm, cloud, or horde
Goldfish	Troubling
Grasshoppers	Cloud
Hornets	Nest
Jellyfish	Smuck or brood
Lice	Flock
Locusts	Swarm, cloud, or plague
Minnows	Shoal, steam, or swarm

Animal	Group name
Oysters	Bed
Sardines	Family
Sharks	School or shoal
Snakes	Bed, knot, den, or pit
Termites	Colony, nest, swarm, or brood
Toads	Nest, knot, or knab
Trout	Hover
Turtles	Bale or dole
Wasps	Nest, herd, or pladge

INSECTS, SPIDERS, ETC.

How many **species of insects** are there?

Estimates of the number of recognized insect species range from about 750,000 to upward of one million—but some experts think that this represents less than half of the number that exists in the world. About 7,000 new insect species are described each year, but unknown numbers are lost annually from the destruction of their habitats, mainly tropical forests.

What is the most **destructive insect** in the world?

The most destructive insect is the desert locust (*Schistocera gregaria*), the locust of the Bible, whose habitat ranges from the dry and semi-arid regions of Africa and the Middle East, through Pakistan and northern India. This short-horn grasshopper can eat its own weight in food a day, and during long migratory flights a large swarm can consume 20,000 tons (18,144,000 kilograms) of grain and vegetation a day.

What are some **beneficial insects**?

Beneficial insects include bees, wasps, flies, butterflies, moths, and others that pollinate plants. Many fruits and vegetables depend on insect pollinators for the production of seeds. Insects are an important source of food for birds, fish, and many animals. In some countries such insects as termites, caterpillars, ants, and bees are eaten as food by people. Products derived from insects include honey and beeswax, shellac, and silk. Some predators such as mantises, ladybugs or lady beetles, and lacewings feed on other harmful insects. Other helpful insects are parasites that live on or in the body of harmful insects. For example, some wasps lay their eggs in caterpillars that damage tomato plants.

What are the stages of **insect metamorphosis**?

There are two types of metamorphoses (marked structural changes in the growth processes): complete and incomplete. In *complete metamorphosis*, the insect (such as the ant, moth, butterfly, termite, wasp, or beetle) goes through all the distinct stages of growth to reach adulthood. In *incomplete metamorphosis*, the insect (such as the grasshopper, cricket, or louse) does not go through all the stages of complete metamorphoses.

Complete metamorphosis

Egg—One egg is laid at a time or many (as much as 10,000).

Larva—What hatches from the eggs is called "larva." A larva can look like a worm.

Pupa—After reaching its full growth, the larva hibernates, developing a shell or "pupal case" for protection. A few insects (e.g., the moth) spin a hard covering called a "cocoon." The resting insect is called a pupa (except the butterfly is called a chrysalis), and remains in the hibernation state for several weeks or months.

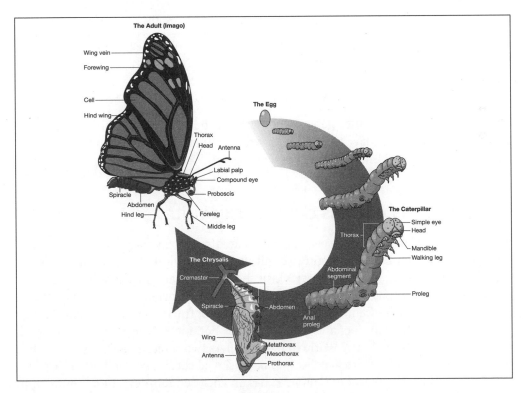

The life cycle of a butterfly represents complete metamorphosis.

Adult—During hibernation, the insect develops its adult body parts. When it has matured physically, the fully grown insect emerges from its case or cocoon.

Incomplete metamorphosis

Egg—One egg or many eggs are laid.

Early-stage nymph—Hatched insect resembles an adult, but smaller in size. However, those insects that would normally have wings have not yet developed them.

Late-stage nymph—At this time, the skin begins to molt (shed), and the wings begin to bud.

Adult—The insect is now fully grown.

Has the U.S. selected a **national insect**?

A group of citizens has petitioned the United States Congress to name the monarch butterfly as the national insect, but, to date, they have not been successful.

How does a **butterfly** differ from a **moth**?

Characteristic	Butterflies	Moths
Antennae	Knobbed	Unknobbed
Active-time of day	Day	Night
Coloration	Bright	Dull
Resting position	Vertically above body	Horizontally beside body

Note: While these guidelines generally hold true, there are exceptions. Moths have hairy bodies, and most have tiny hooks or bristles linking the fore-wing to the hind-wing; butterflies do not have either characteristic.

Which **butterfly gardens** can the public visit?

A number of gardens cultivate special plants that attract the various species of butterfly. The Cecil B. Day Butterfly Center at Callaway Gardens in Pine Mountain, Georgia, is perhaps the largest. Over 100 species visit the outdoor garden. There is also Butterfly World at Tradewinds Park South in Coconut Creek, Florida, and at Marine World Africa U.S.A. in Vallejo, California; the Cincinnati Zoo; the Hummingbird and Butterfly Garden at the Detroit Zoo; and the Des Moines Botanical Gardens with its tropical butterfly house. The Butterfly World in Florida offers two screened aviaries having two to three thousand butterflies, a collection of preserved specimens, and other displays; whereas the Butterfly World in California has an enclosed rain-forest environment in a 5,500 square foot (510 square meter) glass greenhouse.

Who discovered the "dance of the bees"?

In 1943, Karl von Frisch (1886–1982) published his study on the dance of the bees. It is a precise pattern of movements performed by returning forager (worker) honeybees in order to communicate the direction and distance of a food source to the other workers in the hive. The dance is performed on the vertical surface of the hive and two kinds of dances have been recognized: the round dance (performed when food is nearby) and the waggle dance (done when food is further away).

What are "killer bees"?

Africanized honeybees—the term entomologists prefer rather than killer bees—are a hybrid originating in Brazil where African honeybees were imported in 1956. The breeders, hoping to produce a bee better suited to producing more honey in the tropics, instead found that African bees soon hybridized with and mostly displaced the familiar European honeybees. Although they produce more honey, Africanized honeybees also are more dangerous than European bees because they attack intruders in greater numbers. Since their introduction, they have been responsible for approximately 1,000 human deaths. In addition to such safety issues, concern is growing regarding the effect of possible hybridization on the U.S. beekeeping industry.

In October 1990, the bees crossed the Mexican border into the United States. They reached Arizona in 1993 and are expected to colonize parts of the southern United States before being stopped by colder climates, probably by the year 2000. Experts have suggested two possible ways of limiting the spread of the Africanized honeybees. The first is drone-flooding, a process by which large numbers of European drones are kept in areas where comercially-reared European queen bees mate, thereby ensuring that only limited mating occurs between Africanized drones and European queens. The second method is frequent requeening, in which a beekeeper replaces a colony's queen with one of his or her own choosing. The beekeeper can then be assured that the queens are European and that they have already mated with European drones.

What are **migratory beekeepers**?

A migratory beekeeper is a person who transports his or her bee colonies to different areas to produce better honey or to collect fees for pollinating such crops as fruit trees, almonds, and alfalfa. They frequently travel north in the spring and summer to pollinate crops and then back south in the fall and winter to maintain the colonies in the warmer southern weather. Approximately 1,000 migratory beekeepers operate in the United States, transporting approximately two million bee colonies a year.

How are **ants** distinguished from **termites**?

Both insect orders—ants (order Hymenoptera) and termites (order Isoptera)—have segmented bodies with multi-jointed legs. Listed below are some differences.

Characteristic	Ant	Termite
Wings	Two pairs with the front pair being much longer than the back pair	Two pairs of equal length
Antenna	Bends at right angle	Straight
Abdomen	Wasp-waist (pinched in)	No wasp-waist

Do **termites** have any natural predators?

Birds, ants, spiders, lizards, and dragonflies have been seen preying on young, winged termites when they emerge and fly from a home colony to establish new colonies. This time is generally when termites are most vulnerable to predators.

Do male **mosquitoes** bite humans?

No. Male mosquitoes live on plant juices, sugary saps, and liquids arising from decomposition. They do not have a biting mouth that can penetrate human skin as female mosquitoes do. In some species, the females, who lay as many as 200 eggs, need blood to lay their eggs.

What is a "**daddy longlegs**"?

The name applies to two different kinds of invertebrates. The first is a harmless, non-biting long-legged arachnid. Also called a harvestman, it is often mistaken for a spider, but it lacks the segmented body shape that a spider has. Although it has the same number of legs (eight) as a spider, the harvestman's legs are far longer and thinner. These very long legs enable it to raise its body high enough to avoid ants or other small enemies. Harvestmen are largely carnivorous, feeding on a variety of small invertebrates, such as insects, spiders, and mites. They never spin webs as spiders do. They also eat some juicy plants and in captivity can be fed almost anything edible, from bread and milk to meat. Harvesters also need to drink frequently. The term "daddy longlegs" also is used for a cranefly—a thin-bodied insect with long thin legs that has a snout-like proboscis with which it sucks water and nectar.

How many **eggs** does a **spider** lay?

The number of eggs varies according to the species. Some larger spiders lay over 2,000 eggs, but many tiny spiders lay one or two and perhaps no more than a dozen during their lifetime. Spiders of average size probably lay a hundred or so. Most spiders lay all their eggs at one time and enclose them in a single egg sac; others lay eggs over a period of time and enclose them in a number of egg sacs.

Which is stronger—steel or the silk from a **spider's** web?

Spider silk. Well known for its strength and elasticity, the strongest spider silk has tensile strength second only to fused quartz fibers and five times greater than that of steel of equivalent weight. Tensile strength is the longitudinal stress that a substance can bear without tearing apart. The tension necessary to bring a compound thread 0.004 inches (0.01 centimeters) in diameter to the breaking point was found to be 2.8 ounces (80 grams).

How long does it take the average spider to **weave a complete web**?

The average orb-weaver spider takes 30 to 60 minutes to completely spin its web. The order Araneae (the spiders) constitutes the largest division in the class Arachnida, containing about 32,000 species. These species of spiders use silk to capture their food in a variety of ways, ranging from the simple trip wires used by the large bird-eating spiders to the complicated and beautiful webs spun by the orb spiders. Some species produce funnel-shaped webs, and other communities of spiders build communal webs.

A completed web features several spokes leading from the initial structure. The number and nature of the spokes depend on the species. The spider replaces any damaged threads by gathering up the thread in front of it and producing a new one behind it. The orb web must be replaced every few days because it loses its stickiness (and its ability to entrap food).

The largest aerial webs are spun by the tropical orb weavers of the genus *Nephila*, measuring up to 18 feet, 9 inches (six meters) in circumference. The smallest webs are done by the *Glyphesis cottonae* which covers about 0.75 square inches (4.84 square centimeters).

How long have **cockroaches** been on the earth?

The earliest cockroach fossils are about 280 million years old. Some cockroaches measured three to four inches (7.5 to 10 centimeters) long. Cockroaches (order Dictyoptera) are nocturnal scavenging insects that eat not only human food but book-bindings, ink, and whitewash as well.

How many pairs of legs does a **centipede** have?

Centipedes, or members of the class Chilopoda, always have an uneven number of pairs of walking legs, varying from 15 to more than 171. The true centipedes (order Scolopendromorpha) have 21 or 23 pairs of legs. Common house centipedes (*Scutigera coleoptrato*) have 15 pairs of legs.

How do **fleas** jump so far?

The jumping power of fleas comes both from strong leg muscles and from pads of a rubber-like protein called resilin. The resilin is located above the flea's hind legs. To jump, the flea crouches, squeezing the resilin, and then it relaxes certain muscles. Stored energy from the resilin works like a spring, launching the flea. A flea can jump well both vertically and horizontally. Some species can jump 150 times their own length. To match that record, a human would have to spring over the length of two and a quarter football fields—or the height of a 100-story building—in a single bound. The common flea (*Pulex irritans*) has been known to jump 13 inches (33 centimeters) in length and 7.25 inches (18.4 centimeters) in height.

What is the life-span of a **fruit fly**?

The length of adult life can vary considerably. Under ideal conditions, an adult *Drosophila melanogaster* can live as long as 40 days. In crowded conditions, life-span may drop to 12 days. Under normal laboratory conditions, however, adults generally die after only six or seven days.

What causes the **Mexican jumping bean** to move?

The bean moth (*Carpocapa saltitans*) lays its eggs in the flower or in the seed pod of the spurge, a bush known as *Euphorbia sebastiana*. The egg hatches inside the seed pod, producing a larva or caterpillar. The jumping of the bean is caused by the active shifting of weight inside the shell as the caterpillar moves. The jumps of the bean are stimulated by sunshine or by heat from the palm of the hand.

How is the light in fireflies produced?

The light produced by fireflies (*Photinus pyroles*), or lightning bugs, is a kind of heatless light called bioluminescence caused by a chemical reaction in which the substance luciferin undergoes oxidation when the enzyme luciferase is present. The flash is a photon of visible light that radiates when the oxidating chemicals produce a high-energy state and revert back to their normal state. The flashing is controlled by the nervous system and takes place in special cells called photocytes. The nervous system, photocytes, and the tracheal end organs control the flashing rate. The air temperature also seems to be correlated with the flashing rate. The higher the temperature, the shorter the interval between flashes—eight seconds at 65°F (18.3°C) and four seconds at 82°F (27.7°C). Scientists are uncertain as to why this flashing occurs. The rhythmic flashes could be a means of attracting prey or enabling mating fireflies to signal in heliographic codes (that differ from one species to another), or they could serve as a warning signal.

AQUATIC LIFE

See also: Biology—Fungi, Bacteria, Algae, etc.

How is the age of fish determined?

One way to determine the age of a fish is by its scales, which have growth rings just as trees do. Scales have concentric bony ridges or "circuli," which reflect the growth patterns of the individual fish. The portion of the scale that is embedded in the skin contains clusters of these ridges (called "annuli"); each cluster marks one year's growth cycle.

At what speeds do fish swim?

The maximum swimming speed of a fish is somewhat determined by the shape of its body and tail and by its internal temperature. The cosmopolitan sailfish (*Istiophorus platypterus*) is considered to be the fastest fish species, at least for short distances, swimming at greater than 60 miles (95 kilometers) per hour. Some American fishermen believe, however, that the bluefin tuna (*Thunnus thynnus*) is the fastest, but the fastest speed recorded so far is 43.4 miles (69.8 kilometers) per hour. Data is extremely difficult to secure because of the practical difficulties in measuring the speeds. The yellowfin tuna (*Thunnus albacares*) and the wahoe (*Acanthocybium solandri*) are also fast, timed at 46.35 miles (74.5 kilometers) per hour and 47.88 miles (77 kilometers) per hour during 10 to 20 second sprints. Flying fish swim at 40+ miles (64+ kilometers) per hour, dolphins at 37 miles (60 kilometers) per hour, trout at 15 miles (24 kilometers) per hour, and blenny at five miles (eight kilometers) per hour. Humans can swim 5.19 miles (8.3 kilometers) per hour.

What is krill?

Krill (*Euphausiids*) refers to 85 species of marine, planktonic crustaceans that constitute the diet of many whales, particularly baleen whales, and other vertebrates such as fish, penguins, and seabirds. Blue whales, largest of the world's animals, live on krill, and a whale's stomach can contain four tons of the crustacean. Some ecologists have even suggested krill as a potential food source for humans because of the species' abundance and nutritional value.

Ranging in size from one-quarter inch to two inches (8–60 millimeters), krill generally resemble primitive decapods such as shrimp and lobsters. Most are a brilliant red, and sailors will refer to the ocean as "tomato soup" when the krill are numerous enough to color the surface. Krill may be visible at night as well because of their bright luminescence. During the months from January until April in the Antarctic, krill are so abundant that a swarm may contain as much as 35 pounds per cubic yard (20 kilograms per cubic meter) of individual animals.

How can you tell male and female lobsters apart?

The differences between male and female lobsters can only be seen when they are turned on their backs. In the male lobster, the two swimmerets (forked appendages used for swimming) nearest the carapace (the solid shell) are hard, sharp, and bony; in the female the same swimmerets are soft and feathery. The female also has a receptical that appears as a shield wedged between the third pair of walking legs. During mating, the male deposits sperm into this receptical where it remains for as long as several months until the female uses it to fertilize her eggs as they are laid.

How are coral reefs formed?

Coral reefs grow only in warm, shallow water. The calcium carbonate skeletons of dead corals serve as a framework upon which layers of successively younger animals attach themselves. Such accumulations, combined with rising water levels, slowly lead to the formation of reefs that can be hundreds of meters deep and long. The coral animal, or polyp, has a columnar form; its lower end is attached to the hard floor of the reef; the upper end is free to extend into the water. A whole colony consists of thousands of individuals. There are two kinds of corals, hard and soft, depending on the type of skeleton secreted. The polyps of hard corals deposit around themselves a solid skeleton of calcium carbonate (chalk), so most swimmers see only the skeleton of the coral; the animal is in a cup-like formation into which it withdraws during the daytime.

What are **giant tube worms**?

These worms were found in 1977 when the submersible *Alvin* was exploring the ocean floor of the Galapagos Ridge (located 1.5 miles [2.4 kilometers] below the Pacific Ocean surface and 200 miles [322 kilometers] from the Galapagos Islands). *Riftia pachyptila* Jones, named after worm expert Meredith Jones of the Smithsonian Museum of Natural History, were discovered near the hydrothermal (hot water) ocean vents. Growing to lengths of five feet (1.5 meters), the worms lack both mouth and gut, and are topped with feathery plumes composed of over 200,000 tiny tentacles. The phenomenal growth of these worms is due to their internal food source—symbiotic bacteria, over 100 billion per ounce of tissue—that live within the worms' troposome tissues. To these troposome tissues, the tube worms transport absorbed oxygen from the water, together with carbon dioxide and hydrogen sulfide. Utilizing this supply, the bacteria living there in turn produce carbohydrates and proteins that the worms need to thrive.

This was only one of *Alvin*'s discoveries during its historic voyage. Scientists expected to find a "desert" at these ocean depths where no light penetrated. Most of the world's organisms rely on photosynthesis (the use of light to make organic compounds) at the base of their food chains. But in these depths, giant tube worms, vent crabs, and mollusks thrive because these vent communities depend on chemo-autotropic (chemically self-feeding) bacteria, which derive their life-sustaining energy from the oxidation of substances spewing from the vents, or in symbiotic relationships, such as that with the giant tube worms.

How much electricity does an **electric eel** generate?

An electric eel (*Electrophorus electricus*) has current-producing organs made up of electric plates on both sides of its vertebral column running almost its entire body length. The charge—on the average of 350 volts, but as great as 550 volts—is released by the central nervous system. The shock consists of four to eight separate charges, which last only two- to three-thousandths of a second each. These shocks, used as a defense mechanism, can be repeated up to 150 times per hour without any visible fatigue to the eel. The most powerful electric eel, found in the rivers of Brazil, Colombia, Venezuela, and Peru, produces a shock of 400 to 650 volts.

What is a mermaid's purse?

Mermaid's purses are the protective cases in which the eggs of dogfish, skates, and rays are released into the environment. The rectangular purse is leathery and has long tendrils streaming from each corner. The tendrils anchor the case to seaweed or rocks and protects the embryos during the six to nine months it takes for them to hatch. Empty cases often wash up on beaches.

How do **salmon** find the way to their **spawning grounds**?

Scientists do not know exactly how a salmon "remembers" the way back to its native stream after an ocean journey possibly lasting several years and covering several thousand miles. They agree, however, that salmon, like homing pigeons, appear to have an innate compass or "search recognition" mechanism that operates independently of astronomical or physical signs. Some scientists theorize that this internal compass uses the infinitely small electrical voltages generated by the ocean currents as they travel through the earth's magnetic field. Others believe that the salmon's homing mechanism may take its cues from the varying salinities of the water or specific smells encountered along the journey.

How many kinds of **sharks** are there and how many are dangerous?

The United Nations' Food and Agricultural Organization lists 354 species of sharks, ranging in length from six inches (15 centimeters) to 49 feet (15 meters). While 35 species are known to have attacked humans at least once, only a dozen do so on a regular basis. The relatively rare Great White shark (*Carcharodan carcharias*) is the largest predatory fish. The largest specimen accurately measured was 20 feet, 4 inches (6.2 meters) long and weighed 5,000 pounds (2,270 kilograms).

What are the main classes of **mollusk shells**?

Scientists recognize five main classes of mollusks: gastropods, bivalves, tooth shells, chitons, and cephalopods. A sixth class, Monoplacophora, was once thought to be extinct, but scientists have discovered them in very deep ocean waters. They are now considered very rare.

Most shells belong in one of two main classes: gastropods or bivalves. Three-quarters of the world's mollusks, or about 60,000 species, are classified as gastropods,

which possess one-piece shells that are usually coiled. Limpets, cones, olives, murex, cowries, and whelks belong to this class. The 11,000 species of bivalves have two-piece shells, normally hinged along one side. Clams, oysters, cockles, and mussels are some familiar bivalves.

The three minor classes have far fewer species. Scientists recognize about 500 kinds of tooth shells. These shells are tapered, hollow tubes that curve slightly so as to resemble long needles or elephant tusks, prompting some collectors to refer to them as tusk shells. The shells of chitons, of which there are about 600 species, are made up of eight separate movable plates that are kept in place by a leathery oval band called a girdle or belt. They are also called "coat of mail" shells because of their resemblence to armor. The 650 species of cephalopods are quite different from other mollusks. Some have shells that surround their soft bodies. For example, the well-known chambered nautilus inhabits a shell consisting of a series of gradually larger chambers separated by paper-thin walls. Others, such as cuttlefish and squid, have shells inside their bodies to help support them. Octopuses, another kind of cephalopod, have no shells.

REPTILES AND AMPHIBIANS

What is the difference between a reptile and an amphibian?

Reptiles are clad in scales, shields, or plates, and their toes have claws; amphibians have moist, glandular skins, and their toes lack claws. Reptile eggs have a thick, hard or parchment-like shell that protects the developing embryo from moisture loss, even on dry land. The eggs of amphibians lack this protective outer covering and are always laid in water or in damp places. Young reptiles are miniature replicas of their parents in general appearance if not always in coloration and pattern. Juvenile amphibians pass through a larval, usually aquatic, stage before they metamorphose (change in form and structure) into the adult form. Reptiles include alligators, crocodiles, turtles, and snakes. Amphibians include salamanders, toads, and frogs.

How fast can a crocodile run on land?

In smaller crocodiles, the running gait can change into a bounding gallop that can achieve speeds of two to 10 miles (three to 17 kilometers) per hour.

How is the gender of baby alligators determined?

The gender of an alligator is determined by the temperature at which the eggs are incubated. High temperatures of 90°-93°F (32°-34°C) result in males; low tempera- **281**

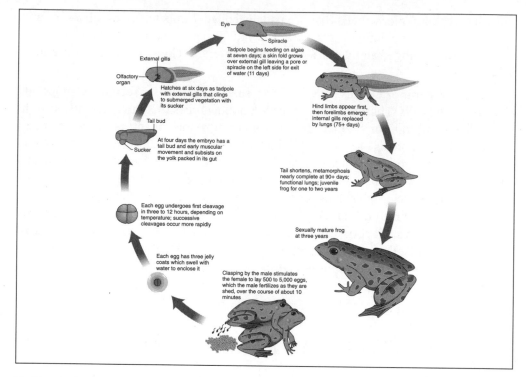

The life cycle of a frog.

tures of 82°-86°F (28°-30°C) yield females. This determination takes place during the second and third week of the two-month incubation. Further temperature fluctuations before or after this time do not alter the gender of the young. The heat from the decaying matter on top of the nest incubates the eggs.

What are a **turtle's** upper and lower **shell** called?

The turtle (order Testudines) uses its shell as a protective device. The upper shell is called the *dorsal carapace* and the lower shell is called the *ventral plastron*. The shell's sections are referred to as the *scutes*. The carapace and the plastron are joined at the sides.

Which **poisonous snakes** are native to the United States?

Snake	Average Length
Rattlesnakes	
Eastern diamondback	
(*Crotalus adamateus*)	33–65 in (84–165 cm)

Snake	Average Length
Rattlesnakes	
Western diamondback (*Crotalus atrox*)	30–65 in (76–419 cm)
Timber rattlesnake (*Crotalus horridus horridus*)	32–54 in (81–137 cm)
Prairie rattlesnake (*Crotalus viridis viridis*)	32–46 in (81–117 cm)
Great Basin rattlesnake (*Crotalus viridis lutosus*)	32–46 in (81–117 cm)
Southern Pacific rattlesnake (*Crotalus viridis helleri*)	30–48 in (76–122 cm)
Red diamond rattlesnake (*Crotalus ruber ruber*)	30–52 in (76–132 cm)
Mojave rattlesnake (*Crotalus scutulatus*)	22–40 in (56–102 cm)
Sidewinder (*Crotalus cerastes*)	18–30 in (46–76 cm)
Moccasins	
Cottonmouth (*Agkistrodon piscivorus*)	30–50 in (76–127 cm)
Copperhead (*Agkistrodon contortrix*)	24–36 in (61–91 cm)
Cantil (*Agkistrodon bilineatus*)	30–42 in (76–107 cm)
Coral snakes	
Eastern coral snake (*Micrurus fulvius*)	16–28 in (41–71 cm)

BIRDS

What names are used for **groups of birds**?

A group of birds in general is called a congregation, flight, flock, volery, or volley.

Bird	Group name
Bitterns	Siege or sedge
Budgerigars	Chatter
Chickens	Flock, run, brood, or clutch

Bird	Group name
Coots	Fleet or pod
Cormorants	Flight
Cranes	Herd or siege
Crows	Murder, clan, or hover
Curlews	Herd
Doves	Flight, flock, or dole
Ducks	Paddling, bed, brace, flock, flight, or raft
Eagles	Convocation
Geese	Gaggle or plump (on water), flock (on land), skein (in flight), or covert
Goldfinches	Charm, chattering, chirp, or drum
Grouses	Pack or brood
Gulls	Colony
Hawks	Cast
Hens	Brood or flock
Herons	Siege, sege, scattering, or sedge
Jays	Band
Larks	Exaltation, flight, or ascension
Magpies	Tiding or tittering
Mallards	Flush, sord, or sute
Nightingales	Watch
Partridges	Covey
Peacocks	Muster, ostentation, or pride
Penguins	Colony
Pheasants	Nye, brood, or nide
Pigeons	Flock or flight
Plovers	Stand, congregation, flock, or flight
Quails	Covey or bevy
Sparrows	Host
Starlings	Chattering or murmuration
Stork	Mustering
Swallows	Flight
Swans	Herd, team, bank, wedge, or bevy
Teals	Spring
Turkeys	Rafter
Turtle doves	Dule
Woodpeckers	Descent
Wrens	Herd

Which birds lay the largest and smallest eggs?

The elephant bird (*Aepyornis maximus*), an extinct flightless bird of Madagascar, also known as the giant bird or roc, laid the largest known bird eggs. Some of these eggs measured as much as 13.5 inches (34 centimeters) in length and 9.5 inches (24 cen-

timeters) in diameter. The largest egg produced by any living bird is that of the North African ostrich (*Struthio camelus*). The average size is six to eight inches (15 to 20.5 centimeters) in length and four to six inches (five to 15 centimeters) in diameter.

The smallest mature egg, measuring less than 0.39 inch (one centimeter) in length, is that of the vervain hummingbird (*Mellisuga minima*) of Jamaica.

Generally speaking, the larger the bird, the larger the egg. However, when compared with the bird's body size, the ostrich egg is one of the smallest eggs, while the hummingbird's egg is one of the largest. The Kiwi bird of New Zealand lays the largest egg, relative to body size, of any living bird. Its egg weighs up to one pound (0.5 kilogram).

Why do birds **migrate** annually?

Migratory behavior in birds is inherited; however, birds will not migrate without certain physiological and environmental stimuli. In the late summer, the decrease in sunlight stimulates the pituitary gland and the adrenal gland of migrating birds, causing them to produce the hormones prolactin and corticosterone respectively. These hormones in turn cause the birds to accumulate large amounts of fat just

Migrating snow geese.

under the skin, providing them with enough energy for the long migratory flights. The hormones also cause the birds to become restless just prior to migration. The exact time of departure, however, is dictated by not only by the decreasing sunlight and hormonal changes, but also by such conditions as the availability of food and the onset of cold weather.

The major wintering areas for North American migrating birds are the southern United States and Central America. Migrating ducks follow four major flyways south: the Atlantic flyway, the Mississippi flyway, the central flyway, and the Pacific flyway. Some bird experts propose that the birds return north to breed for several reasons: (1) Birds return to nest because there is a huge insect supply for their young. (2) The higher the earth's latitude in the summer in the Northern Hemisphere, the longer the daylight available to the parents to find food for their young. (3) Less competition exists for food and nesting sites in the north. (4) In the north, there are fewer mammal predators for nesting birds (which are particularly vulnerable during the nesting stage). (5) Birds migrate south to escape the cold weather, so they return north when the weather improves.

Which bird migrates the **greatest distance**?

The arctic tern (*Sterna paradisaea*) migrates the longest distance of any bird. They breed from subarctic regions to the very limits of land in the arctic of North America **285** and Eurasia. At the end of the northern summer, the arctic tern leaves the north on a migration of more than 11,000 miles (17,699 kilometers) to its sourthern home in Antarctica. A tern tagged in July on the arctic coast of Russia was recovered the next May near Fremantle, Australia, a record 14,000 miles (22,526 kilometers) distant.

When is Buzzard Day in Hinckley, Ohio?

Since 1957, Buzzard Day has been celebrated on the first Sunday after March 15. The buzzards are actually turkey vultures that end their yearly migration north in Hinckley, where they spend their summer. March 15 is usually the day the first "scouting" birds arrive.

When do the swallows come back to Capistrano in California?

According to legend, every year the swallows are expected to return to the Mission San Juan Capistrano, California, on St. Joseph's Day, March 19th, and depart on October 23rd, when they migrate to the Southern Hemisphere. The birds can actually arrive anytime during the month of March and leave anytime in October. The number that return each year has been declining, with the growth of the town and the large number of tourists blamed for the decrease. The legend began when a local innkeeper who considered the birds a nuisance destroyed their nests as an attempt to drive the birds away. One of the mission fathers called the swallows to the mission for shelter and the swallows have returned every year since then.

Do all birds fly?

No. Among the flightless birds, the penguins and the ratites are the best known. Ratites include emus, kiwis, ostriches, rheas, and cassowaries. They are called *ratite* because they lack a keel on the breastbone. All of these birds have wings but lost their power to fly millions of years ago. Many birds that live isolated on oceanic islands (for example, the great auk) apparently became flightless in the absence of predators and the consequent gradual disuse of their wings for escape.

Why do geese fly in formation?

Aerodynamicists have suspected that long-distance migratory birds, such as geese and swans, adapt the "V" formation in order to reduce the amount of energy needed for such long flights. According to theoretical calculations, birds flying in a "V" formation can fly some 10% farther than a lone bird can. Formation flying lessens the drag (the air pressure that pushes against the wings). The effect is similar to flying in a thermal upcurrent, where less total lift power is needed. In addition, when flying, each bird creates behind it a small area of disturbed air. Any bird flying directly behind it would be caught in this turbulence. In the "V" formation of the Canadian geese, each bird flies not directly behind the other, but aside or above the bird in front.

How fast does a **hummingbird** fly and how far does the hummingbird migrate?

Hummingbirds fly at speeds up to 71 miles (80 kilometers) per hour. Small species beat their wings 50 to 80 times per second, higher in courtship displays. For comparison, the following table lists the flight speeds of some other birds:

Bird	Speed	
	Miles per hour	Kilometers per hour
Peregrine falcon	168–217	270.3–349.1
Swift	105.6	169.9
Merganser	65	104.6
Golden plover	50–70	80.5–112.6
Mallard	40.6	65.3
Wandering albatross	33.6	54.1
Carrion crow	31.3	50.4
Herring gull	22.3–24.6	35.9–39.6
House sparrow	17.9–31.3	28.8–50.4
Woodcock	5	8

The longest migratory flight of a hummingbird documented to date is the flight of a rufous hummingbird from Ramsey Canyon, Arizona, to near Mt. Saint Helens, Washington, a distance of 1,414 miles (2,277 kilometers). Bird-banding studies are now in progress to verify that a few rufous hummingbirds do make a 11,000–11,500 mile (17,699–18,503 kilometer) journey along a super Great Basin High route, a circuit that could take a year to complete. Hummingbird studies, however, are difficult to complete because so few banded birds are recovered.

Can any bird fly upside down?

The hummingbird is the only bird that can fly upside down. They can do so because of their angled wing structure, but they can accomplish the maneuver for only a short period of time. Hummingbirds can also fly backwards in order to remove their bills from tube flowers.

Is it best to stop **feeding hummingbirds** after Labor Day?

A difference of opinion exists on this question. Some experts contend that humming-birds can become over-reliant on feeders and, by not experiencing a decrease in their food supply, will not migrate. Others, however, believe that feeders put out at migrat-ing time have little or no effect on hummingbirds leaving a particular area. Some believe that food supplies do not factor into the mechanism that triggers migration, arguing instead that decreasing daylight activates the necessary biochemical mes-sages. Others believe that a decline in another food staple, insects, is the primary cause for the move south. In addition, some birders keep feeders up during migration to help stragglers. However, until further studies are conducted on the subject, experts generally recommend deactivating feeders in Canada and extreme northern states when it is time for migration and taking them down in the extreme southern portions of the United States by mid-October to prevent birds possibly being caught in unseasonably cold weather.

What animal is closely related with the **Canary Islands**?

Ancient explorers named the Canary Islands *Canaria* from the Latin word *Canis* (dog) because of the large, fierce dogs that they found inhabiting them. The Canaries are also the namesake of canary birds, which are native to the islands.

What is unusual about the way the **emperor penguin's eggs** are incubated?

Each female emperor penguin (*Aptenodytes forsteri*) lays one large egg. Initally, both sexes share in incubating the egg by carrying it on his or her feet covered with a fold of skin. After a few days of passing the egg back and forth, the female leaves to feed in the open water of the Arctic Ocean. Balancing their eggs on their feet, the male pen-guins shuffle about the rookery, periodically huddling together for warmth during blizzards and frigid weather. If an egg is inadvertently orphaned, a male with no egg will quickly adopt it. Two months after the female's departure, the chick hatches. The male feeds it with a milky substance he regurgitates until the female returns. Now padded with blubber, the females take over feeding the chicks with fish they have stored in their crops. The females do not return to their mate, however, but wander from male to male until one allows her to take his chick. It is then the males' turn to feed in open water and restore the fat layer they lost while incubating.

What are the natural **predators** of the **penguin**?

The leopard seal (*Hydrurga leptonyx*) is the principal predator of both the adult and juvenile king penguin. The penguin may also be caught by a killer whale while swimming in open water. Eggs and chicks that are not properly guarded by adults are often devoured by skuas and sheathbills.

When was the **bald eagle** adopted as the national bird of the United States?

On June 20, 1782, the citizens of the newly independent United States of America adopted the bald or "American" eagle as their national emblem. At first the heraldic artists depicted a bird that could have been a member of any of the larger species, but by 1902, the bird portrayed on the seal of the United States of America had assumed its proper white plumage on head and tail. The choice of the bald eagle was not unanimous; Benjamin Franklin (1706–1790) preferred the wild turkey. Oftentimes a tongue-in-cheek humorist, Franklin thought the turkey a wily but brave, intelligent, and prudent bird. He viewed the eagle on the other hand as having "a bad moral character" and "not getting his living honestly," preferring instead to steal fish from hardworking fishhawks. He also found the eagle a coward who readily flees from the irritating attacks of the much smaller kingbird.

How does a **homing pigeon** find its way home?

Scientists currently have two hypotheses to explain the homing flight of pigeons. Neither has been proved to the satisfaction of all the experts. The first hypothesis involves an "odor map." The theory proposes that young pigeons learn this map by smelling different odors that reach their home in the winds from varying directions. They would, for example, learn that a certain odor is carried on winds blowing from the east. If a pigeon were transported eastward, the odor would tell it to fly westward to return home. The second hypothesis proposes that a bird may be able to extract its home's latitude and longitude from the earth's magnetic field. It may prove in the future that neither theory explains the pigeon's navigational abilities or that some synthesis of the two theories is plausible.

What is the name of the bird that perches on the black rhinoceros' back?

The bird, a relative of the starling, is called an oxpecker (a member of the Sturnidae family). Found only in Africa, the yellow-billed oxpecker (*Buphagus africanus*) is widespread over much of western and central Africa, while the red-billed oxpecker (*Buphagus erythrorhynchus*) lives in eastern Africa from the Red Sea to Natal.

Seven to eight inches (17–20 centimeters) long with a coffee-brown body, the oxpecker feeds on more than 20 species of ticks that live in the hide of the black rhinoceros (*Diceros bicornis*), also called the hook-lipped rhino. The bird spends most of **289** its time on the rhinoceros or on other animals, such as the antelope, zebra, giraffe, or buffalo. The bird has even been known to roost on the body of its host.

The relationship between the oxpecker and the rhinoceros is a type of symbiosis (a close association between two organisms in which at least one of them benefits) called mutualism. The rhinoceros' relief of its ticks and the bird's feeding clearly demonstrates mutualism (a condition in which both organisms benefit). In addition, the oxpecker, having much better eyesight than the nearsighted rhinoceros, alerts its host with its shrill cries and flight when danger approaches.

Will wild birds reject baby birds that have been **touched by humans**?

No. Contrary to popular belief, birds generally will not reject hatchlings touched by human hands. The best thing to do for newborn birds that have fallen or have been pushed out of the nest is to locate the nest as quickly as possible and gently put them back.

What can an **orphaned wild bird** eat?

An orphaned songbird needs to be fed every 20 minutes during daylight hours for several weeks. The food should be placed deep in its throat. A soft-billed bird (such as a warbler or catbird) may be given grated carrots, chopped hard-boiled eggs, cottage cheese, fresh fruit, or custard. A young hard-billed bird (such as a sparrow or finch) may be given the same food, but rape, millet, and sunflower seeds should be added to this diet when the bird becomes well-developed. A mixture of dry baby cereal and the yolk of a hard-boiled egg moistened with milk can also be given.

What species of birds will nest in **bird houses**?

In general, the only birds that will occupy birdhouses are species that normally chisel nesting holes or use such ready-made cavities as hollow trunks or holes already excavated by other species. Different species of birds require birdhouses of different dimensions, especially concerning the diameter of the entrance hole. Some birds that will nest in birdhouses are: bluebirds, chickadees, finches, flycatchers, purple martins, nuthatches, sparrows, starlings, titmice, woodpeckers, and wrens. In addition, larger birds such as some ducks and owls may be attracted.

How can **bluebirds** be encouraged to nest in a particular location?

Bluebirds may be attracted by providing nesting boxes and perches, having an area of
low or sparse vegetation, and planting nearby trees, vines, or shrubs such as blueber-

ries, honeysuckle, and crabapples. Bluebirds prefer open countryside with low under-growth. Parks, golf courses, and open lawns are their preferred habitats. In the last 40 years eastern bluebird populations have declined 90%, coinciding with the disappearing farmland, widespread use of pesticides, and an increase in nest competitors (house sparrows and European starlings). Artificial nesting boxes sometimes provide more secure nesting places than do natural nest sites, because artificial structures can be built to resist predators. Bluebird boxes can be made with entrance holes small enough to exclude starlings (1.5 inches [4 centimeters] in diameter) and can have special raccoon guards on mounting poles. Mounted three to six feet (one to two meters) above ground to discourage predators, the nesting boxes should be no closer together than 100 feet (30 meters). The box should have a tree within 50 feet (15 meters) so that the fledglings can perch. The box should have a 4-inch by 4-inch floor (10.6 by 10.6 centimeter), walls eight to 12 inches (20–30.5 centimeters) in height, with the entrance hole six to 10 inches (15–25.5 centimeters) above the floor.

MAMMALS

Which mammal has the shortest **gestation period**? Which one has the longest?

Gestation is the period of time between fertilization and birth in oviparous animals. The shortest gestation period known is 12 to 13 days, shared by three marsupials: the American or Virginian opossum (*Didelphis marsupialis*); the rare water opossum, or yapok (*Chironectes minimus*) of central and northern South America; and the eastern native cat (*Dasyurus viverrinus*) of Australia. The young of each of these marsupials are born while still immature and complete their development in the ventral pouch of their mother. While 12 to 13 days is the average, the gestation period is sometimes as short as eight days. The longest gestation period for a mammal is that of the African elephant (*Loxodonta africana*) with an average of 660 days, and a maximum of 760 days.

What names are used for **groups** or **companies** of **mammals**?

Mammal	Group name
Antelopes	Herd
Apes	Shrewdness
Asses	Pace, drove, or herd
Baboons	Troop
Bears	Sloth
Beavers	Family or colony
Boars	Sounder
Buffaloes	Troop, herd, or gang

Mammal	Group name
Camels	Flock, train, or caravan
Caribou	Herd
Cattle	Drove or herd
Deer	Herd or leash
Elephants	Herd
Elks	Gang or herd
Foxes	Cloud, skulk, or troop
Giraffes	Herd, corps, or troop
Goats	Flock, trip, herd, or tribe
Gorillas	Band
Horses	Haras, stable, remuda, stud, herd, string, field, set, team, or stable
Jackrabbits	Husk
Kangaroos	Troop, mob, or herd
Leopards	Leap
Lions	Pride, troop, flock, sawt, or souse
Mice	Nest
Monkeys	Troop or cartload
Moose	Herd
Mules	Barren or span
Oxen	Team, yoke, drove, or herd
Porpoises	School, crowd, herd, shoal, or gam
Reindeer	Herd
Rhinoceri	Crash
Seals	Pod, herd, trip, rookery, or harem
Sheep	Flock, hirsel, drove, trip, or pack
Squirrels	Dray
Swine	Sounder, drift, herd, or trip
Walruses	Pod or herd
Weasels	Pack, colony, gam, herd, pod, or school
Whales	School, gam, mob, pod, or herd
Wolves	Rout, route, or pack
Zebras	Herd

How does the **breath-holding capability** of a human compare with other mammals?

Mammal	Average time in minutes
Human	1
Polar bear	1.5
Pearl diver (human)	2.5
Sea otter	5

Mammal	Average time in minutes
Platypus	10
Muskrat	12
Hippopotamus	15
Sea cow	16
Beaver	20
Porpoise	15
Seal	15 to 28
Greenland whale	60
Sperm whale	90
Bottlenose whale	120

How does a human's **heartbeat** compare with those of other mammals?

Mammal	Resting Heart Rate (beats per minute)
Human	75
Horse	48
Cow	45–60
Dog	90–100
Rat	120
Mouse	498

Do any **mammals fly**?

Bats (order Chiroptera with 986 species) are the only truly flying mammals, although several gliding mammals are referred to as "flying" (such as flying squirrel and flying lemur). The "wings" of bats are double membranes of skin stretching from the sides of the body to the hind legs and tail, and are actually skin extensions of the back and belly. The wing membranes are supported by the elongated fingers of the forelimbs (or arms). Nocturnal (active at night), ranging in length from 1.5 inches (25 millimeters) to 1.3 feet (40.6 centimeters), and living in caves or crevices, bats inhabit most of the temperate and tropical regions of both hemispheres. The majority of species feed on insects and fruit, while some tropical species eat pollen and nectar of flowers, and insects found inside them. Moderate-sized species usually prey on small mammals, birds, lizards, and frogs, and some eat fish. But true vampire bats (three species) eat the blood of animals by making an incision in the animal's skin—from these bats, animals can contract rabies. Most bats do not find their way around by sight but have evolved a sonar system, called "echolocation," for locating solid objects. Bats emit **293** vocal sounds through the nose or mouth while flying. These sounds, usually above the human hearing range, are reflected back as echoes. This method enables bats, when flying in darkness, to avoid solid objects and to locate the position of flying insects. Bats have the most acute sense of hearing of any land animal, hearing frequencies as high as 120 to 210 kilohertz. The highest frequency humans can hear is 20 kilohertz.

What are some animals that have **pouches**?

Marsupials (meaning "pouched" animals) differ from all other living mammals in their anatomical and physiological features of reproduction. Most female marsupials—kangaroos, bandicoots, wombats, banded anteaters, koalas, opossums, wallabies, tasmanian devils, etc.—possess an abdominal pouch (called a marsupium), in which their young are carried. In some small terrestrial marsupials, however, the marsupium is not a true pouch but merely a fold of skin around the mammae (milk nipples).

The short gestation period in marsupials (in comparison to other similarly sized mammals) allows their young to be born in an "undeveloped" state. Consequently, these animals have been viewed as "primitive" or second-class mammals. However, some now see that the reproductive process of marsupials has an advantage over that of placental mammals. A female marsupial invests relatively few resources during the brief gestation period, more so during the lactation (nursing period) when the young are in the marsupium. If the female marsupial loses its young, it can conceive again sooner than a placental mammal in a comparable situation.

How long do **wombats** live and what do they eat?

Native to Australia and Tasmania, the common wombat or coarse-haired wombat (*Vombatus ursinus*) lives between five and 26 years (26 years in zoos). It dines mostly on grasses, roots, mushrooms, fresh shoots, and herbaceous plants. A wombat looks like a small bear in appearance, has a thick heavy body ranging from 2.3 to 4 feet (70 to 120 centimeters) and weighs 33 to 77 pounds (15 to 35 kilograms). Its rough fur ranges from yellowish buff, to gray, to dark brown or black. This marsupial resembles a rodent in its manner of feeding and in its tooth structure—all its teeth are rootless and ever growing to compensate for their wear. Shy, it lives in a burrow and is an active digger.

What freshwater mammal is **venomous**?

The male duck-billed platypus (*Ornithorhynchus anatinus*) has venomous spurs located on its hind legs. When threatened, the animal will drive them into skin of a potential enemy, inflicting a painful sting. The venom this action releases is relatively
mild and generally not harmful to humans.

Which **mammals lay eggs** and **suckle** their young?

The duck-billed platypus (*Ornithorhynchus anatinus*), the short-nosed echidna or spiny anteater (*Tachyglossus aculeatus*), and the long-nosed echidna (*Zaglossus bruijni*), indigenous to Australia, Tasmania, and New Guinea, are the only three species of mammals that lay eggs (a non-mammalian feature) but suckle their young (a mammalian feature). These mammals (order Monotremata) resemble reptiles in that they lay rubbery shell-covered eggs that are incubated and hatched outside the mother's body. In addition, they resemble reptiles in their digestive, reproductive, and excretory systems, and in a number of anatomical details (eye structure, presence of certain skull bones, pectoral [shoulder] girdle and rib and vertebral structures). They are, however, classed as mammals because they have fur and a four-chambered heart, nurse their young from gland milk, are warm-blooded, and have some mammalian skeletal features.

How deep do **marine mammals** dive?

Below are listed the maximum depths and the longest durations of time underwater by various aquatic mammals:

Mammal	Maximum depth Feet	Meters	Maximum time underwater
Weddell seal	1,968	600	70 minutes
Porpoise	984	300	6 minutes
Bottle-nosed whale	1,476	450	120 minutes
Fin whale	1,148	350	20 minutes
Sperm whale	>6,562	>2,000	75–90 minutes

How do the **great whales** compare in weight and length?

Whale	Average weight Tons	Kilograms	Greatest length Feet	Meters
Sperm	35	31,752	59	18
Blue	84	76,204	98.4	30
Finback	50	45,360	82	25
Humpback	33	29,937	49.2	15
Right	50 (est.)	45,360 (est.)	55.7	17
Sei	17	15,422	49.2	15
Gray	20	18,144	39.3	12
Bowhead	50	45,360	59	18
Bryde's	17	15,422	49.2	15
Minke	10	9,072	29.5	9

295

What is the difference between porpoises and dolphins?

Marine dolphins (family Delphinidae) and porpoises (family Phocoenidae) consist of about 40 species. The chief differences between dolphins and porpoises occur in the snout and teeth. True dolphins have a beak-like snout and cone-shaped teeth. True porpoises have a rounded snout and flat or spade-shaped teeth.

What is the name of the **seal-like animal** in Florida?

The West Indian manatee (*Trichechus manatus*), in the winter, moves to more temperate parts of Florida, such as the warm headwaters of the Crystal and Homosassa rivers in central Florida or the tropical waters of southern Florida. When the air temperature rises to 50°F (10°C), it will wander back along the Gulf coast and up the Atlantic coast as far as Virginia. Long-range offshore migrations to the coast of Guyana and South America have been documented. This large, plant-eating, water mammal may have been the inspiration for the mermaid legend. In 1893, when the population of manatees in Florida was reduced to several thousand, the state gave it legal protection from being hunted or commercially exploited. However, many animals continue to be killed or injured by the encroachment of humans. Entrapment in locks and dams, collisions with barges and power boat propellers, etc., cause at least 30% of the manatee deaths, which total 125 to 130 annually.

What is the only **four-horned animal** in the world?

The four-horned antelope (*Tetracerus quadricornis*) is a native of central India. The males have two short horns, usually four inches (10 centimeters) in length, between their ears, and an even shorter pair, one to two inches (2.5 to five centimeters) long, between the brow ridges over their eyes. Not all males have four horns, and in some the second pair eventually falls off. The females have no horns at all.

How many **horses** are there in the world?

According to Dr. D. Fielding of the Edinburgh School of Agriculture (in Edinburgh, United Kingdom) the number of horses worldwide is 65,292,000, the number of donkeys is 41,599,000, and the number of mules is 15,462,000.

What is **Przewalski's horse**?

This native of Mongolia and northeastern China is the last truly wild horse species. Named for Nikolai Przewalski (1839–1888), the Russian colonel who reported its existence in 1870, Przewalski's horse (*Equus przewalskii*) is a stocky, short-legged animal with a dun-colored coat, a pale muzzle and belly, and dark legs, mane, and tail. Its short mane is bristly and erect. This horse has the unusual feature of possessing 66 chromosomes rather then the customary 64 found in a domestic horse. Przewalski's horse was last seen in the wild in 1968 and is believed to be extinct in the wild, although 1,000 or so survive in zoos and wildlife parks.

In June 1994, a small herd bred in captivity was returned to the wild in Mongolia. They were kept in large enclosures for two years while they adjusted to the harsh climate. The herd is flourishing and is expected to reach a self-sustaining population by the year 2000.

Why were **Clydesdale horses** used as war horses?

The Clydesdales were among a group of European horses referred to as the "Great Horses," which were specifically bred to carry the massively armored knights of the Middle Ages. These animals had to be strong enough to carry a man wearing as much as 100 pounds (45 kilograms) of armor as well as up to 80 pounds (36 kilograms) of armor on their own bodies. However, the invention of the musket quickly ended the use of Clydesdales and other Great Horses on the battlefield as speed and maneuverability became more important than strength.

How many letters are permissible in the name of a thoroughbred horse?

Before the name of a thoroughbred can become "official" it must be submitted to the Jockey Club for approval. One of their requirements limits the name to not more than three pronounceable words with a maximum of eighteen letters.

What is the difference between an **African elephant** and an **Indian elephant**?

The African elephant (*Loxodonta africana*) is the largest living land animal, weighing up to 8.25 tons (7,500 kilograms) and standing 10 to 13 feet (three to four meters) at the shoulder. The Indian elephant (*Elephas maximus*) weighs about six tons (5,500 kilograms) with a shoulder height of 10 feet (three meters). Other differences are:

African elephant	Indian elephant
Larger ears	Smaller ears
Gestation period of about 670 days	Gestation period of about 610 days
Ear tops turn backwards	Ear tops turn forwards
Concave back	Convex back
Three toenails on hind feet	Four toenails on hind feet
Larger tusks	Smaller tusks
Two finger-like lips at tips of trunk	One lip at tip of trunk

What is the difference between a **pig** and a **hog**?

In the United States, the term "pig" refers to younger domesticated swine weighing less than 120 pounds (50 kilograms), while the term "hog" refers to older swine weighing more than this. In Great Britain all domesticated swine are referred to as pigs.

Is there a **cat** that lives in the **desert**?

The sand cat (*Felis margarita*) is the only member of the cat family tied directly to desert regions. Found in North Africa, the Arabian peninsula, and the deserts of Turkmenistan in Uzbekistan, western Pakistan, the sand cat has adapted to extremely arid desert areas. The padding on the soles of its feet is well-suited to the loose sandy soil, and it can live without drinking "free" water. Having sandy or grayish-ochre dense fur, its body length is 17.5 to 22 inches (45 to 57 centimeters). Mainly nocturnal (active at night) the cat feeds on rodents, hares, birds, and reptiles.

The Chinese desert cat (*Felis bieti*) does not live in the desert as its name implies, but inhabits the steppe country and mountains. Likewise the Asiatic desert cat (*Felis silvestris ornata*) inhabits the open plains of India, Pakistan, Iran, and Asiatic Russia.

What other names are used for a **cougar**?

A cougar is also known as a puma, painter, screamer, mountain lion, silver ghost, and catamount.

How long does a **gray wolf** live?

The gray wolf (*Canis lupus*), also known as the timber wolf, is the largest and most widespread species of the family Canidae. It can live in the wild for less than 10 years, but under human care, up to 20 years. In many areas, however, it has been hunted and killed because it is believed to pose a threat to humans and domesticated animals (cattle, sheep, and reindeer). It may soon suffer the fate of the red wolf (*Canis rufus*), which once flourished in the southeast and south central United States. The red wolf

Why are Dalmatians "firehouse dogs"?

Before automobiles, coaches and carriages were often accompanied by dogs that kept horses company and guarded them from theft. Dalmatians were particularly well known for the strong bond they formed with horses, and firemen, who often owned the strongest and speediest horses in the area, kept the dogs at the station to deter horse thieves. Although fire engines have replaced horses, Dalmatians have remained a part of firehouse life, both for the appeal of these beautiful dogs and for their nostalgic tie to the past.

has been declared biologically extinct in the wild, now existing in captivity and in a small reintroduced population of captive-bred animals in North Carolina. The endangered gray wolf is declining faster in the New World than in the Old. In the United States, it is limited to Alaska (10,000), Northern Minnesota (1,200), and Isle Royale, Michigan (20), with perhaps a few packs in Wisconsin, northern Michigan, and the Rocky Mountain area; in Canada, they number 15,000. Strongly social, living in packs, and weighing between 75 and 175 pounds (43 to 80 kilograms), in physical appearance the gray wolf resembles a large domestic dog, such as the Alaskan malamute.

Which **bear** lives in a **tropical rain forest**?

The Malayan sun bear (*Ursus malayanus*) is one of the rarest animals in the tropical forests of Sumatra, Malay Peninsula, Borneo, Burma, Thailand, and southern China. The smallest bear, with a length of 3.3 to 4.6 feet (one to 1.4 meters) and weighing 60 to 143 pounds (27 to 65 kilograms), it has a strong, stocky body and black coloring. With powerful paws having long, curved claws to help it climb trees in the dense forests, it is an expert tree climber. The sun bear tears at tree bark to expose insects, larvae, and the nests of bees and termites. Fruit, coconut palm, and small rodents, too, are part of its diet. Sleeping and sunbathing during the day, it is active at night. Unusually shy and retiring, cautious and intelligent, the sun bear is declining in population as the forests are being destroyed.

Do **camels** store water in their humps?

The hump or humps do not store water, since they are fat reservoirs. The ability to go long periods without drinking water, up to ten months if there is plenty of green vegetation and dew to feed on, results from a number of physiological adaptations. One major factor is that camels can lose up to 40% of their body weight with no ill effects. **299**

A camel can also withstand a variation of its body temperature by as much as 14°F (-10°C). A camel can drink 30 gallons of water in ten minutes and up to 50 gallons over several hours. A one-humped camel is called a dromedary or Arabian camel; a Bactrian camel has two humps and lives in the wild on the Gobi desert. Today, the Bactrian is confined to Asia, while most of the Arabian camels are on African soil.

How many quills does a **porcupine** have?

For its defensive weapon, the average porcupine has about 30,000 quills or specialized hairs, comparable in hardness and flexibility to slivers of celluloid and so sharply pointed they can penetrate any hide. The quills that do the most damage are the short ones that stud the porcupine's muscular tail. With a few lashes, the porcupine can send a rain of quills that have tiny scale-like barbs into the skin of its adversary. The quills work their way inward because of their barbs and the involuntary muscular action of the victim. Sometimes the quills can work themselves out, but other times the quills pierce vital organs, and the victim dies.

Slow-footed and stocky, porcupines spend much of their time in the trees, using their formidable incisors to strip off bark and foliage for their food, and supplement their diets with fruits and grasses. Porcupines have a ravenous appetite for salt; as herbivores (plant-eating animals) their diets have insufficient salt. So natural salt licks, animal bones left by carnivores (meat-eating animals), yellow pond lilies, and other items having a high salt content (including paints, plywood adhesives, and the sweated-on clothing of humans) have a strong appeal to porcupines.

Why do **nine-banded armadillos** always have four offspring of the same sex?

A nine-banded armadillo.

The one feature that distinguishes the nine-banded armadillo (*Dasypus novem-cinctus*) is that the female almost always gives birth to four young of the same sex. This consistency results from the division of the one fertilized egg into four parts to produce quadruplets.

What is a **capybara**?

The capybara (*Hydrochoerus hydrochoeris*) is the largest of all living rodents. Also called the water hog, water pig, water cary, or carpincho, it looks like a huge guinea pig. Its body length can be 3.25 to 4.5 feet (one to 1.3 meters), and it usually weighs between 120 and 130 pounds (54 to 59 kilograms) or more. A native of northern South America, this rodent leads a semi-aquatic life, feeding on aquatic plants and grasses. A subspecies, native to Panama, is smaller and weighs between 60 and 75 pounds (27 to 34 kilograms).

What is **chamois**?

The chamois (of the family Bovidae) is a goat-like animal living in the mountainous areas of Spain, central Europe (the Alps and Apennines), south central Europe, the Balkans, Asia Minor, and the Caucasus. Agile and surefooted, with acute senses, it can jump 6.5 feet (two meters) in height and 19.5 feet (six meters) in distance, and run at speeds of 31 miles (50 kilometers) per hour. Its skin has been made into "shammy" leather for cleaning glass and polishing automobiles, although more commonly today the shammy or chamois skins sold are simply specially treated sheepskin.

What is the chemical composition of a **skunk's spray**?

The chief odorous components of the spray have been identified as crotyl mercaptan, isopentyl mercaptan, and methyl crotyl disulfide in the ratio of 4:4:3. The liquid is an oily, pale-yellow, foul-smelling spray that can cause severe eye inflammation. This defensive weapon is discharged from two tiny nipples located just inside the skunk's anus—either as a fine spray or a short stream of rain-sized drops. Although the liquid's range is 6.5 to 10 feet (two to three meters), its smell can be detected 1.5 miles (2.5 kilometers) downwind.

PETS

What are the different **classifications of dogs**?

Dogs are divided into groups according to the purpose for which they have been bred.

Group	Purpose	Representative breeds
Sporting dogs	Retrieving game birds and water fowl	Cocker spaniel, English setter, English springer spaniel, golden retriever, Irish setter, Labradorretriever, pointer
Hounds	Hunting	Basenji, beagle, dachshund, foxhound, greyhound, saluki, Rhodesian ridgeback

Group	Purpose	Representative breeds
Terriers	Hunting small animals such as rats and foxes	Airedale terrier, Bedlington terrier, bull terrier, fox terrier, miniature schnauzer, Scottish terrier, Skye terrier, West Highland white terrier
Toy dogs	Small companions or lap dogs	Chihuahua, Maltese, Pekingese, Pomeranian, pug, Shih Tzu, Yorkshire terrier
Herding dogs	Protect sheep and other livestock	Australian cattle dog, bouviers des Flandres, collie, German shepherd, Hungarian puli, Old English sheepdog, Welsh corgi
Working dogs	Herding, rescue, and sled dogs	Alaskan malamute, boxer, Doberman pinscher, great Dane, mastiff, St. Bernard, Siberian husky
Non-sporting dogs	No specific purpose, not toys	Boston terrier, bulldog, Dalmatian, Japanese akita, keeshond, Lhasa apso, poodle

What is the **oldest breed** of dog?

Dogs are the oldest domestic animal, originating 12,000 to 14,000 years ago. They are believed to be descendants of wild canines, most likely wolves, which began to frequent human settlements where food was more readily available. The more aggressive canines were probably driven off or killed, while the less dangerous ones were kept to guard, hunt, and later herd other domesticated animals, such as sheep. Attempts at selectively breeding desirable traits likely began soon after.

Wolves, like this red wolf, are believed to be the ancestors of domestic dogs.

The oldest pure-bred dog is believed to be the Saluki. Sumerian rock carvings in Mesopotamia that date to about 7000 B.C.E. depict dogs bearing a striking resemblance to the Saluki. The dogs are 23 to 28 inches (58 to 71 centimeters) tall with a long, narrow head. The coat is smooth and silky and can be white, cream, fawn, gold, red, grizzle (bluish-gray) and tan, black and tan, or tricolor (white, black, and tan). The tail is long and feathered. The Saluki has remarkable sight and tremendous speed, which makes him an excellent hunter.

The oldest American pure-bred dog is the American Foxhound. It descends from a pack of foxhounds belonging to an Englishman named Robert Brooke who settled in Maryland in 1650. These dogs were crossed with other strains imported from England, Ireland, and France to develop the American Foxhound. This dog stands 22 to 25 inches (56 to 63.5 centimeters) tall. It has a long, slightly domed head, with a straight, squared-out muzzle. The coat is of medium length and can be any color. They are used primarily for hunting.

Which breed of dogs are **least likely to bite**?

1. Golden retriever
2. Labrador retriever
3. Shetland sheepdog
4. Old English sheepdog
5. Welsh terrier
6. Yorkshire terrier
7. Beagle
8. Dalmatian
9. Pointer

Which breeds of dogs are the **most dangerous**?

The dog breeds responsible for the most fatal attacks on people between 1979 and 1989 are:

Breed	Known fatal attacks
Pit bull	37
German shepherd	9
Husky	7
Malamute	6
Doberman pinscher	5
Rottweiler	5
Great Dane	4
St. Bernard	4

Which dogs are the **most easily trained**?

The top ten dogs rated according to their learning ability are:

1. Border collie
2. Poodle
3. German shepherd
4. Golden retriever
5. Doberman pinscher
6. Shetland sheepdog

7. Labrador retriever

8. Papillon

9. Rottweiler

10. Australian cattle dog

What breeds of dogs **do not shed**?

Poodles, Kerry blue terriers, and schnauzers do not shed.

Which breed is known as the **wrinkled dog**?

The shar-pei, or Chinese fighting dog, is covered with folds of loose skin. It stands 18 to 20 inches (46 to 51 centimeters) and weighs up to 50 pounds (22.5 kilograms). Its solid-colored coat can be black, red, fawn, or cream. The dog originated in Tibet or the northern provinces of China some 2,000 years ago. The People's Republic of China put such a high tax on shar-peis that few people could afford to keep them, and the dog was in danger of extinction. A few specimens were smuggled out ofChina, however, and the breed has made a comeback in the United States, Canada, and the United Kingdom. Although bred as a fighting dog, the shar-pei is generally an amiable dog.

Which breed is known as the **voiceless dog**?

The basenji dog does not bark. When happy, it will make an appealing sound described as something between a chortle and a yodel. It also snarls and growls on occasion. One of the oldest breeds of dogs, and originating in central Africa, the basenji was often given as a present to the Pharaohs of ancient Egypt. Following the decline of the Egyptian civilization, the basenji was still valued in central Africa for its hunting prowess and its silence. The dog was rediscovered by English explorers in the 19th century, although it was not widely bred until the 1940s.

The basenji is a small, lightly built dog with a flat skull and a long rounded muzzle. It measures 16 to 17 inches (40 to 43 centimeters) in height at the shoulder and weighs 22 to 24 pounds (10 to 11 kilograms). The coat is short and silky in texture. The feet, chest, and tail tip are white; the rest of the coat is chestnut red, black, or black and tan.

Where did the **pug dog** originate?

The pug's true origin is unknown, but it has existed in China, its earliest known source, for 1,800 years. A popular pet in Buddhist monasteries in Tibet, it next appeared in Japan and then in Europe. It probably was introduced into Holland by the

> ## How is the age of a dog or cat computed in human years?
>
> When a cat is one year old, it is about 20 years old in human years. Each additional year is multiplied by four. Another source counts the age of a cat slightly differently. At age one, a cat's age equals 16 human years. At age two, a cat's age is 24 human years. Each additional year is multiplied by four.
>
> When a dog is one year old, it is about 15 years old in human years. At age two it is about 24; after age two, each additional year is multiplied by four.

traders of the Dutch East India Company. The name "pug dog" may have come from the dog's facial resemblance to a marmoset monkey. This popular pet in the 1700s was called a "pug," so the term "pug dog" distinguished the dog from the "pug" monkey.

A pug has a square, short compact body, either silver or apricot-fawn in color. Its muzzle is black, short, blunt, and square; its average weight is 14 to 18 pounds (6.4 to 8.2 kilograms). The pug is often described by the motto "Multum in Parvo"—a lot of dog in a small space.

What is the **rarest breed** of dog?

The Tahltan bear dog, of which only a few remain, is thought to be the rarest dog. In danger of extinction, this breed was once used by the Tahltan Indians of western Canada to hunt bear, lynx, and porcupine.

What was the **contribution to medical science** of a dog named **Marjorie**?

Marjorie was a diabetic black-and-white mongrel that was the first creature to be kept alive by insulin (a substance that controls the level of sugar in the blood).

What is the newest **method of tagging** a dog?

There is now a computer-age dog tag. A microchip is implanted between the dog's shoulder blades. The semiconductor carries a 10-digit code, which can be read by a **305** scanner. When the pet is found, the code can be phoned into Infopet, the inventor of the system. Infopet's computers keep such data as the dog's license number, medical condition, and the owner's phone number.

Do **dogs and cats** have good **memories**?

Dogs do have long-term memories, especially for those whom they love. Cats have a memory for things that are important to their lives. Some cats seem to have extraordinary "memories" for finding places. Taken away from their homes, they seem able to remember where they live. The key to this "homing" ability could be a built-in celestial navigation, similar to that used by birds, or the cats' navigational ability could be attributed to the cats' sensitivity to Earth's magnetic fields. When magnets are attached to cats, their normal navigational skills are disrupted.

What is the **original breed of domestic cat** in the United States?

The American shorthair is believed by some naturalists to be the original domestic cat in America. It is descended from cats brought to the New World from Europe by the early settlers. The cats readily adapted to their new environment. Selective breeding to enhance the best traits began early in the 20th century.

The American shorthair is a very athletic cat with a lithe, powerful body, excellent for stalking and killing prey. Its legs are long, heavy, and muscular, ideal for leaping and for coping with all kinds of terrain. The fur, in a wide variety of color and coat patterns, is thick enough to protect the animal from moisture and cold, but short enough to resist matting and snagging.

Although this cat makes an excellent house pet and companion, it remains very self-sufficient. Its hunting instinct is so strong that it exercises the skill even when well-provided with food. The American shorthair is the only true "working cat" in the United States.

What is a **tabby cat**?

"Tabby," the basic feline coat pattern, dates back to the time before cats were domesticated. The tabby coat is an excellent form of camouflage. Each hair has two or three dark and light bands, with the tip always dark. There are four variations on the basic tabby pattern.

The mackerel (also called striped or tiger) tabby has a dark line running down the back from the head to the base of the tail, with several stripes branching down the sides. The legs have stripes, and the tail has even rings with a dark tip. There are two rows of dark spots on the stomach. Above the eyes is a mark shaped like an "M" and dark lines run back to the ears. Two dark necklace-like bands appear on the chest.

The blotched, or classic, tabby markings seem to be the closest to those found in the wild. The markings on the head, legs, tail, and stomach are the same as the mackerel tabby. The major difference is that the blotched tabby has dark patches on the shoulder and side, rimmed by one or several lines.

The spotted tabby has uniformly shaped round or oval dark spots all over the body and legs. The forehead has an "M" on it, and a narrow, dark line runs down the back.

The Abyssinian tabby has almost no dark markings on its body; they appear only on the forelegs, the flanks, and the tail. The hairs are banded except on the stomach, where they are light and unicolored.

What controls the formation of the color **points** in a **Siamese cat**?

The color points are due to the presence of a recessive gene, which operates at cooler temperatures, limiting the color to well-defined areas—the mask, ears, tail, lower legs, and paws—the places at the far reaches of the cardiovascular system of the cat.

There are four classic varieties of Siamese cats. Seal-points have a pale fawn to cream colored coat with seal-brown markings. Blue-points are bluish-white with slate blue markings. Chocolate-points are ivory colored with milk-chocolate brown colored markings. Lilac-points have a white coat and pinkish-gray markings. There are also some newer varieties with red, cream, and tabby points.

The Siamese originated in Thailand (once called Siam) and arrived in England in the 1880s. They are medium-sized and have long, slender, lithe bodies, with long heads and long, tapering tails. Extroverted and affectionate, Siamese are known for their loud, distinctive voices, which are impossible to ignore.

Why do **cats' eyes shine** in the dark?

A cat's eyes contain a special light-conserving mechanism called the *tapetum lucidum*, which reflects any light not absorbed as it passes through the retina of each eye. The retina gets a second chance (so to speak) to receive the light, aiding the cat's vision even more. In dim light, when the pupils of the cat's eyes are opened the widest, this glowing or shining effect occurs when light hits them at certain angles. The *tapetum lucidum*, located behind the retina, is a membrane composed of 15 layers of special, glittering cells that all together act as a mirror. The color of the glow is usually greenish or golden, but the eyes of the Siamese cat reflect a luminous ruby red.

How can pets be treated to remove skunk odor?

From a pet store, purchase one of the products specifically designed to counteract skunk odor. Most of these are of the enzyme or bacterial enzyme variety and can be used withoutwashing the pet first. A dog may also be given a bath with tomato juice, diluted vinegar, or neuthroleum-alpha, or you could try mint mouthwash, aftershave, or soap and water.

Why and how do cats purr?

Experts cannot agree on how or why cats purr, or on where the sound originates. Some think that the purr is produced by the vibration of blood in a large vein in the chest cavity. Where the vein passes through the diaphragm, the muscles around the vein contract, nipping the blood flow and setting up oscillations. These sounds are magnified by the air in the bronchial tubes and the windpipe. Others think that purring is the vibrations of membranes, called false vocal cords, located near the vocal cords. No one knows for sure why a cat purrs, but many people interpret the sound as one of contentment.

Why do cats have whiskers?

The function of a cat's whiskers is not fully understood. They are thought to have something to do with the sense of touch. Removing them can disturb a cat for some time. Some people believe that the whiskers act as antennae in the dark, enabling the cat to identify things it cannot see. The whiskers may help the cat to pinpoint the direction from which an odor is coming. In addition, the cat is thought to point some of its whiskers downwards to guide it when jumping or running over uneven terrain at night.

Which plants are poisonous to cats?

Certain common houseplants are poisonous to cats, who should not be allowed to eat the following:

Caladium (Elephant's ears)

Dieffenbachia (Dumb cane)

Euphorbia pulcherrima (Poinsettia)

Hedera (True ivy)

Mistletoe

Oleander

Philodendron

Prunus laurocerasus (Common or cherry laurel)

Rhododendron (Azalea)

Solanum capiscastrum (Winter or False Jerusalem cherry)

How much does an average adult **potbellied pig** weigh compared to a regular farm pig?

The adult Chinese potbellied pig usually weighs about 70 to 150 pounds (32 to 68 kilograms); adult farm pigs may weigh 1,200 to 1,500 pounds (544 to 680 kilograms). Chinese potbellies are an ancient breed that stand only 16 inches (40 centimeters) tall. They are very intelligent, easily house-broken, and reportedly make affectionate pets.

Which types of **birds** make the best pets?

There are several birds that make good house pets and have a reasonable life expectancy:

Bird	Life expectancy in years	Considerations
Finch	2-3	Easy care
Canary	8-10	Easy care; males sing
Budgerigar	8-15	Easy care
Cockatiel	15-20	Easy care; easy to train
Lovebird	15-20	Cute, but not easy to care for or train
Amazon parrot	50-60	Good talkers, but can be screamers
African grey parrot	50-60	Talkers; never scream

What kind of care do **tadpoles** need, and what do they eat?

Keep the frog eggs and the tadpoles that hatch from them in water at all times, changing half of the water volume no more than once a week. The best diet is probably baby cereal having a high protein content, fresh greens, and bits of egg yolk. Provide a rock island when the legs of the tadpoles appear. A five-gallon (19-liter) tank is sufficient for a half dozen tadpoles. When they mature (lose their tails and have grown legs) they should be released in a pond or by the lake shore.

What do you feed a **hermit crab**?

Hermit crabs are not particular and will eat variety of foods, including algae, beef heart, brine shrimp, earthworms, fish, flake food, fresh shrimp, scallops, tube food, and almost all other commercially prepared foods. Live, fresh, frozen, dry, or freeze-dried, it makes no difference. Hermit crabs may be fed individually two to three times a week, but be careful not to overfeed or underfeed them. Pieces of meat, such as thawed shrimp, scallops, or beef heart, may be soaked in a liquid vitamin complex and presented on the end of a toothpick to the crab. Algae, which is a part of the crab's diet in the wild, may be grown in a separate container with a few small pieces of coral or ordinary shells on the bottom. Within a few weeks, the shells will be covered with algae and may be placed in the display tank for the crabs to pick clean. Fresh spinach and lettuce may be used as a substitute for algae.

What are some unusual animals that have been **White House pets**?

Several unusual animals have resided at the White House. In 1825, the Marquis de Lafayette (1757–1834) toured America and was given an alligator by a grateful citizen. While Lafayette was the guest of President John Quincy Adams (1767–1848), the alligator took up residence in the East Room of the White House for several months. When Lafayette departed, he took his alligator with him. Mrs. John Quincy Adams also kept unusual pets: silkworms that feasted on mulberry leaves. Other residents kept a horned-toad, another a green snake, and still another a kangaroo rat. Theodore Roosevelt brought home a badger that was presented to him as he campaigned in Kansas. The Abraham Lincoln household contained rabbits and a pair of goats named Nanny and Nanko. President Calvin Coolidge kept a raccoon as a pet instead of eating it for Thanksgiving dinner, as was intended by the donors from the State of Mississippi. Given the name Rebecca, the raccoon was kept in a large pen near the President's office.

Other unusual White House pets were:

Martin Van Buren	Two tiger cubs
William Henry Harrison	Billy goat; Durham cow
Andrew Johnson	Pet mice
Theodore Roosevelt	Lion, hyena, wildcat, coyote, five bears, zebra, barn owl, snakes, lizards, roosters, raccoon
William Taft	Cow
Calvin Coolidge	Raccoons, donkey, bobcat, lion cubs, wallaby, pigmy hippo, bear

HUMAN BODY

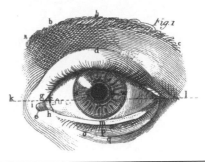

FUNCTIONS, PROCESSES, AND CHARACTERISTICS

Which **chemicals** constitute the human body?

About 24 elements are used by the body in its functions and processes.

Major elements

Element	Percentage	Function
Oxygen	65.0	Part of all major nutrients of tissues; vital to energy production
Carbon	18.5	Essential life element of proteins, carbohydrates, and fats; building blocks of cells
Hydrogen	9.5	Part of major nutrients; building blocks of cells
Nitrogen	3.3	Essential part of proteins, DNA, RNA; essential to most body functions
Calcium	1.5	Form nonliving bone parts; a messenger between cells
Phosphorous	1.0	Important to bone building; essential to cell energy

Potassium, sulfur, sodium, chlorine, and magnesium each occur at 0.35% or less. There are also traces of iron, cobalt, copper, manganese, iodine, zinc, fluorine, boron, aluminum, molybdenum, silicon, chromium, and selenium.

How many **chromosomes** are in a human body cell?

A human being normally has 46 chromosomes (23 pairs) in all but the sex cells. Half

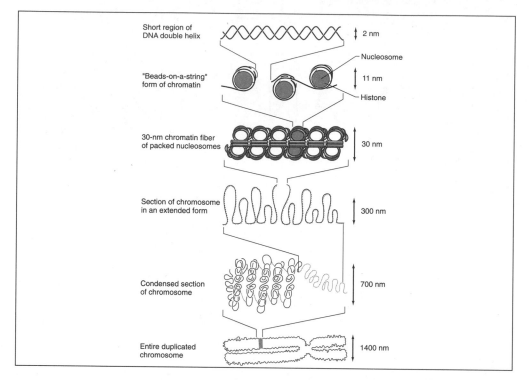

Short region of
DNA double helix — 2 nm

Nucleosome

"Beads-on-a-string"
form of chromatin — 11 nm

Histone

30-nm chromatin fiber
of packed nucleosomes — 30 nm

Section of chromosome
in an extended form — 300 nm

Condensed section
of chromosome — 700 nm

Entire duplicated
chromosome — 1400 nm

How DNA is packaged within chromosomes.

of each pair is inherited from the mother's egg; the other, from the father's sperm. When the sperm and egg unite in fertilization, they create a single cell, or zygote, with 46 chromosomes. When cell division occurs, the 46 chromosomes are duplicated; this process is repeated billions of times over, with each of the cells containing the identical set of chromosomes. Only the gametes, or sex cells, are different. In their cell division, the members of each pair of chromosomes are separated and distributed to different cells. Each gamete has only 23 chromosomes.

Chromosomes contain thousands of genes, each of which has information for a specific trait. That information is in the form of a chemical code, and the chemical compound that codes this genetic information is deoxyribonucleic acid or DNA. A gene can be seen as a sequence of DNA that is coded for a specific protein. These proteins determine specific physical traits (such as height, body shape, color of hair, eyes, skin, etc.), body chemistry (blood type, metabolic functions, etc.), and some aspects of behavior and intelligence. More than 150 human disorders are inherited, and genes are thought to determine susceptibility to many diseases.

How many cells are in the human body?

Sources give figures that vary from 50 to 75 trillion cells.

What is the **average lifespan of cells** in the human body?

Cell type	Length of time
Blood cells	
red blood cells	120 days
lymphocytes	Over 1 year
other white cells	10 hours
platelets	10 days
Bone cells	25–30 years
Brain cells	Lifetime
Colon cells	3–4 days
Skin cells	19–34 days
Spermatozoa	2–3 days
Stomach cells	2 days

How does the **immune system** work?

The immune system has two main components: white blood cells and antibodies circulating in the blood. The antigen-antibody reaction forms the basis for this immunity. When an antigen (*anti*body *gen*erator)—such as a harmful bacterium, virus, fungus, parasite, or other foreign substance—invades the body, a specific antibody is generated to attack the antigen. The antibody is produced by B lymphocytes (B cells) in the spleen or lymph nodes. An antibody may either destroy the antigen directly or it may "label" it so that a white blood cell (called a macrophage, or scavenger cell) can engulf the foreign intruder. After a human has been exposed to an antigen, a later exposure to the same antigen will produce a faster immune system reaction. The necessary antibodies will be produced more rapidly and in larger amounts. Artificial immunization uses this antigen-antibody reaction to protect the human body from certain diseases, by exposing the body to a safe dose of antigen to produce effective antibodies as well as a "readiness" for any future attacks of the harmful antigen.

How do **T cells** differ from **B lymphocytes**?

T cells, responsible for dealing with most viruses, for handling some bacteria and fungi, and for cancer surveillance, are one of the two main classes of lymphocytes. As one variety of white blood cells, lymphocytes are part of the body's immune system; the immune system fights invading organisms that have penetrated the body's general defenses. T lymphocytes, or T cells, compose about 80% of the lymphocytes circulating in the blood. They have been "educated" in the thymus to perform particular functions. Killer T cells are sensitized to multiply when they come into contact with antigens (foreign proteins) on abnormal body cells (cells that have been invaded by

313

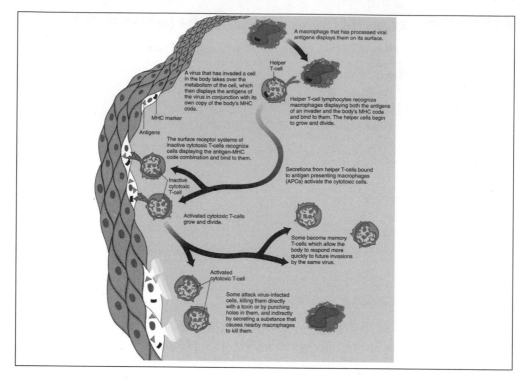

How the immune system works.

viruses, cells in transplanted tissue, or tumor cells). These killer T cells attach themselves to the abnormal cells and release chemicals (lymphokines) to destroy them. Helper T cells assist killer cells in their activities and control other aspects of the immune response. When B lymphocytes, which compose about 10% of total lymphocytes, contact the antigens on abnormal cells, the lymphocytes enlarge and divide to become plasma cells. Then the plasma cells secrete vast numbers of immunoglobulins or antibodies into the blood, which attach themselves to the surfaces of the abnormal cells, to begin a process that will lead to the destruction of the invaders.

What are **endorphins**?

Endorphins and closely related chemicals called enkephalins are part of a larger group called opiods, which have properties very much like drugs such as heroin or morphine. They can act not only as pain killers, but also can induce a sense of well-being or euphoria. Clinical applications of endorphin research include possible treatments for some forms of mental illness; treatment or control of pain for chronic pain sufferers; development of new anesthetics; and the development of nonaddictive, safe, and effective pain relievers.

Is it true that people **need less sleep** as they get older?

As a person ages, the time spent in sleeping changes. The following table shows how long a night's sleep generally lasts.

Age	Sleep time (in hours)
1–15 days	16–22
6–23 months	13
3–9 years	11
10–13 years	10
14–18 years	9
19–30 years	8
31–45 years	7.5
45–50 years	6
50+ years	5.5

What is **REM sleep**?

REM sleep is rapid eye movement sleep. It is characterized by faster breathing and heart rates than NREM (nonrapid eye movement) sleep. The eyes move rapidly, and dreaming, often with elaborate story lines, occurs. The only people who do not have REM sleep are those who have been blind from birth. REM sleep usually occurs in four to five periods, varying from five minutes to about an hour, growing progressively longer as sleep continues.

Scientists do not understand why dreaming is important, but they think the brain is either cataloging the information it picked up during the day and throwing out the data it does not want, or is creating scenarios to work through situations causing emotional distress. Regardless of its function, most people who are deprived of sleep or dreams become disoriented, unable to concentrate, and may even have hallucinations.

Why do people **snore** and how loud can snoring be?

Snoring is produced by vibrations of the soft palate, usually caused by any condition that hinders breathing through the nose. It is more common while sleeping on the back. Research has indicated that a snore can reach 69 decibels, as compared to 70–90 decibels for a pneumatic drill.

How many **calories** does a person burn while **sleeping**?

A 150-pound (68-kilogram) person burns one calorie per minute during bed rest. Approximate caloric expenditure of other activities for a person weighing 150 pounds are given below. Actual numbers may vary, depending on the vigor of the exercise, air temperature, clothing, etc.

Activity	Calories used per hour
Basketball	500
Bicycling (5½ mph)	210
(13 mph)	660
Bowling	220–270
Calisthenics	300
Digging	360–420
Gardening	200
Golfing (using power cart)	150–220
(pulling cart)	240–300
(carrying clubs)	300–360
Football	500
Handball (social)	600–660
(competitive)	>660
Hoeing	300–360
Housework	180
Jogging (5–10 mph)	500–800
Lawn mowing (power)	250
(hand)	420–480
Raking leaves	300–360
Sitting	100
Skiing (cross–country)	600–660
(downhill)	570
Snow shoveling	420–480
Square dancing	350
Standing	140
Swimming moderately	500–700
Tennis (doubles)	300–360
(singles)	420–480
Vacuuming	240–300
Volleyball	350
Walking (2 mph)	150–240
(3.5 mph)	240–300
(4 mph)	300–400
(5 mph)	420–480

Who were the doctor and patient involved in the first studies on **digestion** performed by direct observation of the patient's stomach?

Alexis St. Martin, a French Canadian, was accidentally wounded by a shotgun blast in 1822. Fortunately, William Beaumont (1785–1853), an army surgeon, was nearby and began treatment of the wound immediately. St. Martin's recuperation lasted nearly three

years, and the enormous wound healed except for a small opening leading into his stomach. A fold of flesh covered this opening; when this was pushed aside the interior of the stomach was exposed to view. Through the opening, Beaumont was able to extract and analyze gastric juice and stomach contents at various stages of digestion, observe changes in secretions, and note the stomach's muscular movements. The results of his experiments and observations formed the basis of our modern knowledge of digestion. Today, the use of x-rays and other medical instruments provides the same diagnostic function.

When a person **swallows** solid or liquid food, what prevents it from going down the windpipe?

Once food is chewed, voluntary muscles move it to the throat. In the pharynx (throat), automatic involuntary reflexes take over. The epiglottis closes over the larynx (voice box), which leads to the windpipe. A sphincter at the top of the esophagus relaxes, allowing the food to enter the digestive tract.

How long does it take food to **digest**?

The stomach holds a little under two quarts (1.9 liters) of semi-digested food that

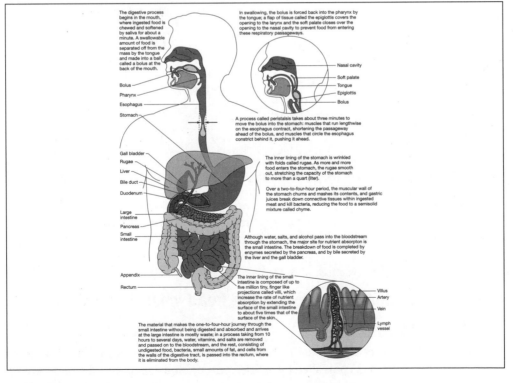

The digestive process.

stays in the stomach three to five hours. The stomach slowly releases food to the rest of the digestive tract. Fifteen hours or more after the first bite started down the alimentary canal, the final residue of the food is passed along to the rectum and is excreted through the anus as feces.

What is the length of the human **intestine**?

The small intestine is about 22 feet (seven meters) long. The large intestine is about five feet (1.5 meters) long.

Who is considered the founder of **physiology**?

Claude Bernard.

As an experimenter, Claude Bernard (1813–1878) enriched physiology by his introduction of numerous new concepts into the field. The most famous of these concepts is that of the *milieu intérieur* or internal environment. The complex functions of the various organs are closely interrelated and are all directed to maintaining the constancy of internal conditions despite external changes. All cells exist in this aqueous (blood and lymph) internal environment, which bathes the cells and provides a medium for the elementary exchange of nutrients and waste material.

Who coined the term **homeostasis**?

Walter Bradford Cannon (1871–1945), who elaborated on Claude Bernard's (1813–1878) concept of the *milieu intérieur* (interior environment), used the term *homeostasis* to describe the body's ability to maintain a relative constancy in its internal environment.

How much **heat** is **lost through the head** when a person is not wearing a hat?

Between 7% and 55% of total body heat can be lost through the head. The amount of blood going to the head is controlled by cardiac output, and the harder the body works, the more blood is circulated to the head, and the more heat is quickly radiated away.

In the United States, what is the **average height and weight** for a man and a woman?

The average female is five feet, 3.75 inches (1.62 meters) tall and weighs 135 pounds (61.24 kilograms). The average male is five feet, nine inches (1.75 meters) tall and weighs 162 pounds (73.48 kilograms). Between 1960 and 1990 the average American male became two inches (five centimeters) taller and 27 pounds (12.25 kilograms) heavier, while the average American woman also grew two inches (five centimeters) taller, but gained only one pound (0.45 kilogram).

What are **desirable weights** for men and women?

Below is listed the desirable weight ranges for adults between the ages of 25 and 59. Height is measured with one-inch (2.5-centimeter) heeled shoes on. Weight is for clothed figures. For nude weight, subtract three pounds for women and five pounds for men.

Men

Height Ft. In.		Small frame	Medium frame	Large frame
5	2	128–134	131–141	138–150
5	3	130–136	133–143	140–153
5	4	132–138	135–145	142–156
5	5	143–140	137–148	144–160
5	6	136–142	139–151	146–164
5	7	138–145	142–154	149–168
5	8	140–148	145–157	152–172
5	9	142–151	148–160	155–176
5	10	144–154	151–163	158–180
5	11	146–157	154–166	161–184
6	0	149–160	157–170	164–188
6	1	152–164	160–174	168–192
6	2	155–168	164–178	172–197
6	3	158–172	167–182	176–202
6	4	162–176	171–187	181–207

Women

Height Ft. In.		Small frame	Medium frame	Large frame
4	10	102–111	109–121	118–131
4	11	103–113	111–123	120–134

Women

Height Ft. In.		Small frame	Medium frame	Large frame
5	0	104–115	113–126	122–137
5	1	106–118	115–129	125–140
5	2	108–121	118–132	128–143
5	3	111–124	121–135	131–147
5	4	114–127	124–138	134–151
5	5	117–130	127–141	137–155
5	6	120–133	130–144	140–159
5	7	123–136	133–147	143–163
5	8	126–139	136–150	146–167
5	9	129–142	139–153	149–170
5	10	132–145	142–156	152–173
5	11	135–148	145–159	155–176
6	0	138–151	148–162	158–179

Considering that 64% of all Americans are overweight, who is the **heaviest person** that ever lived?

John Brower Minnoch (1941–1983) of Bainbridge Island, Washington, weighed 976 pounds (443 kilograms) in 1976 and was estimated to have weighed more than 1,387 pounds (630 kilograms) when he was rushed to the hospital in 1978 with heart and respiratory failure. Much of his weight was due to fluid retention. After two years on a hospital diet, he was discharged at 476 pounds (216 kilograms). He had to be readmitted, however, after reportedly gaining 197 pounds (87 kilograms) in seven days. In 1983 when he died, he weighed 798 pounds (362 kilograms).

The heaviest woman ever recorded was Rosie Carnemolla (b. 1944) of Poughkeepsie, New York, who weighed 850 pounds (386 kilograms). When Mrs. Percy Pearl Washington, who suffered from polydipsia (excessive thirst), died in a Milwaukee hospital in 1972, the scales only registered 800 pounds (363 kilograms) maximum, but she was credited with weighing 880 pounds (400 kilograms).

What are the types of human **body shapes**?

The best known example of body typing (classifying body shape in terms of physiological functioning, behavior, and disease resistance) was devised by American psychologist William Herbert Sheldon (1898–1977). Sheldon's system, known as somatotyping, distinguishes three types of body shapes, ignoring overall size: endomorph, mesomorph, and ectomorph. The extreme endomorph tends to be spherical: a round head, a large fat abdomen, weak penguinlike arms and legs, with heavy upper arms and thighs but

> ## In addition to left- or right-handedness, what other left–right preferences do people have?
>
> Most people have a preferred eye, ear, and foot. In one study, for example, 46% were strongly right-footed, while 3.9% were strongly left-footed; furthermore, 72% were strongly right-handed and 5.3% strongly left-handed. Estimates vary about the proportion of left-handers to right-handers, but it may be as high as one in ten. Some 90% of healthy adults use the right hand for writing; two-thirds favor the right hand for most activities requiring coordination and skill. There is no male-female difference in these proportions.

slender wrists and ankles. The extreme mesomorph is characterized by a massive cubical head, broad shoulders and chest, and heavy muscular arms and legs. The extreme ectomorph has a thin face, receding chin, high forehead, a thin narrow chest and abdomen, and spindly arms and legs. In Sheldon's system there are mixed body types, determined by component ratings. Sheldon assumed a close relationship between body build and behavior and temperament. This system of body typing has many critics.

Who were the congenitally joined twins who gave rise to the term **Siamese twins**?

The term "Siamese twins" originated with the appearance of Chang and Eng Bunker (1811–1874), conjoined Chinese twins born in Siam (now Thailand), who were used as a circus attraction by P. T. Barnum.

Siamese twins are identical twins joined at some point of their bodies, most commonly at the hip, chest, abdomen, buttocks, or head. Like other identical twins, they originate from a single fertilized egg; in the case of congenitally joined twins, however, the egg fails to split into two separate cell masses at the proper time. The condition is relatively rare; only about 500 cases have been reported worldwide. Surgery to separate Siamese twins is a complex task, and often results in the death of one or both of the twins.

What causes **protruding ears**?

If a fold paralleling a part of the outer roll of the ear is sparse, but not absent, the ear will protrude. This trait usually runs in certain families.

Who is the world's **oldest person**?

The greatest authenticated age to which any human has lived is 120 years, 237 days, in the case of Shigechiyo Izumi (1871–1986) of Japan.

How many people living in the United States are **centenarians**?

As of 1990, 37,306 centenarians were living in the United States. Worldwide it was estimated that there were 40,000 centenarians.

How much of the body remains after **cremation**?

During cremation, the intense heat evaporates the large quantity of water that makes up the human body and burns the soft tissues and bone, reducing the body to four to eight pounds (1.8 to 3.6 kilograms) of ash and bone fragments. On average, adult male cremains weigh 7.4 pounds (3.4 kilograms), while adult female cremains weigh 5.8 pounds (2.6 kilograms). Most modern crematoria use electric processors to quickly pulverize residual bone fragments, which will fit into the average urn.

What is **cryonic suspension**?

Suspended animation, as the long-term storage of humans is generally known, has been a topic of scientific speculation since the beginning of the modern era. Cryonic suspension, the controversial process of freezing and storing bodies for later revival, has been practiced since the late 1960s. Ordinarily, people are placed in cryonic suspension only after they are pronounced legally dead.

Opinion among scientists is divided over the feasibility of cryonic suspension. The necessary science and technology needed to revive a cryonically preserved body are not known at this time. The number of cryonics adherents is small. One cryonics group, Alcor Life Extension Foundation, had 26 bodies or heads cryonically preserved as of April 1993. Cryonics is also very expensive. In 1993, the minimum fee charged by one organization was $120,000.

BONES, MUSCLES, AND NERVES

How many bones are in the human body?

Babies are born with about 300 to 350 bones, but many of these fuse together between birth and maturity to produce an average adult total of 206. Bone counts vary accord-

ing to the method used to count them, because some systems treat as multiple bones a structure that other systems treat as a single bone with multiple parts.

Location	Number
Skull	22
Ears (pair)	6
Vertebrae	26
Sternum	3
Throat	1
Pectoral girdle	4
Arms (pair)	60
Hip bones	2
Legs (pair)	58
Total	206

What is the most commonly **broken bone**?

The clavicle (collar bone) is one of the most frequently fractured bones in the body. Fractured clavicles are caused by either a direct blow or a transmitted force resulting from a fall on the outstretched arm.

What is the only **bone** in the human body that **does not touch another bone**?

The hyoid bone is the only bone that does not touch another bone. Found above the larynx, it anchors the tongue muscles. It is also usually broken when a person is hanged or strangled, and therefore will often figure in trials concerning such crimes.

What makes **knuckles crack**?

When a person pulls quickly on his or her finger, a vacuum is created in the joint space between the bones, displacing the fluid liquid normally found in the space. The popping sound occurs when the fluids rush back into the empty gap.

What is the **funny bone**?

The funny bone is not a bone but part of the ulnar nerve located at the the back of the elbow. A bump in this area can cause a tingling sensation or it can make the forearm feel temporarily numb.

What is the **hardest substance** in the body?

Tooth enamel is the hardest substance in the body. It is composed of 96% mineral salts and 4% organic matter and water.

Why do some dentists treat the **molars** and **premolars** of children with **sealants**?

Sealants, a soft plastic coating applied to the tooth surface, can protect a child's first and second permanent molars from decay by filling in the pits and fissures where food and bacteria might otherwise accumulate. The plastic is hardened with a special light or chemical.

How many muscles are in the human body?

There are about 656 muscles in the body, although some authorities make this figure even as high as 850 muscles. No exact figure is available because authorities disagree about which are separate muscles and which ones slip off larger ones. Also, there is a wide variability from one person to another, though the general plan remains the same.

Muscles are used in three body systems. The skeletal muscles move various parts of the body, are striped or striated fibers, and are called voluntary muscles because the person controls their use. The second system includes smooth muscles found in the stomach and intestinal walls, vein and artery walls, and in various internal organs. Called involuntary muscles, they are not generally controlled by the person. The last are the cardiac muscles, or the heart muscles, containing striped and involuntary muscles.

What is the **longest muscle** in the human body?

The longest muscle is the sartorius, which runs from the waist to the knee. Its purpose is to flex the hip and knee. The largest muscle is the gluteus maximus (buttock muscle), which moves the thighbone away from the body and straightens out the hip joint.

What are the **hamstring** muscles?

There are three hamstring muscles, located at the back of the thigh. They flex the leg on the thigh, as in the process of kneeling.

Why does excessive exercise cause **muscles** to become **stiff and sore**?

During vigorous exercise, the circulatory system cannot supply oxygen to muscle fibers quickly enough. In the absense of oxygen, the muscle cells begin to produce lactic acid, which accumulates in the muscle. It is this build-up of lactic acid that causes soreness and stiffness.

What is an **ecorche**?

An ecorche is a flayed figure, a three-dimensional representation of the human body, usually made of plaster, with the envelope of skin and fat removed. Its intent is to depict the surface muscles with precise anatomical correctness.

How many **muscles** does it take to produce a **smile** and a **frown**?

Seventeen muscles are used in smiling. The average frown uses 43.

What is the name of the small fleshy mass hanging from the **back of the mouth**?

The uvula is a small, soft structure, hanging from the free edge of the soft palate. It is composed of muscle, connective tissue, and mucous membrane.

How much **force** does a **human bite** generate?

All the jaw muscles working together can close the teeth with a force as great as 55 pounds (25 kilograms) on the incisors or 200 pounds (90.7 kilograms) on the molars. A force as great as 268 pounds (122 kilograms) for molars has been reported.

What is the **largest nerve** in the body?

The sciatic nerve is the largest in the human body—about as thick as a lead pencil—0.78 inch (1.98 centimeters). It is a broad, flat nerve composed of nerve fibers, and it runs from the spinal cord down the back of the each leg.

ORGANS AND GLANDS

What is the **largest organ** in the human body?

The largest and heaviest human organ is the skin, with a total surface area of about 20 square feet (1.9 square meters) for an average person or 25 square feet (2.3 square meters) for a large person and a weight of 5.6 pounds (2.7 kilograms) on the average. Although generally it is not thought of as an organ, medically it is. An organ is a collection of various tissues integrated into a distinct structural unit and performing specific functions.

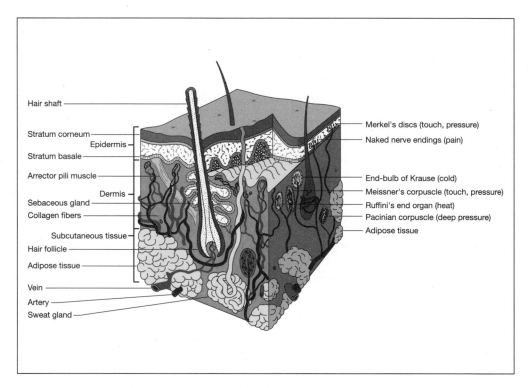

A cross section of the skin. Sensory structures are labeled on the right.

What is the basic unit of the **brain**?

Neurons are the nerve cells that are the major constituent of the brain. At birth the brain has the maximum number of neurons—20 billion to 200 billion neurons. Thousands are lost daily, never to be replaced and apparently not missed, until the cumulative loss builds up in very old age.

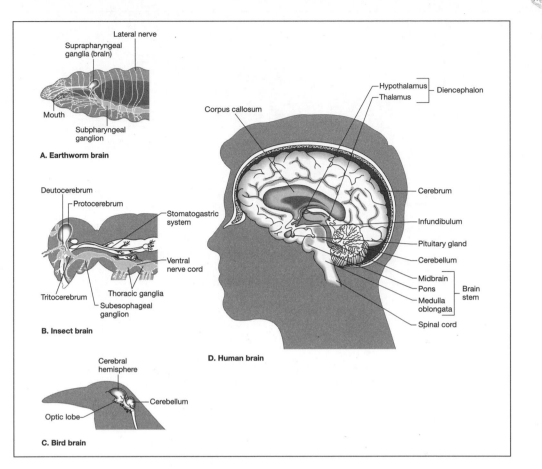

A comparison of the brains of an earthworm, an insect, a bird, and a human.

What is the average **weight** of the human **brain**?

The average human brain weighs three pounds (1.36 kilograms). The average female brain capacity is 79.3 cubic inches, slightly smaller than the male brain of 88.5 cubic inches. The largest human brains may be twice those of average size, but size has no relevance to brain performance.

Whose **brain** is **larger:** that of Neandertal or modern humans?

The capacity of the skull of "classic" Neandertal (or Neanderthal) man was often larger than that of modern humans. The capacity was between 1,350 and 1,700 cubic centimeters with the average being 1,400 to 1,450 cubic centimeters. The mean cranial

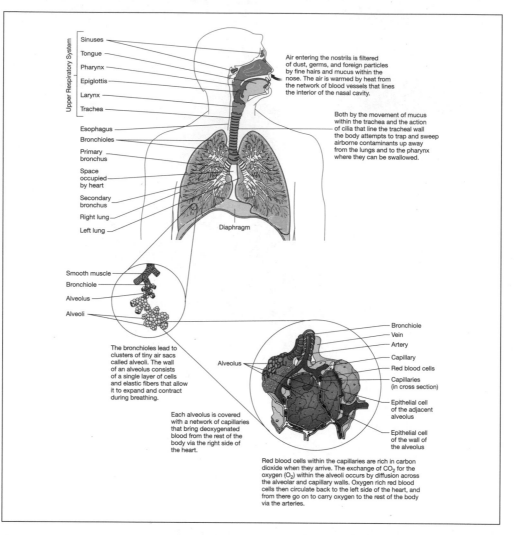

Inside the diagram:

Upper Respiratory System

Sinuses
Tongue
Pharynx
Epiglottis
Larynx
Trachea

Esophagus
Bronchioles
Primary bronchus
Space occupied by heart
Secondary bronchus
Right lung
Left lung

Diaphragm

Air entering the nostrils is filtered of dust, germs, and foreign particles by fine hairs and mucus within the nose. The air is warmed by heat from the network of blood vessels that lines the interior of the nasal cavity.

Both by the movement of mucus within the trachea and the action of cilia that line the tracheal wall the body attempts to trap and sweep airborne contaminants up away from the lungs and to the pharynx where they can be swallowed.

Smooth muscle
Bronchiole
Alveolus
Alveoli

The bronchioles lead to clusters of tiny air sacs called alveoli. The wall of an alveolus consists of a single layer of cells and elastic fibers that allow it to expand and contract during breathing.

Each alveolus is covered with a network of capillaries that bring deoxygenated blood from the rest of the body via the right side of the heart.

Alveolus

Bronchiole
Vein
Artery
Capillary
Red blood cells
Capillaries (in cross section)
Epithelial cell of the adjacent alveolus
Epithelial cell of the wall of the alveolus

Red blood cells within the capillaries are rich in carbon dioxide when they arrive. The exchange of CO_2 for the oxygen (O_2) within the alveoli occurs by diffusion across the alveolar and capillary walls. Oxygen rich red blood cells then circulate back to the left side of the heart, and from there go on to carry oxygen to the rest of the body via the arteries.

The human respiratory system.

capacity of modern man is 1,370 cubic centimeters, with a range of 950 to 2,200 cubic centimeters. However, brain size alone is not an index of intelligence.

How hard does the **heart** work?

The heart squeezes out about two ounces (71 grams) of blood at every beat and daily pumps at least 2,500 gallons (9,450 liters) of blood. On the average, the adult heart beats 70 to 75 times a minute. The rate of the heartbeat is determined in part by the size of the organism. Generally the smaller the size, the faster the heartbeat. Thus women's hearts beat six to eight beats per minute faster than men's hearts do. At birth the heart of a baby can beat as fast as 130 times per minute.

Are the **lungs** identical?

No, the right lung is shorter than the left by one inch (2.5 centimeters); however, its total capacity is greater. The right lung has three lobes, the left lung has two.

How much air does a person breathe in a lifetime?

During his or her life, the average person will breathe about 75 million gallons (284 million liters) of air. Per minute, the human body needs two gallons (7.5 liters) of air when lying down, four gallons (15 liters) when sitting, six gallons (23 liters) when walking, and 12 gallons (45 liters) or more when running.

What was the likely **purpose** of the human **appendix**?

Experts can only theorize on its use. It may have had the same purpose it does in present-day herbivores, where it harbors colonies of bacteria that help in the digestion of cellulose in plant material. Another theory suggests that tonsils and the appendix might manufacture the antibody-producing white blood cells called B lymphocytes; however, B lymphocytes could also be produced by the bone marrow. The third theory is that the appendix may "attract" body infections to localize the infection in one spot that is not critical to body functioning. The earliest surgical removal of the appendix was by Claudries Amyand (1680–1740) in England in 1736.

Which **gland** is the **largest**?

The liver is the largest gland and the second largest organ after the skin. At 2.5 to 3.3 pounds (1.1 to 1.5 kilograms) the liver is seven times larger than it needs to be to perform its estimated 500 functions. It is the main chemical factory of the body. A ducted gland that produces bile to break down fats and reduce acidity in the digestive process, the liver is also a part of the circulatory system. It cleans poisons from the blood and regulates blood composition.

What are the seven **endocrine glands**?

The major endocrine glands include the pituitary, thyroid, parathyroids, adrenals, pancreas, testes, and ovaries. These glands secrete hormones into the blood system, which generally stimulate some change in metabolic activity:

> *Pituitary*—secretes ACTH to stimulate the adrenal cortex, which produces aldosterone to control sodium and potassium reabsorption by the kidneys; FSH to stimulate gonad function and prolactin to stimulate milk secretion of breasts; TSH to stimulate thyroid gland to produce thyroxin; LH to stimulate ovulation

329

in females and testerone production in males; GH to stimulate general growth. Stores oxytocin for uterine contraction.

Thyroid gland—secretes triiodothyronine (T_3) and thyroxine (T_4) to stimulate metabolic rate, especially in growth and development, and secretes calcitonin to lower blood-calcium levels.

Parathyroids—secrete hormone PTH to increase blood-calcium levels; stimulates calcium reabsorption in kidneys.

Adrenals—secrete epinephrine and norepinephrine to help the body cope with stress, raise blood pressure, heart rate, metabolic rate, raise blood sugar levels, etc. Aldosterone secreted by the adrenal cortex maintains sodium-potassium balance in kidneys and cortisol helps the body adapt to stress, mobilizes fat, and raises blood sugar level.

Pancreas—secretes insulin to control blood sugar levels, stimulates glycogen production, fat storage, and protein synthesis. Glucagon secretion raises blood sugar level and mobilizes fat.

Ovaries and testes—secrete estrogens, progesterone, or testosterone to stimulate growth and reproductive processes.

What regulates **body temperature** in humans?

The hypothalamus controls internal body temperature by responding to sensory impulses from temperature receptors in the skin and in the deep body regions. The hypothalamus establishes a "set point" for the internal body temperature, then constantly compares this with its own actual temperature. If the two do not match, the hypothalamus activates either temperature-decreasing or temperature-increasing procedures to bring them into alignment.

BODY FLUIDS

What are the **four humors** of the body?

The four constituent humors of the body were identified as blood, phlegm, yellow bile, and black bile, originating in the heart, brain, liver, and spleen, respectively. Empedocles of Agrigentum (504–433 B.C.E.) probably originated the theory, in which he equated the body fluids to the four elements of nature: earth, fire, air, and water. These humors could determine the health of the body and the personality of the person as well. To be in good health the humors should be in harmony within the body. Ill health could be remedied by treatments to realign the humors and reestablish the harmony.

What is the **normal pH** of blood, urine, and saliva?

Normal pH of arterial blood is 7.4; pH of venous blood is about 7.35. Normal urine pH averages about 6.0. Saliva has a pH between 6.0 and 7.4.

How similar are **seawater** and **blood**?

Component	Seawater (grams/liter)	Blood (grams/liter)
Na (sodium)	10.7	3.2–3.4
K (potassium)	0.39	0.15–0.21
Ca (calcium)	0.42	0.09–0.11
Mg (magnesium)	1.34	0.012–0.036
Cl (chloride)	19.3	3.5–3.8
SO₄ (sulfate)	2.69	0.16–0.34
CO₃ (carbonate)	0.073	1.5–1.9
Protein		70.0

How much blood is in the average human body?

A man weighing 154 pounds (70 kilograms) would have about 5.5 quarts (5.2 liters) of blood. A woman weighing 110 pounds (50 kilograms) would have about 3.5 quarts (3.3 liters).

How many miles of **blood vessels** are contained in the body?

If they could be laid end to end, the blood vessels would total about 60,000 miles (96,500 kilometers).

What is the **largest artery** in the human body?

The aorta is the largest artery in the human body.

How does the body introduce **oxygen** to the **blood** and where does this happen?

Blood entering the right side of the heart (right auricle or atrium) contains carbon dioxide, a waste product of the body. The blood travels to the right ventricle, which pushes it through the pulmonary artery to the lungs. In the lungs, the carbon dioxide is removed and oxygen is added to the blood. Then the blood travels through the pul-

331

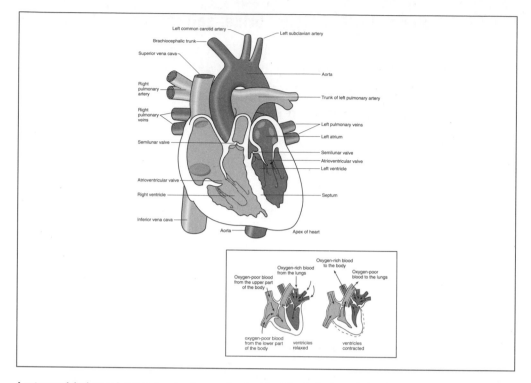

A cutaway of the human heart (top) and a diagram showing blood flow in the heart during diastole (relaxation) and systole (contraction).

monary vein carrying the fresh oxygen to the left side of the heart, first to the left auricle where it goes through a one-way valve into the left ventricle, which must push the oxygenated blood to all portions of the body (except the lungs) through a network of arteries and capillaries. The left ventricle must contract with six times the force of the right ventricle, so its muscle wall is twice as thick as the right.

Which of the major **blood types** are the most common in the United States?

Blood type	Frequency in U.S.
O+	37.4%
O-	6.6%
A+	35.7%
A-	6.3%
B+	8.5%
B-	1.5%
AB+	3.4%
AB-	0.6%

In the world, the preponderance of one blood group varies greatly by locality. Group O is generally the most common (46%), but in some areas Group A predominates.

What is the amount of **carbon dioxide** found in normal blood?

Carbon dioxide normally ranges from 19 to 50 millimeters per liter in arterial blood and 22 to 30 millimeters per liter in venous blood.

Which **blood type** is the rarest?

The rarest blood type is Bombay blood (subtype h-h), found only in a Czechoslovakian nurse in 1961 and in a brother and sister named Jalbert living in Massachusetts in 1968.

What are the **blood group combinations** that can normally be used to prove that a man is not the father of a particular child?

If the mother is	and the child is	the father can be	but not
O	O	O, A, or B	AB
O	A	A or AB	O or B
O	B	B or AB	O or A
A	O	O, A, or B	AB
A	A	any group	
A	B	B or AB	O or A
A	AB	B or AB	O or A
B	O	O, A, or B	AB
B	B	any group	
B	A	A or AB	O or B
B	AB	A or AB	O or B
AB	AB	A, B, or AB	O

No child can acquire a gene, and consequently a blood grouping, if it is not possessed by either parent.

What percent of human body weight is **water**?

The human body is 61.8% water by weight. Protein accounts for 16.6%, fat 14.9%, and nitrogen 3.3%. Other elements are present in lesser amounts.

Why do eyes tear when we work with onions?

When an onion is cut, the pierced cells release a sulfur compound, thio-propanal-s-oxide, through a series of rapid chemical reactions. This substance is irritating to the eyes.

What causes people to sweat when they eat spicy foods?

The chemical capsaicin, a component of spicy foods, causes sweating by stimulating nerve endings in the mouth and tongue that, normally, only respond to a rise in body temperature. As a result, the brain receives a false signal that body temperature has risen, and in turn launches the chain of physiological events that leads to facial sweating.

Why do some people experience a runny nose while eating?

Called prandial rhinorrhea, this condition occurs when eating stimulates the autonomic nervous system to release the compound acetylcholine. This in turn prompts the increased production of saliva, stomach acid, and nasal mucus. Usually, the spicier the meal, the greater the reaction.

SKIN, HAIR, AND NAILS

How much skin does an average person have?

The average human body is covered with about 20 square feet (two square meters) of skin. Weighing six pounds (2.7 kilograms), the skin is composed of two main layers: the epidermis (outer layer) and the dermis (inner layer). The epidermis layer is replaced continually as new cells, produced in the stratum basale, mature and are pushed to the surface by the newer cells beneath; the entire epidermis is replaced in about 27 days. The dermis, the lower layer, contains nerve endings, sweat glands, hair follicles, and blood vessels. The upper portion of the dermis has small fingerlike projections called "papillae," which extend into the upper layer. The patterns of ridges and grooves visible on the skin of the soles, palms, and fingertips are formed from the tops of the dermal papillae. The capillaries in these papillae deliver oxygen and nutrients to the epidermis cells and also function in temperature regulation.

Who first used **fingerprints** as a means of identification?

It is generally acknowledged that Francis Galton (1822–1911) was the first to classify fingerprints. However, his basic ideas were further developed by Sir Edward Henry (1850–1931), who devised a system based on the pattern of the thumb print. In 1901 in England, Henry established the first fingerprint bureau with Scotland Yard called the Fingerprint Branch.

Francis Galton.

Do identical **twins** have the same **fingerprints**?

No. Even identical twins have differences in their fingerprints, which, though subtle, can be discerned by experts.

What is the purpose of **goose-bumps**?

The puckering of the skin that takes place when goose-flesh is formed is the result of contraction of the muscle fibers in the skin. This muscular activity will produce more heat, and raise the temperature of the body.

How can **tattoos** be removed?

Tattoos can be removed by skin grafting, by infrared coagulation treatment, or by salabrasion, in which table salt is scrubbed into the anaesthetized skin. The hypertonic irritant solution disperses the tattoo pigment particles. This procedure will produce scars.

How much does human **hair grow in a year**?

Each hair grows about nine inches (23 centimeters) every year.

Does human **hair grow faster** in summer or winter?

During the summertime, the rate of human hair growth increases by about 10% to 15%. This is because warm weather enhances blood circulation to the skin and scalp, which in turn nourishes hair cells and stimulates growth. In cold weather, when blood is needed to warm internal organs, circulation to the body surface slows and hair cells grow less quickly.

How many hairs does the average person have on his or her head?

The amount of hair covering varies from one individual to another. An average person has about 100,000 hairs on their scalp. Most redheads have about 90,000 hairs, blonds have about 140,000, and brunettes fall in between these two figures. Most people shed between 50 to 100 hairs daily.

What **information** can a forensic scientist determine from a human hair?

A single strand of human hair can identify the age and sex of the owner, drugs and narcotics the individual has taken, and, through DNA evaluation and sample comparisons, from whose head the hair came.

Do the **nails** and **hair** of a **dead person** continue to **grow**?

No. Between 12 and 18 hours after death, the body begins to dry out. That causes the tips of the fingers and the skin of the face to shrink, creating the illusion that the nails and hair have grown.

How fast do **finger nails** grow?

Healthy nails grow about 0.8 inch (two centimeters) each year. The middle fingernail grows the fastest, because the longer the finger, the faster its nail growth. Fingernails grow four times as fast as toenails.

SENSES AND SENSE ORGANS

What are the **floaters** that move around on the eye?

Floaters are semi-transparent specks perceived to be floating in the field of vision. Some originate with red blood cells that have leaked out of the retina. The blood cells

swell into spheres, some forming strings, and float around the areas of the retina. Others are shadows cast by the microscopic structures in the *vitreous humor*, a jellylike substructure located behind the retina. A sudden appearance of a cloud of dark floaters, if accompanied by bright light flashes, could indicate retinal detachment.

What is the difference in the functions of the **rods and cones** found in the eyes?

Rods and cones contain photoreceptors that convert light first to chemical energy and then into electrical energy for transmission to the vision centers of the brain via the optic nerve. Rods are specialized for vision in dim light; they cannot detect color, but they are the first receptors to detect movement and register shapes. There are about 126 million rods in each eye. Cones provide acute vision, functioning best in bright daylight. They allow us to see colors and fine detai!. Cones are divided into three different types, which absorb wavelengths in the short (blue), middle (green), and long (red) ranges. There are about six million cones in each eye.

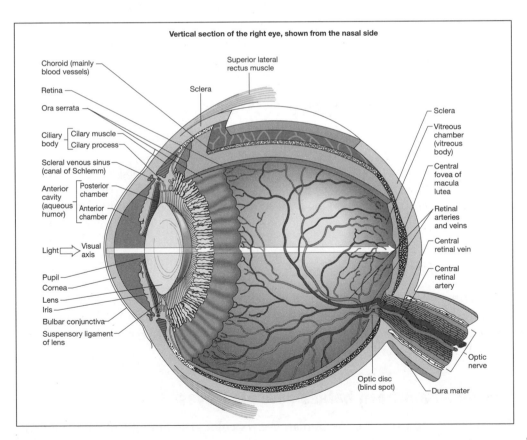

Vertical section of the right eye, shown from the nasal side

The human eye.

How often does the human eye blink?

The rate of blinking varies, but on the average the eye blinks once every five seconds (12 blinks per minute) or 17,000 times each day or 6.25 million times a year. In an award-winning science fair project, fourth-grader Holly Feldman observed that adults blink an average of 16 times per minute, or 5.48 million times a year. Miss Feldman based her calculations on a 16-hour day, concluding that humans don't blink for approximately eight hours each day, when they are asleep.

What are phosphenes?

If the eyes are shut tightly, the lights seen are phosphenes. Technically, the luminous impressions are due to the excitation of the retina caused by pressure on the eyeball.

What does it mean to have 20/20 vision?

Many people think that with 20/20 vision the eyesight is perfect, but it actually means that the eye can see clearly at 20 feet (six meters) what a normal eye can see clearly at that distance. Some people can see even better—20/15, for example. With their eyes, they can view objects from 20 feet away with the same sharpness that a normal-sighted person would have to move in to 15 feet (4.5 meters) to achieve.

Are more people nearsighted or farsighted?

About 30% of Americans are nearsighted to some degree. About 60% are farsighted. If the light rays entering the pupils of the eye converge exactly on the retina, then a sharply focused picture is relayed to the brain. But if the eyeball is shaped differently, the focal point of the light rays is too short or too long, and vision is blurred. Convex lenses for farsightedness correct a too-long focal point. Concave lenses correct nearsightedness when the focal point of light rays, being too short, converge in front of the retina.

Who invented bifocal lenses?

The original bifocal lens was invented in 1784 by Benjamin Franklin (1706–1790). At that time, the two lenses were joined in a metallic frame. In 1899, J.L. Borsch welded the two lenses together. One-part bifocal lenses were developed by Bentron and Emerson in 1910 for the Carl Zeiss Company.

Why do all newborn babies have blue eyes?

The color of the iris gives the human eye its color. The amount of dark pigment, melanin, in the iris is what determines its color. In newborns the pigment is concen-

What is the rare condition called synesthesia?

Synesthesia, or cross perception, is a condition in which a person perceives stimuli not only with the sense for which it is intended, but with others as well. For example, a synesthete may see musical notes as color hues or feel flavors as different textures on the skin. Experiments have determined that the linking of the senses occurs because of some unique physical condition in the brains of these people. For example, blood flow to some parts of the brain, normally increased by sensory stimuli, decreases in synesthetes.

trated in the folds of the iris. When a baby is a few months old, the melanin moves to the surface of the iris and gives the baby his or her permanent eye color.

What causes **eyes** to appear as **red dots** in some photographs?

"Red eye" in some color flash photographs is caused by a reflection from the layer of blood vessels lying between the retina and sclera (whites) of the eye. Red eye usually occurs when the light level is relatively dim and the subject is looking directly at the camera. To minimize the effect, the photographer should move the flash away from the camera lens; if this cannot be done, turning on additional lights in the room may help.

What is the **"sand"** that gathers in the **corners of our eyes** when we sleep?

The "sand" is dried mucus. Glands near the eye secrete the mucus to help the eye retain moisture and protect it against foreign particles. During sleep, the closed eyelids retain the moisture of the eyes, and the mucus may gather in the corners and dry out. When a person wakes, the dried mucus may feel like sand in the eyes.

How do **colors** affect one's **moods**?

According to the American Institute for Biosocial Research, "colors are electromagnetic wave bands of energy." Each color has its own wavelength. The wave bands stimulate chemicals in your eye, sending messages to the pituitary and pineal glands. These master endocrine glands regulate hormones and other physiological systems in the body. Stimulated by response to colors, glandular activities can alter moods, speed up heart rates, and increase brain activity.

What are the three **bones in the ear** called?

The three bones are the malleus, which means hammer; incus, which means anvil; and stapes, which means stirrup. The bones look somewhat like the objects for which they are named. The stapes is the smallest bone in the body, measuring 1.02 to 1.34 inches (2.6 to 3.4 centimeters) and weighing 0.00071 to 0.0015 ounce (0.002 to 0.004 gram). These three tiny bones in the middle ear conduct sound vibrations from the outer to inner ear.

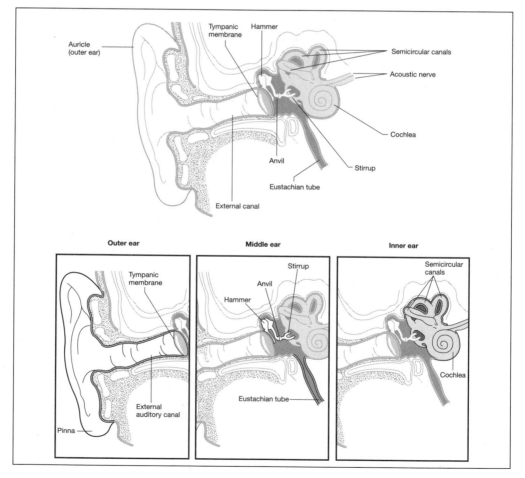

The anatomy of the human ear.

How broad is the **range of sound frequency** that most people can hear?

Most people can hear sounds with frequencies from about 20 to 20,000 hertz. A hertz is a measure of sound frequencies. Environmental sound is measured in decibels to calculate its loudness. Hearing starts with zero decibels; every increase of 10 units is equivalent to a tenfold increase. In comparison, leaves rustling = 10 decibels, a typical office is 50 decibels, pneumatic drills = 80 decibels, riveting machines = 110 decibels, and a jet takeoff at 200 feet (61 meters) measures 120 decibels. Noise above 70 decibels is harmful to hearing; noise at 140 decibels is physically painful.

What are the primary sensations of **taste**?

The four primary categories are sweet, sour, salty, and bitter. The sensitivity and location of these areas on the tongue varies from person to person. Some of the nine thousand taste buds are located in the other areas of the mouth as well. The lips (usually very salt-sensitive), the inner cheeks, the underside of the tongue, the back of the throat, and the roof of the mouth are some examples. The sense of taste is intimately associated with the sense of smell, so that foods taste bland to someone suffering from a cold. Also related are the appearance, texture, and temperature of food.

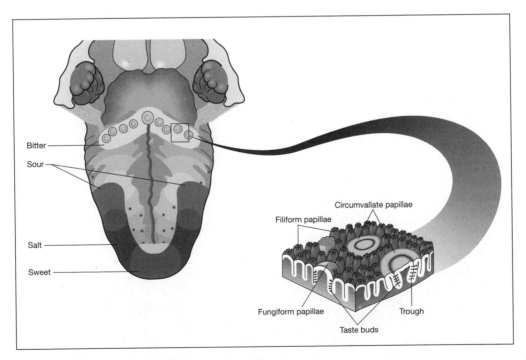

Taste regions of the tongue (left) and taste bud anatomy (right).

HEALTH AND MEDICINE

HEALTH HAZARDS, RISKS, ETC.

Which **risk factors** affect one's health?

Such characteristics as age, gender, work, family history, behavior, and body chemistry are some of the risk factors to consider when deciding whether one is at risk for various conditions. Some risk factors are statistical, describing trends among large groups of people but not giving information about what will happen to individuals. Other risk factors might be described as causative—exposure to them has a direct effect on whether or not the person will become sick.

What are the leading **causes of stress**?

In 1967, when they conducted a study of the correlation between significant life events and the onset of illness, Dr. Thomas H. Holmes and Dr. Richard H. Rahe from the University of Washington compiled a chart of the major causes of stress, with assigned point values. They published their findings on stress effects as "The Social Readjustment Scale," printed in *The Journal of Psychosomatic Research*. The researchers calculated that a score of 150 points indicated a 50–50 chance of the respondent developing an illness or a "health change." A score of 300 would increase the risk to 90%. Of course, many factors enter into an individual's response to a particular event, so this scale, partially represented below, can only be used as a guide.

Event	Point value
Death of spouse	100
Divorce	73

Event	Point value
Marital separation	65
Jail term or death of close family member	63
Personal injury or illness	53
Marriage	50
Fired at work	47
Marital reconciliation or retirement	45
Pregnancy	40
Change in financial state	38
Death of close friend	37
Mortgage over $10,000	31
Foreclosure of mortgage or loan	30
Outstanding personal achievement	28
Trouble with boss	23
Change in work hours or conditions or change in residence or schools	20
Vacation	13
Christmas	12
Minor violations of the law	11

What are the **odds against** being **struck by lightning?**

606,944 to one against.

What are the **odds against** being **killed on a motorcycle?**

1,250 to one against.

Is there **more violence** on the streets and in mental institutions when there is a **full moon?**

A review of 37 studies that attempted to correlate the phases of the moon with violent crime, suicide, crisis center hotline calls, psychiatric disorders, and mental hospital admissions found that there is absolutely no relation between the moon and the mind. Despite these findings, many people continue to believe that the moon is a powerful, and sometimes malevolent, force.

Can **owning a pet** be beneficial to your health?

As a result of several studies, researchers now believe that regular contact with pets can reduce heart rate, blood pressure, and levels of stress. In a study of 93 heart attack patients, only one of 18 pet owners died compared to one of three patients who did not have pets. Pets offer constancy, stability, comfort, security, affection, and intimacy.

What are the leading **causes of death** in the United States?

Of the 2,268,000 deaths in 1994, the leading cause of death was heart disease. Below are listed the four major causes of death in the United States.

Rank	Cause of Death	Number	Percentage of Total Deaths
1	Heart disease	734,090	32.1
2	Cancer	536,860	23.5
3	Stroke	154,350	6.8
4	Chronic obstructive lung diseases and allied conditions	101,870	4.5

HIV infection accounted for 41,930 deaths and ranked 8th.

Did raising the **speed limit** on rural interstate highways from 55 to 65 miles per hour have an effect on the **accident and death rate**?

There was an estimated 20% to 30% increase in deaths on those roads and a 40% increase in serious injuries when the speed limit was raised from 55 miles per hour (88.5 kilometers per hour) to 65 miles per hour (104.5 kilometers per hour) on rural interstate highways.

Are men or women more **accident-prone**?

Women drive and even cross the street more safely than men. Men account for 70% of pedestrian fatalities since 1980. Between the ages of 18 and 45, males outnumber females as fatal crash victims by almost three to one according to the National Highway Traffic Safety Administration. Accidental deaths of all types—from falls, firearms, drownings, fires, even food and other poisonings—also are more common among men than women.

Which direction of impact results in the greatest number of fatalities in **automobile crashes**?

Frontal crashes are responsible for the largest percentage of fatalities in passenger cars.

Which **sport** has the highest rate of **injuries** and what kind of injury is most common?

Football players suffer more injuries than other athletes, collectively. They have 12 times as many injuries as do basketball players, who have the next highest rate of injury. Knee problems are the most common type of injury, with two-thirds of basketball players' injuries and one-third of football players' injuries being knee-related.

Do **electric and magnetic fields** produced by power transmission lines present a health hazard?

No study has produced evidence to allow a firm conclusion on this question. Scientists cannot agree on the significance of the inconsistent and puzzling findings. On electromagnetic fields, in general, a 1990 study by the United States Environmental Protection Agency (EPA) noted a possible statistically significant link between cancer and exposure to extremely low frequency (ELF) electromagnetic fields. ELF waves are non-ionizing electromagnetic radiation that closely resemble the body's micropulsations. Biological studies have yet to prove such a connection. So far the ELF risks are controversial. Effects (from those studies supporting ELF hazards) run the gamut from headaches, to miscarriages, to cancer. In addition, electromagnetic radiation (EMR)—from devices such as electric blankets, video display terminals, microwaves, toasters, and hair dryers, powered by alternating current (AC) power lines—has been the target of study to better understand the health hazards that might be posed.

In May 1995, the American Physical Society reported that it could find no evi-
346 dence that the electromagnetic fields emanating from power lines can cause cancer.

While acknowledging that studies are still underway, the society concluded that existing research does not substantiate any reported adverse health effects.

Can **ozone** be harmful to humans?

Ozone (O_3) in the lower atmosphere contributes to air pollution. It is formed by chemical reactions between sunlight and oxygen in the air in the presence of impurities, such as those found in automobile exhaust. Ozone can damage rubber, plastic, and plant and animal tissue. Exposure to certain concentrations can cause headaches, burning eyes, and irritation of the respiratory tract in many individuals. Asthmatics and others with impaired respiratory systems are particularly susceptible. Exposure to low concentrations for only a few hours can significantly affect normal persons while exercising. Symptoms include chest pain, coughing, sneezing, and pulmonary congestion.

Why is exposure to **asbestos** a health hazard?

Exposure to asbestos has long been known to cause asbestosis. This is a chronic, restrictive lung disease caused by the inhalation of tiny mineral asbestos fibers that scar lung tissues. Asbestos has also been linked with cancers of the larynx, pharynx, oral cavity, pancreas, kidneys, ovaries, and gastrointestinal tract. The American Lung Association reports that prolonged exposure doubles the likelihood that a smoker will develop lung cancer. It takes cancer 15 to 30 years to develop from asbestos. Asbestos fibers were used in building materials between 1900 and the early 1970s as insulation for walls and pipes, as fireproofing for walls and fireplaces, in soundproofing and acoustic ceiling tiles, as a strengthener for vinyl flooring and joint compounds, and as a paint texturizer. Asbestos poses a health hazard only if the tiny fibers are released into the air, but this can happen with any normal fraying or cracking. Asbestos removal aggravates this normal process and multiplies the danger level—it should only be handled by a contractor trained in handling asbestos. Once released, the particles can hang suspended in the air for more than 20 hours.

Why is **radon** a health hazard?

Radon is a colorless, odorless, tasteless radioactive gaseous element produced by the radioactive decay of radium. It has three naturally occurring isotopes found in many natural materials, such as soil, rocks, well water, and building materials. Because the gas is continually released into the air, it makes up the largest source of radiation that humans receive. Some believe that radon may be a significant cancer cause, especially lung cancer. It has been estimated that it may cause as much as 10%, or 5,000 to 20,000 cases, of lung cancer deaths annually. Smokers seem to be at a higher risk than non-smokers. The U.S. Environmental Protection Agency (EPA) recommends that in radon testing, the level should not be more than four picocuries per liter. The estimated national average is 1.5 picocuries per liter. Because EPA's "safe level" is equivalent to 200 chest x-rays per year, some others believe that lower levels are appropriate. The American Society of Heating, Refrigeration, and Air-Conditioning Engineers (ASHRAE) recommends two picocuries/liter. The EPA estimates that nationally 8% to 12% of all houses are above the four picocuries/liter; whereas in another survey in 1987, it was estimated that 21% of homes were above this level.

How is human exposure to **radiation** measured?

The radiation absorbed dose (rad) and the roentgen equivalent man (rem) were used for many years to measure the amount and effect of ionizing radiation absorbed by humans. While officially replaced by the gray and the sievert, both are still used in many reference sources. The rad equals the energy absorption of 100 ergs per gram of irradiated material (an erg is a unit of work or energy). The rem is the absorbed dose of ionizing radiation that produces the same biological effect as one rad of x-rays or gamma rays (which are equal). The rem of x-rays and gamma rays is therefore equal to the rad; for each type of radiation, the number of rads is multiplied by a specific factor to find the number of rems. The millirem, 0.001 rems, is also frequently used; the average radiation dose received by a person in the United States is about 360 millirems per year. Natural radiation accounts for about 82% of a person's yearly exposure, and manufactured sources for 18%. Indoor radon has only recently been recognized as a significant source of natural radiation, with 55% of the natural radiation coming from this source.

In the SI system (*Système International d'Unités*, or International System of Units), the gray and the sievert are used to measure radiation absorbed; these units have largely superseded the older rad and rem. The gray (Gy), equal to 100 rads, is now the base unit. It is also expressed as the energy absorption of one joule per kilogram of irradiated material. The sievert (Sv) is the absorbed dose of radiation that produces the same biological effect as one gray of x-rays or gamma rays. The sievert is equal to 100 rems, and has superseded the rem. The becquerel (Bq) measures the radioactive strength of a source, but does not consider effects on tissue. One becquerel is defined as one disintegration (or other nuclear transformation) per second.

How much radiation does the average **dental x-ray** emit?

Dental examinations are estimated to contribute 0.15 millirems per year to the average genetically significant dose, a small amount when compared to other medical x-rays.

How does the United States Environmental Protection Agency (EPA) classify **carcinogens**?

A carcinogen is an agent that can produce cancer (a malignant growth or tumor that spreads throughout the body, destroying tissue). The EPA classifies chemical and physical substances according to their toxicity to humans.

EPA classification system for carcinogens

Group A. Human carcinogen

This classification indicates that there is sufficient evidence from epidemiological studies to support a cause–effect relationship between the substance and cancer.

Group B. Probable human carcinogen

B_1: Substances are classified as B_1 carcinogens on the basis of sufficient evidence from animal studies, and limited evidence from epidemiological studies.

B_2: Substances are classified as B_2 carcinogens on the basis of sufficient evidence from animal studies, with inadequate or nonexistent epidemiological data.

Group C. Possible human carcinogen

For this classification, there is limited evidence of carcinogenicity from animal studies and no epidemiological data.

Group D. Not classifiable as to human carcinogenicity

The data from human epidemiological and animal studies are inadequate or completely lacking, so no assessment as to the substance's cancer-causing hazard is possible.

Group E. Evidence of noncarcinogenicity for humans

Substances in this category have tested negative in at least two adequate (as defined by the EPA) animal cancer tests in different species and in adequate epidemiological and animal studies. Classification in group E is based on available evidence; substances may prove to be carcinogenic under certain conditions.

What is "good" and "bad" cholesterol?

Chemically a lipid, cholesterol is an important constituent of body cells. This fatty substance, produced mostly in the liver, is involved in bile salt and hormone formation, and in the transport of fats in the bloodstream to the tissues throughout the body. Both cholesterol and fats are transported as lipoproteins (units having a core of cholesterol and fats in varying proportions with an outer wrapping of carrier protein [phospholoids and apoproteins]). An overabundance of cholesterol in the bloodstream can be an inherited trait, can be triggered by dietary intake, or can be the result of a metabolic disease, such as diabetes mellitus. Fats (from meat, oil, and dairy products) strongly affect the cholesterol level. High cholesterol levels in the blood may lead to a narrowing of the inner lining of the coronary arteries from the build-up of a fatty tissue called atheroma. This increases the risk of coronary heart disease or stroke. However, if most cholesterol in the blood is in the form of high density lipoproteins (HDL), **349**

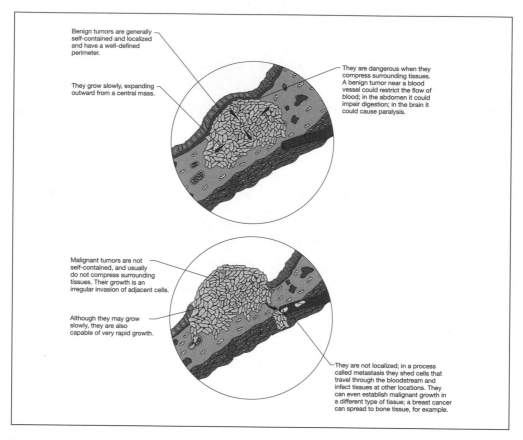

Benign tumors are generally self-contained and localized and have a well-defined perimeter.

They grow slowly, expanding outward from a central mass.

They are dangerous when they compress surrounding tissues. A benign tumor near a blood vessel could restrict the flow of blood; in the abdomen it could impair digestion; in the brain it could cause paralysis.

Malignant tumors are not self-contained, and usually do not compress surrounding tissues. Their growth is an irregular invasion of adjacent cells.

Although they may grow slowly, they are also capable of very rapid growth.

They are not localized; in a process called metastasis they shed cells that travel through the bloodstream and infect tissues at other locations. They can even establish malignant growth in a different type of tissue; a breast cancer can spread to bone tissue, for example.

A comparison of benign and malignant tumor characteristics.

then it seems to protect against arterial disease. HDL picks up cholesterol in the arteries and brings it back to the liver for excretion or reprocessing. HDL is referred to as "good cholesterol." Conversely, if most cholesterol is in the form of low density lipoproteins (LDL), or very low density lipoproteins (VLDL), then arteries can become clogged. "Bad cholesterol" is the term used to refer to LDL and VLDL.

How does the **blood alcohol level** affect the body and behavior?

The effects of drinking alcoholic beverages depend on the amount of actual ethyl alcohol consumed and body weight. The level of alcohol in the blood is calculated in milligrams (one milligram equals 0.035 of an ounce) of pure (ethyl) alcohol per deciliter (3.5 fluid ounces), commonly expressed in percentages.

Number of drinks	Blood alcohol level	Effect
1	0.02–.03%	Changes in behavior, coordination, and ability to think clearly
2	0.05%	Sedation or tranquilized feeling
3	0.08–0.10%	Legal intoxication in many states
5	0.15–0.20%	Person is obviously intoxicated and may show signs of delirium
12	0.30–0.40%	Loss of consciousness
24	0.50%	Heart and respiration become so depressed that they cease to function and death follows

What percentage of the American public are **smokers**?

Smokers constitute a minority, and a shrinking one. The annual prevalence of cigarette smoking among adults in the United States declined 40% during 1965 to 1990 (from 42.4% to 25.5%), but was virtually unchanged during 1990 to 1992. In 1993, an estimated 46 million adults (25%) were current smokers. Of current smokers, an estimated 32 million persons reported they wanted to quit smoking completely. Each year 34% attempt to quit smoking, but only 2.5% successfully stop.

Studies have linked pipe and cigar smoking to oral cavity cancers, and cigarette smoking to lung cancer and to respiratory diseases such as chronic bronchitis, emphysema, and coronary heart disease.

What is the composition of **cigarette smoke**?

Cigarette smoke contains about 4,000 chemicals. Carbon dioxide, carbon monoxide, methane, and nicotine are some of the major components, with lesser amounts of acetone, acetylene, formaldehyde, propane, hydrogen cyanide, toluene, and many others.

Why does the risk of **cancer** diminish rapidly after one quits the **cigarette smoking** habit?

Exposure of a premalignant cell to a promoter converts the cell to an irreversibly malignant state. Promotion is a slow process, and exposure to the promoter must be sustained for a certain period of time. This requirement explains why the risk of cancer diminishes rapidly after one quits smoking; both cancer initiators and promoters appear to be contained in tobacco smoke.

FIRST AID, POISONS, ETC.

How long does it take to **bleed to death**?

Serious bleeding requires immediate attention and care. If a large blood vessel is severed or lacerated, a person can bleed to death in one minute or less. Rapid loss of one quart or more of the total blood volume often leads to irreversible shock and death.

What is the **Heimlich maneuver**?

This effective first-aid technique to resuscitate choking and drowning victims was introduced by Dr. Henry J. Heimlich (b. 1920) of Xavier University, in Cincinnati, Ohio. It is a technique for removing a foreign body from the trachea or pharynx where it is preventing flow of air to the lungs. When the victim is in the vertical position, the maneuver consists of applying subdiaphragmatic pressure by wrapping one's arms around the victim's waist from behind, making a fist with one hand and placing it against the victim's abdomen between the navel and the rib cage, clasping one's fist with the other hand, and pressing in with a quick, forceful thrust. Repeat several times if necessary. When the victim is in the horizontal position (which some experts recommend), the rescuer straddles the victim's thighs.

What safety rules should be observed during a thunder storm?

These safety rules should be observed when lightning threatens:

1. Stay indoors. Seek shelter in buildings. If no buildings are available, the best protection is a cave, ditch, canyon, or under head-high clumps of trees in open forest glades. If there is no shelter, avoid the highest object in the area. Keep away from isolated trees.

2. Get out of the water and off small boats.

3. Do not use the telephone.

4. Do not use metal objects like fishing rods and golf clubs.

5. Stay in your automobile if you are traveling.

6. Do not use plug-in electrical equipment like hair dryers, electric razors, or electric tooth brushes during the storm.

What items should be included in a household **first-aid kit**?

According to the American Medical Association, a first-aid kit should contain:

Antiseptic cream

Antiseptic wipes

Aspirin or an aspirin substitute such as acetaminophen

Adhesive bandages

Elastic bandages

Gauze bandages

Triangular bandage

Calamine lotion

Flashlight

Foil blanket

Hydrogen peroxide or rubbing alcohol

Roll of sterile cotton

Round-ended tweezers

Safety pins

Snub-nosed scissors

Syrup of ipecac

How is **activated charcoal** used medically?

Activated charcoal is an organic substance, such as burned wood or coal, that has been heated to approximately 1,000°F (537°C) in a controlled atmosphere. The result is a fine powder containing thousands of pores that have great absorbent qualities to rapidly absorb toxins and poisons. Activated charcoal is used medically in the treatment of drug overdoses and poisonings.

What is the **deadliest natural toxin**?

Botulinal toxin, produced by the bacterium *Clostridium botulinum*, is the most potent poison of humans. It has an estimated lethal dose in the bloodstream of 10^{-9} milligrams per kilogram. It causes botulism, a severe neuroparalytic disease that travels to the junctions of skeletal muscles and nerves, where it blocks the release of the neurotransmitter acetylcholine, causing muscle weakness and paralysis, and impairing vision, speech, and swallowing. Death occurs when the respiratory muscles are paralyzed; this usually occurs during the first week of illness. Mortality from botulism is about 25%.

Because the bacterium can form the toxin only in the absence of oxygen, canned goods and meat products wrapped in airtight casings are potential sources of botulism. The toxin is more likely to grow in low-acid foods, such as mushrooms, peas, corn, or beans rather than high-acid foods like tomatoes. However, some new tomato hybrids are not acidic enough to prevent the bacteria from forming the toxin. Foods **353** being canned must be heated to a temperature high enough and for a long enough time to kill the bacteria present. Suspect food includes any canned or jarred food product with a swollen lid or can. Ironically, this dreaded toxin in tiny doses is being used to treat disorders that bring on involuntary muscle contractions, twisting, etc. The United States Food and Drug Administration (FDA) has approved the toxin for the treatment of strabismus (misalignment of the eyes), blepharospasm (forcible closure of eyelids), and hemifacial spasm (muscular contraction on one side of the face).

Have childhood deaths from poisoning decreased since the introduction of childproof containers?

After childproof packaging was required on all drugs and medications beginning in 1973, the childhood poisoning death rate declined dramatically. A 50% decrease was noted from 1973 to 1976, and the decline has continued. Other factors in this decline have been the development of poison control centers, changes in products to reduce poisonous agents, and the introduction of single dose packages.

Can toxins in plants in the nightshade family, such as potatoes, tomatoes, and eggplant, cause arthritis in some people?

No scientific evidence supports this belief. Studies have shown that in groups of people who eat lots of potatoes, there is no increased incidence of arthritis.

How deadly is **strychnine**?

The fatal dose of strychnine or deadly nightshade (the plant from which it is obtained) is 15 to 30 milligrams. It causes severe convulsions and respiratory failure. If the patient lives for 24 hours, recovery is probable.

Which part of **mistletoe** is poisonous?

The white berries contain toxic amines, which cause acute stomach and intestinal irritation with diarrhea and a slow pulse. Mistletoe should be considered a potentially dangerous Christmas decoration, especially if children are around.

What is the **poison on arrows** used by South American Indians to kill prey and enemies?

The botanical poison used by the Aucas and similar tribes in the South American jungles is curare. It is a sticky, black mixture with the appearance of licorice and is processed from either of two different vines. One is a liana (*Chondodendron tomentosum*); the other is a massive tree-like vine (*Strychonos quianensis*).

How deadly is *Amanita phalloides*?

The poisonous mushroom *Amanita phalloides* has a fatality rate of about 50%. Ingestion of part of one mushroom may be sufficient to cause death. Over 100 fatalities occur each year from eating poisonous mushrooms, with more than 90% caused by the *Amanita phalloides* group.

What first aid remedies may be used for **bee stings**?

If a person is allergic to bee stings, he or she should seek professional medical care immediately. For persons not allergic to bee stings, the following steps may be taken: The stinger should be removed by scraping with a knife, a long fingernail, or a credit card, rather than by trying to pull it out. A wet aspirin may be rubbed on the area of the sting to help neutralize some of the inflammatory agents in the venom (unless the person is allergic or sensitive to aspirin taken by mouth).

A paste made of meat tenderizer (or other product that contains papain) mixed with water will relieve the pain. Adults may take an antihistamine along with a mild pain reliever such as aspirin, ibuprofen, or acetaminophen.

Which first aid measures can be used for a bite by a black widow spider?

The black widow spider (*Latrodectus mactans*) is common throughout the United States. Its bite is severely poisonous, but no first aid measures are of value. Age, body size, and degree of sensitivity determine the severity of symptoms, which include an initial pinprick with a dull numbing pain, followed by swelling. An ice cube may be placed over the bite to relieve pain. Between 10 and 40 minutes after the bite, severe abdominal pain and rigidity of stomach muscles develop. Muscle spasms in the extremities, ascending paralysis, and difficulty in swallowing and breathing follow. The mortality rate is less than 1%, but anyone who has been bitten should see a doctor; the elderly, infants, and those with allergies are most at risk, and should be hospitalized.

During what period of time may a cut or wound be stitched?

Stitches should be placed within six to eight hours of the injury. The time may be extended to twelve hours if the amount of contamination is small and the wound area is very vascular.

How can the amount of lead in tap water be reduced in an older house having lead-containing pipes?

The easiest way is to let the tap run until the water becomes very cold before using it for human consumption. By letting the tap run, water that has been in the lead-containing pipes for awhile is flushed out. Also, cold water, being less corrosive than warm, contains less lead from the pipes. Lead (Pb) accumulates in the blood, bones, and soft tissues of the body as well as the kidneys, nervous system, and blood-forming organs. Excessive exposure to lead can cause seizures, mental retardation, and behavior disorders. Infants and children are particularly susceptible to low doses of lead and suffer from nervous system damage.

Another source of lead poisoning is old flaking lead paint. Lead oxide and other lead compounds were added to paints before 1950 to make the paint shinier and more durable. 14% of the lead ingested by humans comes from the seam soldering of food cans, according to the United States Food and Drug Administration (FDA). The FDA has proposed a reduction in this lead to 50% over the next five years. Improperly glazed pottery can be a source of poisoning. Acidic liquids such as tea, coffee, wine, and juice can break down the glazes so that the lead can leak out of the pottery. The lead is ingested little by little over a period of time. People can also be exposed to lead in the air. Lead gasoline additives, nonferrous smelters, and battery plants are the most significant contributors of atmospheric lead emissions.

How did **lead** contribute to the **fall of the Roman Empire?**

Some believe Romans from the period around 150 B.C.E. may have been victims of lead poisoning. Symptoms of lead poisoning include sterility, general weakness, apathy, mental retardation, and early death. The lead could have been ingested in water taken from lead-lined water pipes or from food cooked in their lead-lined cooking pots or wine served in lead-lined goblets. Unaware of its dangers, some ancient Romans unwittingly used lead as a sweetening agent or medicinal treatment for diarrhea. Lead poisoning could have caused infertility in women, leading to a subsequent long-term decline in the birth rate of the Roman upper classes. The effect of this inadvertent toxic food additive on Roman history, however, is only speculative.

What often happened to hat makers that caused Lewis Carroll to use the expression **"mad as a hatter"** in *Alice in Wonderland?*

In the 19th century, craftsmen who made hats were known to be excitable and irrational, as well as to tremble with palsy and mix up their words. Such behavior gave rise to familiar expression "mad as a hatter." The disorder, called hatter's shakes, was caused by chronic mercury poisoning from the solution used to treat the felt. Attacking the central nervous system, the toxin led to the behavioral symptoms.

DISEASES, DISORDERS, AND OTHER HEALTH PROBLEMS

Which **disease** is the **most common?**

The most common noncontagious disease is periodontal disease, such as gingivitis or inflammation of the gums. Few people in their lifetime can avoid the effects of tooth decay. The most common contagious disease in the world is coryza or the common cold.

Which **disease** is the **deadliest?**

The most deadly infectious disease was the pneumonic form of the plague, the so-called Black Death of 1347–1351, with a mortality rate of 100%. Today, the disease with the highest mortality (almost 100%) is rabies in humans when it prevents the victim from swallowing water. This disease is not to be confused with being bitten by a rabid animal. With immediate attention, the rabies virus can be prevented from invading the nervous system and the survival rate in this circumstance is 95%. AIDS (acquired immunodeficiency syndrome), first reported in 1981, is caused by HIV (the human immunodeficiency virus). In 1993, HIV infection became the most common cause of death among persons aged 25 to 44 years. In 1994, an estimated 41,930 U.S. residents died from HIV infection, based on information recorded from death certificates. Perhaps as many as 55,000 to 60,000 persons with AIDS died in 1994.

What are the symptoms and signs of **AIDS**?

The early symptoms (AIDS-related complex, or ARC, symptoms) include night sweats, prolonged fevers, severe weight loss, persistent diarrhea, skin rash, persistent cough, and shortness of breath. The diagnosis changes to AIDS (acquired immunodeficiency syndrome) when the immune system is affected and the patient becomes susceptible to opportunistic infections and unusual cancers, such as herpes viruses (herpes simplex, herpes zoster, cytomegalovirus infection), *Candida albicans* (fungus) infection, *Cryptosporidium enterocolitis* (protozoan intestinal infection), *Pneumocystis carinii* pneumonia (PCP, a common AIDS lung infection), toxoplasmosis (protozoan brain infection), progressive multifocal leukoencephalopathy (PML, a central nervous system disease causing gradual brain degeneration), *Mycobacterium avium intracellulare* infection (MAI, a common generalized bacterial infection), and Kaposi's sarcoma (a malignant skin cancer characterized by blue-red nodules on limbs and body, and internally in the gastrointestinal and respiratory tracts, where the tumors cause severe internal bleeding). More than 75% of AIDS victims die within two years of diagnosis.

The signs of AIDS are generalized swollen glands, emaciation, blue or purple-brown spots on the body, especially on the legs and arms, prolonged pneumonia, and oral thrush.

How is the term **zoonosis** defined?

A zoonosis is any infectious or parasitic disease of animals that can be transmitted to humans. Lyme disease and Rocky Mountain spotted fever are indirectly spread to humans from an animal through the bite of a tick. Common household pets also can directly transmit diseases to humans unless preventive measures are taken. Cat-scratch fever and toxoplasmosis may be contracted from cats. Wild animals and dogs can transmit rabies. However, most zoonosis diseases are relatively rare and can be treated once detected. Such sensible actions as regularly vaccinating pets and wearing long sleeved shirts and pants when hiking can prevent the spread of most zoonoses.

What is meant by **vectors** in medicine?

A vector is an animal that transmits a particular infectious disease. A vector picks up
disease organisms from a source of infection, carries them within or on its body, and

later deposits them where they infect a new host. Mosquitoes, fleas, lice, ticks, and flies are the most important vectors of disease to humans.

Which species of mosquito causes **malaria** and **yellow fever** in humans?

The bite of the female mosquito of the genus *Anopheles* can contain the parasite of the genus *Plasmodium*, which causes malaria, a serious tropical infectious disease affecting 200 to 300 million people worldwide. More than one million African babies and children die from the disease annually. The *Aedes aegypti* mosquito transmits yellow fever, a serious infectious disease characterized by jaundice, giving the patient yellowish skin; 10% of the patients die.

What was the contribution of **Dr. Gorgas** to the building of the **Panama Canal**?

Dr. William C. Gorgas (1854–1920) brought the endemic diseases of Panama under control by destroying mosquito breeding grounds, virtually eliminating yellow fever and malaria. His work was probably more essential to the completion of the canal than any engineering technique.

How is **Lyme disease** carried?

The cause of Lyme disease is the spirochete *Borrelia burgdorferi* that is transmitted to humans by the small tick *Ixodes dammini* or other ticks in the Ixodidae family. The tick injects spirochete-laden saliva into the bloodstream or deposits fecal matter on the skin. This multisystemic disease usually begins in the summer with a skin lesion called erythema chronicum migrans (ECM), followed by more lesions, a malar rash, conjunctivitis, and urticaria. The lesions are eventually replaced by small red blotches. Other common symptoms in the first stage include fatigue, intermittent headache, fever, chills, and achiness.

In stage two, which can be weeks or months later, cardiac or neurologic abnormalities sometimes develop. In the last stage (weeks or years later) arthritis develops with marked swelling, especially in the large joints. If tetracycline, penicillin, or erythromycin is given in the early stages, the later complications can be minimized. High dosage of intravenously given penicillin can also be effective on the late stages.

Why is **Legionnaire's disease** known by that name?

Legionnaire's disease was first identified in 1976 when a sudden, virulent outbreak of pneumonia took place at a hotel in Philadelphia, Pennsylvania, where delegates to an **359**

American Legion Convention were staying. The cause was eventually identified as a previously unknown bacterium that was given the name *Legionnella pneumophilia*. The bacterium probably was transmitted by an airborne route. It can spread through cooling tower or evaporation condensers in air-conditioning systems, and has been known to flourish in soil and excavation sites. Usually the disease occurs in late summer or early fall and its severity ranges from mild to life-threatening with a mortality rate as high as 15%. Symptoms include diarrhea, anorexia, malaise, headache, generalized weakness, recurrent chills, and fever accompanied by cough, nausea, and chest pain. Antibiotics such as Erythroycin™ are administered along with other therapies (fluid replacement, oxygen, etc.) that treat the symptoms.

Which name is now used as a synonym for **leprosy**?

Hansen's disease is the name of this chronic, systemic infection characterized by progressive lesions. Caused by a bacterium, *Mycobacterium leprae*, that is transmitted through airborne respiratory droplets, the disease is not highly contagious. Continuous close contact is needed for transmittal. Antimicrobial agents, such as sulfones (dapsone in particular), are used to treat the disease.

Who was **Typhoid Mary**?

Mary Mallon (1855–1938), a cook who lived in New York City at the turn of the century, was identified as a chronic carrier of the typhoid bacilli. Immune to the disease herself, she was the cause of at least three deaths and 51 cases of typhoid fever. She was confined to an isolation center on North Brother Island, near the Bronx, from 1907 to 1910 and from 1914 to 1938. The New York City Health Department released her after the first confinement on the condition that she never accept employment that involved handling food. But when a later epidemic occurred at two places where she had worked as a cook, the authorities returned her to North Brother Island, where she remained until her death from a stroke in 1938.

How many types of **herpes virus** are there?

There are five human herpes viruses:

Herpes simplex type 1—causes recurrent cold sores and infections of the lips, mouth, and face. The virus is contagious and spreads by direct contact with the lesions or fluid from the lesions. Cold sores are usually recurrent at the same sites and reoccur where there is an elevated temperature at the affected site, such as a fever or prolonged sun exposure. Occasionally this virus may occur on the fingers with a rash of blisters. If the virus gets into the eye, it could cause conjunctivitis, or even a corneal ulcer. On rare occasions, it can spread to the brain to cause encephalitis.

Herpes simplex type 2—causes genital herpes and infections acquired by babies at birth. The virus is contagious and can be transmitted by sexual intercourse. The virus produces small blisters in the genital area that burst to leave small painful ulcers, which heal within 10 days to three weeks. Headache, fever, enlarged lymph nodes, and painful urination are the other symptoms.

Varicella-zoster (Herpes zoster)—causes chicken pox and shingles. Shingles can be caused by the dormant virus in certain sensory nerves that re-emerge with the decline of the immune system (because of age, certain diseases, and the use of immunosuppressants), excessive stress, or use of corticosteroid drugs. The painful rash of small blisters dry and crust over, eventually leaving small pitted scars. The rash tends to occur over the rib area or a strip on one side of the neck or lower body. Sometimes it involves the lower half of the face and can affect the eyes. Pain that can be severe and long-lasting affects about half of the sufferers and is caused by nerve damage.

Epstein-Barr—causes infectious mononucleosis (acute infection having high fever, sore throat and swollen lymph glands, especially in the neck, which occurs mainly during adolescence) and is associated with Burkitt's lymphoma (malignant tumors of the jaw or abdomen that occur mainly in African children and in tropical areas).

Cytomegalovirus—usually no symptoms but enlarges the cells it infects; it can cause birth defects when a pregnant mother infects her unborn child.

Three other human herpes viruses are also known: Human herpes virus 6 (HHV-6), commonly associated with roseola, and human herpes viruses 7 and 8 (HHV 7/8), whose disease association is not yet understood. Herpes gestationis is a rare skin-blister disorder occurring only in pregnancy and is not related to the herpes simplex virus.

What is **necrotizing fasciitis**?

This very rare infection is caused by strains of Group A streptococcus, close relatives of the bacteria that cause strep throat and scarlet fever. When this chain-linked bacteria enters the body through a small cut, bite, or scratch, the infected skin becomes discolored, then blisters and cracks, exposing the destroyed tissue below. Within hours, an infected person can lose inches of flesh, or, in extreme cases, his or her life. If the infection is diagnosed early, antibiotics are generally enough to stop the infection. However, amputation of an affected limb may be the only means of curing an advanced case. The bacteria are often called "flesh-eating bacteria" in sensational media accounts.

How are **warts** caused?

A wart is a lump on the skin produced when one of the 30 types of papillomavirus invades skin cells and causes them to multiply rapidly. There are several different types of warts: common warts, usually on injury sites; flat warts on hands, accompa-

Who were the "Blue People" in Appalachia?

The "Blue People" were descendants of Martin Fugate, a French immigrant to Kentucky. He had a recessive gene that limited or stopped the body's production of the enzyme diaphorase. Diaphorase breaks down methemoglobin into hemoglobin in red blood cells. When the enzyme is not present, a disproportionate amount of methemoglobin remains in the blood, giving the cells a bluish tint, rather than the normal pink associated with Caucasians. The condition is strictly one of pigment and does not deprive the person of oxygen.

Despite bluish color, there are no known health risks associated with the deficiency. Fugate's family suffered from the condition because of excessive inbreeding. When both spouses had the recessive gene, their children would be blue. As the family became mobile following World War II and moved out of their Kentucky valley, the inbreeding ceased. As of 1982 there were only two to three members of the family with the condition.

nied by itching; digitate warts having fingerlike projections; filiform warts on eyelids, armpits, and necks; plantar warts on the soles of the feet; and genital warts, pink cauliflower-like areas that, if occurring in a woman's cervix, could predispose her to cervical cancer. Each is produced by a specific virus, and most are usually symptomless. Wart viruses are spread by touch or by contact with the skin shed from a wart.

What is **lactose intolerance**?

Lactose, the principal sugar in cow's milk and found only in dairy products, requires the enzyme lactase for human digestion. Lactose intolerance occurs when the lining of the walls of a person's small intestine does not produce normal amounts of this enzyme. Lactose intolerance causes abdominal cramps, bloating, diarrhea, and excessive gas when more than a certain amount of milk is ingested. Most people are less able to tolerate lactose as they grow older.

A person having lactose intolerance need not eliminate dairy products totally from the diet. Decreasing the consumption of milk products, drinking milk only during meals, and getting calcium from cheese, yogurt, and other dairy products having lower lactose values are options. Another alternative is to buy a commercial lactose preparation that can be mixed into milk. These preparations convert lactose into simple sugars that can be easily digested.

Which **medical condition** is associated with **Abraham Lincoln**'s lanky appearance?

Abraham Lincoln (1809–1865) probably had Marfan's syndrome (Arachnodactyly), which abnormally lengthens the bones. It is a rare inherited degenerative disease of the connective tissue. Besides the excessively long bones, there are chest deformities, scoliosis (spine curvature), an arm span that can exceed height, eye problems (especially myopia or nearsightedness), abnormal heart sounds, and sparse subcutaneous fat. In 1991, researchers identified the gene behind the disease.

Abraham Lincoln may have been a victim of Marfan's syndrome.

What is **carpal tunnel syndrome**?

Carpal tunnel syndrome occurs when a branch of the median nerve in the forearm is compressed at the wrist as it passes through the tunnel formed by the wrist bones (or carpals), and a ligament that lies just under the skin. The syndrome occurs most often in middle age and more so in women than men. The symptoms are intermittent at first, then become constant. Numbness and tingling begin in the thumb and first two fingers; then the hand and sometimes the whole arm becomes painful. Treatment involves wrist splinting, weight loss, control of edema; treatments for arthritis may help also. If not, a surgical procedure in which the ligament at the wrist is cut can relieve pressure on the nerve. Those who work continuously with computer keyboards are particularly vulnerable to carpal tunnel syndrome. To minimize the risk of developing this problem, operators should keep their wrists straight as they type, rather than tilting the hands up. It is also best to place the keyboard at a lower position than a standard desktop.

What is the medical term for **tennis elbow**?

The technical term for tennis elbow is epicondylitis. A result of repeated strain on the forearm, it is a painful inflammation of the muscle and surrounding tissues of the elbow. A number of behaviors can cause its onset, ranging from from playing tennis or golf to carrying a heavy load with the arm extended.

What is **Lou Gehrig's disease**?

Sometimes called Lou Gehrig's disease, amyotrophic lateral sclerosis (ALS) is a motor neuron disease of middle or late life. It results from a progressive degeneration of nerve cells controlling voluntary motor functions that ends in death three to 10 years after onset. There is no cure for it. At the beginning of the disease, the patient notices weakness in the hands and arms, with involuntary muscle quivering and possible muscle cramping or stiffness. Eventually all four extremities become involved. As nerve degeneration progresses, disability occurs and physical independence declines until the patient, while mentally and intellectually aware, can no longer swallow or move.

What is **narcolepsy**?

Although most people think of a narcoleptic as a person who falls asleep at inappropriate times, victims of narcolepsy also share other symptoms, including excessive daytime sleepiness, hallucinations, and cataplexy (a sudden loss of muscle strength following an emotional event). Persons with narcolepsy experience an uncontrollable desire to sleep, sometimes many times in one day. Episodes may last from a few minutes to several hours.

How does **jet lag** affect one's body?

The physiological and mental stress encountered by airplane travelers when crossing four or more time zones is commonly called jet lag. Patterns of hunger, sleep, and elimination, along with alertness, memory, and normal judgement, may all be affected. More than 100 biological functions that fluctuate during the 24-hour cycle (circadian rhythm) can become desynchronized. Most people's bodies adjust at a rate of about one hour per day. Thus after four time zone changes, the body will require about four days to return to its usual rhythms. Flying eastward is often more difficult than flying westward, which adds hours to the day.

What is **factor VIII**?

Factor VIII is one of the enzymes involved in the clotting of blood. Hemophiliacs lack this enzyme and are at high risk of bleeding to death unless they receive supplemental doses of factor VIII. The lack of factor VIII is due to a defective gene, which shows a sex-linked inherited pattern, affecting males (one in 10 thousand). Females can carry the gene. Hemorrhage into joints and muscles usually make up the majority of bleeding episodes.

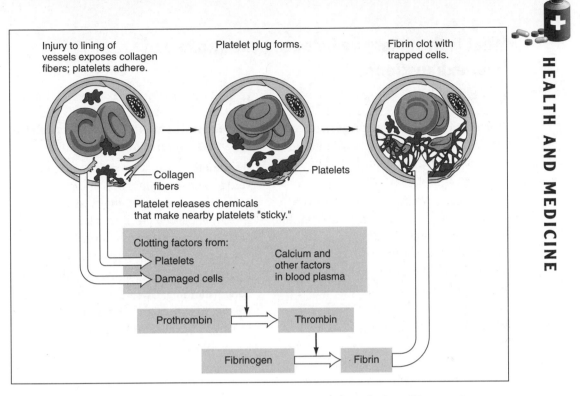

Injury to lining of vessels exposes collagen fibers; platelets adhere.

Platelet plug forms.

Fibrin clot with trapped cells.

Collagen fibers

Platelets

Platelet releases chemicals that make nearby platelets "sticky."

Clotting factors from:

Platelets

Damaged cells

Calcium and other factors in blood plasma

Prothrombin → Thrombin

Fibrinogen → Fibrin

The blood clotting process. Persons with Christmas disease lack a crucial clotting factor that keeps this process from proceeding properly.

What is the "Christmas factor"?

In the clotting of blood, factor IX, or the Christmas factor, is a coagulation factor present in normal plasma, but deficient in the blood of persons with hemophilia B or Christmas disease. It was named after a man named Christmas who, in 1952, was the first patient in whom this genetic disease was shown to be distinct from hemophilia (another genetic blood-clotting disease in which the blood does not have factor VIII).

What is the medical term for a heart attack?

Myocardial infarction is the term used for a heart attack in which part of the heart muscle's cells die as a result of reduced blood flow through one of the main arteries (many times due to arteriosclerosis). The outlook for the patient is dependant on the size and location of the blockage and extent of damage, but 33% of patients die within 20 days after the attack; it is a leading cause of death in the United States. Also, almost half of sudden deaths due to myocardial infarction occur before hospitalization. However, the possibility of recovery improves if vigorous treatment begins immediately.

What is the difference between **heat stroke** and **heat exhaustion**?

Heat Stroke

Caused by: Body cannot regulate its own temperature due to intensive sweating under conditions of high heat and humidity. Advanced age can be a factor.

Symptoms: Weakness, vertigo, nausea, headache, heat cramps, mild heat exhaustion, excessive sweating. Sweating stops just before heatstroke. Temperature rises rapidly (as high as 106°F); blood pressure is elevated. Skin is flushed at first, then turns ashen or purplish. Delirium or coma is common.

First Aid: Heat stroke is a medical emergency. Call for medical assistance. Move person to a cool, indoor place. Loosen or remove clothing. Primary objective is to reduce body temperature, preferably by iced bath or sponging down with cool water until pulse lowers to below 110 per minute and body temperature is below 103°. Caution is necessary.

Heat Exhaustion

Caused by: Person doesn't get enough liquid and salt in very hot, humid weather.

Symptoms: Excessive sweating, weakness, vertigo, and sometimes heat cramps. Skin is cold and pale, clammy with sweat; pulse is thready and blood pressure is low. Body temperature is normal or sub-normal. Vomiting may occur. Unconsciousness is rare.

First Aid: Lay person in cool place. Loosen clothing. Give water to drink with 1 tsp. salt to each quart of water. Fluid intake usually brings about full recovery. Seek medical assistance if severe.

How are the forms of **cancer** classified?

The over 150 different types of cancer are classified into four major groups:

1. Carcinomas—Nine in 10 cancers are carcinomas, which involve the skin and skin-like membranes of the internal organs.
2. Sarcomas—Involve the bones, muscles, cartilage, fat, and linings of the lungs, abdomen, heart, central nervous system, and blood vessels.
3. Leukemias—Develop in blood, bone marrow, and the spleen.
4. Lymphomas—Involve the lymphatic system.

What adverse effects may a person who is allergic to **sulfites** experience?

Sulfites are chemical agents used to prevent discoloration in dried fruits and freshly cut vegetables. They are also used by winemakers to inhibit bacterial growth and fer-

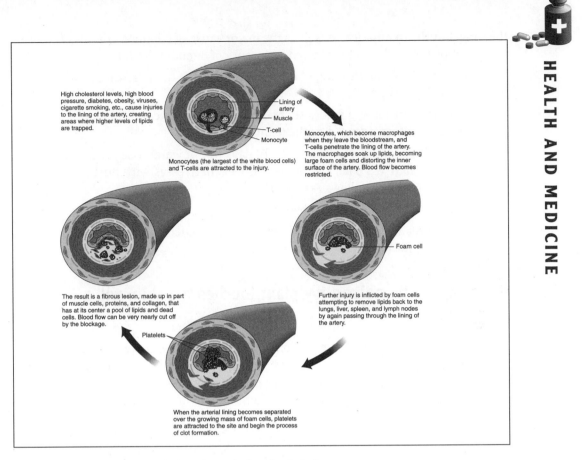

The progression of arteriosclerosis, which may in turn lead to a heart attack.

mentation. If a person is allergic to sulfites, he or she can develop breathing difficulties within minutes of consuming food or drink containing sulfites. Reactions to sulfites can include acute asthma attacks, loss of consciousness, and anaphylactic shock.

What are HeLa cells?

HeLa cells, used in many biomedical experiments, were obtained from a cervical carcinoma in a black woman named Henriette Lacks. Epithelial tissue obtained by biopsy became the first continuously cultured human malignant cells.

What are dust mites?

Dust mites are microscopic arachnids (members of the spider family) commonly found in house dust. Dust mite allergen is probably one of the most important causes of asthma (breathlessness and wheezing caused by the narrowing of small airways of the lungs) in North America, as well as the major cause of common allergies (exaggerated reactions of the immune system to exposure of offending agents).

Thorough, regular cleaning of the home, including the following measures, will help control dust mites:

1. Clean all major appliances such as furnaces and air conditioners, and change filters as recommended by the manufacturer.
2. Launder bedding every seven to 10 days in hot water. Use synthetic or foam rubber mattress pads and pillows. Cover mattresses with dust proof covers. Clean or replace pillows regularly.
3. Keep moist surfaces in kitchen and bathroom clean and free of mold.
4. Vacuum and dust often. A high-efficiency particulate air filter (HEPA) vacuum is especially effective.

If the sap of the **poison ivy** plant touches the skin, will a rash develop?

Studies show that 85% of the population will develop an allergic reaction if exposed to poison ivy, but this sensitivity varies with each individual according to circumstance, age, genetics, and previous exposure. The poison comes mainly from the leaves whose allergens touch the skin. A red rash with itching and burning will develop, and skin blisters will usually develop within six hours to several days after exposure. Washing the affected area thoroughly with mild soap within five minutes of exposure can be effective; sponging with alcohol and applying a soothing and drying lotion, such as calamine lotion, is the prescribed treatment for light cases. If the affected area is large, fever, headache, and generalized body weakness may develop. For severe reactions, a physician should be consulted, who may prescribe a corticosteroid drug. Clothing that touched the plants should also be washed.

What is **dyslexia** and what causes it?

Dyslexia covers a wide range of language difficulties. In general, a person with dyslexia cannot group the meaning of sequences of letters, words, or symbols or the concept of direction. The condition can affect people of otherwise normal intelligence. Dyslexic children may reverse letter and word order, make bizarre spelling errors, and may not be able to name colors or write from dictation. It may be caused by minor visual defects, emotional disturbance, or failure to train the brain. New evidence shows that a neurological disorder may be the underlying cause. Approximately 90% of dyslexics are male.

The term *dyslexia* (of Greek origin) was first suggested by Professor Rudolph of Stuttgart, Germany, in 1887. The earliest references to the condition date as far back as 30 C.E. when Valerius Maximus and Pliny described a man who lost his ability to read after being struck on the head by a stone.

What is **anorexia**?

Anorexia simply means a loss of appetite. Anorexia nervosa is a psychological disturbance that is characterized by an intense fear of being fat. It usually affects teenage or young adult women. This persistent "fat image," however untrue in reality, leads the patient to self-imposed starvation and emaciation (extreme thinness) to the point where one-third of the body weight is lost. There are many theories on the causes of this disease, which is difficult to treat and can be fatal. Between 5% and 10% of patients hospitalized for anorexia nervosa later die from starvation or suicide. Symptoms include a 25% or greater weight loss (for no organic reason) coupled with a morbid dread of being fat, an obsession with food, an avoidance of eating, compulsive exercising and restlessness, binge eating followed by induced vomiting, and/or use of laxatives or diuretics.

Why do deep-sea divers get **the bends**?

Bends is a painful condition in limbs and abdomen. It is caused by the formation and enlargement of bubbles of nitrogen in blood and tissues as a result of rapid reduction of pressure. This condition can develop when a diver ascends too rapidly after being exposed to increased pressure. Severe pain will develop in the muscles and joints of the arms and legs. More severe symptoms include vertigo, nausea, vomiting, choking, shock, and sometimes death. Bends is also known as decompression sickness, caisson disease, tunnel disease, and diver's paralysis.

What is **progeria**?

Progeria is premature old age. There are two distinct forms of the condition, both of which are extremely rare. In Hutchinson-Gilford syndrome, aging starts around the age four, and by 10 or 12, the affected child has all the external features of old age, including gray hair, baldness, and loss of fat, resulting in thin limbs and sagging skin on the trunk and face. There are also internal degenerative changes, such as atherosclerosis (fatty deposits lining the artery walls). Death usually occurs at puberty. Werner's syndrome, or adult progeria, starts in early adult life and follows the same rapid progression as the juvenile form. The cause of progeria is unknown.

How many people in America are estimated to have Alzheimer's disease?

Researchers have concluded that 10% of people over 65 have Alzheimer's disease, including nearly 50% of people over 85. The National Institute on Aging estimated that four million Americans have Alzheimer's disease. Some experts, however, do not agree with these figures.

Alzheimer's disease is a progressive condition in which nerve cells in the brain degenerate and the brain substance shrinks. Although the cause is unknown, some theorize that it is toxic poisoning by a metal such as aluminum. Others believe it to be of genetic origin. There are three stages; in the first, the person becomes forgetful; in the second, the patient experiences severe memory loss and disorientation, lack of concentration, loss of ability to calculate and find the right word to use (dysphasia), anxiety, and sudden personality changes. In the third stage the patient is severely disoriented and confused, suffers from hallucinations and delusions, and has severe memory loss; the nervous system also declines, with regression into infantile behavior, violence, etc., often requiring hospital care.

Alzheimer's disease is emerging as one of the most costly medical and social problems in the United States. Annual expenses run as high as $90 billion in direct and indirect costs. It is the fourth leading cause of death among adults.

How is an **iatrogenic illness** defined?

It is an adverse mental or physical condition caused by the effects of treatment by a physician or surgeon. The term implies that it could have been avoided by judicious care on the part of the physician.

What is **pelvic inflammatory disease?**

Pelvic inflammatory disease (PID) is a term used for a group of infections in the female organs, including inflammations of the Fallopian tubes, cervix, uterus, and ovaries. It is the most common cause of female infertility today. PID is most often found in sexually active women under the age of 25 and almost always results from gonorrhea or chlamydia, but women who use IUDs are also at risk. A variety of organisms have been shown to cause PID, including *Neisseria gonorrhoeae* and such common bacteria as staphylococci, chlamydiae, and coliforms (*Pseudomonas* and *Escherichia coli*). Signs and symptoms of PID vary with the site of the infection, but usually include profuse, purulent vaginal discharge, low grade fever and malaise (especially with *N. gonorrhoeae* infections), and lower abdominal pain. PID is treated with antibiotics, and early diagnosis and treatment will prevent damage to the reproductive system. Severe, untreated PID can result in the development of a pelvic abscess that requires drainage. A ruptured pelvic abscess is a potentially fatal complication, and a patient who develops this complication may require a total hysterectomy.

What is the chemical composition of **kidney stones?**

About 80% are calcium, mainly calcium oxalate and/or phosphate; 5% are uric acid; 2% are amino acid cystine; the remainder are magnesium ammonium phosphate. About 20% of these stones are infective stones, linked to chronic urinary infections, and contain a combination of calcium, magnesium, and ammonium phosphate produced from the alkalinity of the urine and bacteria action on urea (a substance in urine).

What is pica?

Pica refers to the craving for unnatural or non-nutritious substances. It is named after the magpie (*Pica pica*), which has a reputation for sticking its beak into all kinds of things to satisfy its hunger or curiosity. It can happen in both sexes, all races, and in all parts of the world, but is especially noted in pregnant women.

How are **burns** classified?

Type	Causes and Effects
First-degree	Sunburn; steam. Reddening and peeling. Affects epidermis (top layer of skin). Heals within a week.
Second-degree	Scalding; holding hot metal. Deeper burns causing blisters. Affects dermis (deep skin layer). Heals in two to three weeks.
Third-degree	Fire. A full layer of skin is destroyed. Requires a doctor's care and grafting.
Circumferential	Any burns (often electrical) that completely encircle a limb or body region (such as the chest), which can impair circulation or respiration; requires a doctor's care; fasciotomy (repair of connective tissues) is sometimes required.
Chemical	Acid, alkali. Can be neutralized with water (for up to half an hour). Doctor's evaluation recommended.
Electrical	Destruction of muscles, nerves, circulatory system, etc., below the skin. Doctor's evaluation and ECG monitoring required.

If more than 10% of body surface is affected in second-and third-degree burns, shock can develop when large quantities of fluid (and its protein) are lost. When skin is burned, it cannot protect the body from airborne bacteria.

What is **Chinese restaurant syndrome**?

Monosodium glutamate (MSG), a commonly used flavor-enhancer, is thought to cause flushing, headache, and numbness about the mouth in susceptible people. Because many Chinese restaurants use MSG in food preparation, these symptoms may appear after a susceptible person eats Chinese food.

What is the **phobia** of number 13 called?

Fear of the number 13 is known as tridecaphobia, tredecaphobia, and triskaidekapho-bia. Persons may fear any situation involving this number, including a house number, the floor of a building, or the 13th day of the month. Many buildings omit labeling the 13th floor as such, for this reason. A phobia can develop for a wide range of objects, situations, or organisms. The list below demonstrates the variety:

Phobia subject	Phobia term
Animals	Zoophobia
Beards	Pogonophobia
Books	Bibliophobia
Churches	Ecclesiaphobia
Dreams	Oneirophobia
Flowers	Anthophobia
Food	Sitophobia
Graves	Taphophobia
Infection	Nosemaphobia
Lakes	Limnophobia
Leaves	Phyllophobia
Lightning	Astraphobia
Men	Androphobia
Money	Chrometophobia
Music	Musicophobia
Sex	Genophobia
Shadows	Sciophobia
Spiders	Arachnophobia
Sun	Heliophobia
Touch	Haptophobia
Trees	Dendrophobia
Walking	Basiphobia
Water	Hydrophobia
Women	Gynophobia
Work	Ergophobia
Writing	Graphophobia

Was **Napoleon** poisoned?

The most common opinion today is that Napoleon Bonaparte (1769–1821), Emperor of France from 1804 to 1815, died of a cancerous, perforated stomach. A significant minority of doctors and historians have made other claims ranging from various diseases to benign neglect to outright homicide. A Swedish toxicologist, Sten Forshufvud, advanced the theory that Napoleon died of arsenic poisoning, administered by an agent of the French Royalists who was planted in Napoleon's household during his final exile on the island of St. Helena.

HEALTH CARE

Which **symbol** is used to represent **medicine**?

The staff of Aesculapius has represented medicine since 800 B.C.E. It is a single serpent wound around a staff. The caduceus, the twin-serpent magic wand of the god Hermes or Mercury, came into use after 1800 and is commonly used today. The serpent has traditionally been a symbol of healing, and it is an old belief that eating part of a serpent would bring the power of healing to the ingester. Early Greeks saw in the serpent regenerative powers expressed by the serpent's periodic sloughing of its skin, and venerated the serpent. Later, the Greek god of medicine, Asklepius, called Aesculapius by the Romans, performed his functions in the form of a serpent. Sometimes this god is represented in art as an old man with a staff, around which is coiled a serpent.

What is the **Hippocratic Oath**?

The Hippocratic Oath is an oath demanded of physicians who are entering practice, which can be traced back to the Greek physician and teacher Hippocrates (ca. 460–ca. 377 B.C.E.). The oath reads as follows:

"I swear by Apollo the physician, by Aesculapius, Hygeia, and Panacea, and I take to witness all the gods, all the goddesses, to keep according to my ability and my judgement the following Oath:

"To consider dear to me as my parents him who taught me this art; to live in common with him and if necessary to share my goods with him; to look upon his children as my own brothers, to teach them this art if they so desire without fee or written promise; to impart to my sons and the sons of the master who taught me and the disciples who have enrolled themselves and have agreed to rules of the profession, but to these alone, the precepts and the instruction. I will prescribe regiment for the good of my patients according to my ability and my judgement and never to harm anyone. To please no one will I prescribe a deadly drug, nor give advice which may cause his death. Nor will I give a woman a pessary to procure abortion. But I will preserve the purity of my life and my art. I will not cut for stone, even for patients in whom the disease is manifest; I will leave this operation to be performed by practitioners (specialists in this art). In every house where I come I will enter only for the good of my patients, keeping myself far from all intentional ill-doing and all seduction, and especially from the pleasures of love with women or with men, be they free or slaves. All **373** that may come to my knowledge in the exercise of my profession or outside of my profession or in daily commerce with men, which ought not to be spread abroad, I will keep secret and will never reveal. If I keep this oath faithfully, may I enjoy life and practice my art, respected by all men and in all times; but if I swerve from it or violate it, may the reverse be my lot."

The oath varies slightly in wording among different sources.

Who was the founder of **modern medicine**?

Thomas Sydenham (1624–1689), who was also called the English Hippocrates, reintroduced the Hippocratic method of accurate observation at the bedside, and recording of observations, to build up a general clinical description of individual diseases. He is also considered one of the founders of epidemiology and was among the first to describe scarlet fever and Sydenham's chorea.

What was the **first medical college** in the United States?

The College of Philadelphia Department of Medicine, now the University of Pennsylvania School of Medicine, was established on May 3, 1765. The first commencement was held June 21, 1768, when medical diplomas were presented to the ten members of the graduating class.

Who was the **first woman physician** in the United States?

Elizabeth Blackwell (1821–1910) received her degree in 1849 from Geneva Medical College in New York. After overcoming many obstacles, she set up a small practice that expanded into the New York Infirmary for Women and Children, which featured an all-female staff.

When and where did the **first blood bank** open?

Several sites claim the distinction. Some sources list the first blood bank as opening in 1940 in New York City under the supervision of Dr. Richard C. Drew (1904–1950). Others list an earlier date of 1938 in Moscow at the Sklifosovsky Institute (Moscow's central emergency service hospital) founded by Professor Sergei Yudin. The term *blood bank* was coined by Bernard Fantus, who set up a centralized storage depot for blood in 1937 at the Cook County Hospital in Chicago, Illinois.

What is the difference between **homeopathy, osteopathic medicine, naturopathy,** and **chiropractic** medicine?

Developed by a German physician, Christian F. S. Hahneman (1755–1843), the therapy of homeopathy treats patients with small doses of 2,000 substances. Based on the principle that "like cures like," the medicine used is one that produces the same symptoms in a healthy person that the disease is producing in the sick person.

Chiropractic medicine is based on the belief that disease results from the lack of normal nerve function. Relying on physical manipulation and adjustment of the spine for therapy, rather than on drugs or surgery, this therapy, used by the ancient Egyptians, Chinese, and Hindus, was rediscovered in 1895 by American osteopath Daniel David Palmer (1845–1913).

Developed in the United States by Dr. Andrew Taylor Still (1828–1917), osteopathic medicine recognizes the role of the musculoskeletal system in healthy function of the human body. The physician is fully licensed and uses manipulation techniques as well as traditional diagnostic and therapeutic procedures. Osteopathy is practiced as part of standard Western medicine.

Naturopathy is based on the principle that disease is due to the accumulation of waste products and toxins in the body. Practitioners believe that health is maintained by avoiding anything artificial or unnatural in the diet or in the environment.

How many physicians are there in the United States?

In 1994 there were 551,151 male physicians and 113,263 female physicians in the United States.

How many nursing homes are in the United States?

In 1994 there were 15,142 nursing homes in the United States; 11,083 of them were profit-making facilities and 4,059 were non-profit facilities.

What is the difference between the degrees doctor of dental surgery (DDS) and doctor of medical dentistry (DMD)?

The title depends entirely on the school's preference in terminology. The degrees are equivalent.

How many people visit a dentist regularly?

Only about half the population visit a dentist as often as once a year.

What is the difference between an ophthalmologist, optometrist, and optician?

An ophthalmologist is a physician who specializes in care of the eyes. Ophthalmologists conduct examinations to determine the quality of vision and the need for corrective glasses or contact lenses. They also check for the presence of any disorders, such as glaucoma or cataracts. Ophthalmologists may perform surgery or prescribe glasses, contact lenses, or medication, as necessary.

An optometrist is a specialist trained to examine the eyes and to prescribe, supply, and adjust glasses or contact lenses. Because they are not physicians, optometrists may not prescribe drugs or perform surgery. An optometrist refers patients requiring these types of treatment to an ophthalmologist.

An optician is a person who fits, supplies, and adjusts glasses or contact lenses. Because their training is limited, opticians may not examine or test eyes or prescribe glasses or drugs.

DIAGNOSTIC EQUIPMENT, TESTS, ETC.

What is the meaning of the **medical abbreviation NYD**?

Not yet diagnosed.

How is **blood pressure** measured?

A sphygmomanometer is the device used to measure blood pressure. It was invented in 1881 by an Austrian named Von Bash. It consists of a cuff with an inflatable bladder that is wrapped around the upper arm, a rubber bulb to inflate the bladder, and a device that indicates the pressure of blood. Measuring arterial tension (blood pressure) of a person's circulation is achieved when the cuff is applied to the arm over the artery and pumped to a pressure that occludes or blocks it. This gives the systolic measure, or the maximum pressure of the blood, which occurs during contraction of the ventricles of the heart. Air is then released from the cuff until the blood is first heard passing through the opening artery (called Korotkoff sounds). This gives diastolic pressure, or the minimum value of blood pressure that occurs during the relaxation of the arterial-filling phase of the heart muscle.

What is the meaning of the numbers in a **blood pressure reading**?

When blood is forced into the aorta, it exerts a pressure against the walls; this is referred to as blood pressure. In the reading the upper number, the systolic, measures the pressure during the period of ventricular contraction. The lower number, the diastolic, measures the pressure when blood is entering the relaxed chambers of the heart. While these numbers can vary due to age, sex, weight, and other factors, the normal blood pressure is around 110/60 to 140/90 millimeters of mercury.

Is there a name for the **heart-monitoring machine** that people sometimes wear for a day or two while carrying on their normal activities?

A portable version of the electrocardiograph (ECG) designed by J. J. Holter is called a Holter monitor. Electrodes attached to the chest are linked to a small box containing a recording device. The device records the activity of the heart.

What are the normal **test ranges** for total **cholesterol, triglycerides,** low density lipoproteins **(LDL),** and high density lipoproteins **(HDL)?**

The National Cholesterol Education Program has drawn up these guidelines:

	Desirable	Borderline	High Risk
Total Blood Cholesterol	Less than 200 mg/dl	200–239 mg/dl	240 mg/dl or more
LDL	Less than 130 mg/dl	130–159 mg/dl	160 mg/dl or more
HDL	45–65 mg/dl	35–45 mg/dl	Below 35 mg/dl

mg/dl = milligrams per deciliter

What is **nuclear magnetic resonance imaging?**

Magnetic resonance imaging (MRI), sometimes called nuclear magnetic resonance imaging (NMR), is a non-invasive, non-ionizing diagnostic technique. It is useful in detecting small tumors, blocked blood vessels, or damaged vertebral disks. Because it does not involve the use of radiation, it can often be used where x-rays are dangerous. Large magnets beam energy through the body causing hydrogen atoms in the body to resonate. This produces energy in the form of tiny electrical signals. A computer detects these signals, which vary in different parts of the body and according to whether an organ is healthy or not. The variation enables a picture to be produced on a screen and interpreted by a medical specialist.

What distinguishes MRI from computerized x-ray scanners is that most x-ray studies cannot distinguish between a living body and a cadaver, while MRI "sees" the difference between life and death in great detail. More specifically, it can discriminate between healthy and diseased tissues with more sensitivity than conventional radiographic instruments like x-rays or CAT scans. CAT (computerized axial tomography) scanners have been around since 1973 and are actually glorified x-ray machines. They offer three-dimensional viewing but are limited because the object imaged must remain still.

The concept of using MRI to detect tumors in patients was proposed by Raymond Damadian in a 1972 patent application. The fundamental MRI imaging concept used in all present-day MRI instruments was proposed by Paul Lauterbar in an article in *Nature* in 1973. The main advantages of MRI are that it not only gives superior images of soft tissues (like organs), but can measure dynamic physiological changes in a non-invasive manner (without penetrating the body in any way). A disadvantage of MRI is that it cannot be used for every patient. For example, patients with implants, pacemakers, or cerebral aneurysm clips made of metal cannot be examined using MRI because the machine's magnet could potentially move these objects within the body, causing damage.

Ultrasound is another type of 3-D computerized imaging. Using brief pulses of ultrahigh frequency acoustic waves (lasting 0.01 second), it can produce a sonar map of the imaged object.

What is the instrument a doctor uses to check **reflexes**?

A plessor or plexor or percussor is a small hammer, usually with a soft rubber head, used to tap the part directly. Also called a reflex hammer or a percussion hammer, it is used by a doctor to elicit reflexes by tapping on tendons. In the most common test, the patient sits on a surface high enough to allow his legs to dangle freely, and the physician lightly taps the patellar tendon, just below the kneecap. This stimulus briefly stretches the quadriceps muscle on top of the thigh. The stretch causes the muscle to contract, which makes the leg kick forward. The time interval between the tendon tap and the start of the leg extension is about 50 microseconds. That interval is too short for the involvement of the brain and is totally reflexive. This test indicates the status of an individual's reflex control of movement.

DRUGS, MEDICINES, ETC.

What is **pharmacognosy**?

It is the science of natural drugs and their physical, botanical, and chemical properties. Natural products derived from plant, vegetable, animal, and mineral sources have been a part of medical practice for thousands of years. Today about 25% of all prescriptions dispensed in pharmacies contain active ingredients that are extracted from higher plants, and many more are found in over-the-counter products.

What is the meaning of the **abbreviations** often used by a doctor when writing a **prescription**?

Latin phrase	Shortened form	Meaning
quaque hora	qh	every hour
quaque die	qd	every day
bis in die	bid	twice a day
ter in die	tid	three times a day
quarter in die	qid	four times a day
pro re nata	prn	as needed
ante cibum	a.c.	before meals

Latin phrase	Shortened form	Meaning
post cibum	p.c.	after meals
per os	p.o.	by mouth
nihil per os	n.p.o.	nothing by mouth
signetur	sig	let it be labeled
statim	stat	immediately
ad libitum	ad lib	at pleasure
hora somni	h.s.	at bedtime
cum	c	with
sine	s	without
guttae	gtt	drops
semis	ss	a half
et	et	and

What are the common medication measures?

Approximate equivalents of apothecary measures are given below.

Apothecary volume

Volume	Equivalent
1 minim	0.06 milliliters or 0.02 fluid drams or 0.002 fluid ounces
1½ minims	0.1 milliliters
15 minims	1 milliliter
480 minims	1 fluid ounce
1 dram	3.7 milliliters or 60 minims
1 t (teaspoon)	60 drops
3 t (teaspoons)	½ ounce
1 T (tablespoon)	½ ounce
2 T (tablespoons)	1 ounce
1 C (cup)	8 ounces or 30 milliliters

Apothecary weights

Weight	Equivalent
1 grain	60 milligrams or ½ dram
60 grains	1 dram or 3.75 grams
8 drams	1 ounce or 30 grams

How long can a prescription drug be kept?

Generally a prescription drug should not be more than one year old. Some over-the-counter medications have an expiration date on their box or container. A cream should not be used if it has separated into its components. Although some general guidelines are given below, "When in doubt, throw it out."

Remedy	Maximum shelf life (years)
Cold tablets	1 to 2
Laxatives	2 to 3
Minerals	6 or more
Nonprescription painkiller tablets	1 to 4
Prescription antibiotics	2 to 3
Prescription antihypertension tablets	2 to 4
Travel sickness tablets	2
Vitamins (protected from heat, light, and moisture)	6 or more

Which drugs are **prescribed the most**?

In 1995, the drugs most often dispensed in U.S. pharmacies were:

Brand Name	Therapy
Premarin	Symptoms of menopause
Trimox	Penicillin antibiotic
Synthroid	Thyroid hormone replacement
Amoxil	Penicillin antibiotic
Zantac	Anti-ulcer agent
Lanoxin	Treats heart problems
Procardia XL	Treats cardiovascular problems
Vasotec	Treats cardiovascular problems
Prozac	Antidepressant
Proventil Aerosol	Bronchodilator

What is a **double-blind study**?

In drug tests a double-blind study is a study in which neither the investigator administering the drug nor the subject taking it knows if the patient is receiving the experimental drug or a neutral substitute called a placebo. In this manner, bias, either on the part of the administrator or the subject, can be elimated from the study.

What is meant by the term **orphan drugs**?

Orphan drugs are intended to treat diseases that affect fewer than 200,000 Americans. With little chance of making money, a drug company is not likely to undertake the necessary research and expense of finding drugs that might treat these diseases. Also, if the drug is a naturally occurring substance, it cannot be patented in the U.S., and **381** companies are reluctant to invest money in such a medication when it cannot be protected against exploitation by competing drug companies. Encouragingly, the Orphan Drug Act of 1983 offers a number of incentives to drug companies to encourage development of these drugs. The act has provided hope for millions of people with rare and otherwise untreatable conditions.

How many of the **medications** used today are **derived from plants**?

Of the more than 250,000 known plant species, less than 1% have been thoroughly tested for medical applications. Yet out of this tiny portion have come 25% of our prescription medicines. The United States National Cancer Institute has identified 3,000 plants from which anti-cancer drugs are or can be made. This includes ginseng (*Panax quinquefolius*), Asian mayapple (*Podophyllum hexandrum*), western yew (*Taxus brevifolia*), and rosy periwinkle. Seventy percent of these 3,000 come from rain-forests, which also are a source of countless other drugs for diseases and infections. Rainforest plants are rich in so-called secondary metabolites, particularly alkaloids, which biochemists believe the plants produce to protect them from disease and insect attack. However, with the current rate of rainforest destruction, raw materials for future medicines are certainly being lost. Also, as tribal groups disappear, their knowledge of the properties and uses of these plants species will be lost.

From what plant is **taxol** extracted?

Taxol is produced from the bark of the western or Pacific yew (*Taxus brevifolia*). It has been shown to inhibit the growth of HeLa cells (human cancer cells) and is a promising new treatment for several kinds of cancer. Originally it was a scarce drug, but in 1994, two groups of researchers announced its synthesis. The synthesis is a formidable challenge, and better procedures and modifications remain to be developed. Since taxol is developed now from needles instead of tree bark, the natural source is more available, but the synthetic version will be needed to devise modified or "designer" taxols whose cancer-fighting ability may prove more effective.

How long is a **tetanus shot** effective?

In the United States, infants are vaccinated against tetanus at two months, four months, and six months. The vaccination is part of the DPT shot, which protects against diphtheria, tetanus, and pertussis (whooping cough). In order to insure immunity, booster doses are given every 10 years or at the time of a major injury if it occurs more than five years after a dose.

Who discovered **penicillin**?

British bacteriologist Sir Alexander Fleming (1881–1955) discovered the bacteria-killing property of penicillin in 1928. Fleming noticed that no bacteria grew around bits of the *Penicillium notatum* fungus that accidentally fell into a bacterial culture in his laboratory. However, although penicillin was clinically used, it was not until 1941 that Dr. Howard Florey (1898–1968) purified and tested it. The first large-scale plant to produce penicillin was constructed under the direction of Dr. Ernest Chain (1906–1979). By 1945, penicillin was commercially available. In that year, Chain, Florey, and Fleming received a joint Nobel Prize for their work on penicillin.

Ernest Chain.

Today penicillin is still used successfully in the treatment of many bacterial diseases, including pneumonia, strep throat, scarlet fever, gonorrhea, and impetigo. Its discovery also led to the development of other antibiotics that are useful in destroying a broad spectrum of pathogenic bacteria.

Who discovered the antibiotic **streptomycin**?

The Russian-born microbiologist Selman A. Waksman (1888–1973) coined the term "antibiotic" and subsequently discovered streptomycin in 1943. In 1944 Merck and Company agreed to produce it to be used against tuberculosis and tuberculosis meningitis.

Streptomycin ultimately proved to have some human toxicity and was supplanted by other antibiotics, but its discovery changed the course of modern medicine. In addition to its use in treating tuberculosis, it was also used to treat bacterial meningitis, endocarditis, pulmonary and urinary tract infections, leprosy, typhoid fever, bacillary dysentery, cholera, and bubonic plague. Streptomycin saved countless lives, and its development led scientists to search the microbial world for other antibiotics and medicines.

Who developed the **poliomyelitis vaccine** in America?

Immunologist Jonas E. Salk (1914–1995) developed the first vaccine (made from a killed-virus) against poliomyelitis. In 1952 he prepared and tested the vaccine, and in **383**

1954 massive field tests were successfully undertaken. Two years later immunologist Albert Sabin (1906–1993) developed an oral vaccine made from inactivated live viruses of three polio strains. Because of its easy administration and the fact that it requires fewer booster inoculations, Sabin's vaccine has replaced the Salk vaccine as the one to prevent polio. However, Salk remains known as the man who defeated polio.

Who was the first to use chemotherapy?

Chemotherapy is the use of chemical substances to treat diseases, specifically malignant diseases. The drug must interfere with the growth of bacterial, parasitic, or tumor cells, without significantly affecting host cells. Especially effective in types of cancer such as leukemia and lymphoma, chemotherapy was introduced in medicine by the German physician Paul Ehrlich (1854–1915).

Paul Ehrlich.

What are monoclonal antibodies?

Monoclonal antibodies are artificially produced antibodies designed to neutralize a specific foreign protein (antigen). Cloned cells (genetically identical) are stimulated to produce antibodies to the target antigen. Most monoclonal antibody work so far has used cloned cells from mice infected with cancer. In some cases they are used to destroy cancer cells directly; in others they carry other drugs to combat the cancer cells.

Why are anabolic steroids harmful?

Anabolic (protein-building) steroids are drugs that mimic the effects of testosterone and other male sex hormones. They can build muscle tissue, strengthen bone, and speed muscle recovery following exercise or injury. They are sometimes prescribed to treat osteoporosis in postmenopausal women and some types of anemia. Some athletes use anabolic steroids to build muscle strength and bulk, and to allow a more rigorous training schedule. Weight lifters, field event athletes, and body builders are most likely to use anabolic steroids. The drugs are banned from most organized competitions because of the dangers they pose to health and to prevent an unfair advantage.

Adverse effects include hypertension, acne, edema, and damage to liver, heart, and adrenal glands. Psychiatric symptoms can include hallucinations, paranoid delusions, and manic episodes. In men, anabolic steroids can cause infertility, impotence, and premature balding. Women can develop masculine characteristics, such as excessive hair growth, male-pattern balding, disruption of menstruation, and deepening of the voice. Children and adolescents can develop problems in growing bones, leading to short stature.

How is **patient-controlled analgesia (PCA)** administered?

This a drug delivery system that dispenses a preset intravenous (IV) dose of a narcotic analgesic for reduction of pain, when the patient pushes a switch on an electric cord. The device consists of a computerized pump with a chamber containing a syringe holding up to 60 milliliters of a drug. The patient administers a dose of narcotic when the need for pain relief arises. A lockout interval device automatically inactivates the system if the patient tries to increase the amount of narcotic within a preset time period.

What is a **Brompton's cocktail**?

Named for the Brompton Chest Hospital, England, Brompton's cocktail is a mixture of cocaine, morphine, and antiemetics used to reduce pain and induce euphoria, particularly in terminally ill cancer patients.

What were the **birth defects** caused by the drug **Thalidomide**?

In the early 1960s, Thalidomide was marketed as a sedative and antinausea drug. It was found to cause birth defects in babies whose mothers had taken the drug for morning sickness. Some babies were born without arms or legs. Others were born blind or deaf or with heart defects or intestinal abnormalities. Although some were mentally retarded, most were of normal intelligence. This tragedy led to much stricter laws regulating the sale and testing of new drugs.

How does **RU-486** cause an abortion?

A pill containing RU-486 (mifepristone) deprives a fertilized embryo of a compatible uterine environment, terminating a pregnancy within 45 days of fertilization. It is currently used in China and France.

What are **designer drugs,** such as **China White**?

Designer drugs are synthesized chemicals that resemble such available narcotics as fentanyl and meperidine. China white (3-methyl-fentanyl) is one of these drugs and is an analogue of fentanyl. It is 3,000 times more potent than morphine. Even small amounts can be fatal, and it has been responsible for more than 100 overdose deaths in California.

What is a **controlled substance**?

The Comprehensive Drug Abuse Prevention and Control Act of 1971 was designed to control the distribution and use of all depressant and stimulant drugs and other drugs of abuse or potential abuse. Centrally acting drugs are divided into five classes called Schedule I through V.

	Includes	Examples
Schedule I	Experimental and illegal drugs. They are not prescribable and do not have an acceptable medical use.	Heroin, LSD, Peyote
Schedule II	Like Schedule I drugs, Schedule II drugs can be abused. However, they have acceptable medical uses. Prescriptions cannot be renewed.	Amphetamine, Cocaine, Codeine, Morphine
Schedule III	Less likely to be abused than Schedule II drugs. Prescriptions can be refilled up to 5 times in 6 months.	Aspirin with codeine, Methylprylon, Phendimetrazine
Schedule IV	Lower potential for abuse than Schedule I-III. Usually they fall under similar refill regulations as Schedule III drugs.	Chloral hydrate, Diazepam, Phenobarbital
Schedule V	Low potential for abuse. May contain small amounts of narcotics. Regulated in the same manner as non-scheduled prescription drugs.	Lomotil, Parapectolin, Cheracol, Robitussin

Which tests detect **illegal drug use**?

Blood samples are rarely if ever used in routine screening of individuals for drug abuse. Blood samples provide little valuable information unless the drug was consumed a short time before the blood was drawn. Urine, on the other hand, is easily collected and can be analyzed and transported cheaply. Samples of skin, saliva, and hair can also be tested but with greater difficulty.

Urine tests detect cocaine used by a person within the past 24 to 36 hours. Hair analysis can detect cocaine used more than a year ago. Other drugs that can be detected by urine testing are:

PCP (phencylidine)—up to 7–8 days

Barbituates—up to 72 hours
Morphine—1–2 days
Heroin—2–3 days or 4–5 days if larger doses are taken
Methaqualone (Quaalude)—up to 10 days
Cannabis (marijuana)—up to 5 days for infrequent users; up to 10 days for heavy smokers

What is the difference between **cocaine, freebase, and crack**?

Cocaine comes in several different forms. Coca paste is widely used in South America usually added to and smoked in tobacco or marijuana cigarettes. Cocaine hydrochloride, the form most common in the United States, is a white powder. It is inhaled through the nose ("snorted") from tiny spoons, rolled-up dollar bills, or straws. It can also be mixed with water and injected.

Freebase is a purified form of cocaine that is smoked in a water pipe. It is prepared by applying ether, baking powder, or other solvent to cocaine powder and heating the mixture.

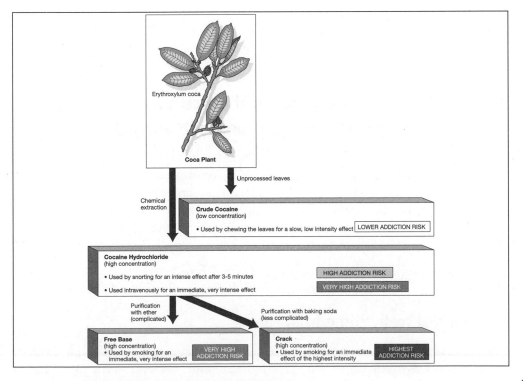

Various forms of cocaine and the addiction risks associated with them.

Crack is freebase that comes in ready-to-smoke chunks or "rocks." Crack is usually smoked in a water pipe. Some users apply it to tobacco or marijuana cigarettes.

Where is **marijuana grown legally** in the United States?

The federal marijuana farm at the University of Mississippi was established in 1968. This farm supplies most of the marijuana (*Cannabis sativa*) used for official medical research in America.

How long do **chemicals from marijuana** stay in the body?

When marijuana is smoked, tetrahydrocannabinol (THC), its active ingredient, is absorbed primarily in the fat tissues. The body transforms the THC into metabolites, which can be detected by urine tests for up to a week. Tests involving radioactively labeled THC have traced the metabolites for up to a month. The retention of labeled THC in humans is about 40% at three days and 30% at one week.

SURGERY AND OTHER NON–DRUG TREATMENTS

What are the most frequent **surgical procedures** for which **second opinions** are most commonly advised?

Back surgery	Hernia repair
Breast surgery	Hip reconstruction
Bunion removal	Hysterectomy
Cataract removal	Knee surgery
Dilatation and curettage	Nasal septum repair
Gall bladder removal	Prostate removal
Heart surgery	Tonsillectomy
Hemorrhoid removal	Varicose vein removal

Does **catgut** really come from cats?

Catgut, an absorbable sterile strand, is obtained from collagen derived from healthy mammals. It was originally prepared from the submucosal layer of the intestines of sheep. It is used as a surgical ligature.

Who was the first African American surgeon to perform heart surgery?

D r. Daniel Hale Williams (1858–1931) was a pioneer in open heart surgery. In 1893, he was able to save a knifing victim by opening up the patient's chest with the help of a surgical team, exposing the beating heart. He sewed the knife wound a fraction of an inch from the heart without the aid of x-rays, blood transfusions, or anesthetics.

Who received the **first heart transplant**?

On December 3, 1967, in Capetown, South Africa, Dr. Christiaan Barnard (b. 1922) and a team of 30 associates performed the first heart transplant. In a five-hour operation the heart of Denise Ann Darval, age 25, an auto accident victim, was transplanted into the body of Louis Washansky, a 55-year-old wholesale grocer. Washansky lived for 18 days before dying from pneumonia.

The first heart transplant performed in the United States was on a $2\frac{1}{2}$-week-old baby boy at Maimonides Hospital, Brooklyn, New York, on December 6, 1967, by Dr. Adrian Kantrowitz (b. 1918). The baby boy lived $6\frac{1}{2}$ hours. The first adult to receive a heart transplant in the United States was Mike Kasperak, age 54, at the Stanford Medical Center in Palo Alto, California, on January 6, 1968. Dr. Norman Shumway performed the operation. Mr. Kasperak lived 14 days.

From December 1967 until March 31, 1993, 14,085 heart transplants have been performed. Interestingly, almost no transplants were done in the 1970s because of the problem of rejection of the new heart by the recipient's immune system. In 1969, Jean-François Borel discovered the anti-rejection drug cyclosporine, but it was not widely used until 1983 when the FDA granted approval. Today heart transplantation is an established medical procedure.

When was the **first artificial heart** used?

On December 2, 1982, Dr. Barney B. Clark (1921–1983), a 61-year-old retired dentist, became the first human to receive a permanently implanted artificial heart. It was known as the Jarvik-7 after its inventor, Dr. Robert Jarvik (b. 1946). The 7.5-hour operation was performed by Dr. William DeVries (b. 1943), a surgeon at the University of Utah Medical Center. Dr. Clark died on March 23, 1983, 112 days later. In Louisville, Kentucky, William Schroeder (1923–1986) survived 620 days with an artificial heart (November 25, 1984 to August 7, 1986). On January 11, 1990, the United States Food and Drug Administration (FDA) recalled the Jarvik-7, which had been the only artificial heart approved by the FDA for use.

How much does the **cardiac pacemaker** weigh?

The modern pacemaker generator is a hermetically sealed titanium metal can weighing from one to 4.5 ounces (30 to 130 grams) and powered by a lithium battery that can last two to 15 years. Used to correct an insufficient or irregular heartbeat, the cardiac pacemaker corrects the low cardiac rhythm through electrical stimulation, which increases the contractions of the heart muscle. The contraction and expansion of the heart muscle produces a heartbeat, one of three billion in an average lifetime, which pumps blood throughout the body. A pacemaker has gold or platinum electrodes, conducting wires, and a pacing box (miniature generator). In both kinds of pacemakers—those implanted in the chest or external—the electrode is attached to the heart's right ventricle (chamber), either directly through the chest or threaded through a vein.

Why are **eye transplants** not available?

It is because the eye's retina is part of the brain, and the retina's cells are derived from brain tissue. Retinal cells and the cells that connect them to the brain are the least amenable to being manipulated outside the body.

Who was the **first test-tube baby**?

Louise Brown, born on July 25, 1978, is the first baby produced from fertilization done in vitro—outside the mother's body. Patrick Steptoe was the obstetrician and Robert Edwards the biologist who designed the method for in-vitro fertilization and early embryo development.

In-vitro fertilization occurs in a glass dish, not a test tube, where eggs from the mother's ovary are combined with the father's sperm (in a salt solution). Fertilization should occur within 24 hours and when cell division begins, these fertilized eggs are placed in the mother's womb (or possibly another woman's womb).

What is **lithotripsy**?

Lithotripsy is the use of ultrasonic or shock waves to pulverize kidney stones (calculi), allowing the small particles to be excreted or removed from the body. There are two different methods: extracorporeal shock wave lithotripsy (ESWL) and percutaneous lithotripsy. The ESWL method, used on smaller stones, breaks up the stones with external shock waves from a machine called a lithotripter. This technique has eliminated the need for more invasive stone surgery in many cases. For larger stones, a type of endoscope, called a nephroscope, is inserted into the kidney through a small incision. The ultrasonic waves from the nephroscope shatter the stones, and the fragments are removed through the nephroscope.

Prior to the condom, what was the main **contraceptive** practice?

Contraceptive devices have been used throughout recorded history. The most traditional of such devices was a sponge soaked in vinegar. The condom was named for its English inventor, the personal physician to Charles II (1630–1685), who used a sheath of stretched, oiled sheep intestine to protect the king from syphilis. Previously penile sheaths were used, such as the linen one made by Italian anatomist, Gabriel Fallopius (1523–1562), but they were too heavy to be successful.

What is **synthetic skin**?

The material consists of a very porous collagen fiber bonded to a sugar polymer (*glycoaminoglycan*) obtained from shark cartilage. It is covered by a sheet of silicon rubber. It was developed by Ioannis V. Yannas and his colleagues at Massachusetts Institute of Technology around 1985. Soon after its introduction, synthetic skin was used to successfully treat more than 100 severely burned victims.

How is a **mustard plaster** made?

Mix one tablespoon of powdered mustard with four tablespoons of flour. Add enough warm water to make a runny paste. Put the mixture in a folded cloth and apply to the chest. Add olive oil first to the skin if the patient has a delicate skin.

What is a **negative ion generator**?

A negative ion generator is an electrostatic air cleaner that sprays a continuous fountain of negatively charged ions into the air. Some researchers say that the presence of these ions causes a feeling of well-being, increased mental and physical energy, and relief from some of the symptoms of allergies, asthma, and chronic headaches. It may also aid in healing of burns and peptic ulcers.

What is **reflexology**?

Reflexology is the application of specific pressures to reflex points in the hands and feet. The reflex points relate to every organ and every part of the body. Massaging of the reflex points is done to prevent or cure diseases. Believed to have been used in

Asian cultures as long as 2,000 years ago, reflexology was introduced to the United States at the turn of the century by Dr. William Fitzgerald and Eunice D. Ingham. Today nearly 25,000 certified practitioners can be found througout the world.

What is **iridology**?

Iridology is the study of the iris of the eye with the intent of diagnosing weaknesses in the body. Iridologists believe that areas of the iris correspond with different body parts. Among the conditions they monitor are color, clarity, texture, fibers, rings, and spots on the iris. Once the diagnosis is made, they recommend natural methods of healing and conditioning of weak areas.

What is **aromatherapy**?

Aromatherapy involves using particular scents derived from essential oils to influence emotions and to treat and cure minor ailments. Rene Maurice Gatlefosse, a French cosmetic chemist, introduced the theory in the late 1970s. It is based on the fact that the olfactory and emotional centers of the body are connected. By inhaling different aromas, emotional concerns as well as physical complaints are said to be eased.

Who developed **psychodrama**?

Psychodrama was developed by Jacob L. Moreno, a psychiatrist born in Romania, who lived and practiced in Vienna until he came to the United States in 1925. He soon began to conduct psychodrama sessions and founded a psychodrama institute in Beacon, New York, in 1934. Largely because of Moreno's efforts it is practiced worldwide.

Psychodrama is defined as a method of group psychotherapy in which personality makeup, interpersonal relationships, conflicts, and emotional problems are explored by means of special dramatic methods.

WEIGHTS, MEASURES, TIME, TOOLS, AND WEAPONS

WEIGHTS, MEASURES, AND MEASUREMENT

See also: Physics and Chemistry—Measurement, Methodology, etc.; Space—Observation and Measurement; Earth—Observation and Measurement; Energy—Measures and Measurement; Health and Medicine—Drugs, Medicines, etc.

How much does the **biblical shekel** weigh in modern units?

A shekel is equal to 0.497 ounces (14.1 grams). Below are listed some ancient measurements with some modern equivalents given.

Biblical
  Volume

omer	=	4.188 quarts (modern) or 0.45 peck (modern) or 3.964 liters (modern)
9.4 omers	=	1 bath
10 omers	=	1 ephah

  Weight

shekel	=	0.497 ounces (modern) or 14.1 grams (modern)

  Length

cubit	=	21.8 inches (modern)

Egyptian
  Weight

60 grams	=	1 shekel
60 shekels	=	1 great mina
60 great minas	=	1 talent

Greek
  Length

cubit	=	18.3 inches (modern)
stadion	=	607.2 or 622 feet (modern)

  Weight

obol or obolos	=	715.38 milligrams (modern) or. 0.04 ounces (modern)
drachma	=	4.2923 grams (modern) or 6 obols
mina	=	0.9463 pounds (modern) or 96 drachmas
talent	=	60 mina

Roman
  Length

cubit	=	17.5 inches (modern)
stadium	=	202 yards (modern) or 415.5 cubits

  Weight

denarius	=	0.17 ounces (modern)

  Volume

amphora	=	6.84 gallons (modern)

What is the SI system of measurement?

French scientists as far back as the 17th and 18th centuries questioned the hodge-podge of the many illogical and imprecise standards used for measurement, and began a crusade to make a comprehensive, logical, precise, and universal measurement system called Système Internationale d'Unités, or SI for short. It uses the metric system as its base. Since all the units are in multiples of 10, calculations are simplified. Today all countries except the United States, Burma, and Liberia use this system. However, some elements within American society do use SI—scientists, exporting/importing industries, and federal agencies (as of November 30, 1992).

The SI or metric system has seven fundamental standards: the meter (for length), the kilogram (for mass), the second (for time), the ampere (for electric current), the kelvin (for temperature), the candela (for luminous intensity), and the mole (for amount of substance). In addition, two supplementary units, the radian (plane angle) and steradian (solid angle), and a large number of derived units compose the current system, which is still evolving. Some derived units, which use special names, are the hertz, newton, pascal, joule, watt, coulomb, volt, farad, ohm, siemens, weber, tesla, henry, lumen, lux, becquerel, gray, and sievert. Its unit of volume or capacity is the cubic decimeter, but many still use "liter" in its place. Very large or very small dimensions are expressed through a series of prefixes, which increase or decrease in multiples of ten. For example, a decimeter is 1/10 of a meter; a centimeter is 1/100 of a meter, and a millimeter is 1/1000 of a meter. A dekameter is 10 meters, a hectometer is 100 meters, and a kilometer is 1,000 meters. The use of these prefixes enable the system to express these units in an orderly way, and avoid inventing new names and new relationships.

How was the length of a **meter** originally determined?

It was originally intended that the meter should represent one ten-millionth of the distance along the meridian running from the North Pole to the equator through Dunkirk, France, and Barcelona, Spain. French scientists determined this distance, working nearly six years to complete the task in November 1798. They decided to use a platinum-iridium bar as the physical replica of the meter. Although the surveyors made an error of about two miles, the error was not discovered until much later. Rather than change the length of the meter to conform to the actual distance, scientists in 1889 chose the platinum-iridium bar as the international prototype. It was used until 1960. Numerous copies of it are in other parts of the world, including the United States National Bureau of Standards.

How is the **length of a meter** presently determined?

The meter is equal to 39.37 inches. It is presently defined as the distance traveled by light in a vacuum during 1/299,792,458 of a second. From 1960 to 1983, the length of a meter had been defined as 1,650,763.73 times the wavelength of the orange light emitted when a gas consisting of the pure krypton isotope of mass number 86 is excited in an electrical discharge.

How did the **yard** as a unit of measurement originate?

In early times the natural way to measure lengths was to use various portions of the body (the foot, the thumb, the forearm, etc.). According to tradition, a yard measured on King Henry I (1068–1135) of England became the standard yard still used today. It was the distance from his nose to the middle fingertip of his extended arm.

Other measures were derived from physical activity such as a pace, a league (distance that equalled an hour's walking), an acre (amount plowed in a day), a furlong (length of a plowed ditch), etc., but obviously these units were unreliable. The ell, based on the distance between the elbow and index fingertip, was used to measure out cloth. It ranged from 0.513 to 2.322 meters depending on the locality where it was used and even on the type of goods measured.

Below are listed some linear measurements that evolved from this old reckoning into U.S. customary measures:

U.S. customery linear measures

1 hand	=	4 inches
1 foot	=	12 inches
1 yard	=	3 feet
1 rod (pole or perch)	=	16.5 feet
1 fathom	=	6 feet

U.S. customery linear measures

1 furlong	=	220 yards or 660 feet or 40 rods
1 (statute) mile	=	1,760 yards or 5,280 feet or 8 furlongs
1 league	=	5,280 yards or 15,840 feet or 3 miles
1 international nautical mile	=	6,076.1 feet

Conversion to metric

1 inch	=	2.54 centimeters
1 foot	=	0.304 meters
1 yard	=	0.9144 meters
1 fathom	=	1.83 meters
1 rod	=	5.029 meters
1 furlong	=	201.168 meters
1 league	=	4.828 kilometers
1 mile	=	1.609 kilometers
1 international nautical mile	=	1.852 kilometers

Why is a **nautical mile** different from a **statute mile**?

Queen Elizabeth I established the statute mile as 5,280 feet (1,609 meters). This measure, based on walking distance, originated with the Romans, who designated 1,000 paces as a land mile.

The nautical mile is not based on human locomotion, but on the circumference of the Earth. There was wide disagreement on the precise measurement, but by 1954 the United States adopted the International Nautical Mile of 1,852 meters (6.076 feet). It is the length on the Earth's surface of one minute of arc.

1 nautical mile (Int.) = 1.1508 statute miles

1 statute mile = 0.868976 nautical miles

How are U.S. customary measures **converted** to metric measures and vice versa?

Listed below is the conversion process for common units of measure:

To convert from	To	Multiply by
acres	meters, square	4,046.856
centimeters	inches	0.394
centimeters	feet	0.0328
centimeters, cubic	inches, cubic	0.06
centimeters, square	inches, square	0.155

How can one use U.S. money as a measuring device?

U.S. paper currency is 6 1/8 inches wide by 2 5/8 inches long. The diameter of a quarter is approximately one inch. The diameter of a penny is approximately three-quarters of an inch.

To convert from	To	Multiply by
feet	meters	0.305
feet, square	meters, square	0.093
gallons, U.S.	liters	3.785
grams	ounces (avoirdupois)	0.035
hectares	kilometers, square	0.01
hectares	miles, square	0.004
inches	centimeters	2.54
inches	millimeters	25.4
inches, cubic	centimeters, cubic	16.387
inches, cubic	liters	0.016387
inches, cubic	meters, cubic	0.0000164
inches, square	centimeters, square	6.4516
inches, square	meters, square	0.0006452
kilograms	ounces, troy	32.15075
kilograms	pounds (avoirdupois)	2.205
kilograms	tons, metric	0.001
kilometers	feet	3,280.8
kilometers	miles	0.621
kilometers, square	hectares	100
knots	miles per hour	1.151
liters	fluid ounces	33.815
liters	gallons	0.264
liters	pints	2.113
liters	quarts	1.057
meters	feet	3.281
meters	yards	1.094
meters, cubic	yards, cubic	1.308
meters, cubic	feet, cubic	35.315
meters, square	feet, square	10.764
meters, square	yards, square	1.196
miles, nautical	kilometers	1.852
miles, square	hectares	258.999

To convert from	To	Multiply by
miles, square	kilometers, square	2.59
miles (statute)	meters	1,609.344
miles (statute)	kilometers	1.609344
ounces (avoirdupois)	grams	28.35
ounces (avoirdupois)	kilograms	0.0283495
ounces, fluid	liters	0.03
pints, liquid	liters	0.473
pounds (avoirdupois)	grams	453.592
pounds (avoirdupois)	kilograms	0.454
quarts	liters	0.946
tons (short/U.S.)	tonne	0.907
ton, long	tonne	1.016
tonne	ton (short/U.S.)	1.102
tonne	ton, long	0.984
yards	meters	0.914
yards, square	meters, square	0.836
yards, cubic	meters, cubic	0.765

Which countries of the world have not formally begun converting to the metric system?

The United States, Burma, and Liberia are the only countries that have not formally converted to the metric system. As early as 1790, Thomas Jefferson, then Secretary of State, proposed adoption of the metric system. It was not implemented because Great Britain, America's major trading source, had not yet begun to use the system.

What are the equivalents for dry and liquid measures?

U.S. customary dry measures

1 pint	=	33.6 cubic inches
1 quart	=	2 pints or 67.2006 cubic inches
1 peck	=	8 quarts or 16 pints or 537.605 cubic inches
1 bushel	=	4 pecks or 2,150.42 cubic inches or 32 quarts
1 barrel	=	105 quarts or 7,056 cubic inches
1 pint, dry	=	0.551 liter
1 quart, dry	=	1.101 liters
1 bushel	=	35.239 liters

U.S. customary liquid measures

1 tablespoon	=	4 fluid drams or 0.5 fluid ounce
1 cup	=	0.5 pint or 8 fluid ounces
1 gill	=	4 fluid ounces
4 gills	=	1 pint or 28.875 cubic inches
1 pint	=	2 cups or 16 fluid ounces
2 pints	=	1 quart or 57.75 cubic ounces
1 quart	=	2 pints or 4 cups or 32 fluid ounces
4 quarts	=	1 gallon or 231 cubic inches or 8 pints or 32 gills or 0.833 British quart
1 gallon	=	16 cups or 231 cubic inches or 128 fluid ounces
1 bushel	=	8 gallons or 32 quarts

Conversion to metric

1 fluid ounce	=	29.57 milliliters or 0.029 liter
1 gill	=	0.118 liter
1 cup	=	0.236 liter
1 pint	=	0.473 liter
1 U.S. quart	=	0.833 British quart or 0.946 liter
1 U.S. gallon	=	0.833 British gallon or 3.785 liters

What is the difference between a **short ton**, a **long ton**, and a **metric ton**?

A short ton or U.S. ton or net ton (sometimes just "ton") equals 2,000 pounds; a long ton or an avoirdupois ton is 2,240 pounds; and a metric ton or tonne is 2,204.62 pounds. Other weights are compared below:

U.S. customary measure

1 ounce	=	16 drams or 437.5 grains
1 pound	=	16 ounces or 7,000 grains or 256 drams
1 (short) hundredweight	=	100 pounds
1 long hundredweight	=	112 pounds
1 (short) ton	=	20 hundredweights or 2,000 pounds
1 long ton	=	20 long hundredweights or 2,240 pounds

Conversion to metric

1 grain	=	65 milligrams
1 dram	=	1.77 grams
1 ounce	=	28.3 grams
1 pound	=	453.5 grams
1 metric ton (tonne)	=	2,204.6 pounds

What are the U.S. and metric units of measurement for **area**?

U.S. customary area measures

1 square foot	=	144 square inches
1 square yard	=	9 square feet or 1,296 square miles
1 square rod or pole or perch	=	30.25 square yards or 272.5 square feet
1 rood	=	40 square rods
1 acre	=	160 square rods or 4,840 square yards or 43,460 square feet
1 section	=	1 mile square or 640 acres
1 township	=	6 miles square or 36 square miles or 36 sections
1 square mile	=	640 acres or 4 roods, or 1 section

International area measures

1 square millimeter	=	1,000,000 square microns
1 square centimeter	=	100 square millimeters
1 square meter	=	10,000 square centimeters
1 are	=	100 square meters
1 hectare	=	100 ares or 10,000 square meters
1 square kilometer	=	100 hectares or 1,000,000 square meters

How much does **water** weigh?

U.S. customary measures

1 gallon	=	4 quarts
1 gallon	=	231 cubic inches
1 gallon	=	8.34 pounds
1 gallon	=	0.134 cubic foot
1 cubic foot	=	7.48 gallons
1 cubic inch	=	.0360 pound
12 cubic inches	=	.433 pound

British measures

1 liter	=	1 kilogram
1 cubic meter	=	1 tonne (metric ton)
1 imperial gallon	=	10.022 pounds
1 imperial gallon salt water	=	10.3 pounds

Which is heavier— a pound of gold or a pound of feathers?

A pound of feathers is heavier than a pound of gold because gold is measured in troy pounds, while feathers are measured in avoirdupois pounds. Troy pounds have 12 ounces; avoirdupois pounds have 16 ounces. A troy pound contains 372 grams in the metric system; an avoirdupois pound contains 454 grams. Each troy ounce is heavier than an avoirdupois ounce.

How are avoirdupois measurements converted to troy measurements and how do the measures differ?

Troy weight is a system of mass units used primarily to measure gold and silver. A troy ounce is 480 grains or 31.1 grams. Avoirdupois weight is a system of units that is used to measure mass, except for precious metals, precious stones, and drugs. It is based on the pound, which is approximately 454 grams. In both systems, the weight of a grain is the same—65 milligrams. The two systems do not contain the same weights for other units, however, even though they use the same name for the unit.

Troy
    1 grain = 65 milligrams
    1 ounce = 480 grains = 31.1 grams
    1 pound = 12 ounce = 5760 grains = 373 grams
Avoirdupois
    1 grain = 65 milligrams
    1 ounce = 437.5 grains = 28.3 grams
    1 pound = 16 ounces = 7000 grains = 454 grams

To Convert From	To	Multiply By
pounds avdp	ounces troy	14.583
pounds avdp	pounds troy	1.215
pounds troy	ounces avdp	1.097
pounds troy	pounds avdp	0.069
ounces avdp	ounces troy	0.911
ounces troy	ounces avdp	1.097

How is the distance to the horizon measured?

Distance to the horizon depends on the height of the observer's eyes. To determine that, take the distance (in feet) from sea level to eye level and multiply by three, then **401** divide by two and take the square root of the answer. The result is the number of miles to the horizon. For example, if eye level is at a height of six feet above sea level, the horizon is almost three miles away. If eye level were exactly at sea level, there would be no distance seen at all; the horizon would be directly in front of the viewer.

What is a **bench mark**?

A bench mark is a permanent, recognizable point that lies at a known elevation. It may be an existing object, such as the top of a fire hydrant, or it may be a brass plate placed on top of a concrete post. Surveyors and engineers use bench marks to find the elevation of objects by reading, through a level telescope, the distance a point lies above some already established bench mark.

What is a **theodolite**?

This optical surveying instrument used to measure angles and directions is mounted on an adjustable tripod and has a spirit level to show when it is horizontal. Similar to the more commonly used transit, the theodolite gives more precise readings; angles can be read to fractions of a degree. It is comprised of a telescope that sights the main target, a horizontal plate to provide readings around the horizon, and a vertical plate and scale for vertical readings. The surveyor uses the geometry of triangles to calculate the distance from the angles measured by the theodolite. Such triangulation is used in road- and tunnel-building and other civil engineering work. One of the earliest forms of this surveying instrument was described by Englishman Leonard Digges (d.1571?) in his 1571 work, *Geometrical Treatise Named Pantometria*.

What is meant by **DIN standards**?

They are German standards for products and procedures, covering a wide range of engineering and scientific fields. The German Institute for Standardization (*Deutsches Institut für Normung*) is the publisher of these standards. DIN also represents Germany in the International Organization for Standardization.

TIME
See also: Biology—Classification, Measurement, and Terms

How is **time** measured?

The passage of time can be measured in three ways. Rotational time is based on the unit of the mean solar day (the average length of time it takes the Earth to complete one rotation on its axis). Dynamic time, the second way to measure time, uses the motion of the moon and planets to determine time and avoids the problem of the Earth's varying rotation. The first dynamic time scale was Ephemeris Time, proposed in 1896 and modified in 1960.

Atomic time is a third way to measure time. This method, using an atomic clock, is based on the extremely regular oscillations that occur within atoms. In 1967, the atomic second (the length of time in which 9,192,631,770 vibrations are emitted by a hot cesium atom) was adopted as the basic unit of time. Atomic clocks are now used as international time standards.

But time has also been measured in other less scientific terms. Listed below are some other "timely" expressions.

Twilight—The first soft glow of sunlight; the sun is still below the horizon; also the last glow of sunlight.

Midnight—12 a.m.; the point of time when one day becomes the next day and night becomes morning.

Daybreak—The first appearance of the sun.

Dawn—A gradual increase of sunlight.

Noon—12 p.m.; the point of time when morning becomes afternoon.

Dusk—The gradual dimming of sunlight.

Sunset—The last diffused glow of sunlight; the sun is below the horizon.

Evening—A term with wide meaning, evening is generally the period between sunset and bedtime.

Night—The period of darkness, lasting from sunset to midnight.

What is the exact length of a **calendar year**?

The calendar year is defined as the time between two successive crossings of the celestial equator by the sun at the vernal equinox. It is exactly 365 days, 5 hours, 48 minutes, 46 seconds. The fact that the year is not a whole number of days has affected the development of calendars, which over time generate an accumulative error. The current calendar used, the Gregorian calendar, named after Pope Gregory XII (1502–1585), attempts to compensate by adding an extra day to the month of February every four years. A "leap year" is one with the extra day added.

When does a **century begin**?

A century has 100 consecutive calendar years. The first century consisted of years 01 through 100. The 20th century started with 1901 and will end with 2000. The 21st century will begin January 1, 2001.

When did **January 1** become the first day of the **new year**?

When Julius Caesar (100–44 B.C.E.) reorganized the Roman calendar and made it solar **403** rather than lunar in the year 45 B.C.E., he moved the beginning of the year to January 1. When the Gregorian calendar was introduced in 1582, January 1 continued to be recognized as the first day of the year in most places. In England and the American colonies, however, March 25, intended to represent the spring equinox, was the beginning of the year. Under this system, March 24, 1700, was followed by March 25, 1701. In 1752, the British government changed the beginning date of the year to January 1.

Besides the Gregorian calendar, what **other kinds of calendars** have been used?

Babylonian calendar—A lunar calendar composed of alternating 29-day and 30-day months to equal roughly 354 lunar days. When the calendar became too misaligned with astronomical events, an extra month was added. In addition, three extra months were added every eight years to coordinate this calendar with the solar year.

Chinese calendar—A lunar month calendar of 12 periods having either 29 or 30 days (to compensate for the 29.5 days from new moon to new moon). The new year begins on the first new moon over China after the sun enters Aquarius (between January 21st and February 19th). Each year has both a number and a name (for example, the year 1992 or 4629 in the Chinese era is the year of the monkey). The calendar is synchronized with the solar year by the addition of extra months at fixed intervals.

Muslim calendar—A lunar 12-month calendar with 30 and 29 days alternating every month for a total of 354 days. The calendar has a 30-year cycle with designated leap years of 355 days (one day added to the last month) in the 30-year period. The Islamic year does not attempt to relate to the solar year (the season). The dating of the beginning of the calendar is 622 C.E. (the date of Mohammed's flight from Mecca to Medina).

Jewish calendar—A blend of the solar and lunar calendar, this calendar adds an extra month (Adar Sheni, or the second Adar or Veadar) to keep the lunar and solar years in alignment. This occurs seven times during a 19-year cycle. When the extra 29-day month is inserted, the month Adar has 30 days instead of 29. In a usual year the 12 months alternately have 30, then 29 days.

Egyptian calendar—The ancient Egyptians were the first to use a solar calendar (about 4236 B.C.E. or 4242 B.C.E.), but their year started with the rising of Sirius, the brightest star in the sky. The year, composed of 365 days, was one-quarter day short of the true solar year, so eventually the Egyptian calendar did not coincide with the seasons. It used twelve 30-day months with five-day weeks and five dates of festival.

Coptic calendar—Still used in areas of Egypt and Ethiopia, it has a similar cycle to the Egyptian calendar: 12 months of 30 days followed by five complementary days. When a leap year occurs, usually preceding the Julian calendar leap year, the complementary days increase to six.

Roman calendar—Borrowing from the ancient Greek calendar, which had a four-year cycle based on the Olympic Games, the earliest Roman calendar (about 738 B.C.E.) had 304 days with 10 months. Every second year a short month of 22 or 23 days was added to coincide with the solar year. Eventually two more months were added at the end of the year (Januarius and Februarius) to increase the year to 354 days. The Roman republican calendar replaced this calendar during the reign of Tarquinius Priscus (616–579 B.C.E.). This new lunar calendar had 355 days, with the month of February having 28 days. The other months had either 29 or 31 days. To keep the calendar aligned with the seasons, an extra month was added every two years. By the time the Julian calendar replaced this one, the calendar was three months ahead of the season schedule.

Julian calendar—Julius Caesar, (100–44 B.C.E.) in 46 B.C.E., wishing to have one calendar in use for all the empire, had the astronomer Sosigenes develop a uniform solar calendar with a year of 365 days with one day ("leap day") added every fourth year to compensate for the true solar year of 365.25 days. The year had 12 months with 30 or 31 days except for February, which had 28 days (or 29 days in a leap year). The first of the year was moved from March 1 to January 1.

Gregorian calendar—Pope Gregory XIII (1502–1585) instituted calendrical reform in 1582 to realign the church celebration of Easter with the vernal equinox (the first day of spring). To better align this solar calendar with the seasons, the new calendar would not have leap year in the century years that were not divisible by 400. Because the solar year is shortening, today a one-second adjustment is made (usually on December 31st at midnight) when necessary to compensate.

Japanese calendar—It has the same structure as the Gregorian calendar in years, months, and weeks. But the years are enumerated in terms of the reigns of emperors as epochs. The last epoch (for Emperor Akihito) is Epoch Heisei, which started January 8, 1989.

Hindu calendars—The principal Indian calendars reckon their epochs from historical events, such as rulers' accessions or death dates, or a religious founder's dates. The Vikrama era (originally from Northern India and still used in western India) dates from February 23, 57 B.C.E., in the Gregorian calendar. The Saka era dates from March 3, 78 C.E., in the Gregorian calendar and is based on the solar year with 12 months of 365 days and 366 days in leap years. The first five months have 31 days; the last seven have 30 days. In leap years, the first six months have 31 days and the last six have 30. The Saka era is the national calendar of India (since 1957). The Buddhist era starts with 543 B.C.E. (believed to be the date of Buddha's death).

Three other secular calendars of note are the *Julian Day calendar* (a calendar astronomers use, which counts days within a 7,980-year period and must be used with a table), the *perpetual calendar* (which gives the days of the week for the Julian and

What is the World Calendar?

Following World War II, the United States led a movement in the United Nations to encourage the international community to adopt a common calendar. Called the World Calendar, it would self-adjust the irregular months, equalize the quarterly divisions of the years, and fix the sequence of weekdays and month dates so that days of the month would always fall on the same day of the week. This calendar would make the normal year 364 days long, divided into four quarters of 91 days each. The quarters could be segmented into three months of 31, 30, and 30 days. Every year would have 52 whole weeks; every quarter would begin with a Sunday and end with a Saturday. An extra day would need to be added to each year. This day, "World's Day," is formally called "W December," observed following the last day of December. Leap Year Day would be a similar insertion in the calendar every fourth year, following June 30, and would be called "W June." Although it was predicted that the calendar would be adopted in 1961, it has repeatedly failed passage in the United Nations.

Gregorian calendars as well), and the *world calendar,* which is similar to the perpetual calendar, having 12 months of 30 or 31 days, a year-day at the end of each year, and a leap-year-day before July 1 every four years.

There have been attempts to reform and simplify the calendar. One such example is the Thirteen-Month or International Fixed calendar, which would have 13 months of four weeks each. The month *Sol* would come before July; there would be a year-day at the end of each year and a leap-year-day every four years just before July 1. A radical reform was made in France when the French republican calendar (1793–1806) replaced the Gregorian calendar after the French Revolution. It had 12 months of 30 days and five supplementary days at the end of the year (six in a leap-year), and weeks were replaced with 10-day decades.

What is the **Julian Day Count**?

This system of counting days rather than years was developed by Joseph Justus Scaliger (1540–1609) in 1583. Still used by astronomers today, the Julian Day Count (named after Scaliger's father, Julius Caesar Scaliger) Julian Day (JD) 1 was January 1, 4113 B.C.E. On this date the Julian calendar, the ancient Roman tax calendar, and the lunar calendar all coincided. This event would not occur again until 7,980 years later. Each day within this 7,980-year period is numbered. December 31, 1991, at noon is the beginning of JD 2,448,622. The figure reflects the number of days that have passed since its inception. To convert Gregorian calendar dates into Julian Day, simple JD conversion tables have been devised for astronomers.

Do all calendars other than the Gregorian calendar use a twelve-month cycle?

No. Some calendars have a varying cycle of months, with their first month falling at a different time. Listed below are some variations with the beginning month of the year in italics:

Months of the year

Gregorian	Hebrew	Hindu
January	Shebat	Magha
February	Adar	Phalguna
March	Nisan	*Caitra*
April	Iyar	Vaisakha
May	Sivan	Jyaistha
June	Tammuz	Asadhe
July	Ab	Sravana
August	Elul	Bhadrapada
September	*Tishri*	Asvina
October	Heshvan	Karttika
November	Kislev	Margasivsa
December	Tebet	Pansa
	Ve-Adar (13th month every three years)	

Muslim	Chinese	
Muharram	*Li Chun*	Li Qui
Safar	Yu Shui	Chu Shu
Rabi I	Jing Zhe	Bai Lu
Rabi II	Chun Fen	Qui Fen
Jumada I	Qing Ming	Han Lu
Jumada II	Gu Yu	Shuang Jiang
Rajab	Li Xia	Li Dong
Sha'ban	Xiao Man	Xiao Xue
Ramadan	Mang Zhong	Da Xue
Shawwal	Xia Zhi	Dong Zhi
Dhu'l-Qa'da	Xiao Shu	Xiao Han
Dhu'l-hijja	Da Shu	Da Han

Which animal designations have been given to the Chinese years?

There are 12 different names, always used in the same sequence: Rat, Ox, Tiger, Hare (Rabbit), Dragon, Snake, Horse, Sheep (Goat), Monkey, Rooster, Dog, and Pig. The following table shows this sequence.

Chinese year cycle

Rat	Ox	Tiger	Hare (Rabbit)	Dragon	Snake
1900	1901	1902	1903	1904	1905
1912	1913	1914	1915	1916	1917
1924	1925	1926	1927	1928	1929
1936	1937	1938	1939	1940	1941
1948	1949	1950	1951	1952	1953
1960	1961	1962	1963	1964	1965
1972	1973	1974	1975	1976	1977
1984	1985	1986	1987	1988	1989
1996	1997	1998	1999	2000	2001

Horse	Sheep (Goat)	Monkey	Rooster	Dog	Pig
1906	1907	1908	1909	1910	1911
1918	1919	1920	1921	1922	1923
1930	1931	1932	1933	1934	1935
1942	1943	1944	1945	1946	1947
1954	1955	1956	1957	1958	1959
1966	1967	1968	1969	1970	1971
1978	1979	1980	1981	1982	1983
1990	1991	1992	1993	1994	1995
2002	2003	2004	2005	2006	2007

The Chinese year of 354 days begins three to seven weeks into the western 365-day year, so the animal designation changes at that time, rather than on January 1.

What were the longest and shortest years on record?

The longest year was 46 B.C.E. when Julius Caesar (100–44 B.C.E.) introduced his calendar, called the Julian calendar, which was used until 1582. He added two extra months and 23 extra days to February to make up for accumulated slippage in the Egyptian Calendar. Thus, 46 B.C.E. was 455 days long. The shortest year was 1582, when Pope Gregory XIII (1502–1585) introduced his calendar, the Gregorian calendar. He decreed that October 5 would be October 15, eliminating 10 days, to make up for the accumulated error in the Julian calendar. Not everyone changed over to this new calendar at once. Catholic Europe adopted it within two years of its inception. Many Protestant continental countries did so in 1699–1700; England imposed it on its colonies in 1752 and Sweden in 1753. Many non-European countries adopted it in the 19th century, with China doing so in 1912, Turkey in 1917, and Russia in 1918. To change from the Julian to the Gregorian calendar, 10 days are added to dates October 5, 1582, through February 28, 1700; after that date add 11 days through February 28, 1800; 12 days through February 28, 1900; and 13 days through February 28, 2100.

When does **leap year** occur?

A leap year occurs when the year is exactly divisible by four except centenary years. A centenary year must be divisible by 400 to be a leap year. There was no February 29 in 1900, which was not a leap year. The next centenary year, 2000, will have February 29.

What is a **leap second**?

The Earth's rotation is slowing down, and to compensate for this lagging motion a leap second is added to a specified day. One leap second was used in 1992 to keep the calendar in close alignment with international atomic time. To complete this change, 23h 59m 59s universal time on June 30, 1992 was followed by 23h 59m 60s and this in turn was followed by 0h 0m 0s on July 1.

Where do the names of the **days of the week** come from?

The English days of the week are named for a mixture of figures in Anglo-Saxon and Roman mythology.

Day	Named after
Sunday	The sun
Monday	The moon
Tuesday	Tiu (the Anglo-Saxon god of war, equivalent to the Norse Tyr or the Roman Mars)
Wednesday	Woden (the Anglo-Saxon equivalent of Odin, the chief Norse god)
Thursday	Thor (the Norse god of thunder)
Friday	Frigg (the Norse god of love and fertility, the equivalent of the Roman Venus)
Saturday	Saturn (the Roman god of agriculture)

What is the **origin** of the **week**?

The week originated in the Babylonian calendar, where one day out of seven was devoted to rest.

How were the **months** of the year **named**?

The English names of the months of the current (Gregorian) calendar come from the Romans, who tended to honor their gods and commemorate specific events by designating them as month names:

January (*Januarius* in Latin), named after Janus, a Roman two-faced god, one face looking into the past, the other into the future.

February (*Februarium*) is from the Latin word *Februare*, meaning "to cleanse." At the time of year corresponding to our February, the Romans performed religious rites to purge themselves of sin.

March (*Martius*) is named in honor of Mars, the god of war.

April (*Aprilis*), after the Latin word *Aperio*, meaning "to open," because plants begin to grow in this month.

May (*Maius*), after the Roman goddess Maia, as well as from the Latin word *Maiores* meaning "elders," who were celebrated during this month.

June (*Junius*), after the goddess Juno and Latin word *iuniores*, meaning "young people."

July (*Iulius*) was, at first, known as *Quintilis* from the Latin word meaning five, since it was the fifth month in the early Roman calendar. Its name was changed to July, in honor of Julius Caesar (100–44 B.C.E.).

August (*Augustus*) is named in honor of the Emperor Octavian (63–14 B.C.E.), first Roman emperor, known as Augustus Caesar. Originally the month was known as *Sextilis* (sixth month of early Roman calendar).

September (*September*) was once the seventh month and accordingly took its name from *septem*, meaning "seven."

October (*October*) takes its name from *octo* (eight); at one time it was the eighth month.

November (*November*) from *novem*, meaning "nine," once the ninth month of the early Roman calendar.

December (*December*) from *decem*, meaning "ten," once the tenth month of the early Roman calendar.

Why are the **lengths of the seasons** not equal?

The lengths of the seasons are not exactly equal because the orbit of the Earth around the sun is elliptic rather than a circular. When the Earth is closest to the sun in January, gravitational forces cause the planet to move faster than it does in the summer months when it is far away from the sun. As a result, the autumn and winter seasons in the Northern Hemisphere are slightly shorter than spring and summer. The duration of the northern seasons are:

spring	92.76 days
summer	93.65 days
autumn	89.84 days
winter	88.99 days

What are the **beginning dates of the seasons** for 1996 to 2000?

The four seasons in the northern hemisphere coincide with astronomical events. The spring season starts with the vernal equinox (around March 21) and lasts until the summer solstice (June 21 or 22); summer is from the summer solstice to the autumnal equinox (about September 21); autumn, from the autumnal equinox to the winter solstice (December 21 or 22); and winter from the winter solstice to the vernal equinox. In the southern hemisphere the seasons are reversed: autumn corresponds to spring; winter to summer. The seasons are caused by the tilt of the Earth's axis, which changes the position of the sun in the sky. In winter the sun is at its lowest position (or angle of declination) in the sky; in summer, it is at its highest position.

Year	Spring	Summer	Fall	Winter
1996	March 20	June 21	September 22	December 21
1997	March 20	June 21	September 22	December 21
1998	March 20	June 21	September 23	December 22
1999	March 21	June 21	September 23	December 22
2000	March 20	June 21	September 22	December 21

How is the date for **Easter** determined?

The rule for establishing the date in Christian churches is that Easter always falls on the first Sunday after the first full moon that occurs on or just after the vernal equinox. The vernal equinox is the first day of spring in the Northern Hemisphere. Because the full moon can occur on any one of many dates after the vernal equinox, the date of Easter can be as early as March 22 and as late as April 25. For the period 1997–2006, Easter will appear on the following dates:

Year	Date
1997	March 30
1998	April 12
1999	April 4

Year	Date
2000	April 23
2001	April 15
2002	March 31
2003	April 20
2004	April 11
2005	March 27
2006	April 16

How is the date for **Passover** determined?

Passover (*Pesah*) begins at sundown on the evening before the 15th day of the Hebrew month of Nisan, which falls in March or April. Celebrated as a public holiday in Israel, the Passover commemorates the exodus of the Israelites from Egypt in 1290 B.C.E. The term "Passover" is a reference to the last of the 10 plagues that "passed over" the Israelite homes at the end of their captivity in Egypt.

When is **Daylight Savings Time** observed in the United States?

In 1967, all states and possessions of the United States were to begin observing Daylight Savings Time at 2 a.m. on the first Sunday in April of every year. The clock would advance one hour at that time until 2 a.m. of the last Sunday of October, when the clock would be turned back one hour. In the intervening years, the length of this time period changed, but on July 8, 1986, the original starting and ending dates were reinstated. A 1972 amendment allowed some areas to be exempt.

This time change was enacted to provide more light in the evening hours. The phrase "fall back, spring forward" indicates the direction in which the clock setting moved during these seasons. Other countries have adopted DST as well. For instance, in western Europe the period is from the last Sunday in March to the last Sunday in September, with the United Kingdom extending the range to the last Sunday in October. Many countries in the Southern Hemisphere generally maintain DST from October to March; countries near the equator maintain standard time.

Which states and territories of the United States are **exempt from Daylight Savings Time**?

Arizona, Hawaii, Puerto Rico, the U.S. Virgin Islands, American Samoa, and most of Indiana are exempt from Daylight Savings Time.

What are some **other names** for **Daylight Saving Time**?

It is also known as fast time or summer time.

How many **time zones** are there in the world?

There are 24 standard time zones that serially cover the Earth's surface at coincident intervals of 15 degrees longitude and 60 minutes Universal Time (UT), as agreed at the Washington Meridian Conference of 1884, thus accounting, respectively, for each 24 hours of the calendar day.

What is unusual about the observance of **time zones** in **Russia** and **China**?

Russia, which spans 11 time zones, is on "advanced time" year round, meaning that it maintains its Standard Time one hour faster than the zone designation. The country also observes Daylight Saving Time from the fourth Sunday in March until the fourth Sunday in September. China, though it lies across five time zones, keeps one time, which is eight hours faster than Greenwich Time.

When traveling from Tokyo to Seattle and crossing the **international date line,** what day is it?

Traveling from west to east (Tokyo to Seattle), the calendar day is set back, i.e., Sunday becomes Saturday. Traveling east to west, the calendar day is advanced, i.e., Tuesday becomes Wednesday. The International Date Line is a zigzag line at approximately the 180th meridian, where the calendar days are separated.

What is meant by **universal time**?

On January 1, 1972, Universal Time (UT) replaced Greenwich Mean Time (GMT) as the time reference coordinate for scientific work. Universal Time is measured by an atomic clock and is seen as the logical development of the adoption of the atomic second in 1968. An advantage of UT is that the time at which an event takes place can be determined very readily without recourse to the time-consuming astronomical observations and calculations that were necessary before the advent of atomic clocks. Universal Time is also referred to as International Atomic Time. GMT is measured according to when the sun crosses the Greenwich Meridian (zero degrees longitude, which passes through the Greenwich Observatory).

Who establishes the **correct time** in the United States?

The United States National Institute of Standards and Technology (NIST) uses a cesium beam clock as its NIST atomic frequency standard to determine atomic time. The atomic second was officially defined in 1967 by the 13th General Conference of

Why do the minute and hour hands on a clock go "clockwise"?

Henry Fried, an expert on timekeeping, postulates that the clockwise motion of minute and hour hands has its origin in the use of sundials before the development of clocks. In the northern hemisphere, the shadow rotates in a clockwise direction, and clock inventors built the hands to copy the natural movement of the sun.

Weights and Measures as 9,192,631,770 oscillations of the atom of cesium-133. This cesium-beam clock of the NIST is referred to as a primary clock because independently of any other reference, it provides highly precise and accurate time.

What is the **United States Time Standard** signal?

Universal Time is announced in International Morse Code each five minutes by radio stations WWV (Fort Collins, Colorado) and WWVH (Puuene, Maui, Hawaii). These stations are under the direction of the U.S. National Institute of Technology and Standards (formerly called National Bureau of Standards). They transmit 24 hours a day on 2.5, 5, 10, 15, and 20 megahertz. The first radio station to transmit time signals regularly was the Eiffel Tower Radio Station in Paris in 1913.

What do the initials **a.m.** and **p.m.** mean?

The initials a.m. stand for *ante meridiem*, Latin for "before noon." The initials p.m. stand for *post meridiem*, Latin for "after noon."

Why do **clocks and watches** with **Roman numerals** on their faces use "IIII" for the number 4, rather than "IV"?

A clock with a "IV" has a somewhat unbalanced appearance. Thus tradition has favored the strictly incorrect "IIII," which more nearly balances the equally heavy "VIII."

What is a **floral clock**?

In the Middle Ages it was believed that one could tell the hour of day by observing flowers, which were believed to open and close at specific times. These would be planted in flower dials. The first hour belonged to the budding rose, the fourth to hyacinths and the twelfth to pansies. The unreliability of this method of timekeeping must have soon become apparent, but floral clocks are still planted in parks and gardens today. The world's largest clock face is that of the floral clock located inside the Rose Building in Hokkaido, Japan. The diameter of the clock is almost 69 feet (21 meters), and the large hand of the clock is almost 28 feet (8.5 meters) in length.

Where did the term grandfather clock come from?

The weight-and-pendulum clock was invented by Dutch scientist Christian Huygens (1629–1695) around the year 1656. In the United States, Pennsylvania German settlers considered such clocks, often called long-case clocks, to be a status symbol. In 1876 American songwriter Henry Clay Work (1832–1884) referred to long-case clocks in his song "My Grandfather's Clock," and the nickname stuck.

Who invented the alarm clock?

Levi Hutchins of Concord, New Hampshire, invented an alarm clock in 1787. His alarm clock, however, rang at only one time—4 a.m. He invented this device so that he would never sleep past his usual waking time. He never patented or manufactured it. The first modern alarm clock was made by Antoine Redier (1817–1892) in 1847. It was a mechanical device; the electric alarm clock was not invented until around 1890. The earliest mechanical clock was made in 725 C.E. in China by Yi Xing and Liang Lingzan.

How is time denoted at sea?

The day is divided into watches and bells. A watch equals four hours except for the time period between 4 p.m. and 8 p.m., which has two short watches. Within each watch there are eight bells—one stroke for each half hour, so that each watch ends on eight bells except the dog watches, which end at four bells. New Year's Day is marked with 16 bells.

Bell	Time equivalent		
1 bell	12:30 or	4:30	or 8:30 A.M. or P.M.
2 bells	1:00	5:00	9:00
3 bells	1:30	5:30	9:30
4 bells	2:00	6:00	10:00
5 bells	2:30	6:30	10:30
6 bells	3:00	7:00	11:00
7 bells	3:30	7:30	11:30
8 bells	4:00	8:00	12:00

What is **military time**?

Military time divides the day into one set of 24 hours, counting from midnight (0000) to midnight of the next day (2400). This is expressed without punctuation.

> Midnight becomes 0000 (or 2400 of the next day)
> 1:00 a.m. becomes 0100 (pronounced oh–one hundred)
> 2:10 a.m. becomes 0210
> Noon becomes 1200
> 6:00 p.m. becomes 1800
> 9:45 p.m. becomes 2145

To translate 24-hour time into familiar time, the a.m. times are obvious. For p.m. times, subtract 1200 from numbers larger than 1200; e.g., 1900–1200 is 7 p.m.

Who set a **doomsday clock** for nuclear annihilation?

The clock first appeared on the cover of the magazine *Bulletin of the Atomic Scientists* in 1947 and was set at 11:53 p.m. The clock, created by the magazine's board of directors, represents the threat of nuclear annihilation, with midnight as the time of destruction. In 1953, just after the United States tested the hydrogen bomb, it was set at 11:58 p.m., the closest to midnight ever. In 1991, following the collapse of the Soviet Union, it was moved back to 11:43 p.m., the farthest from midnight the clock has ever been. However, in 1995, the clock was shifted forward to 11:47, reflecting the instability of the post-cold-war world.

TOOLS, MACHINES, AND PROCESSES

Which **tools** did **Neanderthal man** use?

Neanderthal tool kits are termed *Mousterian* from finds at LeMoustier in France (traditionally dated to the early Fourth Glacial Period, around 40,000 B.C.E.). Using fine-grained glassy stone like flint and obsidian, Neanderthals improved on the already old, established *Levallois* technique for striking one or two big flakes of predetermined shape from a prepared core. They made each core yield many small, thin, sharp-edged flakes, which were then trimmed to produce hide scrapers, points, backed knives, stick sharpeners, tiny saws, and borers. These could have served for killing, cutting, and skinning prey, and for making wooden tools and clothing.

What are the six **simple machines**?

All machines and mechanical devices, no matter how complicated, can be reduced to some combinations of six basic, or simple, machines. The lever, the wheel and axle, the pulley, the inclined plane, the wedge, and the screw were all known to the ancient Greeks, who learned that a machine works because an "effort," which is exerted over an "effort distance," is magnified through "mechanical advantage" to overcome a "resistance" over a "resistance distance." Some consider there to be only five simple machines, and regard the wedge as a moving inclined plane.

How does a **four-stroke** differ from a **two-stroke** engine?

A four-stroke engine functions by going through four cycles: 1) the intake stroke draws a fuel-air mixture in on a down stroke; 2) the mixture is compressed on an upward stroke; 3) the mixture is ignited causing a down stroke; and 4) the mixture is

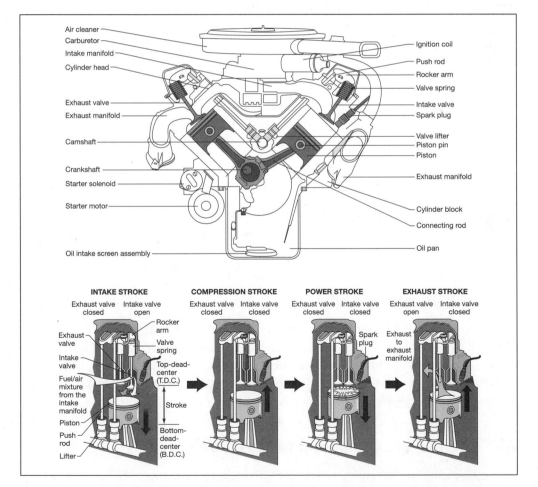

The major componets of an internal combustion engine (top) and the four strokes of its combustion sequence (bottom).

exhausted on an up stroke. A two-stroke engine combines the intake and compression strokes (1 and 2) and the power and exhaust strokes (3 and 4) by covering and uncovering ports and valves in the cylinder wall. Two-stroke engines are typically used in small displacement applications, such as chain saws, some motorcycles, etc.

What does "cc" mean in **engine sizes**?

Cubic centimeters (cc), as applied to an internal combustion engine, is a measure of the combustion space in the cylinders. The size of an engine is measured by theoretically removing the top of a cylinder, pushing the piston all the way down and then filling the cylinder with liquid. The cubic centimeters of liquid displaced (spilled out) when the piston is returned to its high position is the measure of the combustion volume of the cylinder. If a motorcycle has four cylinders, each displacing 200 ccs, it has an 800 cc engine. Automobile engines are sized essentially the same way.

What is a **donkey engine**?

A donkey engine is a small auxiliary engine that is usually portable or semi-portable. It is powered by steam, compressed air, or other means. It is often used to power a windlass or lift cargo on shipboard.

What is a **power take-off**?

The standard power take-off is a connection that will turn a shaft inserted through the rear wall of a gear case. It is used to power accessories such as a cable control unit, a winch, or a hydraulic pump. Farmers use the mechanism to pump water, grind feed, or saw wood. A power take-off drives the moving parts of mowing machines, hay balers, combines, and potato diggers.

Who invented the **compound microscope**?

The principle of the compound microscope, in which two or more lenses are arranged to form an enlarged image of an object, occurred independently, at about the same time, to more than one person. Certainly many opticians were active at the end of the 16th century, especially in Holland, in the construction of telescopes, so that it is likely that the idea of the microscope may have occurred to several of them independently. In all probability, the date may be placed within the period 1590–1609, and the credit should go to three spectacle makers in Holland. Hans Janssen, his son Zacharias (1580–1638), and Hans Lippershey (1570–1619) have all been cited at various times as deserving chief credit. An Englishman, Robert Hooke (1635–1703), was the first to make the best use of a compound microscope, and his book *Micrographia*, published in 1665, contains some of the most beautiful drawings of microscopic observations ever made.

What does the acronym LASER stand for?

"Laser" stands for "light amplification by stimulated emission of radiation." It is a device that produces a narrow, uniform, high-intensity beam of light made up of one very pure color (one wave length) that can be directed over small and large distances. This light beam is so intense that it can vaporize the hardest and most heat-resistant materials. In 1960 Theodore Maiman (b. 1927) demonstrated a working model of a laser, based on the principles of the maser (a device utilizing single–wave length microwaves, developed by Charles Townes [b. 1915] in 1953) using the wave frequencies of visible light. Ordinary light consists of relatively short wave packets; laser light is made up of long stretches of waves of even amplitude (height) and frequency (width), called "coherent light" because the wave packets or photons seem to stick together. The power of the laser lies in this concentration of photons, which strike the target surface simultaneously. Maiman used a ruby crystal to produce photons by exciting the chromium atoms in the ruby from a low-energy to a high-energy state. After a few thousandths of a second, the atoms revert back to their normal state and emit an identical photon. This photon can stimulate the chromium atoms to emit a photon. The beam is built up by billions of these paired photons, which are reflected back and forth by mirrors until they emerge at one end in bursts of red light.

LASER Applications

Semiconductor industry (ultraviolet lasers)	Micromachining of components and circuit boards
Telecommunications (diode laser)	Development of optical fiber communications in the long-distance telephone networks
Retailing	Bar code scanners
Printing	Desktop printers, type-setting machines and color scanners
Military	Target designators
Medical	Diagnostics and therapeutics

419

Who invented the **electron microscope**?

The theoretical and practical limits to the use of the optical microscope were set by the wavelength of light. When the oscilloscope was developed, it was realized that cathode-ray beams could be used to resolve much finer detail because their wavelength was so much shorter than that of light. In 1928, Ernst Ruska (1906–1988) and Max Knoll, using magnetic fields to "focus" electrons in a cathode-ray beam, produced a crude instrument that gave a magnification of 17, and by 1932 they developed an electron microscope having a magnification of 400. By 1937 James Hillier (b. 1915) advanced this magnification to 7,000. The 1939 instrument Vladimir Zworykin (1889–1982) developed gave 50 times more detail than any optical microscope ever could, with a magnification up to two million. The electron microscope revolutionized biological research: for the first time, scientists could see the molecules of cell structures, proteins, and viruses.

What is **holography**?

Hungarian-born scientist Dennis Gabor invented the technique of holography (image in the round) in 1947, but it was not until 1961 when Emmet Leith and Juris Upatnieks produced the modern hologram using a laser, which gave the hologram the strong, pure light it needed. Three-dimensions are seen around an object because light waves are reflected from all around it, overlapping and interfering with each other. This interaction of these collections of waves, called wave fronts, give an object its light, shade, and depth. A camera cannot capture all the information in these wave fronts, so it produces two dimensional objects. Holography captures the depth of an object by measuring the distance light has traveled from the object.

A simple hologram is made by splitting a laser light into two beams through a silvered mirror. One beam, called the object beam, lights up the subject of the hologram. These light waves are reflected onto a photographic plate. The other beam, called a reference beam, is reflected directly onto the plate itself. The two beams coincide to create, on the plate, an "interference pattern." After the plate is developed, a laser light is projected through this developed hologram at the same angle as the original reference beam, but from the opposite direction. The pattern scatters the light to create a projected, three-dimensional, ghost-like image of the original object in space.

In which industries are **robots** being used?

A robot is a device that can execute a wide range of maneuvers under the direction of a computer. Reacting to feedback from sensors or by reprogramming, a robot can alter its maneuvers to fit a changed task or situation. The worldwide population of robots is about 250,000, with approximately 65% being used in Japan and 14% being used in the United States (the second largest user).

Robots are used to do welding, painting, drilling, sanding, cutting, and moving tasks in manufacturing plants. Automobile factories account for more than 50% of robot use in the United States. Robots can work in environments that are extremely threatening to humans or in difficult physical environments. They clean up radioactive areas, extinguish fires, disarm bombs, and load and unload explosives and toxic chemicals. Robots can process light-sensitive materials, such as photographic films that require near darkness—a difficult task for human workers. They can perform a variety of tasks in underwater exploration and in mines (a hazardous, low-light environment). There are only 100 robots in mines, but they produce about one-third of the coal coming from these mines. In the military and security fields, robots are used to sense targets or as surveillance devices. In the printing industry, robots perform miscellaneous tasks, such as sorting and tying bundles of output material, delivering paper to the presses, and applying book covers. In research laboratories, small desktop robots prepare samples and mix compounds.

What film was the first to feature a robot?

In 1886, the French movie *l'Eve Futur* had a Thomas Edison–like mad scientist building a robot in the likeness of a woman. A British lord falls in love with her, in a variation on the Pygmalion theme. True working robots, in contrast to these entertainment devices, are strictly functional in appearance, looking more like machines rather than human beings or animals. However, one early exception to this is the very human-looking "Scribe" built in 1773 by two French inventors, Pierre and Henri-Louis Jacquel-Droz, a father and son team, who produced "The Automaton" to dip a quill pen into an inkwell and write a text of 40 characters maximum.

Who was the founder of cybernetics?

Norbert Weiner (1894–1964) is considered the creator of cybernetics. Derived from the Greek word *kubernetes*, meaning steerman or helmsman, cybernetics is concerned with the common factors of control and communication in living organisms, automatic machines, or organizations. These factors are exemplified by the skill used in steering a boat, in which the helmsman uses continual judgement to maintain control. The principles of cybernetics are used today in control theory, automation theory, and computer programs to reduce many time-consuming computations and decision-making processes formerly done by people.

What is the lost wax process?

This process is used for making valve parts, small gears, magnets, surgical tools, and jewelry. It involves the use of a wax pattern between a two-layered mold. The wax is removed by melting and replaced with molten metal; hence the name "lost wax."

What is **sintering**?

Sintering is the bonding together of compacted powder particles at temperatures below the melting point. This bonding produces larger forms such as cakes and pellets. Sintering is used in powder metallurgy technology, which is the production of useful artifacts from metal powder without passing through the molten state. The components produced are referred to as sintered parts. These parts are normally quite small, and some typical examples made today are shock absorber pistons, belt pulleys, small helical gears, drive gears for chainsaws, and automotive pump gears. Because they are molded, sintered parts can have extremely complex shapes, and do not require machining. The toughness and high strength properties of sintered parts make them especially good for today's high technology systems.

What are **Lichtenberg figures**?

Lichtenberg figures are patterns appearing on a photographic plate or on a plate coated with fine dust, when the plate is placed between electrodes and a high voltage is applied between them. The figures were first produced by George Christopher Litchenberg in 1777, marking the discovery of electrostatic recording.

What is **DNA fingerprinting?**

DNA, or genetic, fingerprinting is a method of determining identity, family relationships, etc. Formulated by Alec Jeffreys, a British geneticist, the genetic fingerprint is based on the assumption that every person (except identical twins) has an unique sequence of DNA (deoxyribonucleic acid)—a substance present in the nucleus of every cell that determines individual characteristics.

Within the DNA molecule, the sequence of the genetic information is repeated many times along the DNA structure, which resembles an endless twisting ladder. The length of the sequence, the number of repetitions, and its precise location within the DNA chain seems to be unique in all cases but identical twins, with the odds being 30 billion to one. A process has been developed that translates these sequences into a visual record that resembles a series of bars on x-ray film. In this process the technician isolates the DNA from blood, saliva, hair follicles, or semen, then the DNA strand is separated into thousands of shorter pieces by placing the DNA into an enzyme solution. Finally the fragments, placed in a gelatin-like material, are subjected to a strong electrical current that separates them according to size and electrical behavior.

In criminal investigations, hair, blood, and skin samples left by the criminal can yield a DNA fingerprint, which can be matched against any suspect's DNA fingerprint. DNA fingerprinting is also used to determine the father in paternity cases, since the infant's DNA strand contains the genetic coding of the parents—half the chromosomes were taken from each of the parents.

WEAPONS
See also: Boats, Trains, Cars, and Planes—Military Vehicles

What is an **onager?**

The onager was the simplest of the early catapults. One type of onager twisted a mass of human hair or animal sinew with one wooden beam inserted into it. Geared winches were used to twist the hair or sinew without letting it unwind. To load it, soldiers manned a windlass, which pulled the beam down until it was horizontal, which added more twist to the fiber. A stone was attached to the end of the beam, and this weapon was fired when a soldier pulled a rope that released the beam from its mooring.

What is the name of the historic weapon consisting of a round, spiked ball attached to a chain?

A flail is a weapon consisting of a stout handle fitted with a short iron-shod bar or wooden rod with iron spikes. The "morning star" flail or mace featured one or more spiked balls on a chain. The flexibility of the chain made the weapon harder to parry.

Who invented the **Bowie knife**?

A popular weapon of the American West, the Bowie knife was named after Jim Bowie (1796–1836), who was killed at the Alamo. According to most reliable sources, his brother Rezin Bowie might have been the actual inventor. The knife's blade measured up to two inches (five centimeters) wide and its length varied from nine to 15 inches (23 to 38 centimeters).

Who invented **mine barrage**?

In 1777, David Bushnell (1742?–1824) conceived the idea of floating kegs containing explosives that would ignite upon contact with ships.

Which **warfare innovations** were introduced during the American **Civil War**?

Barbed wire, trench warfare, hand grenades, land mines, armored trains, ironclad ships, aerial reconnaissance, submarine vessels, machine guns, and even a primitive flamethrower were products of the American Civil War, 1861–1865.

When was the **Colt revolver** patented?

The celebrated six-shooter of the American West was named after its inventor, Samuel Colt (1814–1862). Although he did not invent the revolver, he perfected the design, which he first patented in 1835 in England and then in the United States the following year. Colt had hoped to mass-produce this weapon, but failed to get enough backing to acquire the necessary machinery. Consequently, the guns, made by hand, were expensive and attracted only limited orders. In 1847, the Texas Rangers ordered 1,000 pistols, enabling Colt to finally set up assembly-line manufacture in a plant in Hartford, Connecticut.

Why is a **shot tower** used in shot making?

For shot to be accurate and of high velocity, it should be perfectly round. However, early methods for molding lead for shot often resulted in flawed or misshapen balls. In 1872, a British plumber, William Watts, solved this problem when he devised a simple method. This method consisted of pouring the molten lead through a sieve and then allowing the resulting drops to fall from a great height into a pool of water. The air cooled the drops and the water cushioned their fall, preventing them from being deformed. This new technology spread rapidly and shot towers, from 150 to 215 feet (46 to 65 meters) high appeared across Europe and America. Although steel shot has largely replaced lead due to environmental concerns, about 30 towers still drop lead shot worldwide, including five in the United States. The essentials of the 1782 design remain unchanged.

Who invented the **machine gun**?

The first successful machine gun, invented by Richard J. Gatling (1818–1903), was patented in 1862 during the Civil War. Its six barrels were revolved by gears operated by a hand crank, and it fired 1,200 rounds per minute. Although there had been several partially successful attempts at building a multi-firing weapon, none were able to overcome the many engineering difficulties until Gatling. In his gear-driven machine, cocking and firing were performed by cam action. The United States Army officially adopted the gun on August 24, 1866.

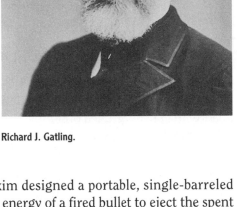

Richard J. Gatling.

The first automatic machine gun was a highly original design by Hiram S. Maxim (1840–1915). In 1884, the clever Maxim designed a portable, single-barreled automatic weapon that made use of the recoil energy of a fired bullet to eject the spent cartridge and load the next.

The original "tommy gun" was the Thompson Model 1928 SMG. This 45-caliber machine gun, designed in 1918 by General John Taliaferro Thompson (1860–1940), was to be used in close-quarter combat. The war ended before it went into production, however, and Thompson's Auto Ordnance Corporation did not do well, until the gun was adopted by American gangsters during Prohibition. The image of a reckless criminal spraying his enemies with bullets from his hand-held "tommy gun" became a symbol of the Depression years. The gun was modified several times and was much used during World War II.

How did the **bazooka** get its name?

It was coined by American comedian Bob Burns (1893–1956). As a prop in his act he used a unique musical instrument that was long and cylindrical and resembled an oboe. When United States Army soldiers in World War II were first issued hollow-tube rocket launchers, they named them bazookas because of their similarity to Burns' instrument.

425

Who was known as the **Cannon King**?

Alfred Krupp (1812–1887), whose father Friedrich (1787–1826) established the family's cast-steel factory in 1811, began manufacturing guns in 1856. Krupp supplied large weapons to so many nations that he became known as the "Cannon King." Prussia's victory in the Franco-German War of 1870–1871 was largely the result of Krupp's field guns. In 1933 when Hitler came to power, this family business began manufacturing a wide range of artillery. Alfred Krupp (1907–1967), the great-grandson of Alfred, supported the Nazis in power and accrued staggering wealth for the company. The firm seized property in occupied countries and used slave labor in its factories. After the war, Alfred was imprisoned for 12 years and had to forfeit all his property. Granted amnesty in 1951, he restored the business to its former position by the early 1960s. On his death in 1967, however, the firm became a corporation and the Krupp family dynasty ended.

How did **Big Bertha** get its name?

This was the popular name first applied to the 16.5-inch (42-centimeter) howitzers used by the Germans and Austrians in 1914, the year World War I started. Subsequently the term included other types of huge artillery pieces used during World War I and II. The large gun was built by the German arms manufacturer Friedrich A. Krupp (1854–1902), and was named after his only child, Bertha Krupp (1886–1957).

These large guns were used to destroy the concrete and steel forts defending Belgium in 1914, and their shells weighed 205 pounds (930 kilograms) and were nearly as tall as a man. Since it was slow and difficult to move such guns, the use of them was practical only in static warfare. In World War II, bomber aircraft took away this role of long-range bombardment from these cumbersome guns.

What was the **Manhattan Project**?

The Manhattan Engineer District was the formal code name for the United States government project to develop an atomic bomb during World War II. It soon became known as the Manhattan Project—a name taken from the location of the office of Colonel James C. Marshall, who had been selected by the United States Army Corps of Engineers to build and run the bomb's production facilities. When the project was activated by the United States War Department in June 1942, it came under the direction of Colonel Leslie R. Groves (1896–1970).

The first major accomplishment of the project's scientists was the successful initiation of the first self-sustaining nuclear chain reaction, done at a University of Chicago laboratory on December 2, 1942. The project tested the first experimental detonation of an atomic bomb in a desert area near Alamogordo, New Mexico, on July 16, 1945. The test site was called Trinity, and the bomb generated an explosive power equivalent to between 15,000 and 20,000 tons (15,240 to 20,320 tonnes) of TNT. Two of the project's bombs were dropped on Japan the following month (Hiroshima on August 6 and Nagasaki on August 9, 1945) resulting in the Japanese surrender to end World War II.

How far can a **Pershing missile** travel?

The surface-to-surface nuclear missile, which is 34.5 feet (10.5 meters) long and weighs 10,000 pounds (4,536 kilograms), has a range of about 1,120 miles (1,800 kilometers). It was developed by the United States Army in 1972. Other surface-to-surface missiles are the Polaris, with a range of 2,860 miles (4,600 kilometers); the Minuteman, with a range of 1,120 miles (1,800 kilometers); the Tomahawk, 2,300 miles (3,700 kilometers); the Trident, 4,600 miles (7,400 kilometers); and the Peacemaker, 6,200 miles (10,000 kilometers).

What is a **nuclear winter**?

The term "nuclear winter" was coined by American physicist Richard P. Turco in a 1983 article in the journal *Science*, in which he describes a hypothetical post-nuclear war scenario having severe worldwide climatic changes: prolonged periods of darkness, below-freezing temperatures, violent windstorms, and persistent radioactive fallout. This would be caused by billions of tons of dust, soot, and ash being tossed into the atmosphere, accompanied by smoke and poisonous fumes from firestorms. In the case of a severe nuclear war, within a few days, the entire northern hemisphere would be under a blanket so thick that as little as 1/10 of 1% of available sunlight would reach the Earth. Without sunlight, temperatures would drop well below freezing for a year or longer, causing dire consequences for all plant and animal life on Earth.

Reaction to this doomsday prediction lead critics to coin the term "nuclear autumn," which downplayed such climatic effects and casualties. In January 1990, the release of *Climate and Smoke: An Appraisal of Nuclear Winter*, based on five years of laboratory studies and field experiments, reinforced the original 1983 conclusions.

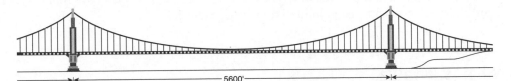

5600'

BUILDINGS, BRIDGES, AND OTHER STRUCTURES

BUILDINGS AND BUILDING PARTS

How many acres of **trees** are used in the construction of a **single-family home**?

On the average, one acre of softwood forest is used for a typical 2,000-square-foot (186-square-meter) house.

How does a **chimney** differ from a **flue**?

A chimney is a brick and masonry construction that contains one or more flues. A flue is a passage within a chimney through which smoke, fumes, and gases ascend. A flue is lined with clay or steel to contain the combustion wastes. By channeling the warm, rising gases, a flue creates a draft that pulls the air over the fire and up the flue. Each heat source needs its own flue, but one chimney can house several flues.

Which part of a door is a **doorjamb**?

The doorjamb is not part of the door, but is the surrounding case into and out of which the door opens and closes. It consists of two upright pieces, called side jambs, and a horizontal head jamb.

What is **crown molding**?

Crown molding is a wood, metal, or plaster finishing strip placed on the wall where it **429** intersects the ceiling. If the molding has a concave face, it is called a cove molding. In inside corners it must be cope-jointed to insure a tight joint.

What is **R-value**?

An R-value, or resistance to the flow of heat, is a special measurement of insulation that represents the difficulty with which heat flows through an insulating material. The higher the R-value, the greater the insulating value of the material. A wall's component R-values can be added up to get its total R-value:

Wall component	R-value
Inside Air Film	0.7
½" Gypsum Wallboard	0.5
R-13 Insulation	13.0
½" Wood Fiber Sheathing	1.3
Wood Siding	0.8
Outside Air Film	0.2
Total R-value	16.5

Building component	R-value
Standard attic ceiling	19
Standard 4-inch-thick insulated wall	11
Typical single-pane glass window	1
Double-glazed window	2
"Superwindows" (inner surface of a pane coated with an infrared radiation reflector material such as tin oxide and argon gas filling in the space between the panes of a double-glazed window.)	4

What is the **BOCA** code?

The Building Officials and Code Administrators (BOCA) International is a service organization that issues a series of model regulatory construction codes for the protection of public health, safety, and welfare. The codes are published in sections, such as the National Building Code, National Plumbing Code, National Fire Prevention Code, etc. They are designed for adoption by state or local governments and may be amended or modified to accomplish desired local requirements.

What is an **STC rating** and what does it mean?

The STC (Sound Transmission Class) tells how well a wall or floor assembly inhibits airborne sound. The higher the number, the greater the sound barrier. Typical STC ratings are as follows:

STC number	What it means
25	Normal speech can be easily understood
30	Loud speech can be understood
35	Loud speech is audible, but not intelligible
42	Loud speech audible as a murmur
45	Must strain to hear loud speech
48	Some loud speech barely audible
50	Loud speech not audible

The degree to which sound barriers work depends greatly on the elimination of air gaps under doors, through electrical outlets, and around heating ducts.

Why are **Phillips screws** used?

The recessed head and cross-shaped slots of a Phillips screw are self-centering and allow a closer, tighter fit than conventional screws. Straight-slotted screws can allow the screwdriver to slip out of the groove, ruining the wood.

Screws were used in carpentry as far back as the 16th century, but slotted screws with a tapering point were made at the beginning of the 19th century. The great advantage of screws over nails is that they are extremely resistant to longitudinal tension. Larger-size screws that require considerable force to insert have square heads that can be tightened with a wrench. Screws provide more holding power than nails and can be withdrawn without damaging the material. Types of screws include wood screws, lag screws (longer and heavier than wood screws), expansion anchors (usually for masonry), and sheet metal screws. The screw sizes vary from 0.25 to six inches (six millimeters to 15 centimeters).

Why is the term **penny** used in nail sizes?

The term "penny" is a measurement relating to the length of nails, originating in England. One explanation is that it refers to cost, with the cost of 100 nails of a certain size being 10 pence or 10d ("d" being the British symbol for a penny). Another explanation suggests that the term refers to the weight of 1,000 nails, with "d" at one time being used as an abbreviation for a pound in weight.

Humans have been using nails for the last 5,000 years or so. Nails are known to have been used in Ur (ancient Iraq) to fasten together sheet metal. Before 1500, nails were made by hand by drawing small pieces of metal through a succession of graded holes in a metal plate. In 1741, 60,000 people were employed in England making nails.

The first nail-making machine was invented by the American Ezekiel Reed. In 1851, Adolphe F. Brown of New York invented a wire-nail-making machine. This enabled nails to be mass-produced cheaply.

What is **Pisé** or **rammed earth**?

Rammed earth is an ancient building technique in which moist earth is compacted into a rough approximation of sedimentary rock. Using forms, rammed earth may be shaped into bricks or entire walls. Dating back as far as 7000 B.C.E., it was used in portions of the 2,000-year-old Great Wall of China as well as temples in Mali and in Morocco. Romans and Phoenicians introduced the technique to Europeans, and it became a popular building technique in France, where it became known as *pisé de terre*. In the United States, it was used for both gracious Victorian homes and low-cost housing.

Today, builders add cement to the earthen mix, which results in stronger, waterproof walls. In traditional rammed-earth construction, hand or compressor-powered tampers are used to compact a mixture of moistened earth and cement between double-sided wooden forms to about 60% of its original volume. In a newer technique, a high-pressure hose sprays the mixture against a single-sided form. Sometimes steel reinforcing bars are also used.

What is a **yurt**?

Originally a Mongolian hut, the yurt has been adapted in the United States as a low-cost structure that can be used as a dwelling. The foundation is built of wood on a hexagonal frame. The wooden lattice-work side walls have a tension cable sandwiched between the wall pieces at the top to keep the walls from collapsing. The walls are insulated and covered with boards, log slabs, canvas, or aluminum siding. A shingle roof, electricity, plumbing, and a small heating stove may be installed. The interior can be finished as desired with shelves, room dividers, and interior siding. The yurt is beautiful, practical, and relatively inexpensive to erect.

When was the **first skyscraper** built?

Designed by William Le Baron Jenney (1832–1907), the first skyscraper, the 10-story Home Insurance Company Building in Chicago, Illinois, was completed in 1885. A skyscraper—a very tall building supported by an internal frame (skeleton) of iron and steel rather than by load-bearing walls—maximizes floor space on limited land. Three technological developments made skyscrapers feasible: a better understanding of how materials behave under stress and load (from engineering and bridge design); the use of steel or iron framing to create a structure, with the outer skin "hung" on the frame;

How much does the leaning tower of Pisa lean?

The leaning tower of Pisa, 184.5 feet (56 meters) tall, is about 17 feet (five meters) out of perpendicular, increasing by about 0.2 inch (1.25 millimeters) a year. The Romanesque-style tower was started by Bonanno Pisano in 1173 as a campanile or bell tower for the nearby baptistry, but was not completed until 1372. Built entirely of white marble, with eight tiers of arched arcades, it began to lean during construction. Although the foundation was dug down to 10 feet (three meters), the builders did not reach bedrock for a firm footing. Ingenious attempts were made to compensate for the tilt by straightening up the subsequent stories and making the pillars higher on the south side than on the north. During the 1960s, cement was added to the foundation to strengthen it, but it is still threatened with collapse.

and the introduction of the first "safety" passenger elevator, invented by Elisha Otis (1811–1861).

When was the **first shopping center** built?

The first shopping center in the world was built in 1896 at Roland Park, Baltimore, Maryland. One of the world's largest shopping centers is the West Edmonton Mall in Alberta, Canada, which covers 5.2 million square feet (480,000 square meters) on a 121-acre (49-hectare) site. It has 828 stores and services, with parking for 20,000 vehicles.

What material was used to construct the exterior of the **Empire State Building**?

The exterior of the Empire State Building is made of Indiana limestone and granite with vertical strips of stainless steel.

What is the ground area of the **Pentagon Building** in Washington, D.C.?

The Pentagon, the headquarters of the United States Department of Defense, is the world's largest office building in terms of ground space. Its construction was com- **433** pleted on January 15, 1943—in just over 17 months. With a gross floor area of over 6.5 million square feet (604,000 square meters), this five-story, five-sided building has three times the floor space of the Empire State Building and is one and a half times larger than the Sears Tower in Chicago. The World Trade Center complex in New York City, completed in 1973, is larger with over nine million square feet (836,000 square meters), but it consists of two structures (towers). Each of the Pentagon's five sides is 921 feet (281 meters) long with a perimeter of 4,610 feet (1,405 meters). The secretary of defense, the secretaries of the three military departments, and the military heads of the army, navy, and air force are all located in the Pentagon. The National Military Command Center, which is the nation's military communications hub, is located where the Joint Chiefs of Staff convene. It is commonly called the "war room."

The largest commercial building in the world under one roof is the flower auction building of the cooperative VBA in Aalsmeer, Netherlands. In 1986, the floor plan was extended to 91 acres (37 hectares). It measures 2,546 × 2,070 feet (776 × 639 meters). The largest building in the United States, and the largest assembly plant in the world, is the Boeing 747 assembly plant in Everett, Washington, with a capacity of 200 million cubic feet (5.5 million cubic meters) and covering 47 acres (19 hectares).

What are the **tallest buildings** in the United States?

The following buildings are the tallest United States buildings and the tallest in the world:

Building	Location	Year built	Height		
			Feet	Meters	Stories
Sears Tower	Chicago, Illinois	1974	1454	443	110
plus two TV towers			1707	520.9	
World Trade Center	New York, New York				
North tower		1972	1368	417	110
South tower		1973	1362	415	110
Empire State Bldg	New York, New York	1931	1250	381	102
plus two TV towers			1414	431	

The tallest self-supporting structure in the world is the CN Tower in Toronto, Canada, at 1,815 feet (533 meters), built in 1975. The tallest structure in the world was the Guyed Warszawa Radio mast at Konstantynow, Poland, at 2,121 feet (646 meters). On August 10, 1991, however, it fell during renovation.

Who invented the **geodesic dome**?

A geodesic line is the shortest distance between two points across a surface. If that surface is curved, a geodesic line across it will usually be curved as well. A geodesic

Buckminster Fuller.

line on the surface of a sphere will be part of a great circle. Buckminster Fuller (1895–1983) realized that the surface of a sphere could be divided into triangles by a network of geodesic lines, and that structures could be designed so that their main elements either followed those lines or were joined along them.

This is the basis of his very successful geodesic dome: a structure of generally spherical form, constructed of many light, straight structural elements in tension, arranged in a framework of triangles to reduce stress and weight. These contiguous tetrahedrons are made from lightweight alloys with high tensile strength.

An early example of a geodesic structure is Britain's Dome of Discovery, built in 1951. It was the first dome ever built with principal framing members intentionally aligned along great circle arcs. The ASM (American Society for Metals) dome, which was built east of Cleveland, Ohio, in 1959–1960, is an open lattice–work geodesic dome. Built in 1965, the Houston Astrodome forms a giant geodesic dome.

Which building has the largest non-air-supported clear span roof?

The Suncoast Dome in St. Petersburg, Florida, completed in 1990, has a clear span of 688 feet (210 meters). Covering an area of 372,000 square feet (34,570 square meters), the fabric-covered dome is a cable roof structure—the newest structural system for **435**

What is the "topping out" party that iron workers have?

When the last beam is placed on a new bridge, skyscraper, or building, ironworkers hoist up an evergreen tree, attach a flag or a handkerchief, and brightly paint the final beam and autograph it.

This custom of raising an evergreen tree goes back to Scandinavia in 700 C.E., when attaching the tree to the building's ridge pole signalled to all who helped that the celebration of its completion would begin.

trussed domes. Its structural behavior is exactly opposite that of the traditional dome: the base ring is in compression rather than tension, and the ring at the crown is in tension rather than compression. Also, the space enclosed is not totally free and unobstructed, but includes structural, top-to-bottom members. To retain its characteristic lightness, the roofing surface employs flexible fabric membranes. These must be flexible since cable structures undergo major structural distortions, and they actually change shape under different load conditions. The largest air-supported building is the 80,600-capacity octagonal Pontiac Silverdome Stadium in Pontiac, Michigan. 522 feet (159 meters) wide and 722 feet (220 meters) long, it is supported by a 10-acre (1.62-hectare) translucent fiberglass roof.

When did Sears, Roebuck and Company sell homes by mail order?

Between 1908 and 1940, Sears manufactured and sold houses in approximately 450 ready-to-assemble designs from mansions to bungalows. Ordered by mail and sent by rail, these popular houses were complete with plumbing and electricity. Over 100,000 were sold at prices ranging from $595 to $5,000.

Sears' success in selling houses was tied, in large part, to its attractive financing plans. By 1911 the company had begun to offer loans for the purchase of materials, and by 1918 it would sometimes advance a portion of the capital required for labor.

Although most homes were sold to individuals, Sears also sold houses to companies for company towns near their factories. Standard Oil Company in Illinois, and Bethlehem Steel in Hellertown, Pennsylvania, were corporate customers.

ROADS, BRIDGES, AND TUNNELS

Who is known as the founder of **civil engineering**?

Thomas Telford (1757–1834), the first president of the Institute of Civil Engineers, is the founder of the British civil engineering profession. Telford established the professional ethos and tradition of the civil engineer—a tradition followed by all engineers today. He built bridges, roads, harbors, and canals. His greatest works include the Menai Strait Suspension Bridge and Pont y Cysyllte Aqueduct, the Gotha Canal in Sweden, the Caledonian Canal, and many Scottish roads. He was the first and greatest master of the iron bridge.

Which state has the **most miles of roads**?

Texas lays claim to the most road mileage with 294,142 miles (473,274 kilometers). California is a distant second with 169,201 miles (272,244 kilometers) of roads. On the other end of the scale, only three states have less than 10,000 miles (16,090 kilometers) of roads: Delaware, Hawaii, and Rhode Island. The total milage count for the United States is 3,904,721 miles (6,282,696 kilometers).

When was the **first U.S. coast-to-coast highway** built?

Completed in 1923, after ten years of planning and construction, the Lincoln Highway was the first transcontinental highway connecting the Atlantic coast (New York) to the Pacific (California). Sometimes called the "Main Street of the United States," the highway was proposed by Carl G. Fisher to a group of automobile manufacturers, who formed the Lincoln Highway Association and promoted the idea. Fisher thought that "Lincoln" would be a good, patriotic name for the road.

Its original length of 3,389 miles (5,453 kilometers) was later shortened by relocations and improvements to 3,143 miles (5,057 kilometers). Crossing 13 states—New York, New Jersey, Pennsylvania, Ohio, Indiana, Illinois, Nebraska, Colorado, Wyoming, Utah, Nevada, and California—in 1925, the Lincoln Highway became, for most of its length, U.S. Route 30.

How are U.S. **highways numbered**?

The main north–south interstate highways always have odd numbers of one or two digits. The system, beginning with Interstate 5 on the West Coast, increases in number as it moves eastward, and ends with Interstate 95 on the East Coast.

The east–west interstate highways have even numbers. The lowest-numbered highway begins in Florida with Interstate 4, increasing in number as it moves northward, and ends with Interstate 96. Coast-to-coast east–west interstates, such as Routes 10, 40, and 80, end in zero. An interstate with three digits is either a beltway or a spur route.

U.S. routes follow the same numbering system as the interstate system, but increase in number from east to west and from north to south. U.S. Route 1, for example, runs along the East Coast; U.S. Route 2 runs along the Canadian border. U.S. route numbers may have anywhere from one to three digits.

Which city had the **first traffic light**?

On December 10, 1868, the first traffic light was erected on a 22-foot (6.7-meter) high cast-iron pillar at the corner of Bridge Street and New Palace Yard off Parliament Square in London, England. Invented by J. P. Knight, a railway signalling engineer, the light was a revolving lantern illuminated by gas, with red and green signals. It was turned by hand using a lever at the base of the pole.

Cleveland, Ohio, installed an electric traffic signal at Euclid Avenue and 105th Street on August 5, 1914. It had red and green lights with a warning buzzer as the color changed.

Around 1913, Detroit, Michigan, used a system of manually operated semaphores. Eventually the semaphores were fitted with colored lanterns for night traffic. New York City installed the first three-color light signals in 1918; these signals were still operated manually.

What is a **Jersey barrier**?

Jersey barriers are concrete highway barriers developed by the New Jersey Department of Transportation. Originally only 12 to 18 inches (30 to 46 centimeters) high, they were designed to prevent left turns at certain intersections. Later barriers, reinforced concrete usually poured on the site, were used as temporary traffic safeguards where construction required motorists to cross over into a lane normally used by oncoming traffic. These barriers were 32 inches (81 centimeters) high. Now the barriers line thousands of miles of American highways as permanent fixtures. Barriers are now 54 inches (137 centimeters) high, thus blocking out the glare of oncoming headlights.

How do cars, buses, and trucks travel in the new **English channel tunnel**?

Cars, buses, and trucks are carried on 2,500-foot (762-meter) long trains traveling at 90 miles per hour (145 kilometers per hour) in the two 31-mile (50-kilometer) long tunnels under the English Channel. Automobile operators drive their vehicles onto the trains and remain inside until the passage is complete. The trains carry cars and buses in large wagons. Truck drivers travel separately from their vehicles, which ride

Why are manhole covers round?

Circular covers are almost universally used on sewer manholes because they cannot drop through the opening. The circular cover rests on a lip that is smaller than the cover, and the cover and the lip are manufactured together, making for a particularly tight fit. Any other shape—such as square or rectangle—could slip into the manhole opening. In addition, round manhole covers can be machined more accurately than other shapes, and, once removed, round covers can be rolled rather than having to be lifted.

in simpler, semi-open wagons. Interspersed with the shuttles are high-speed passenger trains designed to run on the different railroad systems of Britain, Continental Europe, and the tunnel.

What is the world's **longest road tunnel**?

The longest road tunnel is the 10.14-mile (16-kilometer), two-lane St. Gotthard road tunnel from Göschenen to Airolo, Switzerland, which opened to traffic on September 5, 1980. In the United States the longest road tunnel is the 1.69-mile (2.7-kilometer) long twin Eisenhower Memorial Tunnel on Interstate 70 under the Continental Divide in Colorado.

Where is the **longest bridge-tunnel** in the world?

Completed in 1964 after 42 months' work and $200 million and spanning a great distance of open sea, the Chesapeake Bay Bridge-Tunnel is a 17.5-mile (28-kilometer) combination of trestles, bridges, and tunnels that connect Norfolk with Cape Charles in Virginia. Its only rival for crossing so much open and deep water is the Zuider Zee Dam in Holland—a road-carrying structure of similar length, but without the same water depth and same length of open sea.

What are the various **types of bridge** structures?

Four basic types of structures can be used to bridge a stream or similar obstacle: rigid beam, cantilever, arch, and suspension systems.

The rigid beam bridge, the simplest and most common form of bridging, has straight slabs or girders carrying the roadbed. The span is relatively short and its load rests on its supports or piers.

439

The arch bridge is in compression, and thrusts outward on its bearings at each end.

In the suspension bridge, the roadway hangs on steel cables, with the bulk of the load carried on cables anchored to the banks. It can span a great distance without intermediate piers.

Each arm of a cantilever bridge is, or could be, free-standing, with the load of the short central truss span pushing down through the piers of the outer arms and pulling up at each end. The outer arms are usually anchored at the abutments and project into the central truss.

What is a "kissing bridge"?

Covered bridges with roofs and wooden sides are called "kissing bridges," because people inside the bridge could not be seen from outside. Such bridges can be traced back to the early 19th century. Contrary to folk wisdom, they were not designed to produce rural "lovers' lanes," but were covered to protect the structures from deterioration.

How many covered bridges are there in the United States?

More than 10,000 covered bridges were built across the United States between 1805 (when the first was erected in Philadelphia) and the early 20th century. As of January 1980, only 893 of these covered bridges remained—231 in Pennsylvania, 157 in Ohio, 103 in Indiana, 100 in Vermont, 54 in Oregon, and 52 in New Hampshire. Three interstate bridges link New Hampshire and Vermont. The remainder are scattered throughout the country. Non-authentic covered bridges—built or covered for visual effect—appear in each state.

What are the world's longest bridge spans?

The world's longest main-span in a suspension bridge is the Humber Estuary Bridge in England, at 4,626 feet (1,410 meters). Designed by Freeman Fox and Partners and begun on July 27, 1972, it was opened on July 18, 1981. The Humber Bridge is longer than the Verrazano-Narrows Bridge in New York, but it will be surpassed by two bridges now under construction. The double-deck Akashi-Kaikyo Bridge linking Honshū and Shikoku, Japan, beginning construction in 1998, will have a main span of 6,529 feet (1,990 meters). The Messing Bridge that will link Sicily with Calabria on the Italian mainland will become the longest by far when it is completed, with a single span of 10,892 feet (3,320 meters).

The world's longest cable-stayed bridge span is the Pont de Normandie in LeHavre, France, spanning 2,808 feet (856 meters), which opened on January 20, **440** 1995.

The world's longest cantilever bridge is the Quebec Bridge over the St. Lawrence River in Canada, opened in 1917, which has a span of 1,800 feet (549 meters) between piers, with an overall length of 3,239 feet (987 meters).

The world's longest steel arch bridge is the New River Gorge Bridge near Fayetteville, West Virginia, completed in 1977, with a span of 1,700 feet (518 meters).

The world's longest concrete arch bridge is the Jesse H. Jones Memorial Bridge, which spans Houston Ship Canal in Texas. Completed in 1982, the bridge measures 1,500 feet (457 meters).

The world's longest stone arch bridge is the 3,810-foot (1161-meter) Rockville Bridge, completed in 1901, north of Harrisburg, Pennsylvania, with 48 spans containing 216 tons (219 tonnes) of stone.

Where is the **longest suspension bridge** in the United States?

Spanning New York (City) Harbor, the Verrazano-Narrows Bridge is the longest suspension bridge in the United States. With a span of 4,260 feet (1,298 meters) from tower to tower, its total length is 7,200 feet (2,194 meters). Named after Giovanni da Verrazano (1485–1528), the Italian explorer who discovered New York Harbor in April 1524, it was erected under the direction of Othmar H. Ammann (1879–1965) and completed in 1964. To avoid impeding navigation in and out of the harbor, it provides a clearance of 216 feet (66 meters) between the water level and the bottom of the bridge deck. Like other suspension bridges, the bulk of the load of the Verrazano-Narrows Bridge is carried on cables anchored to the banks.

Which United States place has the **most bridges**?

With the possible exception of Venice, Italy, Pittsburgh, Pennsylvania is the bridge capital of the world. There are more than 1,700 bridges in Allegheny County's 731 square miles (1,892 square kilometers). The county has 2.3 bridges per square mile or one bridge for every mile of highway. Nationwide, there are approximately 564,000 bridges.

Are there any **floating bridges** in the United States?

The four floating pontoon bridges in the United States are all located in the state of Washington. The Lacy V. Murrow–Lake Washington Bridge (1993), The Evergreen Point Bridge (1963), and the Third Lake Washington Bridge (1989) in Seattle are 6,543 feet (1,994 meters), 7,518 feet (2,291 meters), and 6,130 feet (1,868 meters) long respectively. The Hood Canal Bridge (1961) in Port Gamble is 6,471 feet (1,972 meters) long.

How was the safety of the **first bridge across the Mississippi** River at St. Louis proved in 1874?

According to a historical appraisal of the bridge by Howard Miller, "Progressively heavier trains shuttled back and forth across the bridge as its engineer, James B. Eads, took meticulous measurements. However, the general public was probably more reassured by a nonscientific test. Everyone knew that elephants had canny instincts and would not set foot on an unsound bridge. The crowd cheered as a great beast from a local menagerie mounted the approach without hesitation and lumbered placidly across to the Illinois side."

Who built the **Brooklyn Bridge**?

John A. Roebling (1806–1869), a German-born American engineer, constructed the first truly modern suspension bridge in 1855. Towers supporting massive cables, tension anchorage for stays, a roadway suspended from the main cables, and a stiffening deck below or beside the road deck to prevent oscillation are all characteristics of Roebling's suspension bridge. In 1867, Roebling was given the ambitious task of constructing the Brooklyn Bridge. In his design he proposed the revolutionary idea of using steel wire for cables rather than the less-resilient iron. Just as construction began, Roebling died of tetanus when his foot was crushed in an accident, and his son, Washington A. Roebling (1837–1926), assumed responsibility for the bridge's construction. Fourteen years later, in 1883, the bridge was completed. At that time, it was the longest suspension bridge in the world, spanning the East River and connecting New York's Manhattan with Brooklyn. The bridge has a central span of 1,595 feet (486 meters), with its masonry towers rising 276 feet (841 meters) above high water. Today, the Brooklyn Bridge is among the best-known of all American civil engineering accomplishments.

Who designed the **Golden Gate Bridge**?

Joseph B. Strauss (1870–1938), formally named chief engineer for the project in 1929, was assisted by Charles Ellis and Leon Moisseiff in the design. An engineering masterpiece that opened to traffic in May 1937, this suspension bridge spans San Francisco Bay, linking San Francisco with Marin County, California. It has a central span of 4,200 feet (1280 meters) with towers rising 746 feet (2274 meters).

MISCELLANEOUS STRUCTURES

Will building a **seawall** protect a beach?

It may for a while, but during a storm, the sand cannot follow its natural pattern of

What is a Texas tower?

A Texas tower is an off-shore platform used as a radar station. Built on pilings sunk into the ocean floor, it resembles the offshore oil derricks or rigs first developed in the Gulf of Mexico off the coast of Texas. In addition to the radar, the components of a typical tower may include crew quarters, a helicopter landing pad, fog signals, and oceanographic equipment.

allowing waves to draw the sand across the lower beach, making the beach flatter. With a seawall, the waves carry off more sand, dropping it into deeper water. A better alternative to the seawall is the revetment. This is a wall of boulders, rubble, or concrete block, tilted back away from the waves. It imitates the way a natural beach flattens out under wave attack.

Where is the **highest dam** in the United States and what is its capacity?

Oroville, the highest dam in the United States, is an earth-fill dam that rises 754 feet (230 meters) and extends more than a mile across the Feather River, near Oroville, California. Built in 1968, it forms a reservoir containing about 3.5 million acre-feet (4.3 million cubic meters) of water. The next highest dam in the United States is the Hoover Dam on the Colorado River, on the Nevada–Arizona border. It is 726 feet (221 meters) high, and was, for 22 years, the world's highest. Presently, nine dams are higher than the Oroville—the highest currently is the 1,098-foot (335-meter) Rogun(skaya) earth-fill dam that crosses the Vaksh River in Tadzhikistan. Built between 1981 and 1987, this dam has a volume of 92.9 million cubic yards (71 million cubic meters).

How big is the **Hoover Dam**?

Formerly called Boulder Dam, the Hoover Dam is located between Nevada and Arizona on the Colorado River. The highest concrete arch dam in the United States, the dam is 1,244 feet (379 meters) long and 726 feet (221 meters) high. It has a base thickness of 660 feet (201 meters) and a crest thickness of 45 feet (13.7 meters). It stores 21.25 million acre-feet of water in the 115-mile (185-kilometer) long Lake Mead reservoir.

The dam was built because the Southwest was faced with constantly recurring cycles of flood and drought. Uncontrolled, the Colorado River had limited value, but once regulated, the flow would assure a stabilized, year-round water supply, and the **443** low-lying valleys would be protected against floods. On December 21, 1928, the Boulder Canyon Project Act became law, and the project was completed on September 30, 1935—two years ahead of schedule. For 22 years, Hoover Dam was the highest dam in the world.

What are the dimensions of the Eiffel Tower?

Number of iron structural components in tower	15,000
Number of rivets	2,500,000
Weight of foundations	306 tons (277,602 kilograms)
Weight of iron	8,092 tons (7,341,214 kilograms)
Weight of elevator systems	1,042 tons (946,000 kilograms)
Total weight	9,441 tons (8,564,816 kilograms)
Pressure on foundations	58–64 pounds per square inch (4–4.5 kilograms per square centimeter), depending on pier
Height of first platform	189 feet (58 meters)
Height of second platform	379 feet 8 inches (116 meters)
Height of third platform	905 feet 11 inches (276 meters)
Total height in 1889	985 feet 11 inches (300.5 meters)
Total height with television antenna	1052 feet 4 inches (320.75 meters)
Number of steps to the top	1,671
Maximum sway at top caused by wind	4.75 inches (12 centimeters)
Maximum sway at top caused by metal dilation	7 inches (18 centimeters)
Size of base area	2.54 acres (10,282 square meters)
Dates of construction	26 January 1887 to 31 March 1889
Cost of construction	7,799,401.31 francs ($1,505,675.90)

How tall is the figure on the Statue of Liberty, and how much does it weigh?

The Statue of Liberty, conceived and designed by the French sculptor Fréderic-Auguste Bartholdi (1834–1904), was given to the United States to commemorate its first centennial. Called (in his patent, U.S. Design Patent no. 11,023, issued February 18, 1879) "Liberty Enlightening the World," it is 152 feet (46 meters) high, weighs 225 tons (204 metric tons), and stands on a pedestal and base that are 151 feet (46 meters) tall. Her flowing robes are made from more than 300 sheets of hand-hammered copper over a steel frame. Constructed and finished in France in 1884, the statue's exterior and interior were taken apart piece by piece, packed into 200 mammoth wooden crates, and shipped to the United States in May 1885. The statue was placed by Bartholdi on Bedloe's Island, at the mouth of New York City Harbor. On October 28, 1886, ten years after the centennial had passed, the inauguration celebration was held.

It was not until 1903 that the inscription "Give me your tired, your poor, Your huddled masses yearning to breathe free ..." was added. The verse was taken from *The New Colossus* composed by New York City poet Emma Lazarus in 1883. The statue, the tallest in the United States, and the tallest metal statue in the world, was recently refurbished for its own centennial, at a cost of $698 million, reopening on July 4, 1986. One visible difference is the flame of her torch is now 24-karat gold-leaf, just as in the original design. In 1916 the flame was redone into a lantern of amber glass. Concealed within the rim of her crown is the observation deck that can be reached by climbing 171 steps or by taking the newly installed hydraulic elevator.

The first ferris wheel, designed for the 1893 Columbian Exposition by George Washington Gale Ferris.

Who invented the **Ferris Wheel** and when?

Originally called "pleasure wheels," the first such rides were described by English traveler Peter Mundy in 1620. In Turkey he saw a ride for children consisting of two vertical wheels, 20 feet (six meters) across, supported by a large post on each side. Such rides were called "ups-and-downs" at the St. Bartholomew Fair of 1728 in England, and in 1860, a French pleasure wheel was turned by hand and carried 16 passengers. They were also in use in the United States by then, with a larger, wooden wheel operating at Walton Spring, Georgia.

Wanting a spectacular attraction to rival that of the 1889 Paris Centennial celebration—the Eiffel Tower—the directors of the 1893 Columbian Exposition had a design competition. The prize was won by the American bridge builder George Washington Gale Ferris (1859–1896). In 1893 he designed and erected a gigantic revolving steel wheel whose top reached 264 feet (80.5 meters) above ground. The wheel—825 feet (251.5 meters) in circumference, 250 feet (76 meters) in diameter, and 30 feet (nine meters) wide—was supported by two 140-foot (43-meter) towers. Attached to the wheel were 36 cars, each able to carry 60 passengers. Opening on June 21, 1893, at the exposition in Chicago, Illinois, it was extremely successful. Thousands lined up to pay 50 cents for a 20-minute ride—a large sum in those days, considering that a merry-go-round ride cost only four cents. In 1904 it was moved to St. Louis, Missouri, for the Louisiana Purchase Exposition. It was eventually sold for scrap. The largest-diameter wheel currently operating is the Cosmoclock 21 at Yokohama City, Japan. It is 345 feet (105 meters) high and 328 feet (100 meters) in diameter.

How many **roller coasters** are there in the United States, and how many people ride them?

There were 164 roller coasters in the United States in 1989, and an estimated 214 million people rode them during that year. Roller coasters have had a long history in thrill-giving. During the 15th and 16th centuries, the first known gravity rides were built in St. Petersburg and were called "Russian Mountains." A wheeled roller coaster, called the "Switchback," was used as early as 1784 in Russia. By 1817, the first roller coaster with cars locked to the tracks operated in France. The first United States roller coaster patent was granted to J. G. Taylor in 1872, and LaMarcus Thompson built the first known roller coaster in the United States at Coney Island in Brooklyn, New York, in 1884. Until recently, the longest roller coaster in the world was "The Beast" at Kings Island, Ohio, which has a run of 1.4 miles (2.25 kilometers) with 800 feet (244 meters) of tunnels. The current record-holder is the "Ultimate" at Lightwater Valley, Ripon, Great Britain, with a run of 1.42 miles (2.28 kilometers).

BOATS, TRAINS, CARS, AND PLANES

BOATS AND SHIPS

What is **dead reckoning**?

Dead reckoning is the determination of a craft's current latitude and longitude by advancing its previous position to the new one on the basis of assumed distance and direction traveled. The influences of current and wind as well as compass errors are taken into account in this calculation, all done without the aid of any celestial or physical observation. This is a real test of a navigator's skill.

Nuclear-powered submarines, which must retain secrecy of movement and cannot ascend to the surface, use the SINS system (Ship's Inertial Navigation System) developed by the United States Navy. It is a fully self-contained system, which requires no receiving or transmitting apparatus and thus involves no detectable signals. It consists of accelerometers, gyroscopes, and a computer. Together they produce inertial navigation, which is a sophisticated form of dead reckoning.

What is the **nautical meaning** of the phrase "by and large"?

On a sailing ship or sailboat, new sailors at the helm are usually ordered to sail "by and large," meaning to sail into the wind at a slightly larger angle than those with more experience might choose. Sailing almost directly into the wind is most efficient, but doing so may cause the sail to flap back against the mast, resulting in loss of speed and control. Sailing "by and large" thus meant they were on the right, if not the perfect, course. Eventually the phrase became generally used as a synonym for approximately.

Why is the right side of a ship called "starboard"?

In the time of the Vikings, ships were steered by long paddles or boards placed over the right side. They were known in Old English as *steorbords*, evolving into the word *starboard*. The left side of a ship, looking forward, is called *port*. Formerly the left side was called *larboard*, originating perhaps from the fact that early merchant ships were always loaded from the left side. Its etymology is Scandinavian, being *lade* (load) and *bord* (side). The British Admiralty ordered *port* to be used in place of *larboard* to prevent confusion with *starboard*.

What is the name of the carved **wooden figure of a woman** on a **sailing ship**?

A carved wooden figure at the top of the stem of a sailing ship, usually in the shape of a woman, is called a figure head.

Which type of **wood** was used to build **Noah's ark**?

According to the Bible, Noah's ark was made of gopher wood. This is identified as *Cupressus sempervirens*, one of the most durable woods in the world. Also called the Mediterranean cypress, the tree is native throughout southern Europe and western Asia. It grows up to 80 feet (24 meters) tall. Similar to this tree is the Monterey cypress (*Cupressus macrocarpa*), which is restricted to a very small area along the coast of central California. It can become as tall as 90 feet (27 meters) with horizontal branches that support a broad, spreading crown. When old, this tree looks very much like the aged cedars of Lebanon.

Where does the term **"mark twain"** originate?

Mark twain is a riverboat term meaning two fathoms (a depth of 12 feet or 3.6 meters). A hand lead is used for determining the depth of water where there is less than 20 fathoms. The lead consists of a lead weight of seven to 14 pounds (three to six kilograms) and a line of hemp or braided cotton, 25 fathoms (150 feet or 46 meters) in length. The line is marked at 2, 3, 5, 7, 10, 15, 17, and 20 fathoms. The soundings are taken by a leadsman who calls out the depths while standing on a platform projecting from the side of the ship, called "the chains." The number of fathoms always forms the last part of the call. When the depth corresponds to any mark on the lead line, it is reported as "By the mark 7," "By the mark 10," etc. When the depth corresponds to a fathom between the marks on the line, it is reported as "By the deep 6," etc. When the line is a fraction greater than a mark, it is reported as "And a half 7," "And a quarter 5"; a fraction less than a mark is "Half less 7," "Quarter less 10," etc. If bottom is not reached, the call is "No bottom at 20 fathoms."

"Mark Twain" was also the pseudonym chosen by American humorist Samuel L. Clemens. Supposedly, he chose the name because of its suggestive meaning, since it was a riverman's term for water that was just barely safe for navigation. One implication of this "barely safe water" meaning was, as his character Huck Finn would later remark, "Mr. Mark Twain ... he told the truth, mostly." Another implication was that "barely safe water" usually made people nervous, or at least uncomfortable.

How is a ship's **tonnage** calculated?

Tonnage of a ship is not necessarily the number of tons that the ship weighs. There are at least six different methods of rating ships; the most common are:

Displacement tonnage—used especially for warships and U.S. merchant ships—is the weight of the water displaced by a ship. Since a ton of sea water occupies 35 cubic feet (one cubic meter), the weight of water displaced by a ship can be determined by dividing the cubic footage of the submerged area of the ship by 35. The result is converted to long tons (2,240 pounds or 1,017 kilograms). Loaded displacement tonnage is the weight of the water displaced when a ship is carrying its normal load of fuel, cargo, and crew. Light displacement tonnage is the weight of water displaced by the unloaded ship.

Gross tonnage (GRST) or *gross registered tonnage* (GRT)—used to rate merchant shipping and passenger ships—is a measure of the enclosed capacity of a vessel. It is the sum in cubic feet of the vessel's enclosed space divided by 100 (100 such cubic feet is considered one ton). The result is gross (registered) tonnage. For example, the old *Queen Elizabeth* did not weigh 83,673 tons, but had a capacity of 8,367,300 cubic feet (236,878 cubic meters).

Deadweight tonnage (DWT)—used for freighters and tankers—is the total weight in long tons (2,240 pounds or 1,017 kilograms) of everything a ship can carry when fully loaded. It represents the amount of cargo, stores, bunkers, and passengers that are required to bring a ship down to her loadline, i.e., the carrying capacity of a ship.

Net registered tonnage (NRT)—used in merchant shipping—is the gross registered tonnage minus the space that cannot be utilized for paying passengers or cargo (crew space, ballast, engine room, etc.)

What does the term **loadline** mean in shipping?

A loadline or load waterline is an immersion mark on the hull of a merchant ship. This indicates her safe load limit. The lines vary in height for different seasons of the year and areas of the world. Also called the "Plimsoll line" or "Plimsoll mark," it was accepted as law by the British Parliament in the Merchant Shipping Act of 1875, primarily at the instigation of Samuel Plimsoll (1824–1898). This law prevented unscrupulous owners from sending out unseaworthy and overloaded, but heavily insured, vessels (so-called "coffin ships"), which risked the crew's lives.

Who created the **Liberty ship**?

The Liberty ship of World War II was the brainchild of Henry J. Kaiser (1882–1967), an American industrialist who had never run a shipyard before 1941. The huge loss of merchant tonnage during the war created an urgent need to protect merchant vessels transporting weapons and supplies, and the Liberty ship was born. It was a standard merchant ship with a deadweight tonnage of 10,500 long tons and a service speed of 11 knots. They were built to spartan standards, and production was on a massive scale. Simplicity of construction and operations, rapidity of building, and large cargo carrying capacity were assets. To these, Kaiser added prefabrication and welding instead of riveting. The ships were a deciding factor on the side of the Allies. In four years 2,770 ships with a deadweight tonnage of 29,292,000 long tons were produced.

When was the first **hospital ship** built?

It is believed that the Spanish Armada fleet of 1587–1588 included hospital ships. England's first recorded hospital ship was the *Goodwill* in 1608, but it was not until after 1660 that the Royal Navy made it a regular practice to set aside ships for hospital use. The United States government outfitted six hospital ships, some of which were permanently attached to the fleet, during the Spanish-American War of 1898. Congress authorized the construction of the USS *Relief* in August 1916. It was launched in 1919 and delivered to the navy in December 1920.

Why did the *Titanic* sink?

On its maiden voyage from Southampton, England, to New York, the British luxury liner *Titanic* sideswiped an iceberg at 11:40 p.m. on Sunday, April 14, 1912, and was badly damaged. The 882-foot (269-meter) long liner, whose eight decks rose to the height of an 11-story building, sank two hours and forty minutes later. Of the 2,227 passengers and crew, 705 escaped in 20 lifeboats and rafts; 1,522 drowned.

Famous as the greatest disaster in transatlantic shipping history, circumstances made the loss of life in the sinking of the *Titanic* exceptionally high. Although Capt. E.

J. Smith was warned of icebergs in shipping lanes, he maintained his speed of 22 knots, and did not post additional lookouts. Later inquiries revealed that the liner *Californian* was only 20 miles (32 kilometers) away and could have helped, had its radio operator been on duty. The *Titanic* had an insufficient number of lifeboats, and those available for use were badly managed, with some leaving the boat only half full. The only ship responding to distress signals was the ancient *Carpathia*, which saved 705 people.

Contrary to a long-held belief, the *Titanic* had not been sliced open by the iceberg. When Dr. Robert Ballard (b. 1942) from Woods Hole Oceanographic Institution descended to the site of the sunken vessel in the research vessel *Alvin* in July 1986, he found that the ship's starboard bow plates had buckled under the impact of the collision. This caused the ship to be opened up to the sea.

Ballard found the bow and the stern more than 600 yards (548 meters) apart on the ocean's floor, and speculated on what happened after the collision with the iceberg. "Water entered six forward compartments after the ship struck the iceberg. As the liner nosed down, water flooded compartments one after another, and the ship's stern rose even higher out of the water, until the stress amidships was more than she could bear. She broke apart ..." and the stern soon sank by itself.

What is the world's **largest ship**?

Among passenger liners, the cruise ship *Sovereign of the Seas*, built in France for the Norwegian Royal Caribbean Cruise Lines, was the world's largest until 1990, with a gross registered tonnage of 73,192. Completed in 1988, its dimensions are 874 × 105 feet (266 × 32 meters) with a depth of 49 feet (15 meters). It can accommodate 2,763 passengers plus crew—more than 3,000 people total. In the autumn of 1990, the cruise ship *Norway*, built in 1961 as the *France* and renamed in 1979, increased her gross registered tonnage from 70,202 to 76,000 to become not only the longest liner at 1,035.5 feet (316 meters), but also the largest. However, the largest passenger liner ever built was Cunard's *Queen Elizabeth*, which was 1,031 feet (314 meters) long and 118.5 feet (36 meters) wide with a final gross registered tonnage of 82,998 (originally 83,673). With the last voyage ending on November 15, 1968, the *Queen Elizabeth* in 1970 became a floating marine university, *Seaside University*, in Hong Kong, and burned on January 9, 1972.

The largest ship of any kind currently in service is the tanker *Hellas Fos*, owned by the Bilinder Marine Corporation of Athens, Greece. Built in 1979, this steam turbine tanker has a deadweight tonnage of 611,832.5 (gross registered tonnage of 254,583). The largest ship in the world is the *Happy Giant*, formerly the *Seawise Giant*, with a deadweight tonnage of 622,571.5, a length of 1,504 feet (458 meters), and a beam of 226 feet (69 meters). Attacked and damaged by Iraqi Mirage jets in the Persian Gulf on December 22, 1987, and again on May 14, 1988, the tanker is in the process of being refitted. The steam turbines are being replaced with a diesel engine, which will decrease her deadweight tonnage to about 420,000 long tons.

When were the first **nuclear-powered vessels** launched?

A controlled nuclear reaction generates tremendous heat, which turns water into steam for running turbine engines. The USS *Nautilus* was the first submarine to be propelled by nuclear power, making her first sea run on January 17, 1955. It has been called the first true submarine since it can remain underwater for an indefinite period of time. The *Nautilus*, 324 feet (99 meters) long, has a range of 2,500 miles (4,023 kilometers) submerged, a diving depth of 700 feet (213 meters), and can travel submerged at 20 knots.

The first nuclear warship was the 14,000-ton cruiser USS *Long Beach*, launched on July 14, 1959. The USS *Enterprise* was the first nuclear-powered aircraft carrier. Launched on September 24, 1960, the *Enterprise* was 1,101.5 feet (336 meters) long, and designed to carry 100 aircraft.

The first nuclear-powered merchant ship was the *Savannah*, a 20,000-ton vessel, launched in 1962. The United States built it largely as an experiment and it was never operated commercially. In 1969, Germany built the *Otto Hahn*, a nuclear-powered ore carrier. The most successful use of nuclear propulsion in non-naval ships has been as icebreakers. The first nuclear-powered icebreaker was the Soviet Union's *Lenin*, commissioned in 1959.

TRAINS AND TROLLEYS

What is a **standard gauge** railroad?

The first successful railroads in England used steam locomotives built by George Stephenson (1781–1848) to operate on tracks with a gauge of four feet, 8.5 inches (1.41 meters) probably because that was the wheel spacing common on the wagons and tramways of the time. Stephenson, a self-taught inventor and engineer, had developed in 1814 the steam-blast engine that made steam locomotives practical. His railroad rival, Isambard K. Brunel (1806–1859), laid out the line for the Great Western Railway at seven feet, 0.25 inches (2.14 meters), and the famous "battle of the gauges" began. A commission appointed by the British Parliament decided in favor of Stephenson's narrower gauge, and the Gauge Act of 1846 prohibited using other gauges. This width eventually became accepted by the rest of the world. The distance is measured between the inner sides of the heads of the two rails of the track at a distance of

⁵⁄₈ inch (16 millimeters) below the top of the rails.

What is the world's **longest railway**?

The Trans-Siberian Railway, from Moscow to Vladivostok, is 5,777 miles (9,297 kilometers) long. If the spur to Nakhodka is included, the distance becomes 5,865 miles (9,436 kilometers). It was opened in sections, and the first goods train reached Irkutsk on August 27, 1898. The Baikal-Amur Northern Main Line, begun in 1938, shortens the distance by about 310 miles (500 kilometers). The journey takes approximately seven days, two hours, and crosses seven time zones. There are nine tunnels, 139 large bridges or viaducts, and 3,762 smaller bridges or culverts on the whole route. Nearly the entire line is electrified.

In comparison, the first American transcontinental railroad, completed on May 10, 1869, is 1,780 miles (2,864 kilometers) long. The Central Pacific Railroad was built eastward from Sacramento, California, and the Union Pacific Railroad was built westward to Promontory Point, Utah, where the two lines met to connect the line.

What is the **fastest train**?

The French SNCF high-speed train TGV (*Train à Grande Vitesse*) Atlantique achieved the fastest speed—320.2 miles per hour (515.2 kilometers per hour)—recorded on any national rail system on May 18, 1990, between Courtalain and Tours.

The Amtrak X2000 is the fastest train in the United States, with a maximum speed of 156 miles per hour (251 kilometers per hour). The train completed a demonstration run between Washington, D.C., and New York on February 1, 1993. It is scheduled for service in 1997.

MAGLEV (*mag*netic *lev*itation) trains under development in Japan and Germany can travel 250 to 300 miles per hour (402 to 483 kilometers per hour) or more. These trains run on a bed of air produced from the repulsion or attraction of powerful magnetic fields (based on the principle that like poles of magnets repel and unlike poles [north and south] attract). The German Transrapid uses conventional magnets to levitate the train. The principle of attraction in magnetism, the employment of wing-like flaps extending under the train to fold under a T-shaped guideway, and the use of electromagnets on board (that are attracted to the non-energized magnetic surface) are the guiding components. Interaction between the train's electromagnets and those built on top of the T-shaped track lift the vehicle 3/8 inch (one centimeter) off the guideway. Another set of magnets along the rail sides provides lateral guidance. The train rides on electromagnetic waves. Alternating current in the magnet sets in the guideway changes their polarity to alternately push and pull the train along. Braking is done by reversing the direction of the magnetic field (caused by reversing the magnetic poles). To increase train speed, the frequency of current is raised.

The Japanese MLV002 uses the same propulsion system, but the difference is in the levitation design, in which the train rests on wheels until it reaches a speed of 100 miles (161 kilometers) per hour. Then it levitates four inches (10 centimeters) above the guideway. The levitation depends on superconducting magnets and a repulsion system (rather than the attraction system that the German system uses).

When was the **first U.S. railroad** chartered?

The first American railroad charter was obtained on February 6, 1815, by Colonel John Stevens (1749–1838) of Hoboken, New Jersey, to build and operate a railroad between the Delaware and Raritan rivers near Trenton and New Brunswick. However, lack of financial backing prevented its construction. The Granite Railway, built by Gridley Bryant, was chartered on October 7, 1826. It ran from Quincy, Massachusetts, to the Neponset River—a distance of three miles (4.8 kilometers). The main cargo was granite blocks used in building the Bunker Hill Monument.

What was the railroad **velocipede**?

In the 19th century, railroad track maintenance workers used a three-wheeled handcar to speed their way along the track. The handcar was used for interstation express and package deliveries and for delivery of urgent messages between stations that could not wait until the next train. Also called an "Irish Mail," this 150-pound (68-kilogram) three-wheeler resembled a bicycle with a sidecar. The operator sat in the middle of the two-wheel section and pushed a crank back and forth, which propelled the triangle-shaped vehicle down the tracks. This manually powered handcar was replaced after World War I by a gasoline-powered track vehicle. This, in turn, was replaced by a conventional pickup truck fitted with an auxiliary set of flanged wheels.

What does the term **gandy dancer** mean?

A track laborer. The name derived from the special tools used for track work made by the Gandy Manufacturing Company of Chicago, Illinois. These tools were used during the 19th century almost universally by section gangs.

What was the route of the *Orient Express*?

This luxury train service was inaugurated in June, 1883, to provide through connection between France and Turkey. It was not until 1889 that the complete journey could be made by train. The route left Paris and went via Chalons, Nancy, and Strasbourg into Germany (via Karlsruhe, Stuttgart, and Munich), then into Austria (via Salzburg, Linz, and Vienna), into Hungary (through Gyor and Budapest), south to Belgrade, Yugoslavia, through Sofia, Bulgaria and finally to Istanbul (Constantinople), Turkey. It ceased operation in May 1977. In 1982, part of the line, the *Venice-Simplon-Orient Express* went into operation.

How does a **cable car**, like those in San Francisco, move?

A cable runs continuously in a channel, between the tracks located just below the street. The cable is controlled from a central station, and usually moves about nine miles (14.5 kilometers) per hour. Each cable car has an attachment, on the underside of the car, called a grip. When the car operator pulls the lever, the grip latches onto the moving cable and is pulled along by the moving cable. When the operator releases the lever, the grip disconnects from the cable and comes to a halt when the operator applies the brakes. Also called an endless ropeway, it was invented by Andrew S. Hallidie (1836–1900) who first operated his system in San Francisco in 1873.

What is a **funicular railway**?

A funicular railway is a type of railway used on steep grades, such as on a mountainside. Two counterbalanced cars or trains are linked by a cable, and when one moves down, the other moves up.

MOTOR VEHICLES

See also: Energy—Consumption and Conservation
Buildings, Bridges, and Other Structures—Roads, Bridges, and Tunnels

How did the term **horsepower** originate?

Horsepower is the unit of energy needed to lift 550 pounds (247.5 kilograms) the distance of one foot (30.48 centimeters) in one second. Near the end of the 18th century the Scottish engineer James Watt (1736–1819) made improvements in the steam engine and wished to determine how its rate of pumping water out of coal mines compared with that of horses, which had previously been used to operate the pumps. In order to define a horsepower, he tested horses and concluded that a strong horse could lift 150 pounds (67.5 kilograms) 220 feet (66.7 meters) in one minute. Therefore, one horsepower was equal to $150 \times 220/1$ or 33,000 foot pounds per minute (also expressed as 745.2 joules per second, 7,452 million ergs per second, or 745.2 watts).

The term horsepower was frequently used in the early days of the automobile because the "horseless carriage" was generally compared to the horse-drawn carriage. Today this inconvenient unit is still used routinely to express the power of motors and engines, particularly of automobiles and aircraft. A typical automobile requires about 20 horsepower to propel it at 50 miles (80.5 kilometers) per hour.

Who invented the **automobile**?

Although the idea of self-propelled road transportation originated long before, Karl **455**

Karl Benz in his first car.

Benz (1844–1929) and Gottlieb Daimler (1834–1900), are both credited with the invention of the gasoline-powered automobile, because they were the first to make their automotive machines commercially practicable. Benz and Daimler worked independently, unaware of each other's endeavors. Both built compact, internal-combustion engines to power their vehicles. Benz built his three-wheeler in 1885; it was steered by a tiller. Daimler's four-wheeled vehicle was produced in 1887.

Earlier self-propelled road vehicles include a steam-driven contraption invented by Nicolas-Joseph Cugnot (1725–1804), who rode the Paris streets at 2.5 miles (four kilometers) per hour in 1769. Richard Trevithick (1771–1833) also produced a steam-driven vehicle that could carry eight passengers. It first ran on December 24, 1801 in Camborne, England. Londoner Samuel Brown built the first practical four-horsepower gasoline-powered vehicle in 1826. The Belgian engineer J. J. Etienne Lenoire (1822–1900) built a vehicle with an internal combustion engine that ran on liquid hydrocarbon fuel in 1862, but he did not test it on the road until September 1863, when it traveled a distance of 12 miles (19.3 kilometers) in three hours. The Austrian inventor Siegfried Marcus (1831–1898) invented a four-wheeled, gasoline-powered handcart in 1864 and a full-size car in 1875; the Viennese police objected to the noise that the car made, and Marcus did not continue its development. Edouard Delamare-Deboutteville invented an eight-horsepower vehicle in 1883, which was not durable enough for road conditions.

Is the **electric automobile** a recent idea?

During the last decade of the 19th century, the electric vehicle became especially popular in the cities. People had grown familiar with electric trolleys and railways, and technology had produced motors and batteries in a wide variety of sizes. The Edison Cell, a nickel-iron battery, became the leader in electric vehicle use. By 1900, electric vehicles nearly dominated the pleasure car field. In that year, 4,200 automobiles were sold in the United States. Of these, 38% were powered by electricity, 22% by gasoline, and 40% by steam. By 1911, the automobile starter motor did away with hand-cranking gasoline cars, and Henry Ford had just begun to mass-produce his Model T's. By 1924, not a single electric vehicle was exhibited at the National Automobile Show, and the Stanley Steamer was scrapped the same year.

Because of the energy crises of the 1970s and the 1990s concern for the environment (as well as "Clean Air" legislation), the large American auto manufacturers, along with the Japanese, are working toward producing a practical electric automobile. Chrysler and Ford have built electric versions of their minivans, and Nissan, Mitsubishi, and Daihatsu are competing, having announced aggressive programs of their own. In Europe, where electric vehicles (EVs) such as the General Motors one-ton van (the Griffon) have been used for years for local deliveries and in service fleets, VW, BMW, Audi, Fiat, and Peugeot are also developing products. But the odds-on favorite for the first electric car to win a mass market is General Motors' Impact, due out in 1998. Prototypes are undergoing public testing, but problems still must be solved.

The basic problem, a technological one, remains—the limitations of battery technology. The electric car remains a poor performer in speed and range, and the cost of battery pack replacement is expensive. Two new types of batteries are under development: the lithium-sulfide battery and the sodium-sulfur unit. Also, manufacturers are experimenting with an alternating-current (AC) engine to replace the present heavier direct-current (DC) power trains.

Who started the first American **automobile company**?

Charles Duryea (1861–1938), a cycle manufacturer from Peoria, Illinois, and his brother, Frank (1869–1967), founded America's first auto-manufacturing firm and became the first to build cars for sale in the United States. The Duryea Motor Wagon company, set up in Springfield, Massachusetts, in 1895, built gasoline-powered, horseless carriages similar to those built by Benz in Germany.

However, the Duryea brothers did not build the first automobile factory in the United States. Ransom Eli Olds (1864–1950) built it in 1899 in Detroit, Michigan, to manufacture his Oldsmobile. More than 10 vehicles a week were produced there by April 1901, for a total of 433 cars produced in 1901. In 1902 Olds introduced the assembly-line method of production and made over 2,500 vehicles in 1902 and 5,508 in 1904. In 1906, 125 companies made automobiles in the United States. In 1908, the

Henry Ford and his first car.

American engineer Henry Ford (1863–1947) improved the automobile assembly-line techniques by adding the conveyor belt system that brought the parts to the workers on the prodution line; this made automotive manufacture quick and cheap, cutting production time to 93 minutes. His company sold 10,660 vehicles that year.

How many workers are needed to build **one car** in one day?

Year	General Motors	Ford	Chrysler	Japanese
1979	5.12	4.71	5.63	—
1989	4.88	3.25	4.58	—
1992	4.55	3.01	3.76	2.0 to 2.5

When was the **Michelin tire** introduced?

The first pneumatic (air-filled) tire for automobiles was produced in France by André (1853–1931) and Edouard Michelin (1859–1940) in 1885. The first radial-ply tire, the Michelin X, was made and sold in 1948. In radial construction, layers of cord materials called plies are laid across the circumference of the tire from bead to bead (perpendicular to the direction of the tread centerline). The plies can be made of steel wires or belts that circle the tire. Radial tires are said to give longer tread life, better handling, and a softer ride at medium and high speeds than bias or belted bias tires (both of which have plies laid diagonally). Radials give a firm, almost hard, ride at low speeds.

What is a **rumble seat**?

A rumble seat is a folding external seat situated in the rear deck of some older two-door coupes, convertibles, and roadsters.

When were **tubeless automobile tires** first manufactured?

In Akron, Ohio, the B.F. Goodrich Company announced the manufacture of tubeless tires on May 11, 1947. Dunlop was the first British firm to make tubeless tires in 1953.

What do the **numbers** mean on automobile **tires**?

The numbers and letters associated with tire sizes and types are complicated and confusing. The "Metric P" system of numbering is probably the most useful method of indicating tire sizes. For example, if the tire had P185/75R-14, then "P" means the tire is for a passenger car. The number 185 is the width of the tire in millimeters. 75 indicates the aspect ratio, i.e., that the height of the tire from the rim to the road is 75% of the width. R indicates that it is a radial tire. 14 is the wheel diameter in inches. 13 and 15 inches are also common sizes.

Which vehicle had the first modern automobile **air conditioner**?

The first air-conditioned automobile was manufactured by the Packard Motor Car Company in Detroit, Michigan, and was exhibited publicly November 4–12, 1939 at the 40th Automobile Show in Chicago, Illinois. Air in the car was cooled to the temperature desired, dehumidified, filtered, and circulated. The first fully automatic air conditioning system was Cadillac's "Climate Control," introduced in 1964.

What was the first car manufactured with an automatic transmission?

The first of the modern generation of automatic transmissions was General Motors' Hydramatic, first offered as an option on the Oldsmobile during the 1940 season. Between 1934 and 1936, a handful of 18 horsepower Austins were fitted with the American-designed Hayes infinitely variable gear. The direct ancestor of the modern automatic gearbox was patented in 1898.

Has there ever been a **nuclear-powered automobile**?

In the 1950s, Ford automotive designers envisioned the Ford Nucleon, which was to be propelled by a small atomic reactor core, located under a circular cover at the rear of the car. It was to be recharged with nuclear fuel. The car was never built.

Where was the first automobile **license plate** issued?

Leon Serpollet of Paris, France, obtained the first license plate in 1889. They were first required in the United States by New York State in 1901. Registration was required within 30 days. Owners had to provide their names and addresses as well as a description of their vehicles. The fee was one dollar. The plates bore the owner's initials and were required to be over three inches (7.5 centimeters) high. Permanent plates made of aluminum were first issued in Connecticut in 1937.

What information is available from the **vehicle identification number (VIN), body number plate,** and **engine** on a car?

These coded numbers reveal the model and make, model year, type of transmission, plant of manufacture, and sometimes even the date and day of the week a car was made. The form and content of these codes is not standardized and often changes from one year to the next for the same manufacturer. Various components of a car may be made in different plants, so a location listed on a VIN may differ from one on the engine number. The official shop manual lists the codes for a particular make of car.

How many motor vehicles are registered in the United States?

The total United States registration of motor vehicles in 1994 is estimated to be 195,469,000. Of the total, 147,171,000 were automobiles and 48,298,000 were trucks and buses. Worldwide, in 1993 there were 617,087,061 total motor vehicles registered (469,460,221 passenger cars).

How much does it **cost to operate** an automobile in the United States?

Below is listed the average cost per mile to operate an automobile in the United States in cents per mile. Figures are given for suburban driving conditions:

	Large	Intermediate	Compact	Subcompact	Passenger van
Depreciation	9.6	8.6	7.3	5.9	10.7
Maintenance	6.0	5.2	4.6	5.1	6.9
Gas and oil	7.0	5.7	4.6	4.4	9.1
Parking and tolls	0.9	0.9	0.9	0.9	0.9
Insurance	4.9	5.6	4.3	5.0	8.9
Taxes	2.2	1.8	1.6	1.4	2.7
Total costs	30.6	27.8	23.3	22.7	39.2

How many new passenger cars in the United States are imported cars?

In 1994, imported cars accounted for 19.3% of the total passenger car sales. On total sales of 8,990,483 cars, 7,255,303 were domestic and 1,735,180 were imports. Japanese car sales (1,239,450) account for 13.8% of total car sales, and 71.5% of total import car sales; Germany sold 192,241 imports, and 95,399 of import sales were U.S. sponsored.

What is the **braking distance** for an automobile at different speeds?

Average stopping distance is directly related to vehicle speed. On a dry, level concrete surface, the minimum stopping distances are as follows (including driver reaction time to apply brakes):

Speed		Reaction time distance		Braking distance		Total distance	
Mph	Kph	Feet	Meters	Feet	Meters	Feet	Meters
10	16	11	3.4	9	2.7	20	6.1
20	32	22	6.7	23	7.0	45	13.7
30	48	33	10.1	45	13.7	78	23.8
40	64	44	13.4	81	24.7	125	38.1
50	80	55	16.8	133	40.5	188	57.3
60	97	66	20.1	206	62.8	272	82.9
70	113	77	23.5	304	92.7	381	116.1

How can one find out about **safety recalls** on automobiles?

The National Highway Traffic Safety Administration keeps records of recalls and takes reports of safety problems experienced by consumers. You can call their 24-hour hotline at 1-800-424-9393 or write the administration at NHTSA, Department of Transportation, Washington, DC 20590. Be sure to include the make, model, year, and vehicle identification number of the vehicle, and a description of the problem or part in question. You will get any recall information the NHTSA has, either on the phone or by a mailed printout.

What day of the week do most **fatal automotive accidents** occur?

Hour of Day	Sun	Mon	Tues	Wed	Thurs	Fri	Sat	Total
12–3 am	1,442	470	380	445	527	619	1,467	5,350
3–6 am	681	308	248	253	307	409	794	3,000
6–9 am	428	535	572	578	584	624	519	3,840
9–Noon	482	576	565	599	539	580	619	3,960
Noon–3 pm	791	741	677	743	719	853	876	5,400
3–6 pm	973	943	896	926	948	1,131	963	6,780
6–9 pm	989	676	713	737	818	1,117	1,190	6,240
9 pm–12 am	804	671	569	639	718	1,297	1,132	5,830
Total	6,590	4,920	4,620	4,920	5,160	6,630	7,560	40,400

When did **seat belts** become mandatory equipment on United States motor vehicles?

The U.S. National Highway Safety Bureau first required the installation of lap belts for all seats and shoulder belts in the front seats of cars in 1968. However, most Americans did not regularly use safety belts until after 1984, when the first state laws were introduced that penalized drivers and passengers who did not use the device. As of 1992, 49% of automobile occupants regularly use their seat belts.

Which **colors** of cars are the **safest**?

Tests at the University of California concluded that either blue or yellow is the best color for car safety. Blue shows up best during daylight and fog; yellow is best at night. The worst color from the visibility standpoint is gray. In another study by Mercedes-Benz in Germany, white ranked the highest in all-around visibility, except in situations of completely snow-covered roads or white sand. In such extremes, bright yellow and bright orange ranked second and third respectively in visibility. The least visible car color in the Mercedes-Benz test was dark green.

How did Ralph Nader's book *Unsafe at Any Speed* contribute to the demise of the **Corvair** automobile?

Nader intended the book as an indictment of all the sins of the Detroit automobile

When was a speed trap first employed to apprehend speeding automobile drivers?

In 1905, William McAdoo, police commissioner of New York City, was stopped for traveling at 12 miles per hour (19 kilometers per hour) in an eight miles per hour (13 kilometers per hour) zone in rural New England. The speed detection device consisted of two lookout posts, camouflaged as dead tree trunks, spaced one mile (1.6 kilometers) apart. A deputy with a stopwatch and a telephone kept watch for speeders. When a car appeared to be traveling too fast, the deputy pressed his stopwatch and telephoned ahead to his confederate who immediately consulted a speed-mileage chart and phoned ahead to another constable manning a road block to apprehend the speeder. McAdoo invited the New England constable to set up a similar device in New York City.

One of the most famous speed traps was in the Alabama town of Fruithurst, on the Alabama-Georgia border. In one year, this town of 250 people collected over $200,000 in fines and forfeitures from unwary "speeders."

manufacturers, and principally of General Motors. Actually, the Corvair is discussed only in the first chapter. Nader believed that General Motors executives had marketed a car they knew to be unsafe because their desire for profit outweighed all other considerations.

Nader, at the time of the book's publication, was working on the staff of Senator Abraham Ribicoff, who chaired a Senate subcommittee that was crafting a bill to establish standards for automobile design. Thus the book received widespread attention, and Nader was called on as an expert witness during hearings on various automobile concerns, including the safety of the Corvair. Nader's testimony, along with some well-timed publicity, set the stage for passage of a strong National Traffic and Motor Vehicle Safety Act in September 1966.

Negative publicity about the car had done its damage, and even though design modifications were made, sales dropped catastrophically. Production was discontinued in 1969.

Which states allow a **right** or **left turn** on a **red light**?

All states permit drivers to turn right on a red signal after a complete stop if the intersection is not designated otherwise by posted signs. New York City now is the only major jurisdiction that prohibits the turn. According to the Federal Highway Administration, fewer accidents occur when drivers turn right on a red light than when they turn right on a green light. The statute also saves each driver an average of 14 seconds at a turn, cuts gasoline consumption and exhaust emissions, and allows intersections to handle more traffic.

Forty-one states permit left turns on a red signal, but only after a complete stop and only from a one-way street into another one-way street. Those states that prohibit the turn are: Connecticut, Maryland, Mississippi, Missouri, New Jersey, North Carolina, Rhode Island, Vermont, and Wisconsin. The District of Columbia and New York City also prohibit the turn.

How does **VASCAR** work?

Invented in 1965, VASCAR (Visual Average Speed Computer and Recorder) is a calculator that determines a car's speed from two simple measurements of time and distance. No radar is involved. VASCAR can be used at rest or while moving to clock traffic in both directions. The patrol car can be behind, ahead of, or even perpendicular to the target vehicle. The device measures the length of a speed trap and then determines how long it takes the target car to cover that distance. An internal calculator does the math and displays the average speed on an LED readout. Most police departments now use several forms of moving radar, which are less detectable and more accurate.

How does **police radar** work?

The Austrian physicist, Christian Doppler (1803–1853), discovered that the reflected waves bouncing off a moving object are returned at a different frequency (shorter or longer waves, cycles, or vibrations). This phenomenon, called the *Doppler effect*, is the basis of police radar. Directional radio waves are transmitted from the radar device. The waves bounce off the targeted vehicle and are received by a recorder. The recorder compares the difference between the sent and received waves, translates the information into miles per hour, and displays the speed on a dial.

Which states do not allow **radar detection devices** in motor vehicles?

All states and Canadian provinces use radar in their speed enforcement programs, and all but eight—Connecticut, Manitoba, Newfoundland, Ontario, Prince Edward Island, Quebec, and Virginia—as well as the District of Columbia permit drivers to install radar detectors for advance warning.

How does an **air bag** work to prevent injury in an automobile crash?

When a frontal collision occurs, sensors trigger the release and reaction of sodium azide with iron, which produces large quantities of nitrogen gas. This gas fully inflates the bag in about two-tenths of a second after impact, to create a protective cushion. The air bag deflates immediately thereafter, and the harmless nitrogen gas escapes through holes in the back.

An air bag will deploy only after the car has an impact speed of 11 to 14 miles per hour (17 to 22 kilometers per hour) or greater. It will not be set off by a minor fender bender, by hitting a cement stop in a parking space, or if someone kicks the bumpers. The National Highway Traffic Safety Administration estimates that between 1987 and 1993, air bags saved 1,026 lives. Federal safety officials recommended that owners of vehicles with air bags not use rear-facing infant seats in the front passenger seat. In that location, an inflating air bag can strike the child seats with enough force to cause injury.

When was the **air bag invented**?

Patented ideas on air bag safety devices began appearing in the early 1950s. U.S. patent 2,649,311 was granted on August 18, 1953, to John W. Hetrick for an inflated safety cushion to be used in automotive vehicles. The Ford Motor Company studied the use of air bags around 1957, and other undocumented work was carried out by Mr. Assen Jordanoff before 1956. There are other earlier uses of an air bag concept, including a rumored method of some World War II pilots inflating their life vests before a crash.

In the mid-1970s, General Motors geared up to sell 100,000 air bag–equipped cars a year in a pilot program to offer them as a discounted option on luxury models. GM dropped the option after only 8,000 buyers ordered air bags in three years. As of September 1, 1989, all new passenger cars produced for sale in the United States are required to be equipped with passive restraints (either automatic seatbelts or air bags). Today, nearly 20 million cars and trucks on the road have air bags. Federal law requires dual air bags in all cars by 1998 and on all light trucks the following year.

Which automobile is the one **most often stolen**?

Automobile theft has been occurring since an automobile mechanic stole Baron de Zuylen's Peugeot in Paris in June 1896. Now, every 20 seconds a vehicle is stolen in the United States. In general, cars with the lowest overall theft losses are small and midsize four-door cars and station wagons. Sports and luxury models, especially convertibles, have the highest losses.

The Highway Loss Data Institute published the following data for 1991–93 passenger vehicles:

Least likely to be stolen
Chevrolet Cavalier station wagon
Pontiac Grand Prix 4 door
Oldsmobile Cutlass 4 door
Oldsmobile Cutlass 2 door

Most likely to be stolen
Volkswagen Cabriolet
Ford Mustang convertible
Cadillac De Ville 2 door
Ford Mustang
Honda Civic 2 door

What is the difference between a **medium truck** and a **heavy truck**?

Medium trucks weigh 14,001 to 33,000 pounds (6,351 to 14,969 kilograms). They span a wide range of sizes and have a variety of uses, from step-van route trucks to truck tractors. Common examples include beverage trucks, city cargo vans, and garbage trucks. Heavy trucks weigh 33,001 pounds (14,969 kilograms) or greater. Heavy trucks include over-the-road 18-wheelers, dump trucks, concrete mixers, and fire trucks. These trucks have come a long way from the first carrying truck, built in 1870 by John Yule, which moved at a rate of three-quarters of a mile (1.2 kilometers) per hour.

What is the origin of the term **taxicab**?

The term taxicab is derived from two words—*taximeter* and *cabriolet*. The taximeter,

When was the parking meter introduced?

Carlton C. Magee, editor of the Oklahoma City *Daily News* and a member of the Chamber of Commerce traffic committee, became concerned about the parking problem in larger cities. He proposed a device to charge people for parking spaces. He entered into a partnership with Gerald A. Hale, a professor at Oklahoma Agricultural and Mechanical College, to perfect the mechanism. In 1932, Magee applied for a patent on a parking meter. In July 1935, meters were installed on some streets in Oklahoma City. These machines now help solve traffic and parking problems in major cities throughout the world.

an instrument invented by Wilhelm Bruhn in 1891, automatically recorded the distance traveled and/or the time consumed. This enabled the fare to be accurately measured. The cabriolet is a two-wheeled, one-horse carriage, which was often rented.

The first taxicabs for hire were two Benz-Kraftdroschkes operated by "Droschkenbesitzer" Dütz in the spring of 1896 in Stuttgart, Germany. In May 1897 Friedrich Greiner started a rival service. In a literal sense, Greiner's cabs were the first "true" taxis because they were the first motor cabs fitted with taximeters.

AIRCRAFT

See also: Boats, Trains, Cars, and Planes—Military Vehicles

Why did the dirigible *Hindenburg* explode?

Despite the official United States and German investigations into the explosion, it still remains a mystery today. The most plausible explanations are structural failure, St. Elmo's Fire, static electricity, or sabotage. The *Hindenburg*, built following the great initial success of the *Graf Zeppelin*, was intended to exceed all other airships in size, speed, safety, comfort, and economy. At 803 feet (245 meters) long, it was 80% as long as the liner *Queen Mary*, 135 feet (41 meters) in diameter, and could carry 72 passengers in its spacious quarters.

In 1935, the German Air Ministry virtually took over the Zeppelin Company to use it to spread Nazi propaganda. After its first flight in 1936, the airship was very popular with the flying public. No other form of transport could carry passengers so swiftly, reliably, and comfortably between continents. During 1936, 1,006 passengers flew over the North Atlantic Ocean in the *Hindenburg*. On May 6, 1937, while landing at Lakehurst, New Jersey, its hydrogen burst into flames, and the airship was completely destroyed. Of the 97 people aboard, 62 survived.

What was the name of the **Wright brothers' airplane**?

The name of the Wright brothers' plane was the *Flyer*. A wood and fabric biplane, the *Flyer* was originally used by the brothers as a glider and measured 40 feet, 4 inches (12 meters) from wing-tip to wing-tip. For their historic flight, Wilbur and Orville Wright outfitted it with a four-cylinder, 12-horsepower gasoline engine and two propellers, all of their own design. On December 17, 1903, at Kitty Hawk, North Carolina, Orville Wright made the first engine-powered, heavier-than-air craft flight lying in the middle of the lower wing to pilot the craft, which flew 120 feet (37 meters) in 12 seconds. The brothers made three more flights that day, with Wilbur Wright completing the longest one—852 feet (260 meters) in 59 seconds.

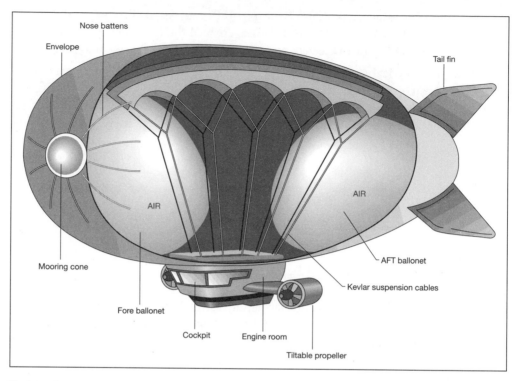

The internal structure of an airship.

Who made the first **nonstop transatlantic flight**?

The first nonstop flight across the Atlantic Ocean, from Newfoundland, Canada, to Ireland, was made by two British aviators, Capt. John W. Alcock (1892–1919) and Lt. Arthur W. Brown (1886–1948), on June 14–15, 1919. The aircraft, a converted twin-engined Vickers Vimy bomber, took 16 hours, 27 minutes to fly 1,890 miles (3,032 kilometers). Later Charles A. Lindbergh (1902–1974) made the first solo crossing flight on May 20–21, 1927, in the single-engined Ryan monoplane *Spirit of St. Louis*, with a wing spread of 46 feet (15 meters) and a chord of seven feet (2.2 meters). His flight from New York to Paris covered a distance of 3,609 miles (5,089 kilometers) and lasted 33.5 hours. The first woman to fly solo across the Atlantic was Amelia Earhart (1897–1937), who flew from Newfoundland to Ireland May 20–21, 1932.

Who made the first **supersonic flight**?

Supersonic flight is flight at or above the speed of sound. The speed of sound is 760 miles (1,223 kilometers) per hour in warm air at sea level. At a height of about 37,000 feet (11,278 kilometers), its speed is only 660 miles (1,062 kilometers) per hour. The first person credited with reaching the speed of sound (Mach 1) was Major Charles E.

(Chuck) Yeager (b. 1923) of the United States Air Force. In 1947, he attained Mach 1.45 at 60,000 feet (18,288 meters) while flying the Bell *X-1* rocket research plane designed by John Stack and Lawrence Bell. This plane had been carried aloft by a B-29 and released at 30,000 feet (9,144 meters). In 1949, the Douglas *Skyrocket* became the first supersonic jet–powered aircraft to reach Mach 1 when Gene May flew at Mach 1.03 at 26,000 feet (7,925 meters).

When was the first **nonstop, unrefueled, round-the-world** airplane flight?

Dick Rutan (b. 1943) and Jeana Yeager (b. 1952) flew the *Voyager*, a trimaran monoplane, in a closed circuit loop westbound and back to Edwards Air Force Base, California, December 14–23, 1986. The flight lasted nine days, three minutes, 44 seconds, and covered 24,986.7 miles (40,203.6 kilometers). The first successful round-the-world flight was made by two Douglas World Cruisers between April 6 and September 28, 1924. Four aircraft originally left Seattle, Washington, and two went down. The two successful planes completed 27,553 miles (44,333 kilometers) in 175 days—with 371 hours, 11 minutes being their actual flying time. Between June 23 and July 1, 1931, Wiley Post (1900–1935) and Harold Gatty (1903–1957) flew around the world, starting from New York, in their Lockheed Vega, *Winnie Mae*.

What is **avionics**?

Avionics, a term derived by combining aviation and electronics, describes all of the electronic navigational, communications, and flight management aids with which airplanes are equipped today. In military aircraft it also covers electronically controlled weapons, reconnaissance, and detection systems. Until the 1940s, the systems involved in operating aircraft were purely mechanical, electric, or magnetic, with radio apparatus being the most sophisticated instrumentation. The advent of radar and the great advance made in airborne detection during World War II led to the general adoption of electronic distance-measuring and navigational aids. In military aircraft such devices improve weapon delivery accuracy and in commercial aircraft they provide greater safety in operation.

Where is the **black box** carried on an airplane?

Actually painted bright orange to make it more visible in an aircraft's wreckage, the black box is a tough metal and plastic case containing two recorders. Installed in the rear of the aircraft—the area most likely to survive a crash—the case has two shells of stainless steel with a heat-protective material between the shells. The case must be able to withstand a temperature of 2,000°F (1,100°C) for 30 minutes. Inside it, mounted in a shockproof base, is the aircraft's flight data and cockpit voice recorders. **469**

> ## Why don't tires on airplanes blow out when the airplane lands?
>
> The Federal Aviation Agency requires airplane tires to meet rigid FAA standards to prevent accidental blowouts. A plug built into the tire will pop out when the air pressure gets too high, and the tire will deflate in an orderly fashion.

The flight data recorder provides information about airspeed, direction, altitude, acceleration, engine thrust, and rudder and spoiler positions from sensors that are located around the aircraft. The data is recorded as electronic pulses on stainless steel tape, which is about as thick as aluminum foil. When the tape is played back, it generates a computer printout. The cockpit voice recorder records the previous 30 minutes of the flight crew's conversation and radio transmission on a continuous tape loop. If a crash does not stop the recorder, vital information can be lost.

When was the first full-scale wind tunnel for testing airplanes used?

It began operations on May 27, 1931, at the Langley Research Center of the National Advisory Committee for Aeronautics, Langley Field, Virginia. This tunnel, still in use, is 30 feet (nine meters) high and 60 feet (18 meters) wide. A wind tunnel is used to simulate air flow for aerodynamic measurement; it consists essentially of a closed tube, large enough to hold the airplane or other craft being tested, through which air is circulated by powerful fans.

Who designed the *Spruce Goose*?

Howard Hughes (1905–1976) designed and built the all-wood H-4 Hercules flying boat, nicknamed the *Spruce Goose*. The aircraft had the greatest wingspan ever built and was powered by eight engines. It was only flown once—covering a distance of less than one mile at Los Angeles harbor on November 2, 1947, lifting only 33 feet (10.6 meters) off the surface of the water.

After the attack on Pearl Harbor on December 7, 1941, and the subsequent entry of the United States into World War II, the United States government needed a large, cargo-carrying airplane that could be made from noncritical wartime materials, such as wood. Henry J. Kaiser (1882–1967), whose shipyards were producing Liberty ships at the rate of one per day, hired Howard Hughes to build such a plane. Hughes eventually produced a plane that weighed 400,000 pounds (181,440 kilograms) and had a wingspan of 320 feet (97.5 meters). Unfortunately, the plane was so complicated that it was not finished by the end of the war. In 1947, Hughes flew the plane himself during its only time off the ground—supposedly just to prove that something that big could fly. The plane was on public display in Long Beach, California, but was sold in 1992 to Delford Smith, an aviation enthusiast, and shipped to McMinnville, Oregon. Mr. Smith intends to make the Spruce Goose the centerpiece of an air museum at that location.

What is the maximum **seating capacity** in a Boeing 747?

The seating capacity of the 747 and some other jets servicing cities in the United States are listed below.

Airplane	Maximum seating capacity
Boeing 707	179
Boeing 707-320, 707-420	189
Boeing 720	149
Boeing 727	125
Boeing 747	498
Boeing 757	196
Boeing 767	289
Boeing 777	375
Concorde (SST)	110
Lockheed L-1011 TriStar	345
McDonnell Douglas DC-8	189
McDonnell Douglas DC-9	
Series 20	119
Series 30 & 40	125
Series 50	139
McDonnell Douglas DC-10	380
Tupolev Tu-144 (Soviet SST)	140

What is the difference between an **amphibian plane** and a **seaplane**?

The primary difference is that an amphibian has retractable wheels that enable it to operate from land as well as water, while a seaplane is limited to water take-offs and landings, having only pontoons without wheels. Because its landing gear cannot retract, a seaplane is less aerodynamically efficient than an amphibian.

471

MILITARY VEHICLES

Where did the military **tank** get its name?

During World War I, when the British were developing the tank, they called these first armored fighting vehicles "water tanks" to keep their real purpose a secret. This code word has remained in spite of early efforts to call them "combat cars" or "assault carriages."

Who invented the **culin device** on a tank?

In World War II, American tank man Sergeant Curtis G. Culin devised a crossbar welded across the front of the tank with four protruding metal tusks. This device made it possible to break through the German hedgerow defenses. In the hedgerow country of Normandy, France, countless rows or stands of bushes or trees surrounded the fields, limiting tank movement. The culin device, also known as the "Rhinoceros" because its steel angled teeth formed a tusk-like structure, cut into the base of the hedgerow and pushed a complete section ahead of it into the next field, burying any enemy troops dug in on the opposite side.

What is a **Hummve**?

The U.S. Army originally developed the HMMWV (High Mobility Multipurpose Wheeled Vehicle), or Hummve, in 1979 as a possible replacement for the M-151 or Jeep. Today, the military uses more than 100,000 "Hummers," which can operate in all

What is a Sopwith Camel and why is it so called?

The most successful British fighter plane of World War I, the Camel was a development of the earlier Sopwith Pup, with a much larger rotary engine. Its name "camel" was derived from the humped shape of the covering of its twin synchronized machine guns. The highly maneuverable Camel, credited with 1,294 enemy aircraft destroyed, proved far superior to all German types as dogfighters, until the introduction of the Fokker D. VII in 1918. Altogether, 5,490 Camels were built by Sopwith Aircraft. Its top speed was 118 miles per hour (189 kilometers per hour) and it had a ceiling of 24,000 feet (7,300 meters).

weather extremes and are designed as troop transports, light-weapon platforms, ambulances, and mobile shelters.

A civilian version is also available with such refinements as air conditioning, sound proofing, bucket seats, and a stereo sound system. It generally sells for around $50,000.

Who was the **Red Baron**?

Manfred von Richthofen (1892–1918), a German fighter pilot during World War I, was nicknamed "Red Baron" by the Allies because he flew a red-painted Albatros fighter. Although he became the top ace of the war by shooting down 80 Allied planes, only 60 of his kills were confirmed by both sides. The others are disputed and could have been joint kills by Richthofen and his squadron, the Flying Circus (so-named because of their brightly painted aircraft). Von Richthofen died on April 21, 1918, when he was attacked over the Semme River in France by Roy Brown, a Canadian ace, and Australian ground machine-gunners. Both parties claimed responsibility for his death.

When was the **B-17 Flying Fortress** introduced?

A Fortress prototype first flew on July 28, 1935, and the first Y1B-17 was delivered to the Air Corps in March 1937, followed by an experimental Y1B-17A fitted with turbo-super-charged engines in January 1939. An order for 39 planes was placed for this model under the designation B-17B. In addition to its bombing function, the B-17 was used for many experimental duties, including serving as a launching platform in the U.S.A.A.F. guided missile program and in radar and radio-control experiments. It was called a "Flying Fortress" because it was the best defended bomber of World War II. Altogether, it carried 13 50-caliber Browning M-2 machine guns, each having about 700 pounds (317.5 kilograms) of armor-piercing ammunition. Ironically, the weight of all its defensive armament and manpower severely restricted the space available for bombs.

Who were the **Flying Tigers**?

They were members of the American Volunteer Group who were recruited early in 1941 by Major General Claire Lee Chennault (1890–1958) to serve in China as mercenaries. Some 90 veteran United States pilots and 150 support personnel served from December 1941 until June 1942 during World War II. The airplanes they flew were P-40 Warhawks, which had the mouths of tiger sharks painted on the planes' noses. It was from these painted-on images that the group got its nickname "Flying Tigers."

Why was the designation **MiG** chosen for the Soviet fighter plane used in World War II?

The *MiG* designation, formed from the initials of the plane's designers, Artem I.

Mikoyan and Mikhail I. Gurevich, sometimes is listed as the Mikoyan-Gurevich MiG. Appearing in 1940 with a maximum speed of 400 miles per hour (644 kilometers per hour), the MiG-3, a piston-engined fighter, was one of the few Soviet planes whose performance was comparable with Western types during World War II. One of the best-known fighters, the MiG-15, first flown in December 1947, was powered by a Soviet version of a Rolls-Royce turbo jet engine. This high performer saw action during the Korean Conflict (1950–1953). In 1955 the MiG-19 became the first Soviet fighter capable of supersonic speed in level flight.

What is the name of the airplane that carried the first atomic bomb?

During World War II, the *Enola Gay*, a modified Boeing B-29 bomber, dropped the first atomic bomb on Hiroshima, Japan, at 8:15 a.m. on August 6, 1945. It was piloted by Col. Paul W. Tibbets Jr. of Miami, Florida. The bombardier was Maj. Thomas W. Ferebee of Mocksville, North Carolina. Bomb designer Capt. William S. Parsons was aboard as an observer.

Three days later, another B-29 called *Bock's Car* dropped a second bomb on Nagasaki, Japan. The Japanese surrendered unconditionally on August 15, which confirmed the American belief that a costly and bloody invasion of Japan could be avoided at Japanese expense.

The *Enola Gay* is currently undergoing restoration at the National Air and Space Museum's Silver Hill, Maryland facility. *Bock's Car* is on display at the U.S. Air Force Museum at Wright-Patterson Air Force Base, Dayton, Ohio.

COMMUNICATIONS

SYMBOLS, WRITING, AND CODES

Which **animals** other than horses have been used to **deliver the mail**?

During the 19th century, cows hauled mail wagons in some German towns. In Texas, New Mexico, and Arizona, camels were used. In Russia and Scandinavia, reindeer pulled mail sleighs. The Belgian city of Liége even tried cats, but they proved to be unreliable.

What is the **standard phonetic alphabet**?

Letter	Phonetic equivalent
A	Alpha
B	Bravo
C	Charlie
D	Delta
E	Echo
F	Fox Trot
G	Golf
H	Hotel
I	India
J	Juliett
K	Kilo
L	Lima

Letter	Phonetic equivalent
M	Mike
N	November
O	Oscar
P	Papa
Q	Quebec
R	Romeo
S	Sierra
T	Tango
U	Uniform
V	Victor
W	Whiskey
X	X-ray
Y	Yankee
Z	Zulu

Who invented the **Braille** alphabet?

The Braille system, used by the blind to read and write, consists of combinations of raised dots that form characters corresponding to the letters of the alphabet, punctuation marks, and common words such as "and" and "the." Louis Braille (1809–1852), blind himself since the age of three, began working on developing a practical alphabet for the blind shortly after he started a school for the blind in Paris. He experimented with a communication method called night-writing, which the French army used for nighttime battlefield missives. With the assistance of an army officer, Captain Charles Barbier, Braille pared the method's 12-dot configurations to a 6-dot one and devised a code of 63 characters. The system was not widely accepted for several years; even Braille's own Paris school did not adopt the system until 1854, two years after his death. In 1916, the United States sanctioned Louis Braille's original system of raised dots, and in 1932 a modification called "Standard English Braille, Grade 2" was adopted throughout the English-speaking world. The revised version changed the letter-by-letter codes into common letter combinations, such as "ow," "ing," and "ment," making reading and writing a faster activity.

Before Braille's system, one of the few effective alphabets for the blind was devised by another Frenchman, Valentin Haüy (1745–1822), who was the first to emboss paper to help the blind read. Haüy's letters in relief were actually a punched alphabet, and imitators immediately began to copy and improve on his system. Another letter-by-letter system of nine basic characters was devised by Dr. William Moon (1818–1894) in 1847, but it is less versatile in its applications.

What is the **Morse Code**?

The success of any electrical communication system lies in its coding interpretation,

What is a hornbook?

Found in English and American classrooms from the 15th century to the 18th century, the hornbook was a flat board with a handle that beginning students used. On the board was pasted a sheet of paper usually containing the alphabet, the Benediction, the Lord's Prayer, and the Roman numerals. A thin, flat piece of clear horn covered the whole board to protect the paper, which was scarce and expensive at the time. Hornbooks were used as early as 1442 and became standard equipment in English schools by the 1500s. They were discontinued around 1800, when books became cheaper.

for only series of electric impulses can be transmitted from one end of the system to the other. These impulses must be "translated" from and into words, numbers, etc. This problem plagued early telegraphy until American painter-turned-scientist Samuel F. B. Morse (1791–1872), with the help of Alfred Vail (1807–1859), devised in 1835 a code composed of dots and dashes to represent letters, numbers, and punctuation. Telegraphy uses an electromagnet—a device that becomes magnetic when activated and raps against a metal contact. A series of short electrical impulses repeatedly can make and break this magnetism, resulting in a tapped-out message.

Samuel F. B. Morse.

Having secured a patent on the code in 1837, Morse and Vail established a communications company on May 24, 1844. The first long-distance telegraphed message was sent by Morse in Washington, D.C., to Vail in Baltimore, Maryland. This was the same year that Morse took out a patent on telegraphy; Morse never acknowledged the unpatented contributions of Joseph Henry (1797–1878), who invented the first electric motor and working electromagnet in 1829 and the electric telegraph in 1831.

The International Morse Code (shown below) uses sound or a flashing light to send messages. The dot is a very short sound or flash; a dash equals three dots. The pauses between sounds or flashes should equal one dot. An interval of the length of one dash is left between letters; an interval of two dashes is left between words.

A .-	J .---	S ...
B -...	K -.-	T -
C -.-.	L .-..	U ..-
D -..	M --	V ...-
E .	N -.	W .--
F ..-.	O ---	X -..-
G --.	P .--.	Y -.--
H	Q --.-	Z --..
I ..	R .-.	
1 .----	6 -....	Period .-.-.-
2 ..---	7 --...	Comma --..--
3 ...--	8 ---..	
4 ....-	9 ----.	
5	0 -----	

What were **Enigma** and **Purple** in **World War II**?

Enigma and *Purple* were the electric rotor cipher machines of the Germans and Japanese, respectively. The Enigma machine, used by the Nazis, was invented in the 1920s and was the best known cipher machine in history. One of the greatest triumphs in the history of cryptanalysis was the Polish and British solution of the German Enigma ciphers. This played a major role in the Allies' conduct of World War II.

In 1939, the Japanese introduced a new cipher machine adapted from *Enigma*. Code-named *Purple* by U.S. cryptanalysts, the new machine used telephone stepping switches instead of rotors. U.S. cryptanalysts were able to solve this new system as well.

Cryptography—the art of sending messages in such a way that the real meaning is hidden from everyone but the sender and the recipient—is done in two ways: code and cipher. A code is like a dictionary in which all the words and phrases are replaced by codewords or codenumbers. A codebook is used to read the code. A cipher works with single letters, rather than complete words or phrases. There are two kinds of ciphers: transposition and substitution. In a transposition cipher, the letters of the ordinary message (or plain text) are jumbled to form the cipher text. In substitution, the plain letters can be replaced by other letters, numbers, or symbols.

What are the **10-codes**?

Almost as many different codes exist as agencies using codes in radio transmission. The following are officially suggested by the Associated Public Safety Communications

Ten-1   Cannot understand your message.
Ten-2   Your signal is good.
Ten-3   Stop transmitting.
Ten-4   Message received ("O.K.").
Ten-5   Relay information to _____.
Ten-6   Station is busy.
Ten-7   Out of service.
Ten-8   In service.
Ten-9   Repeat last message.
Ten-10 Negative ("no").
Ten-11 _____ in service.
Ten-12 Stand by.
Ten-13 Report _____ conditions.
Ten-14 Information.
Ten-15 Message delivered.
Ten-16 Reply to message.
Ten-17 Enroute.
Ten-18 Urgent.
Ten-19 Contact _____.
Ten-20 Unit location.
Ten-21 Call _____ by telephone.
Ten-22 Cancel last message.
Ten-23 Arrived at scene.
Ten-24 Assignment completed.
Ten-25 Meet _____.
Ten-26 Estimated time of arrival is _____.
Ten-27 Request for information on license.
Ten-28 Request vehicle registration information.
Ten-29 Check records.
Ten-30 Use caution.
Ten-31 Pick up.
Ten-32 Units requested.
Ten-33 Emergency! Officer needs help.
Ten-34 Correct time.

What do the lines in a UPC **bar code** mean?

A Universal Product Code (UPC) or bar code is a product description code designed to be read by a computerized scanner or cash register. It consists of 11 numbers in groups of "0"s (dark strips) and "1"s (white strips). A bar will be thin if it has only one strip or thicker if there are two or more strips side by side.

The first number describes the type of product. Most products begin with a "0"; exceptions are variable weight products such as meat and vegetables (2), health-care products (3), bulk-discounted goods (4), and coupons (5). Since it might be misread as a bar, the number 1 is not used.

The next five numbers describe the product's manufacturer. The five numbers after that describe the product itself, including its color, weight, size, and other distinguishing characteristics. The code does not include the price of the item. When the identifying code is read, the information is sent to the store's computer database, which checks it against a price list and returns the price to the cash register.

The last number is a check digit, which tells the scanner if there is an error in the other numbers. The preceding numbers, when added, multiplied, and subtracted in a certain way will equal this number. If they do not, a mistake exists somewhere.

What does the code that follows the letters ISBN mean?

ISBN, or International Standard Book Number, is an ordering and identifying code for book products. It forms a unique number to identify that particular item. The first number of the series relates to the language the book is published in, for example, the zero is designated for the English language. The second set of numbers identifies the publisher, and the last set of numbers identifies the particular item. The very last number is a "check number," which mathematically makes certain that the previous numbers have been entered correctly.

RADIO AND TELEVISION

Who invented radio?

Guglielmo Marconi (1874–1937), of Bologna, Italy, was the first to prove that radio signals could be sent over long distances. Radio is the radiation and detection of signals propagated through space as electromagnetic waves to convey information. It was first called wireless telegraphy because it duplicated the effect of telegraphy without using wires. On December 12, 1901, Marconi successfully sent Morse code signals from Newfoundland to England.

In 1906, the American inventor Lee de Forest (1873–1961) built what he called "the Audion," which became the basis for the radio amplifying vacuum tube. This device made voice radio practical, because it magnified the weak signals without distorting them. The next year, de Forest began regular radio broadcasts from Manhattan, New York. As there were still no home radio receivers, de Forest's only audience was ship wireless operators in New York City Harbor.

What was the first **radio broadcasting station**?

The identity of the "first" broadcasting station is a matter of debate since some pioneer AM broadcast stations developed from experimental operations begun before the institution of formal licensing practices. According to records of the Department of Commerce, which then supervised radio, WBZ in Springfield, Massachusetts, received the first regular broadcasting license on September 15, 1921. However, credit for the first radio broadcasting station has customarily gone to Westinghouse station KDKA in Pittsburgh for its broadcast of the Harding-Cox presidential election returns on November 2, 1920. Unlike most other earlier radio transmissions, KDKA used electron tube technology to generate the transmitted signal and hence to have what could be described as broadcast quality. It was the first corporate-sponsered radio station and the first

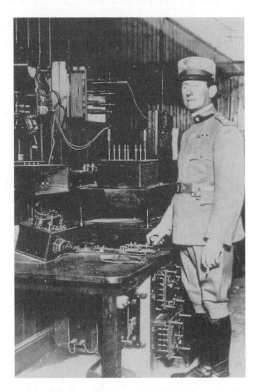

Guglielmo Marconi with his wireless radio.

to have a well-defined commercial purpose—it was not a hobby or a publicity stunt. It was the first broadcast station to be licensed on a frequency outside the amateur bands. Altogether, it was the direct ancestor of modern broadcasting.

How are the **call letters** beginning with "K" or "W" assigned to **radio stations**?

These beginning call letters are assigned on a geographical basis. For the majority of radio stations located east of the Mississippi River, their call letters begin with the letter "W"; if the stations are west of the Mississippi, their first call letter is the letter "K". There are exceptions to this rule. Stations founded before this rule went into effect kept their old letters. So, for example, KDKA in Pittsburgh has retained the first letter "K"; likewise some western pioneer stations have retained the letter "W". Since many

AM licensees also operate FM and TV stations, a common practice is to use the AM call letters followed by "–FM" or "–TV".

Why do **FM radio stations** have a limited broadcast range?

Usually radio waves higher in frequency than approximately 50 to 60 megahertz are not reflected by the Earth's ionosphere, but are lost in space. Television, FM radio, and high frequency communications systems are therefore limited to approximately line-of0sight ranges. The line-of-sight distance depends on the terrain and antenna height, but is usually limited to from 50 to 100 miles (80 to 161 kilometers). FM (frequency–modulation) radio uses a wider band than AM (amplitude–modulation) radio to give broadcasts high fidelity, especially noticeable in music—crystal clarity to high frequencies and rich resonance to base notes, all with a minimum of static and distortion. Invented by Edwin Howard Armstrong (1891–1954) in 1933, FM receivers became available in 1939.

Edwin Howard Armstrong.

Why do **AM stations** have a wider **broadcast range at night**?

This variation is caused by the nature of the ionosphere of the Earth. The ionosphere consists of several different layers of rarefied gases in the upper atmosphere that have become conductive through the bombardment of the atoms of the atmosphere by solar radiation, by electrons and protons emitted by the sun, and by cosmic rays. These layers, sometimes called the Kennelly–Heaviside layer, reflect AM radio signals, enabling AM broadcasts to be received by radios that are great distances from the transmitting antenna. With the coming of night, the ionosphere layers partially dissipate and become an excellent reflector of the short waveband AM radio waves. This causes distant AM stations to be heard more clearly at night.

Can **radio transmissions** between **space shuttles** and ground control be picked up by shortwave radio?

Amateur radio operators at Goddard Space Flight Center, Greenbelt, Maryland, retransmit shuttle space-to-ground radio conversations on shortwave frequencies. These retransmissions can be heard freely around the world. To hear astronauts talking with ground controllers during liftoff, flight, and landing, a shortwave radio capable of receiving single-sideband signals should be tuned to frequencies of 3.860, 7.185, 14.295, and 21.395 megahertz. British physics teacher Geoffrey Perry, at the Kettering Boys School, has taught his students how to obtain telemetry from orbiting Russian satellites. Since the early 1960s Perry's students have been monitoring Russian space signals using a simple taxicab radio, and using the data to calculate position and orbits of the spacecraft.

Who was the founder of **television**?

The idea of television (or "seeing by electricity," as it was called in 1880) was offered by several people over the years, and several individuals contributed a multiplicity of partial inventions. For example, in 1897 Ferdinand Braun (1850–1918) constructed the first cathode ray oscilloscope, a fundamental component to all television receivers. In 1907, Boris Rosing proposed using Braun's tube to receive images, and in the following year Alan Campbell-Swinton likewise suggested using the tube, now called the cathode-ray tube, for both transmission and receiving. The figure most frequently called the father of television, however, was a Russian-born American named Vladimir K. Zworykin (1889–1982). A former pupil of Rosing, he produced a practical method of amplifying the electron beam so that the light/dark pattern would produce a good image. In 1923, he patented the iconoscope (which would become the television camera), and in 1924 he patented the kinoscope (television tube). Both inventions rely on streams of electrons for both scanning and creating the image on a fluorescent screen. By 1938, after adding new and more sensitive photo cells, Zworykin demonstrated his first practical model.

Another "father" of television is the American Philo T. Farnsworth. He was the first person to propose that pictures could be televised electronically. He came up with the basic design for an apparatus in 1922 and discussed his ideas with his high school teacher. This documented his ideas one year before Zworykin and was critical in settling a patent dispute between Farnsworth and his competitor at the Radio Corporation of America. Farnsworth eventually licensed his television patents to the growing industry and let others refine and develop his basic inventions.

During the early 20th century others worked on different approaches to television. The best-known is John Logie Baird (1888–1946), who in 1936 used a mechanized scanning device to transmit the first recognizable picture of a human face. Limitations in his designs made any further improvements in the picture quality impossible.

How does **rain** affect **television reception** from a satellite?

The incoming microwave signals are absorbed by rain and moisture, and severe rainstorms can reduce signals by as much as 10 decibels (reduction by a factor of 10). If **483** the installation cannot cope with this level of signal reduction, the picture may be momentarily lost. Even quite moderate rainfall can reduce signals enough to give noisy reception on some receivers. Another problem associated with rain is an increase in noise due to its inherent noise temperature. Any body above the temperature of absolute zero ($0°K$ or $-459°F$ or $-273°C$) has an inherent noise temperature generated by the release of wave packets from the body's molecular agitation (heat). These wave packets have a wide range of frequencies, some of which will be within the required bandwidth for satellite reception. The warm Earth has a high noise temperature, and consequently rain does as well.

What name is used for a **satellite dish** that picks up **TV broadcasts**?

Earth station is the term used for the complete satellite receiving or transmitting station. It includes the antenna, the electronics, and all associated equipment necessary to receive or transmit satellite signals. It can range from a simple, inexpensive, receive-only Earth station that can be purchased by the individual consumer, to elaborate, two-way communications stations that offer commercial access to the satellite's capacity. Signals are captured and focused by the antenna into a feedhorn and low noise amplifier. These are relayed by cable to a down converter and then into the satellite receiver/modulator.

Satellite television became widely available in the late 1970s when cable television stations, equipped with satellite dishes, received signals and sent them to their subscribers by coaxial cable. Taylor Howard designed the first satellite dish for personal use in 1976. By 1984 there were 500,000 installations, and in recent years that number has increased worldwide to 3.7 million.

What is **high definition television**?

The amount of detail shown in a television picture is limited by the number of lines that make it up and by the number of picture elements on each line. The latter is mostly determined by the width of the electron beam. To obtain pictures closer to the quality associated with 35-millimeter photography, a new television system, HDTV (High Definition Television) will have more than twice the number of scan lines with a much smaller picture element. Currently American and Japanese television has 525 scanning lines, while Europe uses 625 scanning lines. HDTV has received wide publicity in recent years, but it is currently in an engineering phase, and not yet commercially available.

The Japanese are generally given credit for being pioneers in HDTV, ever since the Japanese broadcasting company NHK began research in 1968. In fact, the original pioneer was RCA's Otto Schade who began his research after the end of World War II.

Can a TV satellite dish be painted a different color?

Although not recommended, TV satellite dishes can be painted a different color as long as the same standards adhered to in manufacture are maintained. The paint used should not be optically reflective. Metallic paints or gloss finishes may focus the sun's radiation on the head unit, causing performance problems. Only "vinyl matte" finish paints should be used. They exhibit lower solar reflection properties, and they cause a minimal amount of microwave absorption and reflection errors. Finally, the paint should be applied as smoothly as possible, as any bumps or drips may cause reflection errors.

Schade was ahead of his time, and decades passed before television pickup tubes and other components became available to take full advantage of his research.

HDTV cannot be used in the commercial broadcast bands until technical standards are approved by the United States Federal Communications Commission (FCC) or the various foreign regulating agencies. The more immediate problem, however, has been a technological one—HDTV needs to transmit five times more data than is currently assigned to each television channel. One approach is signal compression—squeezing the 30-megahertz bandwidth signal that HDTV requires into the six-megahertz bandwidth currently used for television broadcasting. The Japanese and Europeans have explored analog systems that use wavelike transmission, while the Americans based their HDTV development on digital transmission systems. In 1994, the television industry cleared this hurdle when it accepted a digital signal transmission system developed by Zenith. However, HDTV sets won't be available to the public until 1997 or later, and at prices ranging from $3,500 to $5,000.

How do submerged **submarines communicate**?

Using frequencies from very high to extremely low, submarines can communicate by radio when submerged if certain conditions are met, and depending on whether or not detection is important. Submarines seldom transmit on long-range high radio frequencies if detection is important, as in war. However, Super (SHF), Ultra (UHF), or Very High Frequency (VHF) two-way links with cooperating aircraft, surface ships, via satellite, or with the shore are fairly safe with high data rate, though they all require that the boat show an antenna or send a buoy to the surface.

TELECOMMUNICATIONS, RECORDINGS, THE INTERNET, ETC.

When was the first **commercial communications satellite** used?

In 1960 *ECHO 1*, the first communications satellite, was launched. Two years later, on July 10, 1962, the first commercially funded satellite, *Telstar 1* (paid for by American Telephone and Telegraph), was launched into low Earth orbit. It was also the first true communications satellite, being able to relay not only data and voice, but television as well. The first broadcast, which was relayed from the United States to England, showed an American flag flapping in the breeze. The first commercial satellite (in which its operations are conducted like a business) was *Early Bird*, which went into regular service on June 10, 1965, with 240 telephone circuits. *Early Bird* was the first satellite launched for Intelsat (International Telecommunications Satellite Organization). Still in existence, the system is owned by member nations—each nation's contribution to the operating funds are based on its share of the system's annual traffic.

How does a **fax machine** work?

Telefacsimile (also telefax or facsimile or fax) transmits graphic and textual information from one location to another through telephone lines. A transmitting machine uses either a digital or analog scanner to convert the black and white representations of the image into electrical signals that are transmitted through the telephone lines to a designated receiving machine. The receiving unit converts the transmission back to an image of the original and prints it. In its broadest definition, a facsimile terminal is simply a copier equipped to transmit and receive graphics images.

The fax was invented by Alexander Bain of Scotland in 1842. His crude device, along with scanning systems invented by Frederick Bakewell in 1848, evolved into several modern versions. In 1924, faxes were first used to transmit wire photos from Cleveland to New York, a boon to the newspaper industry.

Can a **fax** and an **answering machine** be used on the same telephone line?

Most fax machines come with an interface that allows it to work with an answering machine. The fax "listens" for the incoming call and sends it to the answering machine if no one picks up the phone. As the message is being recorded, the fax machine listens for a fax tone. If it hears the tone, it sends the fax through. If not, the answering machine continues to function as it normally would. Fax machines with built–in answering machines are also available, making such an interface unnecessary.

What is a **fiber optic cable**?

A fiber optic cable is composed of many very thin strands of coated glass fibers that transmit light through the process of "cladding," in which total internal reflection of light is achieved by using material that has a lower refractive index. Once light enters the fiber, the cladding layer inside it prevents light loss as the beam of light zigzags inside the glass core. Glass fibers can transmit messages or images by directing beams of light inside itself over very short or very long distances up to 13,000 miles (20,917 kilometers) without significant distortion. The pattern of light waves forms a code that carries a message. At the receiving end, the light beams are converted back into electric current and decoded. Since light beams are immune to electrical noise and can be carried greater distances before fading, this technology is used heavily in telecommunications. Other applications include using medical fiber optic viewers, such as endoscopes and fiberscopes, to see internal organs; fiber optic message devices in aircraft and space vehicles; and fiber optic connections in automotive lighting systems.

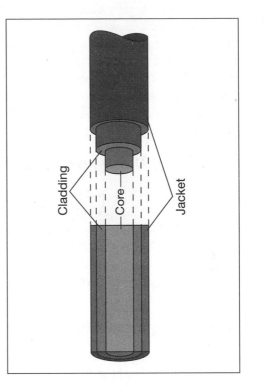

A cross section of a fiber optic cable.

What is a **Clarke belt**?

Back in 1945, Arthur C. Clarke (b. 1917), the famous scientist and science fiction writer, predicted that an artificial satellite placed at a height of 22,248 miles (35,803 kilometers) directly above the equator would orbit the globe at the same speed with which the Earth was rotating. As a result, the satellite would remain stationary with respect to any point on the Earth's surface. This equatorial belt, rather like one of Saturn's rings, is affectionately known as the Clarke belt.

What are the types of **cellular telephones**?

There are three types of cellular phones. The first and oldest variety of mobile cellular **487** phones are permanently attached to an automobile and are powered by the car's battery. They also have an antenna that must be mounted outside the vehicle. The second type are transportable, or bag, cellular phones. These are essentially mobile phones with their own battery packs that allow owners to detach them from the car and carry them in a pouch. However, most weigh about five pounds (2.25 kilograms) and are not very practical when used this way. The third type are portable cellular phones. Similar in appearance to a cordless phone handset, a portable generally weighs less than a pound and is the most versatile type of cellular phone. It is also the most expensive and has a transmitter of less power than a mobile or transportable cellular phone. Kits are available for some models, however, that boosts the transmitter's power.

What is the **Dolby** noise reduction system?

The magnetic action of a tape produces a background hiss—a drawback in sound reproduction on tape. A noise reduction system known as *Dolby*—named after R. M. Dolby (b. 1933), its American inventor—is widely used to deal with the hiss. In quiet passages, electronic circuits automatically boost the signals before they reach the recording head, drowning out the hiss. On playback, the signals are reduced to their correct levels. The hiss is reduced at the same time, becoming inaudible.

What is **digital audio tape** (DAT)?

DAT, a new concept in magnetic recording, produces a mathematical value for each sound based on the binary code. When the values are reconstructed during playback, the reconstructed sound is so much like the original that the human ear cannot distinguish the difference. The reproduction is so good that American record companies have lobbied lawmakers to prevent DAT from being sold in the United States, claiming that it could encourage illegal CD copying.

How are **compact discs** (CDs) made?

The master disc for a CD is an optically flat glass disc coated with a resist. The resist is a chemical that is impervious to an etchant that dissolves glass. The master is placed on a turntable. The digital signal to be recorded is fedto the laser, turning the laser off and on in response to the binary on-off signal. When the laser is on, it burns away a small amount of the resist on the disc. While the disc turns, the recording head moves across the disc, leaving a spiral track of elongated "burns" in the resist surface. After the recording is complete, the glass master is placed in the chemical etchant bath. This developing removes the glass only where the resist is burned away. The spiral track now contains a series of small pits of varying length and constant depth. To play a recorded CD, a laser beam scans the three miles (five kilometers) of playing track and converts the "pits" and "lands" of the CD into binary codes. A pho-

What is virtual reality?

Virtual reality combines state-of-the-art imaging with computer technology to allow users to experience a simulated environment as reality. Several different technologies are integrated into a virtual reality system, including holography, which uses lasers to create three-dimensional images; liquid crystal displays; high definition television; and multimedia techniques that combine various types of displays in a single computer terminal.

Despite the widespread attention the media pays to virtual reality, the field remains in a rudimentary state since supporting technologies have yet to meet human expectations.

todiode converts these into a coded string of electrical impulses. In October 1982, the first CDs were marketed; they were invented by Phillips (Netherlands) Company and Sony in Japan in 1978.

What is the lifespan of a **CD-ROM** disc?

Although manufacturers claim that a CD-ROM disc will last 20 years, recent statements by the United States National Archives and Records Administration suggest that a lifespan of three to five years is more accurate. The main problem is that the aluminum substratum on which the data is recorded is vulnerable to oxidation.

What is the **information highway**?

A term originally coined by Vice President Al Gore, the information highway is envisioned as an electronic communications network of the near future that would easily connect all users to one another and provide any every type of electronic service possible, including shopping, electronic banking, education, medical diagnosis, video conferencing, and game playing. Initially implemented on a national scale, it would eventually become a global network.

The exact form of the information highway is a matter of some debate. Two principle views currently exist. One visualizes the highway as a more elaborate form of the Internet, the principle purpose of which would be to gather and exchange written information via a global electronic mail network. The other possibility centers around **489** plans to create an enhanced interactive television network that would provide video services on demand.

What is the **Internet**?

The Internet is the world's largest computer network. It links computer terminals together via wires or telephone lines in a web of networks and shared software. With the proper equipment, an individual can access vast amounts of information and search databases on various computers connected to the Internet, or communicate with someone located anywhere in the world as long as he or she has the proper equipment. Researchers estimate that 20 to 30 million people accessed this system in mid-1995.

Originally created in the late 1960s by the U.S. Department of Defense Advanced Research Projects Agency to share information with other researchers, the Internet mushroomed when scientists and academics using the network discovered its great value. Despite its origin, however, the Internet is not owned or funded by the U.S. government or any other organization or institution. A group of volunteers, the Internet Society, address such issues as daily operations and techincal standards.

What is the **Netplex**?

The Netplex is the name given to an area around Washington, D.C., that has become the world center of the data communications industry and the focal point of the Internet. The businesses in the Netplex include companies that build and manage optical fiber networks, sell Internet connections to companies and individuals, or offer other services. It has been compared to such other "technology centers" as California's Silicon Valley or the Research Triangle of North Carolina, where a large concentration of corporations involved in the telecommunication and computer industries are located.

COMPUTERS

What is an **algorithm**?

An algorithm is a set of clearly defined rules and instructions for the solution of a problem. It is not necessarily applied only in computers, but can be a step-by-step procedure for solving any particular kind of problem. A nearly 4,000-year-old Babylonian banking calculation inscribed on a tablet is an algorithm, as is a computer program that consists of step-by-step procedures for solving a problem.

The term is derived from the name of Muhammad ibn Musa al Kharizmi (ca. 780–ca. 850), a Baghdad mathematician who introduced Hindu numerals (including

0) and decimal calculation to the West. When his treatise was translated into Latin in the 12th century, the art of computation with Arabic (Hindu) numerals became known as *algorism*.

Who invented the **computer**?

Computers developed from calculating machines. One of the earliest mechanical devices for calculating, still widely used today, is the abacus—a frame carrying parallel rods on which beads or counters are strung. Herodotus, the Greek historian who lived around 400 B.C.E., mentions the use of the abacus in Egypt. In 1617, John Napier (1550–1617) invented "Napier's Bones"—marked pieces of ivory for multiples of numbers. In the middle of the same century, Blaise Pascal (1623–1662) produced a simple mechanism for adding and subtracting. Multiplication by repeated addition was a feature of a stepped drum or wheel machine of 1694 invented by Gottfried Wilhelm Leibniz (1646–1716). In

Charles Babbage.

1823, the English visionary Charles Babbage (1792–1871) persuaded the British government to finance an "analytical engine." This would have been a machine that could undertake any kind of calculation. It would have been driven by steam, but the most important innovation was that the entire program of operations was stored on a punched tape. Babbage's machine was not completed and would not have worked if it had been. The standards required were far beyond the capabilities of the engineers of the time, and in any case, rods, levers, and cogs move too slowly for really quick calculations. Modern computers use electrons, which travel at near the speed of light. Although he never built a working computer, Babbage thought out many of the basic principles that guide modern computers.

Based on the concepts of British mathematician Alan M. Turing (1912–1954), the earliest programmable electronic computer was the 1,500-valve "Colossus," formulated by Max Newman (1897–1985), built by T. H. Flowers, and used by the British government in 1943 to crack the German codes generated by the coding machine "Enigma."

What was the first major use for **punched cards**?

Punched cards were a way of programming, or giving instructions to, a machine. In 1801, Joseph Marie Jacquard (1752–1834) built a device that could do automated pattern weaving. Cards with holes were used to direct threads in the loom, creating pre-defined patterns in the cloth. The pattern was determined by the arrangement of holes in the cards, with wire hooks passing through the holes to grab and pull through specific threads to be woven into the cloth.

By the 1880s, Herman Hollerith (1860–1929) was using the idea of punched cards to give machines instructions. He built a punched card tabulator that processed the data gathered for the 1890 United States Census in six weeks (three times the speed of previous compilations). Metal pins in the machine's reader passed through holes punched in cards the size of dollar bills, momentarily closing electric circuits. The resulting pulses advanced counters assigned to details such as income and family size. A sorter could also be programmed to pigeonhole cards according to pattern of holes, an important aid in analyzing census statistics. Later, Hollerith founded Tabulating Machines Co., which in 1924 became IBM. When IBM adopted the 80-column punched card (measuring $7\frac{3}{8} \times 3\frac{1}{4}$ inches [18.7 × 8.25 centimeters] and 0.007 inches [0.17 millimeters] thick), the de facto industry standard was set, which has endured for decades.

What is meant by **fifth generation computers**? What are the other four generations?

The evolution of computers has advanced so much in the past few decades that "generations" are used to describe these important advances:

First generation computer—a mammoth computer using vacuum tubes, drum memories, and programming in machine code as its basic technology. Univax 1, used in 1951, was one of the earliest of these vacuum-tube based electronic computers. The generation starts at the end of World War II and ends about 1957.

Second generation computer—a computer using discrete transistors as its basic technology. Solid-state components replaced the vacuum tubes during this period from 1958 to 1963. Magnetic core memories store information. This era includes the development of high-level computer languages.

Third generation computer—a computer having integrated circuits, semiconductor memories, and magnetic disk storage. New operating systems, minicomputer systems, virtual memory, and timesharing are the advancements of this period from 1963 to 1971.

Fourth generation computer—a computer using microprocessors and large-scale integrated chips as its basic technology, which made computers accessible to a large segment of the population. Networking, improved memory, database management systems, and advanced languages mark the period from 1971 to the end of the 1980s.

Fifth generation computer—a computer that uses inference to draw reasoned conclusions from a knowledge base, and interacts with its users via an intelligent

What is the origin of the expression "Do not fold, spindle, or mutilate"?

This is the inscription on an IBM punched card. Frequently, office workers organize papers and forms by stapling or folding them together, or by impaling them on a spindle. Because Hollerith (punched) card readers scan uniform rectangular holes in a precise arrangement, any damage to the physical card makes it unusable. In the 1950s and 1960s, when punched cards became widespread, manufacturers printed a warning on each card; IBM's "Do not fold, spindle, or mutilate" was the best known. In 1964, the student revolution at the University of California, Berkeley used the phrase as a symbol of authority and regimentation.

user interface to perform such functions as speech recognition, machine translation of natural languages, and robotic operations. These computers using artificial intelligence have been under development since the early 1980s, especially in Japan, as well as in the United States and Europe. In 1991, however, Japan began a new 10-year initiative to investigate neural networks, which will probably divert resources from development of the fifth generation as traditionally defined.

A lot of people have heard of ENIAC, the first large electronic computer. What was MANIAC?

MANIAC (mathematical analyzer, numerator, integrator, and computer) was built at the Los Alamos Scientific Laboratory under the direction of Nicholas C. Metropolis between 1948 and 1952. It was one of several different copies of the high-speed computer built by John von Neumann (1903–1957) for the Institute for Advanced Studies (IAS). It was constructed primarily for use in the development of atomic energy applications, specifically the hydrogen bomb.

It was originated with the work on ENIAC (electronic numerical integrator and computer), the first fully operational, large-scale, electronic digital computer. ENIAC was built at the Moore School of Electrical Engineering at the University of Pennsylvania between 1943 and 1946. Its builders, John Prosper Eckert Jr. and John William Mauchly (1907–1980), virtually launched the modern era of the computer with ENIAC.

What is an **expert system**?

An expert system is a type of software that analyzes a complex problem in a particular field and recommends possible solutions based on information previously programmed into it. The person who develops an expert system first analyzes the behavior of a human expert in a given field, then inputs all the explicit rules resulting from their study into the system. Expert systems are used in equipment repair, insurance planning, training, medical diagnosis, and other areas.

For what purpose was **MADAM** designed?

MADAM (Manchester automatic digital machine) is a chess-playing machine designed by Alan M. Turing (1912–1954) in 1950. Turing was one of the first individuals to program a computer to play chess. His machine was a very poor chess player and made foolish moves. After several moves the machine would be forced to give up. Today it is possible to play a fairly advanced game of chess with a computer. However, no machine has been designed that analyzes every possible strategy corresponding to any move. Even if a machine could play a million chess games a second, it would take 10^{108} years to play all the possible games.

What was the first successful **video-arcade game**?

Pong, a simple electronic version of a tennis game, was the first successful video-arcade game. Although it was first marketed in 1972, Pong was actually invented 14 years earlier in 1958 by William Higinbotham, who headed instrumentation design at Brookhaven National Laboratory at the time. Invented to amuse visitors touring the laboratory, the game was so popular that visitors would stand in line for hours to play it. Higinbotham dismantled the system two years later, and, considering it a trifle, did not patent it. In 1972, Atari released Pong, an arcade version of Higinbotham's game, and Magnavox released Odyssey, a version that could be played on home televisions.

What was the name of the **microcomputer** introduced by **Apple** in the early 1980s?

Lisa was the name of the microcomputer that Apple introduced. The forerunner of the Macintosh microcomputer, Lisa has a graphical user interface and a mouse.

What is a **silicon chip**?

A silicon chip is an almost pure piece of silicon, usually less than one centimeter square and about half a millimeter thick. It contains hundreds of thousands of microminiature electronic circuit components, mainly transistors, packed and interconnected in layers beneath the surface. These components can perform control, logic, and/or memory functions. There is a grid of thin metallic strips on the surface of the chip; these wires are used for electrical connections to other devices. The silicon chip was developed independently by two researchers: Jack Kilby of Texas Instruments in 1958, and Robert Noyce (b. 1927) of Fairchild Semiconductor in 1959.

While silicon chips are essential to most computer operation today, a myriad of other devices depend on them as well, including calculators, microwave ovens, automobile diagnostic equipment, and VCRs.

What are the sizes of silicon chips?

SSI—small scale integration

MSI—medium scale integration

LSI—large scale integration

VLSI—very large scale integration

ULSI—ultra large scale integration

GSI—gigascale integration

The number of components packed into a single chip is very loosely defined. ULSI units can pack millions of components on a chip. GSI, a long-term target for the industry, will potentially hold billions of components on a chip.

Are any devices being developed to replace silicon chips?

When transistors were introduced in 1948, they demanded less power than fragile, high-temperature vacuum tubes; allowed electronic equipment to become smaller, faster, and more dependable; and generated less heat. These developments made computers much more economical and accessible; they also made portable radios practical. However, the smaller components were harder to wire together, and hand wiring was both expensive and error-prone.

In the early 1960s, circuits on silicon chips allowed manufacturers to build increased power, speed, and memory storage into smaller packages, which required less electricity to operate and generated even less heat. While through most of the 1970s manufacturers could count on doubling the components on a chip every year without increasing the size of the chip, the size limitations of silicon chips are becoming more restrictive. Though components continue to grow smaller, the same rate of shrinking cannot be maintained.

Researchers are investigating different materials to use in making circuit chips. Gallium arsenide is harder to handle in manufacturing, but it has potential for greatly increased switching speed. Organic polymers are potentially cheaper to manufacture, and could be used for liquid-crystal and other flat screen displays, which need to have their electronic circuits spread over a wide area. Unfortunately, organic polymers do not allow electricity to pass through as well as the silicons do. Several researchers are working on hybrid chips, which could combine the benefits of organic polymers with those of silicon. Researchers are also in the initial stages of developing integrated optical chips, which would use light rather than electric current. Optical chips would generate little or no heat, would allow faster switching, and would be immune to electrical noise.

How is a **hard disk** different from a **floppy disk**?

Both types of disk use a magnetic recording surface to record, access, and erase data, in much the same way as magnetic tape records, plays, and erases sound or images. A read/write head, suspended over a spinning disk, is directed by the central processing unit (CPU) to the sector where the requested data is stored, or where the data is to be recorded. A hard disk uses rigid aluminum disks coated with iron oxide to store data. It has much greater storage capacity than several floppy disks (from 10 to hundreds of megabytes). While most hard disks used in microcomputers are "fixed" (built into the computer), some are removable. Minicomputer and mainframe hard disks include both fixed and removable hard disks (in modules called disk packs or disk cartridges). A floppy disk, also called a diskette, is made of plastic film covered with a magnetic coating, which is enclosed in a nonremovable plastic protective envelope. Floppy disks vary in storage capacity from 100 thousand bytes to more than two megabytes. Floppy disks are generally used in minicomputers and microcomputers.

In addition to storing more data, a hard disk can provide much faster access to storage than a floppy disk. A hard disk rotates from 2,400 to 3,600 revolutions per minute (rpm) and is constantly spinning (except in laptops, which conserve battery life by spinning the hard disk only when in use). An ultra-fast hard disk has a separate read/write head over each track on the disk, so that no time is lost in positioning the head over the desired track; accessing the desired sector takes only milliseconds, the time it takes for the disk to spin to the sector. A floppy disk does not spin until a data transfer is requested, and the rotation speed is only about 300 rpm.

Why does a computer **floppy disk** have to be **"formatted"**?

A disk must first be organized so that data can be stored on and retrieved from it. The data on a floppy disk or a hard disk is arranged in concentric tracks. Sectors, which can hold blocks of data, occupy arc-shaped segments of the tracks. Most floppy disks are soft-sectored, and formatting is necessary to record sector identification so that data blocks can be labeled for retrieval. Hard-sectored floppy disks use physical marks to identify sectors; these marks cannot be changed, so the disks cannot be reformatted. The way that sectors are organized and labeled dictates system compatibility: disks formatted for DOS computers can only be used in other DOS machines; those formatted for Macintoshes can only be used in other Macintoshes. Formatting erases any pre-existing data on the disk. Hard disk drives are also formatted before being initialized, and should be protected so that they are not reformatted unintentionally.

How much **data** can a **floppy disk** hold?

The three common floppy disk (diskette) sizes vary widely in storage capacity.

Envelope size (inches)	Storage capacity
8	100,000–500,000 bytes
5.25	100 kilobytes–1.2 megabytes
3.5	400 kilobytes–more than 2 megabytes

An 8-inch or 5-inch diskette is enclosed in a plastic protective envelope, which does not protect the disk from bending or folding; parts of the disk surface are also exposed, and can be contaminated by fingerprints or dust. The casing on a 3.5-inch floppy disk is rigid plastic, and includes a sliding disk guard that protects the disk surface, but allows it to be exposed when the disk is inserted in the disk drive. This protection, along with the increased data storage capacity, makes the 3.5-inch disk currently the most popular.

Who invented the computer **mouse**?

A computer "mouse" is a hand-held input device that, when rolled across a flat surface, causes a cursor to move in a corresponding way on a display screen. A prototype mouse was part of an input console demonstrated by Douglas C. Englehart in 1968 at the Fall Joint Computer Conference in San Francisco. Popularized in 1984 by the Macintosh from Apple Computer, the mouse was the result of 15 years devoted to exploring ways to make communicating with computers simpler and more flexible.

The physical appearance of the small box with the dangling, tail-like wire suggested the name of "mouse."

What is **Hopper's rule**?

Electricity travels one foot in a nanosecond (a billionth of a second). This is one of a number of rules compiled for the convenience of computer programmers. This is also considered to be a fundamental limitation on the possible speed of a computer—signals in an electrical circuit cannot move any faster.

Who was the first programmer?

According to historical accounts, Lord Byron's daughter, Augusta Ada Byron, the Countess of Lovelace, was the first person to write a computer program for Charles Babbage's (1792–1871) "analytical engine." This machine, never built, was to work by means of punched cards that could store partial answers that could later be retrieved for additional operations, and that would print results. Her work with Babbage and the essays she wrote about the possibilities of the "engine" established her as a "patron saint," if not a founding parent, of the art and science of programming. The programming language called "Ada" was named in her honor by the United States Department of Defense. In modern times the honor goes to Commodore Grace Murray Hopper (1906–1992) of the United States Navy. She wrote the first program for the Mark I computer.

Is an **assembly language** the same thing as a **machine language**?

While the two terms are often used interchangeably, an assembly language is a more "user friendly" translation of a machine language. A machine language is the collection of patterns of bits recognized by a central processing unit (CPU) as instructions. Each particular CPU design has its own machine language. The machine language of the CPU of a microcomputer generally includes about 75 instructions; the machine language of the CPU of a large mainframe computer may include hundreds of instructions. Each of these instructions is a pattern of 1's and 0's that tells the CPU to perform a specific operation.

An assembly language is a collection of symbolic, mnemonic names for each instruction in the machine language of its CPU. Like the machine language, the assembly language is tied to a particular CPU design. Programming in assembly language requires intimate familiarity with the CPU's architecture, and assembly language programs are difficult to maintain and require extensive documentation.

The computer language C, developed in the late 1980s, is now frequently used instead of assembly language. It is a high-level programming language that can be compiled into machine languages for almost all computers, from microcomputers to mainframes, because of its functional structure.

Who invented the **COBOL** computer language?

COBOL (common business oriented language) is a prominent computer language designed specifically for commercial uses, created in 1960 by a team drawn from several computer makers and the Pentagon. The best-known individual associated with COBOL was then-Lieutenant Grace Hopper (1906–1992) who made fundamental contributions to the United States Navy standardization of COBOL. COBOL excels at the most common kinds of data processing for business—simple arithmetic operations performed on huge files of data. The language endures because its syntax is very much like English and because a program written in COBOL for one kind of computer can run on many others without alteration.

How is a **byte** defined?

A byte, a common unit of computer storage, holds the equivalent of a single character, such as a letter ("A"), a number ("2"), a symbol ("$"), a decimal point, or a space. It is usually equivalent to eight "data bits" and one "parity bit." A bit (a binary digit), the smallest unit of information in a digital computer, is equivalent to a single "0" or "1". The parity bit is used to check for errors in the bits making up the byte. Although eight data bits per byte is the most common size, computer manufacturers are free to define a differing number of bits as a byte. Six data bits per byte is another common size.

What does it mean to **"boot"** a computer?

Booting a computer is starting it, in the sense of turning control over to the operating system. The term comes from bootstrap, because bootstraps allow an individual to pull on boots without help from anyone else. Some people prefer to think of the process in terms of using bootstraps to lift oneself off the ground, impossible in the physical sense, but a reasonable image for representing the process of searching for the operating system, loading it, and passing control to it. The commands to do this are embedded in a *read only memory* (ROM) chip that is automatically executed when a microcomputer is turned on or reset. In mainframe or minicomputers, the process usually involves a great deal of operator input. A *cold boot* powers on the computer and passes control to the operating system; a *warm boot* resets the operating system without powering off the computer.

Should a PC be **turned off** when not in use?

Personal computers (PCs) currently account for up to 5% of the nation's commercial energy use, and that percentage could double by the year 2000. While shutting off personal computers for one or two hours during the work day is not a cost-effective practice, turning off the monitor and leaving on the central processing unit (CPU) for the same amount of time saves a substantial fraction of the PC's energy use. However, to save energy and extend the computer's lifetime, both the CPU and the monitor should be shut off at the end of the day and before the weekend.

What is the correct way to **face a computer** screen?

Correct positioning of the body at a computer is essential to preventing physical problems such as carpal tunnel syndrome and back pain. You should sit so that your eyes are 18 to 24 inches (45 to 61 centimeters) from the screen, and at a height so that they are six to eight inches (15 to 20 centimeters) above the center of the screen. Your hands should be level with or slightly below the arms.

Correct posture is also necessary. You should sit upright, keeping the spine straight. Sit all the way back in the chair with the knees level with or below the thighs. Both feet should be on the floor. The arms may rest on the desk or chair arms, but make sure you do not slouch. If you need to bend or lean forward, do so from the waist.

Where did the term **bug** originate?

The slang term *bug* is used to describe problems and errors occurring in computer programs. The term may have originated during the early 1940s at Harvard University, when computer pioneer Grace Murray Hopper discovered that a dead moth had caused the breakdown of a machine on which she was working. When asked what she was doing while removing the corpse with tweezers, she replied, "I'm debugging the machine." The moth's carcass, taped to a page of notes, is preserved with the trouble log notebook at the Virginia Naval Museum.

Grace Murray Hopper.

What is a computer **virus** and how is it spread?

Taken from the obvious analogy with biological viruses, a computer "virus" is a program that searches out other programs and "infects" them by replicating itself in them. When the programs are executed, the embedded virus is executed too, thus propagating the "infection." This normally happens invisibly to the user. A virus cannot infect other computers, however, without assistance. It is spread when users communicate by computer, often when they trade programs. The virus might do nothing but propagate itself and then allow the program to run normally. Usually, however, after propagating silently for a while, it starts doing other things—possibly inserting "cute" messages or destroying all of the user's files. Computer "worms" and "logic bombs" are similar to viruses, but they do not replicate themselves within programs as viruses do. A logic bomb does its damage immediately—destroying data, inserting garbage into data files, or reformatting the hard disk; a worm can alter the program and database either immediately or over a period of time.

In the 1990s, viruses, worms, and logic bombs have become such a serious problem, especially among IBM PC and Macintosh users, that the production of special detection and "inoculation" software has become an industry.

What is a **fuzzy search**?

Fuzzy search is a feature of some software programs that allows a user to search for text that is similar to but not exactly the same as what he or she specifies. It can produce results when the exact spelling is unknown, or it can help users obtain information that is loosely related to a topic.

What is a **pixel**?

A pixel (from the words *pix*, for picture, and *el*ement) is the smallest element on a video display screen. A screen contains thousands of pixels, each of which can be made up of one or more dots or a cluster of dots. On a simple monochrome screen, a pixel is one dot; the two colors of image and background are created when the pixel is switched either on or off. Some monochrome screen pixels can be energized to create different light intensities, to allow a range of shades from light to dark. On color screens, three dot colors are included in each pixel—red, green, and blue. The simplest screens have just one dot of each color, but more elaborate screens have pixels with clusters of each color. These more elaborate displays can show a large number of colors and intensities. On color screens, black is created by leaving all three colors off; white by all three colors on; and a range of grays by equal intensities of all the colors.

The most economical displays are monochrome, with one bit per pixel, with settings limited to on and off. High-resolution color screens, which can use a million pixels, with each color dot using four bytes of memory, would need to reserve many megabytes just to display the image.

What does **DOS** stand for?

DOS stands for "disk operating system," a program that controls the computer's transfer of data to and from a hard or floppy disk. Frequently it is combined with the main operating system. The operating system was originally developed at Seattle Computer Products as SCP-DOS. When IBM decided to build a personal computer and needed an

501

operating system, it chose the SCP-DOS after reaching an agreement with the Microsoft Corporation to produce the actual operating system. Under Microsoft, SCP-DOS became MS-DOS, which IBM referred to as PC-DOS (personal computer), and which everyone eventually simply called DOS.

What is **E mail**?

Electronic mail, also known as E mail or e-mail, uses communication facilities to transmit messages. Many systems use computers as transmitting and receiving interfaces, but fax communication is also a form of E mail. A user can send a message to a single recipient, or to many. Different systems offer different options for sending, receiving, manipulating text, and addressing. For example, a message can be "registered," so that the sender is notified when the recipient looks at the message (though there is no way to tell if the recipient has actually read the message). Many systems allow messages to be forwarded. Usually messages are stored in a simulated "mailbox" in the network server or host computer; some systems announce incoming mail if the recipient is logged onto the system. An organization (such as a corporation, university, or professional organization) can provide electronic mail facilities; national and international networks can provide them as well. In order to use E mail, both sender and receiver must have accounts on the same system or on systems connected by a network.

What is a **hacker**?

A hacker is a skilled computer user. The term originally denoted a skilled programmer, particularly one skilled in machine code and with a good knowledge of the machine and its operating system. The name arose from the fact that a good programmer could always hack an unsatisfactory system around until it worked.

The term later came to denote a user whose main interest is in defeating password systems. The term has thus acquired a pejorative sense, with the meaning of one who deliberately and sometimes criminally interferes with data available through telephone lines. The activities of such hackers have led to considerable efforts to tighten security of transmitted data.

What is a **kludge**?

A kludge (also spelled kluge) is a sloppy, crude, cumbersome solution to a problem. It refers to a makeshift solution as well as to any poorly designed product, or a product that becomes unmanageable over time.

Who coined the term **technobabble**?

John A. Barry used the term "technobabble" to mean the pervasive and indiscriminate use of computer terminology, especially as it is applied to situations that have nothing at all to do with technology. He first used it in the early 1980s.

COMMUNICATIONS

GENERAL
SCIENCE
AND TECHNOLOGY

NUMBERS

When was a symbol for the concept **zero** first used?

Hindu mathematicians are usually given credit for developing a symbol for the concept "zero"; it appears in an inscription at Gwalior dated 870 C.E. It is certainly older than that; it is found in inscriptions dating from the seventh century in Cambodia, Sumatra, and Bangka Island (off Sumatra). While there is no documentary evidence for the zero in China before 1247, some historians believe that it originated there, and arrived in India via Indochina.

What are **Roman numerals**?

Roman numerals are symbols that stand for numbers. They are written using seven basic symbols: I (1), V (5), X (10), L (50), C (100), D (500), and M (1,000). Sometimes a bar is place over a numeral to multiply it by 1,000. A smaller numeral appearing before a larger numeral indicates that the smaller numeral is subtracted from the larger one. This notation is generally used for 4s and 9s; for example, 4 is written IV, 9 is IX, 40 is XL, and 90 is XC.

What is a **perfect number**?

A perfect number is a number equal to the sum of all its proper divisors (divisors smaller than the number) including 1. The number 6 is the smallest perfect number; the sum of its divisors 1, 2, and 3 equals 6. The next three perfect numbers are 28, **505**

496, and 8,126. No odd perfect numbers are known. The highest known perfect number is:

$$(2^{859,433}-1) \times 2^{859,433}$$

What are **Fibonacci numbers**?

Fibonacci numbers are a series of numbers where each, after the second term, is the sum of the two preceding numbers—for example, 1, 1, 2, 3, 5, 8, 13, 21 .... They were first described by Leonard Fibonacci (ca. 1180–ca. 1250), also known as Leonard of Pisa, as part of a thesis on series in his most famous book *Liber abaci* (*The Book of the Calculator*), published in 1202 and later revised by him. In addition to their function as recreational mathematics (providing entertainment to mathematicians who enjoy calculating series), Fibonacci numbers have proved useful in describing the positioning of leaves around plant stems, the spiral patterns in the heads of sunflowers, and the genealogy of honeybees.

What is the **largest prime number** presently known?

A prime number is one that is evenly divisible only by itself and 1. The integers 1, 2, 3, 5, 7, 11, 13, 17, and 19 are prime numbers. Euclid (ca. 300 B.C.E.) proved that there is no "largest prime number," because any attempt to define the largest results in a paradox. If there is a largest prime number (P), adding 1 to the product of all primes up to and including P, $1 + (1 \times 2 \times 3 \times 5 \times ... \times P)$, yields a number that is itself a prime number, because it cannot be divided evenly by any of the known primes. In 1993, scientists Paul Gage and David Slowinski at Cray Research in Eagan, Minnesota determined the 33rd known prime number by computer. The number is 258,716 digits long. It is: $2^{859,433} - 1$.

There is no apparent pattern to the sequence of primes. Mathematicians have been trying to find a formula since the days of Euclid, but to no avail.

What is the **largest number** mentioned in the **Bible**?

The largest number specifically named in the Bible is a thousand thousand; i.e., a million. It is found in 2 Chronicles 14:9.

How are names for large and small **quantities** **constructed** in the **metric system**?

Each prefix listed below can be used in the metric system and with some customary units. For example, centi + meter = centimeter, meaning one-hundredth of a meter.

Prefix	Power	Numerals
Exa-	10^{18}	1,000,000,000,000,000,000
Peta-	10^{15}	1,000,000,000,000,000
Tera-	10^{12}	1,000,000,000,000
Giga-	10^{9}	1,000,000,000
Mega-	10^{6}	1,000,000
Myria-	10^{5}	100,000
Kilo-	10^{3}	1,000
Hecto-	10^{2}	100
Deca-	10^{1}	10
Deci-	10^{-1}	0.1
Centi-	10^{-2}	0.01
Milli-	10^{-3}	0.001
Micro-	10^{-6}	0.000001
Nano-	10^{-9}	0.000000001
Pico-	10^{-12}	0.000000000001
Femto-	10^{-15}	0.000000000000001
Atto-	10^{-18}	0.000000000000000001

How large is a **googol**?

A googol is 10^{100} (the number 1 followed by 100 zeros). Unlike most other names for numbers, it does notrelate to any other numbering scale. The American mathematician Edward Kasner first used the term in 1938; when searching for a term for this large number, Kasner asked his nephew, Milton Sirotta, then about nine years old, to suggest a name. The googolplex is 10 followed by a googol of zeros, represented as 10^{googol}.

Other very large numbers

Name	Value in powers of 10	Number of 0's	Number of groups of three 0's after 1,000
Billion	10^{9}	9	2
Trillion	10^{12}	12	3
Quadrillion	10^{15}	15	4
Quintillion	10^{18}	18	5
Sextillion	10^{21}	21	6
Septillion	10^{24}	24	7
Octillion	10^{27}	27	8
Nonillion	10^{30}	30	9
Decillion	10^{33}	33	10
Undecillion	10^{36}	36	11
Duodecillion	10^{39}	39	12
Tredecillion	10^{42}	42	13
Quattuor-decillion	10^{45}	45	14
Quindecillion	10^{48}	48	15
Sexdecillion	10^{51}	51	16
Septen-decillion	10^{54}	54	17
Octodecillion	10^{57}	57	18
Novemdecillion	10^{60}	60	19
Vigintillion	10^{63}	63	20
Centillion	10^{303}	303	100

The British, French, and Germans use a different system for naming denominations above one million. The googol and googolplex are rarely used outside the United States.

What is the **value of pi** out to 30 digits past the decimal point?

Pi (π) represents the ratio of the circumference of a circle to its diameter, used in calculating the area of a circle (πr^2) and the volume of a cylinder ($\pi r^2 h$) or cone. It is a "transcendental number," an irrational number with an exact value that can be measured to any degree of accuracy, but that can't be expressed as the ratio of two integers. In theory, the decimal extends into infinity, though it is generally rounded to 3.1416. Rounded to 30 digits past the decimal point, it equals 3.141592653589793238462643383279. In 1989, Gregory and David Chudnovsky, at Columbia University, New York City, calculated the value of pi to 1,011,961,691 decimal places. They performed the calculation twice on an IBM 3090 mainframe and on a CRAY-2 super computer with matching results. In 1991, they calculated pi to 2,260,321,336 decimal places.

Why is **seven a magical** number?

In magical lore and mysticism, all numbers are ascribed certain properties and energies. Seven is a number of great power, a magical number, a lucky number, a number of psychic and mystical powers, of secrecy and the search for inner truth. The origin of belief in seven's power lies in the lunar cycle. Each of the moon's four phases lasts about seven days. The Sumerians, who based their calendar on the moon, gave the week seven days and declared the seventh and last day of each week to be uncanny. Life cycles on Earth also have phases demarcated by seven, there are said to be seven years to each stage of human growth, and there are seven colors to the rainbow, seven notes in the musical scale, seven petitions in the Lord's Prayer, and seven deadly sins. The seventh son of a seventh son is said to be born with formidable magical and psychic powers. The number seven is widely held to be a lucky number, especially in matters of love and money.

MATHEMATICS

What is the most **enduring mathematical work** of all time?

The *Elements* of Euclid (fl. about 300 B.C.E.) has been the most enduring and influential mathematical work of all time. In it, the ancient Greek mathematician presented the work of earlier mathematicians and included his own many innovations. The *Ele-*

Is it possible to count to infinity?

No. Very large finite numbers are not the same as infinite numbers. Infinite numbers are defined as being unbounded, or without limit. Any number that can be reached by counting or by representation of a number followed by billions of zeros is a finite number.

ments is divided into 13 books: the first six cover plane geometry; seven to nine address arithmetic and number theory; 10 treats irrational numbers; and 11 to 13 discuss solid geometry. In presenting his theorems, Euclid used the synthetic approach, in which one proceeds from the known to the unknown by logical steps. This method became the standard procedure for scientific investigation for many centuries, and the *Elements* probably had a greater influence on scientific thinking than any other work.

How long has the **abacus** been used? Is it still used?

The abacus grew out of early counting boards, with hollows in a board holding pebbles or beads used to calculate. It has been documented in Mesopotamia back to around 3500 B.C.E. The current form, with beads sliding on rods, dates back at least to 15th-century China. Before the use of decimal number systems, which allowed the familiar paper-and-pencil methods of calculation, the abacus was essential for almost all multiplication and division. The abacus is still used in many countries where modern calculators are not available. It is also still used in countries, such as Japan and China, that have long traditions of abacus use. As recently as the mid-1970s, most Japanese shopkeepers used abaci for totalling customers' bills. While the calculator is now more widely used, many people still prefer to check the results on an abacus. At least one manufacturer offers calculators with small, built-in abaci.

Can a person using an **abacus calculate more rapidly** than someone using a calculator?

In 1946, the Tokyo staff of *Stars and Stripes* sponsored a contest between a Japanese abacus expert and an American accountant using the best electric adding machine then available. The abacus operator proved faster in all calculations except the multiplication of very large numbers. While today's electronic calculators are much faster and easier to use than the adding machines used in 1946, undocumented tests still show that an expert can add and subtract faster on an abacus than someone using an electronic calculator. It also allows long division and multiplication problems with more digits than a hand calculator can accommodate.

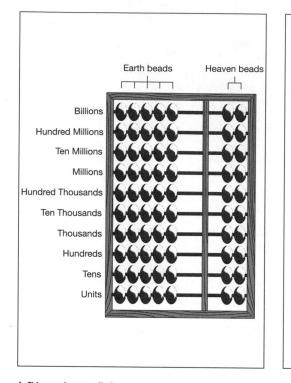

Earth beads   Heaven beads

Billions
Hundred Millions
Ten Millions
Millions
Hundred Thousands
Ten Thousands
Thousands
Hundreds
Tens
Units

A Chinese abacus called a suan pan.

Enter 32. Numbers are entered by moving beads toward the crossbar.

Add 7 to get 39.   Plus 5   Plus 2

Add 1. All five earth beads on the first rod are now used....

Cancel the section by moving the beads away from the crossbar and moving one heaven bead down. Now both heaven beads are used....

Cancel the two heaven beads by moving them away from the crossbar and moving up one earth bead on the next rod. The abacus now reads 40.

An example of addition on a suan pan. The heaven beads have five times the value of the earth beads below them.

What are **Napier's bones**?

In the 16th century, the Scottish mathematician John Napier (1550–1617), Baron of Merchiston, developed a method of simplifying the processes of multiplication and division, using exponents of 10, which Napier called *logarithms* (commonly abbreviated as *logs*). Using this system, multiplication is reduced to addition and division to subtraction. For example, the log of 100 (10^2) is 2; the log of 1000 (10^3) is 3; the multiplication of 100 by 1000, $100 \times 1000 = 100,000$, can be accomplished by adding their logs: $\log[(100)(1000)] = \log(100) + \log(1000) = 2 + 3 = 5 = \log(100,000)$. Napier published his methodology in *A Description of the Admirable Table of Logarithms* in 1614. In 1617 he published a method of using a device, made up of a series of rods in a

John Napier.

frame, marked with the digits 1 through 9, to multiply and divide using the principles of logarithms. This device was commonly called "Napier's bones" or "Napier's rods."

What are **Cuisenaire rods**?

The Cuisenaire method is a teaching system used to help young students independently discover basic mathematical principles. Developed by Emile-Georges Cuisenaire, a Belgian school teacher, the method uses rods of 10 different colors and lengths that are easy to handle. The rods help students understand mathematical principles rather than merely memorizing them. They are also used to teach elementary arithmetic properties such as associative, commutative, and distributive properties.

Who invented the **slide rule**?

The slide rule is based on the use of logarithmic scales, which were invented by John Napier (1550–1617), Baron of Merchiston, and published in 1614. In 1620, Edmund Gunter (1581–1626) of Gresham College, London, England, described an immediate forerunner of the slide rule, his "logarithmic line of numbers." William Oughtred (1574–1660), Rector of Aldbury, England, made the first rectilinear slide rule in 1621. This slide rule consisted of two logarithmic scales that could be manipulated together for calculation. His former pupil, Richard Delamain, published a description of a circular slide rule in 1630, three years before Oughtred published a description of his invention (at least one source says that Delamain published in 1620). Oughtred accused Delamain of stealing his idea, but evidence indicates that the inventions were probably arrived at independently. The earliest existing straight slide rule using the modern design of a slider moving in a fixed stock dates from 1654. A wide variety of specialized slide rules were developed by the end of the 17th century, for trades such as masonry, carpentry, and excise tax collecting. Peter Mark Roget (1779–1869), best known for his *Thesaurus of English Words and Phrases*, invented a log-log slide rule for calculating the roots and powers of numbers in 1814. While the slide rule was popular as a calculating tool for several centuries, it has largely been superseded by the electronic calculator.

How is **casting out nines** used to check the results of addition or multiplication?

The method of "casting out nines" is based on the excess of nines in digits of whole numbers (the remainder when a sum of digits is divided by 9). Illustrating this process in the multiplication example below, the method begins by adding the digits in both the multiplicand (one of the terms that is being multiplied) and the multiplier (the other term being multiplied). In the example below, this operation leads to the results **511** of "13" and "12," respectively. If these results are greater than 9 (>9), then the operation is repeated until the resulting figures are less than 9 (<9). In the example below, the repeated calculation gives the results as "4" and "3," respectively. Multiply the resulting "excess" from the multiplicand by the excess from the multiplier (4 × 3 below). Add the digits of the result to eventually yield a number equal to or less than 9 (≤). Repeat the process of casting out nines in the multiplication product (the result of the multiplication process). The result must equal the result of the previous set of transactions, in this case "3." If the two figures disagree, then the original multiplication procedure was done incorrectly. "Casting out nines" can also be applied to check the accuracy of the results of addition.

$$
\begin{array}{r}
328 \rightarrow 13 \rightarrow 4 \\
\underline{624} \rightarrow 12 \rightarrow \underline{3} \\
1312 \qquad 12 \rightarrow 3 \\
656 \\
\underline{1968} \\
204672 \rightarrow 21 \rightarrow 3
\end{array}
$$

What is the difference between a **median** and a **mean**?

If a string of numbers is arranged in numerical order, the median is the middle value of the string. If there are an even number of values in the string, the median is found by adding the two middle values and dividing by two.

The arithmetic mean, also known as the simple average, is found by taking the sum of the numbers in the string and dividing by the number of items in the string. While easy to calculate for relatively short strings, the arithmetic mean can be misleading, as very large or very small values in the string can distort it. For example, the mean of the salaries of a professional football team would be skewed if one of the players was a high-earning superstar; it could be well above the salaries of any of the other players. The mode is the number in a string that appears most often.

For the string 111222234455667: The median is the middle number of the series, 3. The arithmetic mean is the sum of numbers ÷ the number of numbers in the series, 51 ÷ 15 = 3.4. The mode is the number that occurs most often, 2.

What are **Venn diagrams**?

Venn diagrams are graphical representations of set theory, which use circles to show the logical relationships of the elements of different sets, using the logical operators AND, OR, and NOT. John Venn (1834–1923) first used them in his 1881 *Symbolic Logic*, in which he interpreted and corrected the work of George Boole (1815–1864) and Augustus de Morgan (1806–1871). While his attempts to clarify perceived inconsistencies and ambiguities in Boole's work are not widely accepted, the new method of diagramming is considered to be an improvement. Venn used shading to better illus-

When does 0 × 0 = 1?

Factorials are the product of a given number and all the factors less than that number. The notation n! is used to express this idea. For example, 5! (five factorial) is $5 \times 4 \times 3 \times 2 \times 1 = 120$. For completeness, 0! is assigned the value 1, so $0 \times 0 = 1$.

trate inclusion and exclusion. Charles Dodgson (1832–1898), better known as Lewis Carroll, refined Venn's system, in particular by enclosing the diagram to represent the universal set.

When did the concept of **square root** originate?

The concept of square root has been in existence for many thousands of years. Exactly how it was discovered is not known, but several different methods of exacting square roots were used by early mathematicians. Babylonian clay tablets from 1900 to 1600 B.C.E. contain the squares and cubes of integers 1–30. The early Egyptians used square roots around 1700 B.C.E., and during the Greek Classical Period (600 to 300 B.C.E.) better arithmetic methods improved square root operations. In the 16th century, French mathematician René Descartes was the first to use the square root symbol, $\sqrt{}$.

What are the common mathematical formulas for **volume**?

Volume of a sphere:
Volume = 4/3 times pi times the cube of the radius
$V = 4/3 \times \pi r^3$

Volume of a pyramid:
Volume = 1/3 times the area of the base times the height
$V = 1/3bh$

Volume of a cylinder:
Volume = area of the base times the height
$V = Ah$

Volume of a circular cylinder (with circular base):
Volume = pi times the square of the radius of the base times the height
$V = \pi r^2 h$

Volume of a cube:
Volume = the length of one side cubed
$V = S^3$

Volume of a cone:
Volume = 1/3 times pi times the square of the radius of the base times the height.
$V = 1/3\ \pi r^2 h$

Volume of a rectangular solid:
Volume = length times width times height
$V = lwh$

What are the common mathematical formulas for **area**?

Area of a rectangle:
Area = length times width
$A = lw$

Area = altitude times base
$A = ab$

Area of a circle:
Area = pi times the radius squared
$A = \pi r^2$ or $A = 1/4\pi d^2$

Area of a triangle:
Area = one half the altitude times the base
$A = 1/2ab$

Area of the surface of a sphere:
Area = four times pi times the radius squared
$A = 4\pi r^2$ or $A = \pi d^2$

Area of a square:
Area = length times width, or length of one side squared
$A = s^2$

Area of a cube:
Area = square of the length of one side times 6
$A = 6s^2$

Area of an ellipse:
Area = long diameter times short diameter times 0.7854.

How many feet are on each side of an **acre** that is square?

514 An acre that is square in shape has about 208.7 feet (64 meters) on each side.

Who discovered the formula for the **area of a triangle**?

Heron (or Hero) of Alexandria (first century B.C.E.) is best known in the history of mathematics for the formula that bears his name. This formula calculates the area of a triangle with sides a, b, and c, with s = half the perimeter: $A = \sqrt{[s(2-a)(s-b)(s-c)]}$. The Arab mathematicians who preserved and transmitted the mathematics of the Greeks reported that this formula was known earlier to Archimedes (ca. 287–212 B.C.E.), but the earliest proof now known is that appearing in Heron's *Metrica*.

How is **Pascal's triangle** used?

Pascal's triangle is an array of numbers, arranged so that every number is equal to the sum of the two numbers above it on either side. It can be represented in several slightly different triangles, but this is the most common form:

```
              1
          1       1
       1      2       1
     1     3      3      1
   1    4      6     4      1
 1    5    10    10     5     1
```

The triangle is used to determine the numerical coefficients resulting from the computation of higher powers of a binomial (two numbers added together). When a binomial is raised to a higher power, the result is expanded, using the numbers in that row of the triangle. For example, $(a+b)^1 = a^1 + b^1$, using the coefficients in the second line of the triangle. $(a+b)^2 = a^2 + 2ab + b^2$, using the coefficients in the next line of the triangle. (The first line of the triangle correlates to $(a+b)^0$.) While the calculation of coefficients is fairly straightforward, the triangle is useful in calculating them for the higher powers without needing to multiply them out. Binomial coefficients are useful in calculating probabilities; Blaise Pascal was one of the pioneers in developing laws of probability.

Blaise Pascal.

As with many other mathematical developments, there is some evidence of a previous appearance of the triangle in China. Around 1100 C.E., the Chinese mathematician Chia Hsien wrote about "the tabulation system for unlocking binomial coefficients"; the first publication of the triangle was probably in a book called *Piling-Up Powers and Unlocking Coefficients*, by Liu Ju-Hsieh.

What is the **Pythagorean theorem?**

In a right triangle (one where two of the sides meet in a 90 degree angle), the hypoteneuse is the side opposite the right angle. The Pythagorean theorem, also known as the rule of Pythagoras, states that the square of the length of the hypoteneuse is equal to the sum of the squares of the other two sides ($h^2 = a^2 + b^2$). If the lengths of the sides are: h = 5 inches, a = 4 inches, and b = 3 inches, then

$$h = \sqrt{a^2 + b^2} = \sqrt{4^2 + 3^2} = \sqrt{16 + 9} = \sqrt{25} = 5$$

The theorem is named for the Greek philosopher and mathematician Pythagoras (ca. 580–ca. 500 B.C.E.). Pythagoras is credited with the theory of the functional significance of numbers in the objective world and numerical theories of musical pitch. As he left no writings, the Pythagorean theorem may actually have been formulated by one of his disciples.

What are the **Platonic solids?**

The Platonic solids are the five regular polyhedra: the four-sided tetrahedron, the six-sided cube or hexahedron, the eight-sided octahedron, the twelve-sided dodecahedron, and the twenty-sided icosahedron. While they had been studied as long ago as the time of Pythagorus (around 500 B.C.E.), they are called the Platonic solids because they were first described in detail by Plato around 400 B.C.E. The ancient Greeks gave mystical significance to the Platonic solids: the tetrahedron represented fire, the icosahedron represented water, the stable cube represented the Earth, the octahedron represented the air. The twelve faces of the dodecahedron corresponded to the twelve signs of the zodiac, and this figure represented the entire universe.

What is the ancient Greek problem of **squaring the circle?**

This problem was to construct, with a straight-edge and compass, a square having the same area as a given circle. The Greeks were unable to solve the problem because the task is impossible, as was shown by the German mathematician Ferdinand von Lindemann (1852–1939) in 1882.

What does the expression **tiling the plane** mean?

It is a mathematical expression describing the process of forming a mosaic pattern (a "tessellation") by fitting together an infinite number of polygons so that they cover an entire plane. Tesselations are the familiar patterns that can be seen in designs for quilts, floor coverings, and bathroom tilework.

What is a **golden section**?

Golden section, also called the divine proportion, is the division of a line segment so that the ratio of the whole segment to the larger part is equal to the ratio of the larger part to the smaller part. The ratio is approximately 1.61803 to 1. A golden rectangle is one whose length and width correspond to this ratio. The ancient Greeks thought this shape had the most pleasing proportions. Many famous painters have used the Golden Rectangle in their paintings, and architects have used it in their design of buildings, the most famous example being the Greek Parthenon.

What is a **Möbius strip**?

A Möbius strip is a surface with only one side, usually made by connecting the two ends of a rectangular strip of paper after putting a half-twist (180 degrees relative to the opposite side) in the strip. Cutting a Möbius strip in half down the center of the length of the strip results in a single band with four half-twists. Devised by the German mathematician August Ferdinand Möbius (1790–1868) to illustrate the properties of one-sided surfaces, it was presented in a paper that was not discovered or published until after his death. Another 19th-century German mathematician, Johann Benedict Listing, developed the idea independently at the same time.

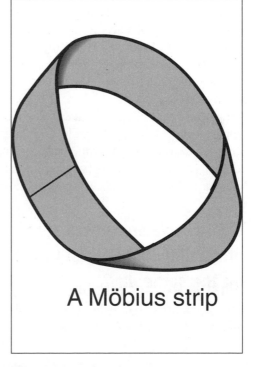

A Möbius strip

Möbius Strip

What are **fractals**?

A fractal is a set of points that is too irregular to be described by traditional geometric terms, but that often have some degree of self-similarity; that is, they are made of parts that resemble the whole. They are used in image processing to compress data and to depict apparently chaotic objects in nature such as mountains or coastlines. Scientists also use fractals to better comprehend rainfall trends, patterns formed by clouds and waves, and the distribution of vegetation. Fractals are also used to create computer-generated art.

How is the **rule of 70** used?

This rule is a quick way of estimating the period of time it will take a quantity to double given the percentage of increase. Divide the percentage of increase into 70. For example, if a sum of money is invested at 6% interest, the money will double in value in $70 \div 6 = 11.7$ years.

How is **percent of increase** calculated?

To find the percent of increase, divide the amount of increase by the base amount. Multiply the result by 100%. For example, a raise in salary from $10,000 to $12,000 would have percent of increase = $(2,000 \div 10,000) \times 100\% = 20\%$.

What is the **law of very large numbers**?

Formulated by Persi Diaconis and Frederick Mosteller of Harvard University, this long-understood law of statistics states that "with a large enough sample, any outrageous thing is apt to happen." Therefore, seemingly amazing coincidences can actually be expected if given sufficient time or a large enough pool of subjects. For example, when a New Jersey woman won the lottery twice in four months, the media publicized it as an incredible long shot of 1 in 17 trillion. However, when statisticians looked beyond this individual's chances and asked what were the odds of the same happening to *any* person buying a lottery ticket in the United States over a six-month period, the number dropped dramatically to 1 in 30. According to researchers, coincidences arise often in statistical work, but some have hidden causes and therefore are not coincidences at all. Many are simply chance events reflecting the luck of the draw.

If 30 people are chosen at random, what is the probability that at least two of them have their **birthday on the same day**?

The probability that at least two people in a group of 30 share the same birthday is about 70%.

How many **different bridge games** are possible?

Roughly 54 octillion different bridge games are possible.

> ## What is the probability of a successful triple play occurring in a single baseball game?
>
> The odds against a triple play in a game of baseball are 1,400 to 1.

What is **Zeno's paradox**?

Zeno of Elea (ca. 490–ca. 425 B.C.E.), a Greek philosopher and mathematician, is famous for his paradoxes, which deal with the continuity of motion. One form of the paradox is: If an object moves with constant speed along a straight line from point 0 to point 1, the object must first cover half the distance (1/2), then half the remaining distance (1/4), then half the remaining distance (1/8), and so on without end. The conclusion is that the object never reaches point 1. Because there is always some distance to be covered, motion is impossible. In another approach to this paradox, Zeno used an allegory telling of a race between a tortoise and Achilles (who could run 100 times as fast), where the tortoise started running 10 rods in front of Achilles. Because the tortoise always advanced 1/100 of the distance that Achilles advanced in the same time period, it was theoretically impossible for Achilles to pass him. The English mathematician and writer Charles Dodgson (1832–1898), better known as Lewis Carroll, used the characters of Achilles and the tortoise to illustrate his paradox of infinity.

TERMS AND THEORIES

What is **High Technology** or **High Tech**?

This buzz term used mainly by the lay media (as opposed to scientific, medical, or technological media) appeared in the late 1970s. It was initially used to identify the newest, "hottest" application of technology to fields such as medical research, genetics, automation, communication systems, and computers. It usually implied a distinction between technology to meet the information needs of society and traditional heavy industry, which met more material needs. By the mid-1980s, the term had become a catch-all applying primarily to the use of electronics (especially computers) to accomplish everyday tasks.

How is a **therblig** defined?

Frank Bunker Gilbreth (1868–1924), the founder of modern motion study technique, called the fundamental motions of the hands of a worker "therbligs" (Gilbreth roughly **519**

What is the new science of chaos?

Chaos or chaotic behavior is the behavior of a system whose final state depends very sensitively on the initial conditions. The behavior is unpredictable and cannot be distinguished from a random process, even though it is strictly determinate in a mathematical sense. Chaos studies the complex and irregular behavior of many systems in nature, such as changing weather patterns, flow of turbulent fluids, and swinging pendulums. Scientists once thought they could make exact predictions about such systems, but found that a tiny difference in starting conditions can lead to greatly different results. Chaotic systems do obey certain rules, which mathematicians have described with equations, but the science of chaos demonstrates the difficulty of predicting the long-range behavior of chaotic systems.

spelled backwards). He concluded that any and all operations are made up of series of these 17 divisions. The 17 divisions are search, select, grasp, reach, move, hold, release, position, pre-position, inspect, assemble, disassemble, use, unavoidable delay, avoidable delay, plan, and test to overcome fatigue.

Gilbreth developed many of the concepts that became part of modern management techniques, and he also patented many inventions useful in the construction industry. One device he used in time and motion studies was his cyclograph or "motion recorder." An ordinary camera and a small electric bulb showed the path of movement. The light patterns reveal all hesitation or poor habits interfering with a workers's dexterity.

What does the term **ergonomics** mean?

The study of human capability and psychology in relation to the worker's working environment and equipment is variously known as ergonomics, human engineering, human factors engineering, or engineering psychology. Ergonomics is based on the premise that tools humans use and the environment they work in should be matched with their capabilities and limitations, rather than forcing humans to adapt to the physical environment. Researchers in ergonomics try to determine optimum conditions in communication, cognition, reception of sensory stimuli, physiology, and psychology, and examine the effect of adverse conditions. Specific areas of study include design of work areas (including seats, desks, consoles, and cockpits) in terms of human physical size, comfort, strength, and vision; effects of physiological stresses such as work speed, work load, decision making, fatigue, and demands on memory and perception; and design of visual displays to enhance the quality and speed of interpretation.

How did a total **solar eclipse** confirm Einstein's **theory of general relativity**?

When formulating his theory of general relativity, Albert Einstein proposed that the curvature of space near a massive object like the Sun would bend light that passed close by. For example, a star seen near the edge of the sun during an eclipse would appear to have shifted by 1.75 arc seconds from its usual place. The British astronomer Arthur Eddington confirmed Einstein's hypothesis during an eclipse on May 29, 1919. The subsequent attention given Eddington's findings helped establish Einstien's reputation as one of science's greatest figures.

What is the law of **parsimony**?

The law of parsimony, also called the law of economy or Ockham's razor, proposes that a problem should be stated in its basic and simplest terms. In scientific terms, it states that the simplest theory that fits the facts of a problem should be the one selected. Credit for outlining the law is usually given to William of Ockham (1284?–1347?), an English philosopher and theologian, who wrote that "entities must not be multiplied beyond what is necessary."

Further Reading

Books

AAMA Motor Vehicle Facts & Figures '95. Washington, DC: American Automobile Manufacturers Association, 1995.

The AARL General Class License Manual for Radio Amateur. Newington, CT: American Radio Relay League, 1990.

The AARL Handbook for Radio Amateurs 1996. 73rd ed. Newington, CT: American Radio Relay League, 1995.

Abel, Bob. *The Book of Beer*. Chicago, IL: Regnery, 1976.

Abell, George O. *Realm of the Universe*. New York: Holt, Rinehart and Winston, Inc., 1976.

Academic American Encyclopedia. Danbury, CT: Grolier, 1992.

Ackerknecht, Erwin H. *A Short Story of Medicine*. New York: Ronald Press, 1955.

Acronyms Initialisms & Abbreviations Dictionary. 19th ed. Detroit, MI: Gale Research, 1995.

Adams, Edward Dean. *Niagara Power*. Niagara Falls, NY: Niagara Falls Power Company, 1927.

Adams, Ramon F. *The Language of the Railroader*. Norman, OK: University of Oklahoma Press, 1977.

Adler, Bill. *Outwitting Critters*. New York: HarperCollins, 1992.

Adler, Bill. *Whole Earth Quiz Book: How Well Do You Know the Planet*. New York: Quill, 1991.

Agent Orange and Its Associated Dioxin: Assessment of a Controversy. New York: Elsevier, 1988.

Agress, Clarence M. *Energetics*. New York: Grosset & Dunlap, 1978.

Ahrens, C. Donald. *Meteorology Today*. 2nd ed. St. Paul, MN: West Publishing, 1985.

Ainsworth, G.C. *Ainsworth's & Bisby's Dictionary of the Fungi*. 5th ed. London: Commonwealth Agricultural Bureau, 1961.

Ali, Sheikh R. *The Peace and Nuclear War Dictionary*. Santa Barbara, CA.: ABC-CLIO, 1989.

Allaby, Michael. *Dictionary of the Environment*, 3rd ed. New York: New York University Press, 1989.

The Almanac of Science and Technology. San Diego, CA: Harcourt Brace Jovanovich, 1990.

Altman, Roberta. *The Complete Book of Home Environmental Hazards*. New York: Facts on File, 1990.

Amazing Animals. Alexandria, VA: Time-Life Books, 1990.

American Academy of Dermatology. *Poison Ivy* (Pamphlet). Washington, DC: American Academy of Dermatology, 1990.

The American Geological Institute. *Dictionary of Geological Terms*. Rev. ed. Garden City, NY: Anchor Press, 1976.

American Horticultural Society Encyclopedia of Gardening. New York: Dorling Kindersley, 1993.

American Kennel Club. *The Complete Dog Book*. New York: Howell Book House, Inc., 1985.

The American Medical Association Encyclopedia of Medicine. New York: Random House, 1989.

American Medical Association Family Medical Guide. Rev. ed. New York: Random House, 1987.

Amory, Cleveland. *Animail*. New York: Windmill Books, Inc., and E.P. Dutton & Co., Inc., 1976.

Anderson, B.W. *Gem Testing*. 10th ed. Stoneham, MA: Butterworth, 1990.

Anderson, Jean. *The Nutrition Bible*. New York: William Morrow, 1995.

Anderson, Kenneth. *Orphan Drugs*. Los Angeles, CA: The Body Press, 1987.

Anderson, Norman D., and Walter R. Brown. *Ferris Wheels*. New York: Pantheon Books, 1983.

Angelo, Joseph A. *The Dictionary of Space Technology*. New York: Facts on File, 1982.

Angelo, Joseph A. *The Extraterrestrial Encyclopedia*. Rev. & updated ed. New York: Facts On File, 1991.

Annual Energy Review 1990. Washington, DC: U.S. Department of Energy, Energy Information Administration, 1990.

Arem, Joel E. *Color Encyclopedia of Gemstones*. 2nd ed. New York: Van Nostrand Reinhold, 1987.

Arnett, Ross H., Jr. *Insect Life*. Englewood Cliffs, NJ: Prentice-Hall, 1985.

Argenzio, Victor. *Diamonds Eternal*. New York: David McKay, 1974.

Armstrong, Joseph E. *Science in Biology*. Prospect Heights, IL: Waveland Press, 1990.

The ARRL Handbook for Radio Amateurs. 68th ed. Newington, CT: American Radio Relay League, 1991.

Ashby, W. Ross. *Introduction to Cybernetics*. New York: John Wiley & Sons, 1958.

Ashworth, William. *The Encyclopedia of Environmental Studies*. New York Facts on File, 1991.

Asimov, Isaac. *Asimov On Chemistry*. New York: Anchor Books, 1975.

Asimov, Isaac. *Asimov On Numbers*. New York: Doubleday, 1977.

Asimov, Isaac. *Asimov's Biographical Encyclopedia of Science and Technology*. 2nd rev. ed. Garden City, NY: Doubleday & Company, Inc., 1982.

Asimov, Isaac. *Asimov's Chronology of Science and Discovery*. New York: Harper and Row, 1989.

Asimov, Isaac. *Asimov's New Guide to Science*. Rev. ed. New York: Basic Book, Inc., 1984.

Asimov, Isaac. *The Human Body*. New rev. ed. New York: A Mentor Book, 1992.

Asimov, Isaac. *Isaac Asimov's Book of Science and Nature Questions*. New York: Grove Weidenfeld, 1988.

Asimov, Isaac. *Isaac Asimov's Guide to Earth and Space*. New York: Random House, 1991.

Asimov, Isaac. *Understanding Physics*. New York: Dorset Press, 1988. 3 vols. in one.

Asimov, Isaac. *Words of Science*. Boston, MA: Houghton Mifflin, 1959.

Aslett, Don. *The Cleaning Encyclopedia*. New York: Bantam Doubleday Dell.

Aslett, Don. *How Do I Clean the Moosehead?* New York: New American Library, 1989.

Aslett, Don. *Pet Clean-up Made Easy*. Cincinnati, OH: Writer's Digest Books, 1988.

Aslett, Don. *Stainbusters Bible*. New York: Penguin, 1990.

Astronauts and Cosmonauts Biographical and Statistical Data Report to the Committee on Science, Space, and Technology U.S. House of Representatives, 1989. Washington, DC: Committee on Science, Space and Technology, 1989.

Astronomical Almanac 1992. Washington, DC: U.S. Government Printing Office, 1991.

Austic, Richard E. *Poultry Production*. 13th ed. Philadelphia: Lea & Febiger, 1990.

Automobile Book. Lincolnwood, IL: Publications Inter- national, 1996.

Automotive Encyclopedia. Rev. ed. South Holland, IL: Goodheart-Willcox Company, 1989.

Aveni, Anthony F. *Empires of Time*. New York: Basic Books, 1989.

Babbitt, Harold E. *Sewage and Sewage Treatment*. 8th ed. New York: Wiley, 1958.

Back to Basics. Pleasantville, NY: The Reader's Digest Association, 1991.

Bagel, Marilyn, and Tom Bagel. *The Bagel's Bagel Book*. Herndon, VA: Acropolis Books, 1985.

Bagenal, Philip, and Jonathan Meades. *The Illustrated Atlas of the World's Great Buildings*. London: Salamander Books, Ltd., 1980.

Bailey, Adrian. *Mrs. Bridges' Upstairs, Downstairs Cookery Book*. New York: Simon and Schuster, 1974.

Bailey, Janet. *Keeping Food Fresh*. Rev. ed. New York: Harper & Row, Publishers, 1989.

Bair, Frank E. *The Weather Almanac*. 6th ed. Detroit, MI: Gale Research Inc., 1992.

Baker, David. *The History of Manned Space Flight*. New York: Crown Publishers, Inc., 1982.

Baker, Susan P., et al. *The Injury Fact Book*. 2nd ed. New York: Oxford University Press, 1992.

Balfour, Henry H. *Herpes Diseases and Your Health*. Minneapolis, MN: University of Minnesota Press, 1984.

Bali, Mrinal. *Space Exploration: A Reference Handbook*. Santa Barbara, CA: ABC-CLIO, 1990.

Ballast, David Kent. *Architects' Handbook of Formulas, Tables and Mathematical Calculations*. New York: Prentice-Hall, 1988.

Bamberger, Richard. *Physics Through Experiment*. New York: Sterling, 1969.

Barach, Arnold B. *Famous American Trademarks*. Washington, D. C.: Public Affairs Press, 1972.

Barnard, Christiaan. *The Body Machine*. New York: Crown, 1981.

Barndt, Herb. *How to Remove Spots and Stains*. New York: Perigee Books, 1987.

Barnhart, Robert K. *The American Heritage Dictionary of Science*. Boston, MA: Houghton, Mifflin, 1986.

Barr, Roger. *Radios: Wireless Sound*. San Diego, CA, Lucent Books, 1994.

Barrett, James A. *Biology*. Englewood Cliffs, NJ: Prentice-Hall, 1986.

Barry, John. *Technobabble*. Cambridge, MA: MIT Press, 1991.

Bartholomew, Mel. *Square Foot Gardening*. Emmaus, PA: Rodale Press, 1981.

Bartlett, John. *Familiar Quotations*. Boston, MA: Little, Brown, 1980.

Bates, Robert, and Julia A. Jackson. *Glossary of Geology*. 3rd ed. Alexandria VA: American Geological Institute, 1987.

Battan, Louis J. *Weather in Your Life*. New York: W.H. Freeman, 1983.

Baylin, Frank, and Brent Gale. *Home Satellite TV Installation and Troubleshooting Manual*. 1986 ed. Boulder, CO: Baylin/Gale Productions, 1985.

Bear, Marina, and John Bear. *How to Repair Food*. Berkeley, CA: Ten Speed Press, 1987.

Beard, James. *James Beard's American Cookery*. Boston, MA: Little, Brown, 1972.

Beatty, J. Kelly, Brian O'Leary, and Andrew Chaikin. *The New Solar System*. Cambridge, MA: Sky Publishing Corp., 1981.

Beck, James H. *Rail Talk*. Gretna, NE: James Publications, 1978.

Beeching, W.A. *Century of the Typewriter*. New York: St. Martin's Press, 1974.

Berg, Richard E. *The Physics of Sound*. Englewood Cliffs, NJ: Prentice-Hall, 1982.

Bergamini, David. *Life Science Library: Mathematics*. New York: Time Incorporated, 1963.

Berliner, Barbara. *The Book of Answers*. Englewood Cliffs, NJ: Prentice-Hall, 1990.

Bernard, Josef. *The Cellular Connection*. Mendocino, CA: Quantum Publishing, 1987.

Berry, James. *Exploring Crystals*. New York: Crowell-Collier Press, 1969.

Best, Charles H. *Best and Taylor's Physiological Basis of Medical Practice*. Baltimore, MD: Williams & Wilkins, 1985.

Beyer, Don E. *The Manhattan Project*. New York: Watts, 1991.

Beyer, William H. *CRC Standard Mathematical Tables*. 28th ed. Boca Raton, FL: CRC Press, 1987.

Bingham, Anne. *Buying Jewelry*. New York: McGraw-Hill, 1989.

The Biocycle Guide to Maximum Recycling. Emmaus, PA: JG Press, 1993.

Biographical Dictionary of Scientists. 2nd ed. New York: Oxford University Press, 1994.

Biographical Encyclopedia of Scientists. 2nd ed. Bristol: Institute of Physics, 1994.

The Birds Around Us. San Ramon, CA: Ortho, 1986.

Bishop, Peter. *Fifth Generation Computers*. Hempstead, Eng.: Ellis Horwood, Ltd., 1986.

Blacks in Science. New Brunswick, Transaction Books, 1983.

Blackwell, Will H. *Poisonous and Medicinal Plants*. Englewood Cliffs, NJ: Prentice-Hall, 1990.

Blair, Ian. *Taming the Atom*. Bristol, Eng.: Adam Hilger, 1983.

Block, E.B. *Fingerprinting: Magic Weapon Against Crime*. New York: McKay, 1969.

Blocksma, Mary. *Reading the Numbers*. New York: Penguin, 1989.

The BOCA National Building Code 1993. 12th ed. Country Club Hills, IL: Building Officials and Code Administrators International, 1993.

Bodinski, Lois H. *The Nurse's Guide to Diet Therapy*. New York: Wiley, 1987.

Bogner, Bruce F. *Vehicular Traffic Radar Handbook for Attorneys*. Mount Holly, NJ: The Brehn Corporation, 1979.

Bohren, Craig F. *Clouds in a Glass of Beer*. New York: Wiley, 1987.

Bolton, W.C. *Physics Experiments and Projects*. Elmsford, NY: Pergamon, 1968.

Bomberger, Audrey S., and Betty A. Dannenfelser. *Radiation and Health*. Gaithersburg, MD: Aspen Pubs., Inc., 1984.

Bonnet, Robert L. *Botany: 49 Science Fair Projects*. Blue Ridge Summit, PA: Tab Books, 1989.

Booth, Nicholas. *The Concise Illustrated Book of Planets and Stars*. New York: Gallery Books, 1990.

Bothamley, Jennifer. *Dictionary of Theories*. London: Gale Research International, 1993.

Boulware, Marcus H. *Snoring*. Rockaway, NJ: American Faculty Press, 1974.

Bowler, Peter J. *Evolution, the History of an Idea*. Berkeley, CA: University of California Press, 1984.

Boyer, Carl B. *A History of Mathematics*. 2nd ed. New York: Wiley, 1989.

Boyer, Rick. *Places Rated Almanac*. Englewood Cliffs, NJ: Prentice-Hall, 1989.

Bradbury, Savile. *The Evolution of the Microscope*. Elmsford, NY: Pergamon Press, 1967.

Bradford, Gershom. *A Glossary of Sea Terms*. New York: Dodd, Mead, 1942.

Brady, George S. *Materials Handbook*. 13th ed. New York: McGraw-Hill, 1991.

Bragonier, Reginald, and David Fisher. *What's What*. Maplewood, NJ: Hammond Incorporated, 1981.

Brandreth, Gyles. *Your Vital Statistics*. New York: Citadel, 1986.

Branson, Gary D. *The Complete Guide to Recycling at Home*. Whitehall, VA: Betterway Publications, 1991.

Braun, Wernher von, and Frederick I. Ordway III. *Space Travel: A History*. New York: Harper & Row, 1985.

Breakthroughs and Discoveries. New York: John Wiley, 1994.

Brennan, Richard P. *Dictionary of Scientific Literacy*. New York: John Wiley & Sons, Inc., 1992.

Brennan, Richard P. *Levitating Trains and Kamikaze Genes*. New York: Harper Perennial, 1990.

Brewer, Brian. *Eclipse*. 2nd ed. Seattle, WA: Earth View, 1991.

Britannica Book of the Year 1991. Chicago, IL: Encyclopaedia Britannica, 1991.

Britten, Frederick J. *Britten's Old Clocks and Watches and Their Makers*. 8th ed. New York: Dutton, 1973.

Broadcasting and Cable Yearbook 1995. New Providence, NJ: Bowker, 1995.

Broadcasting Yearbook 1991. New York: Broadcasting Publications, Inc., 1991.

Brody, Jane E. *Jane Brody's Good Food Book*. New York: W.W. Norton, 1985.

Brown, Robert Hanbury. *Man and the Stars*. Oxford: Oxford University Press, 1978.

Brown, Robert J. *200 Illustrated Science Experiments for Children*. Blue Ridge Summit, PA: TAB Books, 1987.

Brown, Theodore L. *Chemistry*. 4th ed. Englewood Cliffs, NJ: Prentice-Hall, 1988.

Brown, Travis. *Historical First Patents*. Metuchen, NJ: Scarecrow Press, 1994.

Brown, Victor J. *Engineering Terminology*. Chicago, IL: Gillette, 1938.

Bruno, Leonard C. *On the Move*. Detroit: Gale Research, 1993.

Buchman, Dian Dincin. *Dian Dincin Buchman's Herbal Medicine*. New York: Gramercy, 1980.

Buchsbaum, Ralph. *The Lower Animals*. Garden City, NY: Doubleday, 1960.

Buehner, Jim. *The Complete Handbook of Model Railroading*. Blue Ridge Summit, PA: TAB Books, 1975.

The Bumper Book of Things a Boy Can Make. Blue Ridge Summit, PA: TAB Books, 1978.

Bunch, Bryan. *The Handbook of Current Science & Technology*. Detroit: Gale, 1996.

Burnam, Tom. *The Dictionary of Misinformation*. New York: Perennial Library, 1986.

Burt, McKinley. *Black Inventors of America*. Portland, OR: National Book Company, 1989.

Burt, William Henry. *A Field Guide to the Mammals*. 3rd ed. Boston, MA: Houghton Mifflin, 1976.

Burton, Benjamin T., and Willis R. Foster. *Human Nutrition*. 4th ed. New York: McGraw-Hill, 1988.

Burton, J.L. *Essentials of Dermatology*. 3rd ed. New York: Churchill Livingstone, 1990.

Burton, Maurice. *Encyclopaedia of Animals in Colour*. London: Octopus Books, 1972.

Burton, Maurice, and Robert Burton. *Encyclopedia of Insects and Arachnids*. New York: Crescent Books, 1975.

Bush, Grace A. *Foundations of Mathematics*. New York: McGraw-Hill, 1968.

Busha, William, and Stephen Morris. *The Book of Heat*. Brattleboro, VT: Stephen Greene Press, 1982.

Bynum, W.F., et al. *Dictionary of the History of Science*. Princeton, NJ: Princeton University Press, 1985.

Byrne, Austin T. *A Treatise on Highway Construction*. New York: John Wiley & Sons, 1896.

Cairis, Nicholas. *Cruise Ships of the World*. Boston, MA: Pegasus, 1988.

Calasibetta, Charlotte M. *Fairchild's Dictionary of Fashion*. New York: Fairchild Publications, 1988.

Calder, Nigel. *The Comet Is Coming*. New York: Penguin Books, 1982.

Callahan Philip S. *Bird Behavior*. New York: Four Winds Press, 1975.

The Cambridge Dictionary of Science and Technology. New York: Cambridge University Press, 1988.

The Cambridge Encyclopedia of Ornithology. New York: Cambridge University Press, 1991.

The Cambridge Encyclopedia of Space. New York: Cambridge University Press, 1990.

Campbell, Neil A. *Biology*. 2nd ed. Redwood City, CA: Benjamin/Cummings Publishing Co., Inc., 1990.

Cancer Free: The Comprehensive Cancer Prevention Program. New York: Simon & Schuster, 1995, p. 29.

Can Elephants Swim? New York: Time-Life Books, 1969.

Carlson, Neil R. *Foundations of Physiological Psychology*. Needham Heights, MA: Allyn Bacon, Inc., 1988.

Carroll, Anstice, and Embree De Persiis Vona. *The Health Food Dictionary with Recipes*. Englewood Cliffs, NJ: Prentice-Hall, Inc., 1973.

Carter, E.F. *Dictionary of Inventions and Discoveries*. New York: Crane Russak, 1974.

Cartnell, Robert. *The Incredible Scream Machine: A History of the Roller Coaster*. Fairview Park, OH: Amusement Park Books, 1987.

Cartwright, Rudolph. *Doctors Are Easy to Understand If You Speak Their Language*. New York: Vantage Press, 1987.

Carwell, Hattie. Blacks in Science: Astrophysicist to Zoologist. Oakland, CA: Exposition Press, 1977.

Cary, James. *Tanks and Armor in Modern Warfare*. New York: Franklin Watts, 1966.

Cassel, Don. *Understanding Computers*. Englewood Cliffs, NJ: Prentice-Hall, 1990.

Cassens, B. *Preventive Medicine and Public Health*. New York: Harwal Publishing Co., 1987.

Catalog of American Car ID Numbers 1970-79. Sidney, OH: Amos Press, Inc., 1991.

Cazeau, Charles J. *Science Trivia*. New York: Berkley Books, 1986.

Cecil Textbook of Medicine. 18th ed. Philadelphia, PA: Saunders, 1988. 2 vols.

Chalmers, Irena. *Great American Food Almanac*. New York: Harper & Row, 1986.

Chalmers, Irena. *The Great Food Almanac*. San Francisco, CA: Collins, 1994.

Chambers Science and Technology Dictionary. Cambridge, Eng. & Edinburgh, Scotland: W&R Chambers, Ltd., and Cambridge University Press, 1988.

Chapman, Eugenia. *Clean Your House and Everything in It*. Rev. and updated ed. New York: Perigee Books, 1991.

Charney, Leonard. *Build A Yurt*. New York: Macmillan, 1974.

Chiasson, Robert B. *Laboratory Anatomy of the Cat*. 6th ed. Dubuque, IA: Wm. C. Brown, 1977.

Childs, W.H.J. *Physical Constants*. 9th ed. New York: Chapman and Hall, 1972.

Chinn, George M. *The Machine Gun*. Washington, DC: U.S. Department of the Navy, 1951.

Choukas-Bradley, Melanie, and Polly Alexander. *City of Trees*. Rev. ed. Baltimore, MD: Johns Hopkins University Press, 1987.

Churchill, James E. *The Backyard Building Book*. Harrisburg, PA: Stackpole Books, 1976.

Churchill's Medical Dictionary. New York: Churchill Livingstone, 1989.

Churchman, Lee W. *Survey of Electronics*. San Francisco, CA: Rinehart Press, 1971.

Cipolla, Carlo M., and Derek Birdsall. *The Technology of Man*. New York: Holt, Rinehart and Winston, 1980.

Cities of the United States: The West. Detroit, MI: Gale Research, 1989.

Clark, Jerome. *Unexplained!* Detroit: Visible Ink Press, 1993.

Clarke, Donald. *The Encyclopedia of How It Works From Abacus to Zoom Lens*. New York: A&W Publishers, 1977.

Clearing the Air: Perspectives on Environmental Tobacco Smoke. Lexington, MA: Lexington Books, 1988.

Cleveland-Peck, Patricia. *Making Cheeses, Butters, Cream and Yogurt at Home*. Wellingborough, Eng.: Thorsons Publishing Limited, 1980.

Clifford, Martin. *The New Handbook for Electricians*. Englewood Cliffs, NJ: PTR Prentice-Hall, 1993.

Coated Abrasives: Modern Tool of Industry. New York: McGraw-Hill, 1958.

Cocks, Elijan E. *Who's Who on the Moon*. Greensboro, NC: Tudor, 1995.

Cody, John. *Visualizing Muscles*. Lawrence, KS: University Press of Kansas, 1990.

Cohen, Daniel. *The Last Hundred Years: Household Technology*. New York: M. Evans & Co., 1982.

Cohen, Daniel. *Marbling on Fabric*. Loveland, CO: Interweave Press, 1990.

Cohen, I. Bernard. *Revolution in Science*. Cambridge, MA: Belknap Press, 1985.

Collin, P.H. *Dictionary of Ecology and the Environment*. Teddington, Eng.: Peter Collin Publishing, 1988.

Columbia University College of Physicians and Surgeons. *Complete Home Medical Guide*. New York: Crown, 1985.

The Complete Encyclopedia of Arms & Weapons. New York: Simon & Schuster, 1982.

The Complete Encyclopedia of the Animal World. London: Octopus Books, 1980.

Complete Guide to Prescription and Non-Prescription Drugs 1996. New York: Berkley Publishing Group, 1995.

Comprehensive Textbook of Psychiatry. 5th ed. Baltimore, MD: Williams & Wilkins, 1989. 2 vols.

Compton, William David. *Where No Man Has Gone Before*. Washington, DC: Superintendent of Documents, 1980.

Conant, Roger. *A Field Guide to Reptiles and Amphibians: Eastern and Central North America*. 3rd updated ed. Boston, MA: Houghton Mifflin Company, 1991.

Concise Chemical and Technical Dictionary. 4th enlarged ed. New York: Chemical Publ., Co., Inc., 1986.

Concise Encyclopedia Chemistry. Berlin: deGruyter, 1994.

Cone, Robert J. *How the New Technology Works*. Phoenix, AZ: Oryx Press, 1991.

Congram, Marjorie. *Horsehair: A Textile Resource*. Martinsville, NJ: Dockwra Press, 1987.

Considine, Douglas M. *Energy Technology Handbook*. New York: McGraw-Hill, 1977.

Constantine, Albert. *Know Your Woods*. New York: Home Craftsman Publishing Corp., 1959.

Conway, W. Fred. *Discovering America's Fire Museums*. New Albany, IN: FBH Publishers, 1993.

Conway, W. Fred. *Firefighting Lore*. New Albany, IN: FBH Publishers, 1993.

Corbeil, Jean-Claude. *The Facts on File Visual Dictionary*. New York: Facts on File, 1986.

Corliss, William R. *Tornadoes, Dark Days, Anomalous Precipitation, with Related Weather Phenomena*. Glen Arm, MD: Sourcebook Project, 1983.

Cornell, Felix. *American Merchant Seaman's Manual*. Centreville, MD: Cornell, Maritime, 1964.

Cornell, James. *The Great International Disaster Book*. 3rd ed. New York: Charles Scribner's, 1982.

Cortada, James W. *Historical Dictionary of Data Processing: Technology*. Westport, CT: Greenwood Press, 1987.

Costello, David F. *The World of the Porcupine*. Philadelphia, PA: Lippincott, 1966.

Coughlin, Roberta M. *The Gardener's Companion*. New York: HarperCollins, 1991.

Council on Environmental Quality. *Environmental Quality*. Washington, DC: Council on Environmental Quality, 1992.

A Country Christmas. New York: Time-Life Books, 1989.

Country Living's Country Look and How to Get It. New York: Hearst Books, 1991.

Course, A. G. *A Dictionary of Nautical Terms*. New York: Philosophical Library, 1963.

Cox, James M. *Mark Twain: The Fate of Humor*. Princeton, NJ: Princeton University Press, 1966.

Crager, Meg. *Christmas Trees*. New York: Grove Weidenfeld, 1986.

CRC Handbook of Physics and Chemistry. 76th ed. Boca Raton, FL: CRC Press, 1995.

Crockett, James U. *Crockett's Indoor Garden*. Boston, MA: Little, Brown, 1978.

Crockett, Lawrence J. *Wildly Successful Plants*. NY: Macmillan, 1977.

Crocodiles and Alligators. New York: Facts On File, 1989.

Crowson, Phillip. *Minerals Handbook, 1990-1991*. New York: Stockton Press, 1990.

Cruickshank, Allan D. *1001 Questions Answered About Birds*. New York: Dodd, Mead, 1958.

Cuff, David J. *The United States Energy Atlas*. 2nd ed. New York: Macmillan, 1986.

Cunningham, William P., and Barbara Woodhouse Saigo. *Environmental Science: A Global Concern*. Dubuque, IA: Wm. C. Brown Publishers, 1990.

Current Medical Diagnosis and Treatment 1995. 34th ed. Norwalk, CT: Appleton & Lange, 1995.

Curtis, Anthony R. *Monitoring NASA Communications*. Lake Geneva, WI: Tiare, 1992.

Curtis, Anthony R. *Space Almanac*. Woodsboro, MD: ARCsoft, 1990.

Curtis, Helena, and N. Sue Barnes. *Invitation to Biology*. 4th ed. New York: Worth Publ., Inc., 1985.

D'Adamo, James. *One Man's Food—Is Someone Else's Poison*. New York: R. Marek, 1980.

Daintith, John. *The Facts on File Dictionary of Physics*. New York: Facts On File, 1988.

Daintith, John, and Amanda Isaacs. *Medical Quotes*. New York: Facts On Files, 1989.

Dalley, Robert L. *Are You Burning Money?* New York: Reston, 1982.

Dance, S. Peter. *Shells*. New York: Dorling Kindersly, 1992.

Danforth's Obstetrics and Gynecology. 7th ed. Philadelphia, PA: Lippincott, 1994.

Danilov, Victor J. *America's Science Museums*. Westport, CT: Greenwood, 1990.

Darwin, Charles. *On the Origin of Species*. Cambridge, MA: Harvard University Press, 1964.

Davie, Michael. *Titanic: The Death and Life of a Legend*. New York: Alfred Knopf, 1987.

Davis, G. J. *Automotive Reference*. Boise, ID: Whitehorse, 1987.

Davis, Joel. *Endorphins*. Garden City, NY: Dial, 1984.

Day, David. *The Doomsday Book of Animals*. New York: Viking, 1983.

Day, John, and C. Eng. *The Bosch Book of the Motor Car*. New York: St. Martin's Press, 1976.

Dean, John A. *Lange's Handbook of Chemistry*. 13th ed. New York: McGraw Hill, 1985.

De Bono, Edward. *Eureka!* New York: Holt, Rinehart and Winston, 1974.

Deming, Richard. *Metric Power*. Nashville, TN: Nelson, 1974.

Desmond, Kevin. *A Timetable of Inventions and Discoveries*. New York: M. Evans & Co., 1982.

Der Marderosian, Ara H. *Natural Products Medicine*. Philadelphia, PA: George F. Stickley, 1988.

De Voney, Chris. *MS-DOS User's Guide*. 2nd ed. Indianapolis, IN: Que Corporation, 1987.

Diagram Group. *Comparisons*. New York: St. Martin's Press, 1980.

Diagram Group. *Weapons*. New York: St. Martin's Press, 1980.

Diamond, Freda. *The Story of Glass*. San Diego, CA: Harcourt, Brace and Co., 1953.

Dickerson, Richard Earl. *Chemical Principles*. 3rd ed. Menlo Park, CA: The Benjamin/Cummings Publ., Co., Inc., 1979.

Dickinson, Terence, and Alan Dyer. *The Backyard Astronomer's Guide*. Ontario, Can.: Camden House, Publishing, 1991.

Dictionary of American Medical Biography. Westport, CT: Greenwood, 1984. 2 vols.

Dictionary of Occupational Titles. 4th ed., rev. Washington, DC: U.S. Department of Labor, 1991. 2 vols.

The Dictionary of Science. New York: Simon & Schuster, 1994.

Dictionary of Scientific Biography. New York: Charles Scribner's Sons, 1973.

Dictionary of Visual Science. 4th ed. Radnor, PA: Chilton Trade Book, 1989.

Diseases and Disorders Handbook. Springhouse PA: Springhouse Corporation, 1990.

Ditzel, Paul C. *Fire Engines, Firefighters*. New York: Crown, 1976.

Doctor, Ronald M. *The Encyclopedia of Phobias, Fears, and Anxieties*. New York: Facts on File, 1989.

The Doctors' Book of Home Remedies II. Emmaus, PA: Rodale, 1993.

Dolensek, Emil P. *A Practical Guide to Impractical Pets*. New York: Viking Press, 1976.

Donovan, Richard T. *World Guide to Covered Bridges*. Rev. ed. Worcester, MA: The National Society for the Preservation of Covered Bridges, 1980.

Doo, Jack. *The Ultimate Owner's Manual*. Alhambra, CA: Edmund, 1993.

Dorland's Illustrated Medical Dictionary. 27th ed. Philadelphia, PA: Saunders, 1988.

Dougans, Inge. *Reflexology*. New York: Element, 1991.

Douglas, R.W., and Susan Frank. *A History of Glassmaking*. London: G.T. Foulis & Co., 1972.

Dowling, Harry F. *Fighting Infection*. Cambridge, MA: Harvard University Press, 1977.

Downing, Douglas, and Michael Covington. *Dictionary of Computer Terms*. 2nd ed. Hauppauge, NY: Barron, 1989.

Downs, Robert B. *Landmarks in Science: Hippocrates to Carson*. Littleton, CO: Libraries Unlimited, Inc., 1982.

Downs, Robert B. *Scientific Enigmas*. Littleton, CO: Libraries Unlimited, Inc., 1987.

Dowson, Gordon. *Powder Metallurgy: The Process and Its Products*. London: Adam Hilger, 1990.

Drake, George R. *Weatherizing Your Home*. New York: Reston Publishing Co., 1978.

Dreisbach, Robert H. *Handbook of Poisoning*. 12th ed. Norwalk, CT: Appleton & Lange, 1987.

Drimmer, Frederick. *The Elephant Man*. New York: Putnam, 1985.

Drug Testing in the Workplace. Chicago, IL: ASCP Press, 1989.

Dublin, Louis I. *Factbook on Man from Birth to Death*. 2nd ed. New York: Macmillan, 1965.

Duensing, Edward. *Talking to Fireflies, Shrinking the Moon*. New York: Penguin, 1990.

Dull, Charles E. *Modern Physics*. New York: Henry Holt, 1960.

Dunbar, Ian. *Dog Behavior: Why Dogs Do What They Do*. Neptune, NJ: T.F.H. Publications, 1979.

Dunne, Levon J. *Nutrition Almanac*. 3rd ed. New York: McGraw-Hill, 1990.

Duplaix, Nicole, and Noel Simon. *World Guide to Mammals*. New York: Crown Publishers, 1976.

DuPraw, E. J. *DNA and Chromosomes*. New York: Holt, Rinehart and Winston, 1970.

DuVall, Nell. *Domestic Technology*. Boston, MA: G.K. Hall, 1988.

Duxbury, Alyn C., and Alison Duxbury. *An Introduction to the World's Oceans*. Reading, MA: Addison-Wesley Publishing Company, Inc., 1984.

Dyson, James L. *The World of Ice*. New York: Knopf, 1962.

Eagleman, J. R. *Severe and Unusual Weather*. New York: Van Nostrand Reinhold, 1983.

Eating to Lower Your High Blood Cholesterol (Pamphlet). Washington, DC: U.S. Department of Health and Human Services, 1989.

Edelson, Edward. *Sports Medicine*. New York: Chelsea House, 1988.

Eden, Maxwell. *Kiteworks*. New York: Sterling, 1989.

Edmund's Car Savvy. Alhambra, CA: Edmund Publications, 1991.

Edmunds, Robert A. *The Prentice-Hall Encyclopedia of Information Technology*. Englewood Cliffs, NJ: Prentice-Hall, Inc., 1989.

Egg Science and Technology. 3rd ed. Westport, CT: AVI, 1986.

Eldridge, Wayne B. *The Best Pet Name Book Ever*. Hauppauge, NY: Barron, 1990.

Elkort, Martin. *The Secret Life of Food*. Los Angeles, CA: Jeremy P. Tarcher, 1991.

Ellis, John. *The Social History of the Machine Gun*. London: Croom Helm, Ltd., 1975.

Ellis, Keith. *Thomas Telford*. Duluth, MN: Priory Press, 1974.

Emergency Medical Procedures for the Home, Auto & Workplace. 2nd rev. ed. New York: Prentice-Hall, 1990.

Emerging Issues (pamphlet). Washington, D. C.: Congressional Institute for the Future, 1993.

Emiliani, Cesare. *The Scientific Companion*. New York: Wiley Science Editions, 1988.

Encyclopaedic Dictionary of Physical Geography. London: Blackwell, 1985.

Encyclopedia Americana. Danbury, CT: Grolier, 1990. 30 vols.

Encyclopedia of Associations. 27th ed. Detroit, MI: Gale Research, 1993.

Encyclopedia of Aviation. New York: Scribners, 1977.

Encyclopedia of Chemical Technology. 4th ed. New York: Wiley, 1992.

The Encyclopedia of Crafts. New York: Scribners, 1980. 3 vols.

Encyclopedia of Human Evolution and Prehistory. New York: Garland Publ., 1988.

The Encyclopedia of Insects. New York: Facts On File, 1986.

The Encyclopedia of Mammals. New York: Facts on File, 1984.

Encyclopedia of Microbiology. San Diego, CA: Academic Pres, 1992.

Encyclopedia of Physical Science and Technology. San Diego, CA: Academic Press, 1987. 15 vols.

Encyclopedia of Practical Photography. Garden City, NY: Amphoto, 1979.

The Encyclopedia of Solid Earth Sciences. Oxford, Blackwell Scientific Publications, 1993.

Encyclopedia of Textiles. Englewood Cliffs, NJ: Prentice-Hall, 1980.

Encyclopedia of Twentieth Century Warfare. New York: Orion, 1989.

Encyclopedic Dictionary of Science. New York: Facts On File, 1988.

Engineering and the Advancement of Human Welfare. Washington, DC: National Academy Press, 1989.

English Translations of German Standards Catalog, 1991. Braintree, MA: Beuth Verlag Gmbh., 1991.

Environmental Viewpoints. Detroit, MI: Gale Research, 1992.

Erickson, Joan Beth. *Flower Garden Plans*. San Ramon, CA: Ortho Books, 1991.

Evanoff, Vlad. *Fishing with Natural Baits*. Englewood Cliffs, NJ: Prentice-Hall, 1975.

Everett, Thomas H. *Living Trees of the World*. New York: Doubleday, 1968.

Everett, Thomas H. *The New York Botanical Garden Illustrated Encyclopedia of Horticulture*. Hamden, CT: Garland, 1981.

The Facts on File Dictionary of Astronomy. 3rd ed. New York: Facts on File, 1994.

The Facts On File Dictionary of Chemistry. Rev. and enl. ed. New York: Facts On File, 1988.

The Facts on File Dictionary of Marine Science. New York: Facts on File, 1988.

The Facts On File Dictionary of Physics. New York: Facts On File, 1988.

Farb, Peter. *The Insects*. Alexandria, VA: Time-Life Books, 1977.

Farber, Edward. *Nobel Prize Winners in Chemistry 1901-1961*. Rev. ed. New York: Ablard-Schuman, 1963.

Farndon, John. *Eyewitness Question & Answer Book*. New York: Dorling Kindersley, 1993.

Fejer, Eva, and Cecilia Fitzsimons. *An Instant Guide to Rocks and Minerals*. Stamford, CT: Longmeadow Press, 1988.

Feldman, David. *Do Penguins Have Knees?* New York: Harper Perennial, 1991.

Feldman, David. *When Do Fish Sleep? And Other Imponderables of Everyday Life*. New York: Harper & Row, 1989.

Feldman, David. *Why Do Clocks Run Clockwise? and Other Imponderables*. New York: Perennial Library, 1988.

Feldman, David. *Why Do Dogs Have Wet Noses? and Other Imponderables of Everyday Life*. New York: Harper Perennial, 1991.

Felton, Bruce, and Mark Fowler. *Felton & Fowler's Best, Worst, and Most Unusual*. New York: Crowell, 1975.

Feltwell, John. *The Natural History of Butterflies*. New York: Facts On File, 1986.

Fenton, Carroll L. *The Fossil Book*. New York: Doubleday, 1989.

Field, Frank. *Doctor Frank Field's Weather Book*. New York: Putnam, 1981.

Field, Gary C. *Color and its Reproduction*. Pittsburgh, PA: Graphic Arts Technical Foundation, 1988.

Field, Leslie. *The Queen's Jewels*. New York: Harry N. Abrams, 1987.

50 Simple Things You Can Do to Save the Earth. Berkeley, CA: Earth Works Press, 1989.

Findling, John E. *Historical Dictionary of World's Fairs and Expositions, 1851-1988*. Westport, CT: Greenwood, 1990.

Fire Protection Handbook. 16th ed. Quincy, Mass: National Fire Protection Assoc., 1986.

First Aid Book. Washington, DC: U.S. Mine Safety & Health Administration, 1991.

Fisher, Arthur. *The Healthy Heart*. New York: Time-Life Books, 1981.

Fisher, David J. *Rules of Thumb for Engineers and Scientists*. Houston, TX: Gulf, 1991.

Flakus, Greg. *Living with Killer Bees*. Oakland, CA: Quick Trading Co., 1993.

Flaste, Richard. *The New York Times Book of Science Literacy*. New York: Times Books, Random, 1991.

Flatow, Ira. *Rainbows, Curve Balls: And Other Wonders of the Natural World Explained*. New York: Harper & Row Publishers, 1988.

Fletcher, Edward. *Pebble Collecting and Polishing*. New York: Sterling, 1973.

Flynn, John C. *Cocaine*. New York: Carol Publishing Group, 1991.

Fogle, Bruce. *Know Your Cat*. New York: Dorling Kindersley, Inc., 1991.

Foods & Nutrition Encyclopedia. 2nd ed. Boca Raton, FL: CRC Press, 1994.

Food Factors for Older Adults. U. S. Department of Agriculture. Home and Garden Bulletin, no. 251 (1993).

Foodworks. Redding, MA: Addison-Wesley, 1987.

Forrester, Frank H. *1001 Questions Answered About the Weather*. New York: Grosset & Dunlap, 1957.

Fowler, Virginie. *Folk Arts Around the World*. Englewood Cliffs, NJ: Prentice-Hall, 1981.

Fox, Michael W. *The Animal Doctor's Answer Book*. New York: Newmarket, 1984.

Fox, Michael W. *Understanding Your Cat*. New York: Bantam, 1974.

Franck, Irene. *The Green Encyclopedia*. New York: Prentice-Hall, 1992.

Frankel, Edward. *Poison Ivy, Poison Oak, Poison Sumac, and Their Relatives*. Pacific Grove, CA: Boxwood Press, 1991.

Franklin, Linda Campbell. *300 Years of Kitchen Collectibles*. 3rd ed. Florence, AL: Books Americana, 1991.

Freedman, Alan. *The Computer Glossary*. 6th ed. New York: AMACOM, 1993.

Freese, Arthur S. *The Miracle of Vision*. New York: Harper & Row, 1977.

Freiberger, Paul, and Michale Siwaine. *Fire in the Valley: The Making of the Personal Computer*. Berkeley, CA: Osborne/McGraw-Hill, 1984.

Frew, Timothy. *Salmon*. New York: Mallard Press, 1991.

Freydberg, Nicholas. *The Food Additives Book*. New York: Bantam, 1982.

Fritts, Harold C. *Tree Rings and Climate*. New York: Academic Press, 1976.

Frost, Harwood. *The Art of Roadmaking*. New York: Engineering News Publishing Company, 1910.

Fruits and Vegetables: 1001 Gardening Questions Answered. Pownal, VT: Storey Communications, Inc., 1990.

Funk & Wagnalls New Standard Dictionary of the English Language. New York: Funk & Wagnalls, 1959.

Funk, Charles E. *Horse Feathers and Other Curious Words*. New York: Harper, 1958.

Gaddis, Vincent H. *The Curious World of Twins*. New York: Hawthorn Books, 1972.

Gale Book of Averages. Detroit, MI: Gale Research 1994.

Gall, Timothy L. *Consumer's Guide to Product Grades and Terms*. Detroit, MI: Gale Research, 1993.

Galperin, Anne. *Gynecological Disorders*. New York: Chelsea House, 1991.

Gardiner, Mary S. *The Biology of Invertebrates*. New York: McGraw-Hill, 1972.

Gardner, Pat. *Dough Creations*. Radnor, PA: Chilton, 1979.

Garrison, Ervan G. *A History of Engineering and Technology: Artful Methods*. Boca Raton, FL: CRC Press, 1991.

Garrison, Webb. *How It Started*. Nashville, TN: Abingdon Press, 1972.

Gascoigne, Robert M. *A Chronology of the History of Science 1450-1900*. New York: Garland Publishing, Inc., 1987.

Gatland, Kenneth. *The Illustrated Encyclopedia of Space Technology*. New York: Orion Books, 1989.

Gay, Kathlyn. *The Greenhouse Effect*. New York: Franklin Watts, 1986.

Gay, Kathlyn. *Ozone*. New York: Franklin Watts, 1989.

Gebhardt, Susan E., and Ruth H. Matthews. *Nutritive Value of Foods*. Washington, DC: U.S. Department of Agriculture. Human Nutrition Information Service, 1991.

530 *Gene Hughes' Police Call Radio Guide*. Los Angeles, CA: Hollins Radio Data, 1990.

George, L. David, and Jennifer J. George. *Marine Life*. New York: Wiley Interscience, 1979.

Gerken, Louis C. *Airships: History and Technology*. Chula Vista, CA: American Scientific Corporation, 1990.

Gertsch, Willis J. *American Spiders*. New York: Van Nostrand Reinhold, 1979.

Gibson, Carol. *The Facts On File Dictionary of Mathematics*. Rev. ed. New York: Facts On File, Inc., 1988.

Giedion, Siegfried. *Mechanization Takes Command*. New York: Oxford University Press, 1948.

Gies, Joseph and Frances Gies. *The Ingenious Yankees*. New York: Thomas Y. Cromwell Co., 1976.

Giscard d'Estaing, Valerie-Anne. *The World Almanac Book of Inventions*. New York: World Almanac Publications, 1985.

Giscard d'Estaing, Valerie-Anne. *The Second World Almanac Book of Inventions*. New York: World Almanac, 1986.

Giwojna, Pete. *Marine Hermit Crabs*. Hong Kong: T. F. H. Publications, 1978.

G.K. Hall Encyclopedia of Modern Technology. Boston, MA: Equinox, 1987.

Glover, Thomas J. *DeskRef*. Littleton, CO: Sequoia Publishing, 1993.

Godish, Thad. *Indoor Air Pollution Control*. Chelsea, MI: Lewis Publishers, 1989.

Gong, Victor. *AIDS: Facts and Issues*. New Brunswich, NJ: Rutgers University Press, 1980.

Gore, Louise L. *Meet the Pug*. Wilsonville, OR: Doral, 1990.

Goulty, George A. *A Dictionary of Landscape*. Brookfield, VT: Gower Publishing Co., 1991.

Graedon, Joe, and Dr. Teresa Graedon. *Graedons' Best Medicine*. New York: Bantam Book, 1991.

Graf, Rudolf F., and George J. Whalen. *The Reston Encyclopedia of Biomedical Engineering Terms*. New York: Reston Publishing, 1977.

Graham, John. *Facts on File Dictionary of Telecommunications*. Rev. ed. New York: Facts On File, 1991.

Gray, Henry. *Anatomy of the Human Body*. 28th ed. Malvern, PA: Lea & Febiger, 1966.

Gray, Peter. *The Encyclopedia of the Biological Sciences*. New York: Van Nostrand Reinhold, 1970.

Great Britain Meteorological Office. *Meteorological Glossary*. New York: Chemical Publishing, 1972.

Great Disasters. New York: Reader's Digest Association, 1989.

Great Engineers and Pioneers in Technology. New York: St. Martin's Press, 1981.

The Great Scientists. Danbury, CT: Grolier, 1989.

Green, James Harry. *The Dow Jones-Irwin Handbook of Telecommunications*. Homewood, IL: Dow Jones-Irwin, 1986.

Greenfield, Ellen J. *House Dangerous*. New York: Vintage Books, 1987.

Griffin, Heather. *Introduction to Batik*. Cincinnati, OH: North Light Books, 1990.

Griffith, H. Winter. *Complete Guide to Vitamins, Minerals & Supplements*. Tucson, AZ: Fisher Books, 1988.

Grimm, William C. *The Illustrated Book of Trees*. Harrisburg, PA: Stackpole, 1983.

Grimm, William C. *The Trees of Pennsylvania*. Harrisburg, PA: Stackpole, 1950.

Grossman, Harold J. *Grossman's Guide to Wines, Beers, and Spirits*. 7th ed., rev. New York: Charles Scribner's Sons, 1983.

Groves, Don. *The Ocean Book*. New York: Wiley, 1989.

Grzimek's Animal Life Encyclopedia. New York: Van Nostrand Reinhold Company, 1974. 13 vols.

Grzimek's Encyclopedia of Mammals. 2nd ed. New York: McGraw-Hill, 1990. 5 vols.

Guedes, Pedro. *The Macmillan Encyclopedia of Architecture and Technological Change*. London: Macmillan Press, 1979.

Guiley, Rosemary E. *Moonscapes*. Englewood Cliffs, NJ: Prentice-Hall, 1991.

The Guinness Book of Answers. 8th ed. Enfield, Eng.: Guinness Publishing, 1991.

Guinness Book of Records 1996. New York: Bantam Book, 1995.

Gurney, Gene. *Space Shuttle Log*. Blue Ridge Summit, PA: TAB, 1988.

Guyton, Arthur C. *Basic Human Physiology*. Philadelphia, PA: Saunders, 1977.

Guyton, Arthur C. *Textbook of Medical Physiology*. 8th ed. Philadelphia, PA: Saunders, 1991.

Haber, Louis. *Odyssey Black Pioneers of Science and Invention*. San Diego, CA: An Odyssey Book, Harcourt Brace Jovanovich, Publishers, 1970.

Hackh, Ingo W.D. *Grant & Hackh's Chemical Dictionary*. 5th ed. New York: McGraw-Hill, 1987.

Haggard, Howard W. *The Lame, the Halt, and the Blind*. New York: Harper, 1932.

Hale, Mason E., Jr. *The Biology of Lichens*. 2nd ed. London: Edward Arnold, Ltd., 1974.

Halliday, Tim R., ed. *The Encyclopedia of Reptiles and Amphibians*. New York: Facts on File, 1986.

Halliday, William R. *Depths of the Earth*. New York: Harper, 1976.

Halstead, B. W. *Dangerous Aquatic Animals of the World*. Princeton, NJ: Darwin Press, 1992.

Hamilton, William R. *The Henry Holt Guide to Minerals, Rocks and Fossils*. New York: Henry Holt, 1989.

Hampel, Clifford A. *Glossary of Chemical Terms*. 2nd ed. New York: Van Nostrand Reinhold Co., Inc., 1982.

Hand, A.J. *Home Energy How-To*. New York: Harper & Row, 1977.

Handbook of Air Conditioning, Heating, and Ventilating. 3rd ed. New York: Industrial Press, 1979.

Handbook of Glass Manufacture. 3rd ed. New York: Ashlee Publishing, 1984.

Hanson, M. J. *The Boomerang Book*. Harmondsworth, Middlesex: Puffin Books, 1974.

Hapgood, Charles H. *Maps of the Ancient Sea Kings*. Radnor, PA: Chilton, 1966.

Harding, Anthony. *Car Facts and Feats*. London: Guinness Superlatives, 1975.

Harding, Anthony. *The Guinness Book of Car Facts and Feats*. London: Guinness Superlatives, 1980.

Harding, Anthony. *The Guinness Book of the Car*. London: Guinness Superlatives, 1987.

Harrington, Geri. *The Wood-Burning Stove Book*. New York: Macmillan, 1977.

Harris, Ben. *Make Use of Garden Plants*. New York: Barre, 1978.

Harris, Harry. *Good Old-Fashioned Yankee Ingenuity*. Chelsea, MI: Scarborough House, 1990.

Harte, John. *Toxics A to Z*. Berkeley, CA: University of California Press, 1991.

Harrison, C. William. *Conservation*. New York: Julian Messner, 1973.

Hartmann, William K., and Ron Miller. *Cycles of Fire*. New York: Workman Publishing, 1987.

Hawkes, Nigel. *Structures*. New York: Macmillan, 1990.

Hawley's Condensed Chemical Dictionary. 12th ed. New York: Van Nostrand Reinhold, 1993.

Hawthorne, Douglas B. *Men and Women of Space*. San Diego, CA: Univelt, 1992.

Haygreen, John G. *Forest Products and Wood Science*. 2nd ed. Ames, IA: Iowa State University Press, 1989.

Hazen, Robert M., and James Trefil. *Science Matters: Achieving Scientific Literacy*. New York: Anchor Books, 1991.

Headstrom, Richard. *Spiders of the United States*. Stamford, CT: A.S. Barnes, 1973.

Health on File. New York: Facts on File, 1995.

Hechtlinger, A. *Modern Science Dictionary*. 2nd ed. Palisade, NJ: Franklin Publ. Co., Inc., 1975.

Hegstad, Lorrie N. *Essential Drug Dosage Calculations*. Bowie, MD: R.J. Brady, 1983.

Heintzelman, Donald S. *A Guide to Eastern Hawk Watching*. University Park, PA: Pennsylvania State University Press, 1976.

Helms, Harry L. *Shortwave Listening Handbook*. Englewood Cliffs, NJ: Prentice-Hall, 1987.

Heloise. *All New Hints from Heloise*. New York: Putnam, 1989.

Heloise. *Heloise Hints for a Healthy Planet*. New York: Perigee, 1990.

Henderson's Dictionary of Biological Terms. 11th ed. New York: John Wiley, 1995.

Hendrickson, Robert. *The Ocean Almanac*. Garden City, NY: Doubleday, 1984.

Henrickson, Charles H. *Chemistry for the Health Professions*. New York: Van Nostrand, 1980.

Heraud, Daniel P. *Chilton's Road Report*. Radnor, PA: Chilton, 1994.

Herbert, Don. *Mr. Wizard's Experiments for Young Scientists*. New York: Doubleday, 1959.

Herbs. Pownal, VT: Storey Communications, 1990.

Herbst, Sharon Tyler. *The Food Lover's Tiptionary*. New York: Hearst Books, 1994.

Herbst, Sharon Tyler. *New Food Lover's Companion*. Hauppauge, NY: Barron, 1995.

Hériteau, Jacqueline. *The National Arboretum Book of Outstanding Garden Plants*. New York: Simon and Schuster, 1990.

Hershey, David R. *Plant Biology Science Projects*. New York: John Wiley, 1995.

Hershey, Robert L. *How to Think With Numbers*. Los Altos, CA: William Kaufmann, 1982.

Hickman, Cleveland P., et al. *Integrated Principles of Zoology*. 7th ed. St. Louis, MO: Times Mirror/Mosby College Publishing, 1984.

Hill, John W. *Chemistry and Life: An Introduction to General Organic and Biological Chemistry*. New York: Macmillan, 1993.

Hillman, Harold. *Kitchen Science*. Rev. ed. Boston, MA: Houghton Mifflin Company, 1989.

Hiscox, Gardner D. *Henley's Twentieth Century Book of Formulas, Processes, and Trade Secrets*. New York: NY Books, Inc., 1963.

Historical Dictionary of World's Fairs and Expositions, 1851-1988. New York: Greenwood, 1990.

Hofstadter, Douglas R. *Gödel, Escher, Bach: An Eternal Golden Braid*. New York: Vintage Books, 1979.

Hogg, Ian V. *The Illustrated Encyclopedia of Artillery*. London: Stanley Paul & Co., 1987.

Holmes, Ann M. *Nutrition & Vitamins*. New York: Facts On File, 1983.

Holmes, Gwendolyn. *Handbook of Environmental Management and Technology*. New York: Wiley, 1993.

Hooper, Meredith. *Everyday Inventions*. London: Angus & Robertson, 1972.

Hooper, Meredith. *More Everyday Inventions*. London: Angus and Robertson, 1974.

Hopkins, Jeanne. *Glossary of Astronomy and Astrophysics*. Chicago, IL: University of Chicago Press, 1976.

Hopkins, Nigel J., John W. Mayne, and John R. Hudson. *The Numbers You Need*. Detroit, MI: Gale Research, 1992.

Horton, Edward. *The Illustrated History of the Submarine*. London: Sidgwick & Jackson, 1974.

Household Hints & Handy Tips. Pleasantville, NY: The Reader's Digest Association, 1988.

Household Hints and Tips. Des Moines, IA: Meredith Corporation, 1989.

How in the World? Pleasantville, NY: The Reader's Digest Association, 1990.

How Products are Made. Detroit, MI: Gale Research, 1994.

How Things Work in Your Home. New York: Holt, Rinehart, and Winston, 1985.

How Things Work: Structures. New York: Time-Life Books, 1991.

How to Do Just About Anything. Pleasantville, NY: Reader's Digest Association, 1986.

Howard, A.V. *Chamber's Dictionary of Scientists*. London: W. & R. Chambers, Ltd., 1955.

Howes, F.N. *A Dictionary of Useful and Everyday Plants and Their Common Names*. Cambridge, Eng.: Cambridge University Press, 1974.

Hoyle, Russ. *Gale Environmental Almanac*. Detroit, MI: Gale Research, 1993.

Hudgeons, Marc. *The Official Investors Guide; Buying, Selling Gold, Silver, Diamonds*. Orlando, FL: House of Collectibles, 1981.

The Human Brain. Englewood Cliffs, NJ: Prentice-Hall, 1977.

Hunnicutt, R.P. *Sherman: A History of the American Medium Tank*. San Rafeal, CA: Taurus Enterprises, 1978.

Hunt, V. Daniel. *The Gasohol Handbook*. New York: Industrial Press, 1981.

Hunter, Linda Mason. *The Healthy Home*. New York: Pocket Books, 1989.

Hutchinson, Robert. *Meteorites*. New York: Sterling, 1992.

Huxley, Thomas H. *The Crayfish*. Cambridge, MA: MIT Press, 1974.

Hyde, Lee. *The McGraw-Hill Essential Dictionary of Health Care*. New York: McGraw-Hill, 1988.

Hyne, Norman J. *Dictionary of Petroleum Exploration, Drilling & Production*. Tulsa, OK: PennWell, 1991.

Illingworth, Valerie. *The Facts On File Dictionary of Astronomy*. New York: Facts On File, 1979.

Illustrated Dictionary of Botany. Chestnut Ridge, NY: Triune Books, 1979.

The Illustrated Encyclopedia of Wildlife. Lakeville, CT: Grey Castle Press, 1991. 15 vols.

The Illustrated Science and Invention Encyclopedia. International ed. Westport, CT: H.S. Stuttman Publishers, 1983, 23 vols.

Industrial Engineering Terminology. Rev. ed. New York: McGraw-Hill, 1991.

Inglis, Andrew F. *Behind the Tube: A History of Broadcasting Technology and Business*. London: Focal Press, 1990.

International Encyclopedia of Astronomy. New York: Orion, 1987.

International Encyclopedia of Robotics. New York: Wiley, 1988.

International Petroleum Encyclopedia. Tulsa, OK: PennWell, 1992.

Inventions and Discoveries 1993. New York: Facts on File, 1993.

Inventive Genius. New York: Time-Life Books, 1991.

The Inventive Yankee. Camden, ME: Yankee Books, 1989.

Involuntary Smoking. Washington, DC: U.S. Public Health Service, 1979.

Iserson, Kenneth V. *Death to Dust*. Tucson, AZ: Galen Press, 1994.

Iver, David F. *Dictionary of Astronomy, Space, and Atmospheric Phenomena*. New York: Van Nostrand Reinhold Co., 1979.

Jackson, Donald C. *Great American Bridges and Dams*. Washington, DC: The Preservation Press, 1988.

Jacobs, Harold R. *Mathematics: A Human Endeavor*. San Francisco, CA: W.H. Freeman, 1970.

James, Glenn. *Mathematics Dictionary*. 4th ed. New York: Van Nostrand Reinhold, 1976.

James, Robert C. *Mathematics Dictionary*. 5th ed. New York: Van Nostrand Reinhold, 1992.

Jane's All the World's Aircraft 1947. London: Sampson Low, Marston, 1947.

Jane's Encyclopedia of Aviation. New York: Portland House, 1989.

Jaramillo, Alex. *Cracker Jack Prizes*. New York: Abbeville Press, 1989.

Jayne, Kate Lindley, and Claudette Suzanne Mautor. *Living with Potpourri*. New York: Peter Pauper, 1988.

Jelinek, Jan. *The Pictorial Encyclopedia of the Evolution of Man*. London: Hamlyn, 1975.

Jerram, Mike. *The World's Classic Aircraft*. London: Frederick Muller, Ltd., 1981.

Jerrard, H.G. *A Dictionary of Scientific Units*. 4th ed. New York: Chapman and Hall, 1980.

Jespersen, James. *RAMS, ROMS and Robots*. New York: Atheneum, 1984.

Johnson, Duane. *How a House Works*. Pleasantville, NY: Reader's Digest Association, 1994.

Johnson, Leland G. *Biology*. Dubuque, IA: Wm. C. Brown, 1983.

Johnson, Lorraine. *How to Restore & Repair Practically Everything*. Rev. ed. London: The Penguin Group, 1989.

Johnstone, William D. *For Good Measure*. Fort Worth, TX: Holt, Rinehart and Winston, 1975.

Jones, Julia, and Barbara Deer. *Royal Pleasures and Pastimes*. Devon, Eng.: David and Charles, 1990.

Jones, Mablen. *Taking Care of Clothes*. New York: St. Martin's, 1982.

Joseph, Lawrence E. *Gaia*. New York: St. Martin's Press, 1990.

Kane, Joseph N. *Famous First Facts*. 4th ed. New York: Wilson, 1981.

Kaplan, Eugene H. *Field Guide to Coral Reefs*. Boston, MA: Houghton Mifflin Co., 1982.

Karlen, Arno. *Napoleon's Glands*. Boston, MA: Little, Brown, 1984.

Karush, William. *Webster's New World Dictionary of Mathematics*. Englewood Cliffs, NJ: Webster's New World, 1989.

Kaufman, Wallace. *The Beaches Are Moving*. New York: Anchor Press, 1979.

Keeler, Harriet L. *Our Early Wild Flowers*. New York: Charles Scribner's Sons, 1916.

Keene, Ann T. *Earthkeepers*. New York: Oxford University Press, 1994.

Kelly, Niall. *Presidential Pets*. New York: Abbeville Press Publishers, 1992.

Kemp, Peter. *Encyclopedia of Ships and Sailing*. Dobbs Ferry, NY: Stanford Maritime, 1989.

Kemp, Peter. *The History of Ships*. New York: Galahad, 1979.

Kendig, Frank, and Richard Hutton. *Life-Spans*. New York: Holt, Rinehart and Winston, 1979.

Kennedy, Kenneth A.R. *Neanderthal Man*. Minneapolis, MN: Burgess, 1975.

Kerrod, Robin. *The Concise Dictionary of Science*. New York: Arco Publ. Inc., 1985.

Kidder, Frank. *Architects' and Builders' Handbook*. New York: Wiley, 1931.

Klein, Hilary D. *Tiny Game Hunting*. New York: Bantam, 1991.

Klinowska, Margaret. *Dolphins, Porpoises and Whales of the World*. Gland, Switz.: IUCN, 1991.

Kogelman, Stanley, and Barbara R. Heller. *The Only Math Book You'll Ever Need*. New York: Facts On File Publications, 1986.

Krantz, Les. *The Best and Worst of Everything*. New York: Prentice Hall General Reference, 1991.

Kress, Stephen W. *The Audubon Society Guide to Attracting Birds*. New York: Charles Scribner's Sons, 1985.

Kroschivitz, Jacqueline I. *Chemistry*. New York: McGraw-Hill, 1990.

Kuttner, Paul. *Science's Trickiest Questions*. New York: Henry Holt, 1994.

Labatut, Jean, and J.L. Wheaton. *Highways in Our National Life*. Princeton, NJ: Princeton University Press, 1950.

Lambert, David. *Field Guide to Early Man*. New York: Facts On File, 1987.

Lane, Ferdinand C. *Earth's Grandest Rivers*. New York: Doubleday, 1949.

Langenkamp, R. D. *Handbook of Oil Industry Terms and Phrases*. 5th ed. Tulsa, OK: Pennwell, 1994.

Larijani, L. Casey. *The Virtual Reality Primer*. New York: McGraw-Hill, 1994.

Larousse Dictionary of Scientists. New York: Larousse Kingfisher Chambers, Inc., 1994.

Lawrence, Eleanor. *Henderson's Dictionary of Biological Terms*. 10th ed. New York: John Wiley and Sons, 1989.

Layton, Cryil W. T. *Dictionary of Nautical Words and Terms*. 3rd ed., rev. Glasgow: Brown, Son & Ferguson, 1987.

Lean, Geoffrey, Don Hinrichsen, and Adam Markham. *WWF Atlas of the Environment*. Boston, MA: Willard Grant Press, 1991.

LeBlanc, Raymond. *Gold-Leaf Techniques*. Cincinnati, OH: ST Publications, 1986.

Lee, Sally. *Predicting Violent Storms*. New York: Franklin Watts, 1989.

Leet, L. Don, and Sheldon Judson. *Physical Geology*. 4th ed. Englewood Cliffs, NJ: Prentice-Hall, 1971.

Leff, Jonathan. *Consumer Reports Health Answer Book*. Yonkers, NY: Consumer Reports Books, 1993.

Leggett, Jeremy. *Global Warming*. Oxford: Oxford University Press, 1990.

Lenfestey, Tom. *The Facts on File Dictionary of Nautical Terms*. New York: Facts on File, 1994.

Lennes, N.J. *New Practical Mathematics*. New York: Macmillan, 1939.

Leopold, Luna B. *Water*. New York: Time, 1966.

Leug, Albert Y. *Encyclopedia of Common Natural Ingredients*. New York: Wiley, 1980.

Levenstein, Mary K. *Caring for Your Cherished Possessions*. New York: Crown, 1989.

Levy, Richard C. *Inventing and Patenting Sourcebook*. Detroit, MI: Gale Research Inc., 1990.

Levy Richard C. *The Inventor's Desktop Companion*. Detroit, MI: Visible Ink Press, 1991.

Lewis, Richard J. *Food Additives Handbook*. New York: Van Nostrand Reinhold, 1989.

Libien, Lois. *Paint It Yourself*. New York: Morrow, 1978.

Lincoln, John W. *Driving Without Gas*. Pownal, VT: Garden Way, 1980.

Lincoln, R.J. *A Dictionary of Ecology, Evolution, and Systematics*. New York: Cambridge University Press, 1982.

The Little Scented Library. New York: Simon and Schuster, 1991. 4 vols.

Living Invertebrates. Palo Alto, CA: Blackwell Scientific Publications, 1987.

Lloyd, Elizabeth J. *Enchanted Circles*. New York: Simon and Schuster, 1991.

Logan, Carolynn. *Logan's Medical and Scientific Abbreviations*. Philadelphia, PA: Lippincott, 1987.

Log of Apollo 11 (NASA EP-72). Washington, D.C.: NASA, 1969.

Long, James W. *The Essential Guide to Prescription Drugs*. New York: Harper & Row, 1987.

Longley, Dennis, and Michael Shain. *Van Nostrand Reinhold Dictionary of Information Technology*. 3rd. ed. New York: Van Nostrand Reinhold, 1989.

Loomer, Alice. *Famous Flaws*. New York: Macmillan, 1976.

Ludlum, David M. *The Audubon Society Field Guide to North American Weather*. New York: Knopf, 1991.

Luetzelschwab, John. *Household Energy Use & Conservation*. Chicago, IL: Nelson Hall, 1980.

Mabberley, D.J. *The Plant Book*. New York: Cambridge University Press, 1987.

Macauley, David. *The Way Things Work*. Boston, MA: Houghton Mifflin Co., 1988.

MacEachern, Diane. *Save Our Planet*. New York: Dell, 1990.

Mackay, Alan L. *A Dictionary of Scientific Quotations*. 2nd ed. Bristol: Institute of Physics Publishing, 1991.

Maclean, Norman. *Dictionary of Genetics and Cell Biology*. New York: New York University Press, 1987.

The Macmillan Dictionary of Quotations. New York: Macmillan, 1989.

Macmillan Illustrated Animal Encyclopedia. New York: MacMillan, 1984.

The Macmillan Visual Desk Reference. New York: Macmillan, 1993.

The Macmillan Visual Dictionary. New York: Macmillan, 1992.

Maerz, A. *A Dictionary of Color*. 2nd ed. New York: McGraw-Hill, 1950.

Magill, Frank N. *Great Events from History II: Science and Technology Series*. Englewood Cliffs, NJ: Salem Press, 1991. 5 vols.

Magill, Frank N. *Magill's Survey of Science. Applied Science Series*. Pasadena, CA: Salem Press, 1993.

Magill, Frank N. *Magill's Survey of Science: Earth Science Series*. Englewood Cliffs, NJ: Salem Press, 1990.

Magill, Frank N. *Magill's Survey of Science: Life Science Series*. Englewood Cliffs, NJ: Salem Press, 1991. 6 vols.

Magill, Frank N. *Magill's Survey of Science. Physical Science Series*. Englewood Cliffs, NJ: Salem Press, 1992. 6 vols.

Magill, Frank N. *Magill's Survey of Science: Space Exploration Series*. Englewood Cliffs, NJ: Salem Press, 1989.

Magill, Frank N. *Nobel Prize Winners, Physiology or Medicine*. Englewood Cliffs, NJ: Salem Press, 1991.

Maginley, C.J. *Models of America's Past*. San Diego, CA: Harcourt, Brace & World, 1969.

Magner, Lois N. *A History of the Life Sciences*. New York: Marcel Dekker, 1979.

The Making, Shaping and Treating of Steel. 10th ed. Pittsburgh, PA: United States Steel, 1985.

Managing the Future of America's Forests (Pamphlet). Washington, DC: American Forest Council, 1989.

Manchester, Richard B. *Mammoth Book of Fascinating Information*. New York: A&W Visual Library, 1980.

Manchester, William R. *The Arms of Krupp, 1587-1968*. Boston, MA: Little Brown, 1968.

Maniquet, Xavier. *The Jaws of Death*. Dobbs Ferry, NY: Sheridan House, 1991.

Manko, Howard H. *Solders & Soldering*. 2nd ed. New York: McGraw-Hill, 1979.

Mansfield, George Rogers. *Origin of the Brown Mountain Light in North Carolina*. Washington, DC: U.S. Geological Survey, 1971.

The Map Catalog. New York: Vintage, 1986.

Marchok, Janice. *Oh No! Not My Electric Blanket, Too?* Latrobe, PA: Jetmarc Group, 1991.

Marcin, Marietta Marshall. *The Herbal Tea Garden*. Pownall, VT: Storey Communications, 1993.

Margen, Sheldon. *The Wellness Encyclopedia of Food and Nutrition*. New York: Rebus, 1992.

Margo. *Growing New Hair*. Brookline, MA: Autumn Press, 1980.

Margulis, Lynn. *Five Kingdoms*. New York: W.H. Freeman and Company, 1988.

Mariani, John F. *The Dictionary of American Food and Drink*. New York: Ticknor & Fields, 1994.

Mark's Standard Handbook for Mechanical Engineers. 9th ed. New York: McGraw-Hill, 1987.

Marshall Cavendish Illustrated Encyclopedia of Family Health. London: Marshall Cavendish, 1984. 24 vols.

Marshall Cavendish International Wildlife Encyclopedia. London: Marshall Cavendish, 1989. 24 vols.

Marshall, John. *The Guinness Railway Book*. London: Guinness Books, 1989.

Marshall, John. *Rail: The Records*. London: Guinness Books, 1985.

Matlins, Antoinette L. *Jewelry & Gems*. 3rd ed. Woodstock, VT: GemStone Press, 1993.

Mathematics Encyclopedia. New York: Doubleday, 1977.

Matthews, L. Harrison. *The Life of Mammals*. New York: Universe Books, 1971.

Matthews, Rupert O. *The Atlas of Natural Wonders*. New York: Facts On File, 1988.

May, John. *The Greenpeace Book of Antarctica: A New View of the Seventh Continent*. 1st ed. New York: Doubleday, 1989.

May, John. *The Greenpeace Book of the Nuclear Age*. New York: Pantheon, 1989.

Mayhew, Susan, and Anne Penny. *The Concise Oxford Dictionary of Geography*. New York: Oxford University Press, 1992.

Mayo Clinic Family Health Book. New York: Morrow, 1990.

McAleer, Neil. *The Body Almanac*. New York: Doubleday, 1985.

McAleer, Neil. *The OMNI Space Almanac*. New York: World Almanac, 1987.

McCarthy, Eugene J., et al. *The Second Opinion Handbook*. New York: Nick Lyons Books, 1987.

McClane, Albert J. *McClane's Fish Buyer's Guide*. New York: Henry Holt, 1990.

McCully, Helen. *Nobody Ever Tells You These Things About Food and Drink*. Fort Worth, TX: Holt, Rinehart and Winston, 1967.

McCutcheon, Marc. *The Compass in Your Nose*. Los Angeles: Jeremy P. Tarcher, 1989.

McElroy, Thomas P. *The New Handbook of Attracting Birds*. New York: Knopf, 1960.

McEwan, W.A., and A.H. Lewis. *Encyclopedia of Nautical Knowledge*. Centreville, MD: Cornell Maritime Press, 1953.

McGee, Harold. *On Food and Cooking*. New York: Collier Books, 1988.

McGoon, Michael D. *Mayo Clinic Heart Book*. New York: William Morrow, 1993.

McGraw-Hill Dictionary of Physics and Mathematics. New York: McGraw-Hill Book Co., 1978.

The McGraw-Hill Dictionary of Scientific and Technical Terms. 5th ed. New York: McGraw-Hill, 1994.

McGraw-Hill Encyclopedia of Science and Technology. 7th ed. New York: McGraw Hill, Inc., 1992. 20 vols.

McGraw-Hill Yearbook of Science and Technology 1991. New York: McGraw-Hill, 1990.

McGraw-Hill Yearbook of Science and Technology 1992. New York: McGraw-Hill, 1991.

McGraw-Hill Yearbook of Science and Technology 1995. New York: McGraw-Hill, 1994.

McGraw-Hill Yearbook of Science & Technology 1996. New York: McGraw-Hill, 1995.

McGrayne, Sharon Bertsch. *365 Surprising Scientific Facts, Breakthroughs, and Discoveries*. New York: John Wiley, 1994.

McKinnell, Robert G. *Cloning of Frogs, Mice, and Other Animals*. Rev. ed. Minneapolis, MN: University of Minnesota Press, 1985.

McNair, James K. *Adventures in Italian Cooking*. San Ramon, CA: Ortho, 1980.

McNeil, Ian. *An Encyclopedia of the History of Technology*. London: Routledge, 1990.

McNulty, Faith. *Wholly Cats*. New York: Bobbs-Merrill, 1962.

Means Illustrated Construction Dictionary. Kingston, MA: R.S. Means, 1985.

Medawar, P.B., and J.S. Medawar. *Aristotle to Zoos*. Cambridge MA: Harvard University Press, 1983.

Medicine. New York: Time-Life Books, 1991.

Melaragno, Michele. *An Introduction to Shell Structures*. New York: Van Nostrand Reinhold, 1991.

Melnick, Mimi. *Manhole Covers*. Cambridge, MA: MIT Press, 1994.

Melonakos, K. *Saunders Pocket Reference for Nurses*. Philadelphia, PA: Saunders, 1990.

Memmler, Ruth L. *Structure and Function of the Human Body*. Philadelphia, PA: Lippincott, 1987.

Mendelsohn, Oscar A. *The Dictionary of Drink and Drinking*. London: Macmillan, 1965.

Menzel, Donald H., and Jay M. Pasachoff. *A Field Guide to Stars and Planets*. 2nd ed. Boston, MA: Houghton Mifflin Co., 1990.

Menninger, Edwin. *Fantastic Trees*. New York: Viking, 1967.

Merck Manual of Diagnosis and Therapy. 15th ed. West Point, PA: Merck, Shark & Dohme, 1987.

The Merck Veterinary Manual. 7th ed. Rahway, NJ: Merck, 1991.

Merilees, Bill. *Attracting Backyard Wildlife*. Stillwater, MN: Voyageur Press, 1989.

Mery, Fernand. *The Life, History, and Magic of the Dog*. New York: Grosset & Dunlap, 1970.

Messadié, Gerald. *Great Modern Inventions*. Edinburgh: Chambers, 1991.

Metal Statistics 1994. 86th ed. New York: American Metal Market, 1994.

Michard, Jean-Guy. *The Reign of the Dinosaurs*. New York: Harry N. Abrams, Incorporated, 1992.

Mierhof, Annette. *The Dried Flower Book*. New York: Dutton, 1981.

Milestones of Aviation. Washington, DC: Smithsonian Institution, 1989.

Miller, E. Willard. *Environmental Hazards: Toxic Waste and Hazardous Material*. Santa Barbara, CA: ABC-CLIO, 1991.

Miller, Ron, and William K. Hartmann. *The Grand Tour: A Traveler's Guide to the Solar System*. New York: Workman Publishing, 1981.

Millichap, J. Gordon. *Dyslexia as the Neurologist and Educator Read It*. Springfield, IL: Thomas, 1986.

Milner, Richard. *The Encyclopedia of Evolution*. New York: Facts on File, 1990.

Minerals Yearbook, 1993. Washington, DC: U.S. Bureau of Mines, 1995.

Mitchell, Harris. *1200 Household Hints You Wanted to Know*. Toronto: Bestsellers, Inc., 1982.

Mondey, David. *The Guinness Book of Aircraft*. London: Guinness, 1988.

Moorcroft, William H. *Sleep, Dreaming, and Sleep Disorders*. Lanham, MD: University Press of America, 1989.

Moore, John E. *Submarine Warfare*. Bethesda, MD: Alder & Alder, 1987.

Moore, Laurence A. *Lightning Never Strikes Twice and Other False Facts*. New York: Avon Books, 1994.

Moore, Patrick, et al. *The Atlas of the Solar System*. New York: Crescent Books with the Royal Astronomical Society, 1990.

Moore, Patrick. *International Encyclopedia of Astronomy*. New York: Orion Books, 1987.

Moore-Landecker, Elizabeth. *Fundamentals of the Fungi*. 3rd ed. Englewood Cliffs, NJ: Prentice Hall, 1990.

Morgan, Christopher. *The Computer Museum Presents the Official Computer Bowl Trivia Book*. New York: Crown Trade Paperbacks, 1996.

Morgan, George W. *Geodesic and Geodetic Domes and Space Structures*. Madison, WI: Sci-Tech Publications, 1985.

Morgans, W.M. *Outlines of Paint Technology*. New York: Halsted Press, 1990.

Morlan, Michael. *Kitty Hawk to NASA*. Shawnee Mission, KS: Bon a Tirer, 1991.

Mort, J. *The Anatomy of Xerography*. Jefferson, NC: McFarland, 1989.

Mosby's Medical, Nursing and Allied Health Dictionary. 3rd ed. St. Louis, MO: Mosby, 1990.

The Motor Gasoline Industry. Washington, DC: U.S. Department of Energy. Energy Information Administration, 1991.

Motz, Lloyd. *The Story of Mathematics*. New York: Plenum Press, 1993.

Motz, Lloyd, and Jefferson Hane Weaver. *Conquering Mathematics*. New York: Plenum Press, 1991.

Mount, Ellis, and Barbara A. List. *Milestones in Science and Technology; the Ready Reference Guide to Discoveries, Inventions, and Facts*. Phoenix, AZ: Oryx Press, 1987.

Mr. Boston Official Bartender's Guide. 63rd ed., rev. and updated. New York: Warner Books, 1988.

Mull, Kayla. *Pot-Bellied Pet Pigs*. Orange, CA: All Publishing, 1990.

Müller, Ulrike. *The New Cat Handbook*. Woodbury, NY: Barron, 1984.

Murmurs of Earth: The Voyager Interstellar Record. New York: Random House, 1978.

MVMA Motor Vehicle Facts and Figures '91. Detroit, MI: Motor Vehicle Manufacturers Association of the United States, 1991.

Mysteries of the Human Body. Alexandria, VA: Time-Life Books, 1990.

Naar, Jon. *Design for a Livable Planet*. New York: Harper & Row, Publishers, 1990.

Nassau, Kurt. *Gems Made by Man*. Radnor, PA: Chilton, 1980.

The National Inventors Hall of Fame. Washington, DC: U.S. Patent and Trademark Office, 1990.

National Safety Council Accident Facts, 1989. Washington, DC: National Safety Council, 1989.

Nature on the Rampage. Washington, DC: National Geographic Society, 1986.

Nayler, Joseph L. *Aviation: Its Technical Development*. Chester Springs, PA: Dufour Editions, 1965.

Nebeker, Frederik. *Calculating the Weather*. San Diego: Academic Press, 1995.

Nebel, Bernard J. *Environmental Science*. Englewood Cliffs, NJ: Prentice-Hall, 1990.

Netboy, Anthony. *The Salmon*. Boston: Houghton Mifflin. 1974.

The New American State Papers, Science and Technology, vol. 4: Patents. Wilmington, DE: Scholarly Resources, 1973.

The New Book of Popular Science. Danbury, CT: Grolier, 1988. 6 vols.

A New Dictionary of Physics. Bristol, Eng.: Longman Group, 1975.

The New Dog Encyclopedia. Harrisburg, PA: Stackpole, 1970.

New Encyclopaedia Britannica. 15th ed. Chicago, IL: Encyclopaedia Britannica, 1990. 29 vols.

The New Good Housekeeping Family Health and Medical Guide. New York: Hearst Books, 1989.

New Illustrated Science and Invention Encyclopedia. Westport, CT: Stuttman, 1988. 23 vols.

The New Larousse Encyclopedia of Animal Life. New York: Bonanza Books, 1984.

New York Public Library Desk Reference. New York: Webster's New World, 1989.

New York Times Book of Indoor and Outdoor Gardening Questions. New York: Quadrangle, 1975.

Newman, Renée. *The Pearl Buying Guide*. 2nd ed. Los Angeles, CA: International Jewelry Publications, 1994.

Newmark, Joseph. *Mathematics as a Second Language*. 4th ed. Redding, MA: Addison-Wesley, 1987.

Newton, Michael. *Armed and Dangerous*. Cincinnati, OH: Writer's Digest Books, 1990.

The Next Step: 50 More Things You Can Do To Save the Earth. Berkeley, CA: Earth Works Group, 1991.

Nichols, Herbert L. *Moving the Earth*. 3rd ed. Greenwich, CT: North Castle Books, 1976.

Nickon, Alex, and Ernest F. Silversmith. *Organic Chemistry: The Name Game*. New York: Pergamon Press, 1987.

Niebel, Benjamin W. *Motion and Time Study*. 7th ed. Homewood, IL: Irwin, 1982.

The 1992 Information Please Environmental Almanac. Boston, MA: Houghton Mifflin Company, 1992.

The Nobel Prize Winners: Chemistry. Pasadena, CA: Salem Press, 1990.

The Nobel Prize Winners: Physics. Pasadena, CA: Salem Press, 1989.

The Nobel Prize Winners: Physiology or Medicine. Pasadena, CA: Salem Press, 1991.

Nobile, Philip. *Complete Ecology Fact Book*. New York: Doubleday, 1972.

Nock, O.S. *Encyclopedia of Railways*. London: Octopus Books, 1977.

Norman, Bruce. *Secret Warfare: The Battle of Codes and Ciphers*. Reston, VA: Acropolis Books, 1973.

Norman, David. *Dinosaur!* New York: Prentice-Hall, 1991.

Notable Twentieth Century Scientists. Detroit: Gale Research, 1995.

Nowak, Robert M. *Walker's Mammals of the World*. 5th ed. Baltimore, MD: The Johns Hopkins University Press, 1991. 2 vols.

The Nuclear Waste Primer. New York: Nick Lyons Books, 1985.

Nugent, Nancy. *Food and Nutrition*. Emmaus, PA: Rodale Press, 1983.

Nunn, Richard V. *Home Paint Book*. Birmingham, AL: Oxmoor House, 1976.

Nunn, Richard V. *Saving Home Energy*. Rev. ed. Birmingham, AL: Oxmoor House, 1978.

Oberrecht, Kenn. *The Practical Angler's Guide to Successful Fishing*. New York: Winchester Press, 1978.

O'Brien, Robert. *Machines*. New York: Time Inc., 1964.

O'Brien, Tim. *Where the Animals Are*. Old Saybrook, CT: Globe Pequot Press, 1992.

The Odds on Virtually Everything. New York: G.P. Putnam's Sons, 1980.

Odum, Eugene. *Fundamentals of Ecology*. 3rd ed. Philadelphia, PA: Saunders, 1971.

The Official World Wildlife Fund Guide to Endangered Species of North America. Washington, DC: Beacham Publishing, 1990-1991. 3 vols.

Oglesby, Clarkson H., and R. Gary Hicks. *Highway Engineering*. New York: John Wiley & Sons, 1982.

Ojakargas, Richard. *Schaum's Outline of Theory and Problems of Introductory Geology*. New York: McGraw-Hill, 1991.

Oklahoma University Science and Public Policy Program. Technology Assessment Group. *Energy Under the Oceans*. Norman, OK: University of Oklahoma, 1973.

Olney, Ross. *Americans in Space*. New York: Nelson, 1970.

101 Ways to Save Money & Save Our Planet. New Orleans, LA: Paper Chase Press, 1992.

Ortho's Complete Guide to Successful Gardening. San Ramon, CA: Ortho Books, 1983.

Otto, James H. *Modern Biology*. Fort Worth, TX: Holt, Rinehart and Winston, 1981.

The Oxford Dictionary for Scientific Writers and Editors. Oxford, Eng.: Oxford University Press, 1991.

Oxford Illustrated Encyclopedia of Invention and Technology. Oxford, Eng.: Oxford University Press, 1992.

Pais, Abraham. *'Subtle Is the Lord —'* New York: Oxford University Press, 1982.

Pagana, Kathleen Deska. *Mosby's Diagnostic and Laboratory Test Reference*. St. Louis, MO: Mosby-YearBook, 1992.

Palmer, Ephram Laurence. *Fieldbook of Natural History*. 2nd ed. New York: McGraw-Hill, 1974.

Palmer, Joan. *Dog Facts*. New York: Dorset Press, 1991.

Panati, Charles. *Panati's Browser's Book of Beginnings*. Boston, MA: Houghton Mifflin, 1984.

Panati, Charles. *Panati's Extraordinary Origins of Everyday Things*. New York: Perennial Library, 1987.

Pappas, Theoni. *The Magic of Mathematics*. San Carlos, CA: Wide World/Tetra, 1994.

Parker, Robert M. *Parker's Wine Buyer's Guide*. 3rd ed. New York: Simon & Schuster, 1993.

Parker, Sybil P. *McGraw-Hill Concise Encyclopedia of Science and Technology*. 2nd ed. New York: McGraw-Hill, 1989.

Parker, Sybil P. *Synopsis & Classification of Living Organisms*. New York: McGraw-Hill, 1982.

Parkinson, Clair L. *Breakthroughs: A Chronicle of Great Achievements in Science and Mathematics*. Boston, MA: G.K. Hall, 1985.

Partington, J.R. *A Short History of Chemistry*. 3rd ed. New York: Dover, 1989.

Pasachoff, Jay M. *Contemporary Astronomy*. Philadelphia, PA: W.B. Saunders, Co., 1977.

Passarin, d'Entreves P. *The Secret Life of Insects*. New York: Chartwell, 1976.

Passport to World Band Radio. Penn's Park, PA: International Broadcasting Services, 1992.

Pawley, Martin. *Building For Tomorrow: Putting Waste To Work*. San Francisco, CA: Sierra Club Books, 1982.

Pawley, Martin. *Garbage Housing*. New York: Halsted, 1975.

Pearce, B.G. *Health Hazards of VDT's*. New York: John Wiley & Sons, 1984.

Pearl, Richard M. *1001 Questions Answered About the Mineral Kingdom*. New York: Dodd, Mead, 1959.

Pearl, Richard M. *The Wonder World of Metals*. New York: Harper & Row, 1966.

Pendergrast, Mark. *For God, Country, and Coca-Cola*. New York: Charles Scribner's Sons, 1993.

Penny, Malcolm. *Rhinos: Endangered Species*. New York: Facts On File, 1988.

Pennycook, Bob. *Building with Glass Blocks*. New York: Doubleday, 1987.

The Pentagon: A National Institution. Berlin, MD: D'OR Press, 1986.

Personal Health Reporter. Detroit, MI: Gale, 1993.

Peters, George H. *The Plimsoll Line*. London: Barry Rose, Ltd., 1975.

Petroski, Henry. *The Pencil: A History of Design and Circumstance*. New York: Knopf, 1990.

Pettingill, O.E. *Born to Run*. New York: Arco, 1973.

Pfadt, Robert E. *Fundamentals of Applied Entomology*. 3rd ed. New York: Macmillan, 1978.

Pfeffer, Pierre. *Predators and Predation*. New York: Facts On File, 1989.

Phipps, William E. *Cremation Concerns*. Springfield, IL: CC Thomas, 1989.

Physicians' Guide to Rare Diseases. Montvale, NJ: Dowden, 1992.

Picken, Mary Brooks. *The Fashion Dictionary*. Rev. and enlarged ed. New York: Funk & Wagnalls, 1973.

Pickering, James S. *1001 Questions Answered About Astronomy*. New York: Dodd, Mead, 1958.

Pinkham, Mary Ellen. *Mary Ellen's Clean House!* New York: Crown, 1993.

Pinkney, Cathey. *The Patient's Guide to Medical Tests*. 3rd ed. New York: Facts On File, 1986.

Planetary and Lunar Coordinates for the Years 1984-2000. London: H.M. Stationery Office, 1983.

Plants: Their Biology and Importance. New York: Harper & Row, Publishers, 1989.

The Plastic Waste Primer. New York: Lyons & Burford, 1993.

Platt, Rutherford. *1001 Questions Answered About Trees*. New York: Dodd, Mead, 1959.

Pleasant, Barbara. *The Gardener's Bug Book*. Ponwal, VT: Storey Communications, 1994.

Plumridge, John H. *Hospital Ships and Ambulance Trains*. London: Seeley, 1975.

Plunkett, Edward R. *Folk Name & Trade Diseases*. Stamford, CT: Barrett Book Co., 1978.

Pogue, William R. *How Do You Go to the Bathroom in Space?* New York: Tom Doherty Associates, 1985.

Poirier, René. *The Fifteen Wonders of the World*. New York: Random House, 1961.

Poisonous Snakes of Pennsylvania. Pittsburgh, PA: Carnegie Museum of Natural History, 1955.

Poisonous Snakes of the World. New York: Dover, 1991.

Pond, Alonzo W. *The Desert World*. Westport, CT: Greenwood, 1975, pp. 40-58.

Popular Encyclopedia of Plants. New York: Cambridge University Press, 1982.

Powell, Claire. *The Meaning of Flowers*. London: Jupiter Books Ltd., 1977.

Power, Rex. *How to Beat Police Radar*. New York: Arco Publishing, 1977.

Practical Botany. Reston, VA: Reston Publishing Co., Inc., 1983.

Prentice-Hall Encyclopedia of Mathematics. Englewood Cliffs, NJ: Prentice-Hall, 1982.

Press, Frank. *Earth*. 2nd ed. San Francisco, CA: W.H. Freeman, 1978.

Preston-Mafham, Rod. *The Book of Spiders and Scorpions*. New York: Crescent Books, 1991.

Prevention's Giant Book of Health Facts. Emmaus, PA: Rodale Press, 1991.

Price, Lowi. *Concoctions*. New York: E. P. Dutton, 1976.

Professional Guide to Diseases. 4th ed. Springhouse, PA: Springhouse Corp., 1992.

Prosser, C. Ladd, ed. *Environmental and Metabolic Animal Physiology*. New York: Wiley-Liss, 1991.

Provenzo, Eugene F. *47 Easy-To-Do-Classic Science Experiments*. New York: Dover, 1989.

Prudden, Theodore M. *About Lobsters*. Freeport, ME: The Bond Wheelwright Co., 1973.

The Public Health Consequences of Disasters, 1989. Atlanta, GA: Centers for Disease Control, 1989.

Pugh, Anthony. *Polyhedra*. Berkeley, CA: University of California Press, 1976.

Purnell's Encyclopedia of Inventions. London: Purnell & Sons, Ltd., 1976.

Putnam, R.E., and G.E. Carlson. *Architectural and Building Trades Dictionary*. 3rd ed. Chicago, IL: American Technical Society, 1974.

Putnam, Robert E. *Builder's Comprehensive Dictionary*. 2nd ed. Carlsbad, CA: Craftsman Book Company, 1989.

Rackensky, Stanley. *Getting Pests to Bug Off*. New York: Crown, 1978.

Raymond, Eric S. *The New Hacker's Dictionary*. Cambridge, MA: The MIT Press, 1991.

Read, Oliver. *From Tin Foil to Stereo*. Indianapolis, IN: Howard W. Sams, 1976.

Reader's Digest Consumer Advisor. Pleasantville, NY: Reader's Digest Association, 1989.

Reader's Digest Fix-It-Yourself Manual. Pleasantville, NY: Reader's Digest Association, 1978.

Reader's Digest Practical Problem Solver. Pleasantville, NY: Reader's Digest Association, 1991.

Renmore, C.D. *Silicon Chips and You*. New York: Beaufort Books, 1980.

Resh, Howard M. *Hydroponic Food Production*. Santa Barbara, CA: Woodbridge Press, 1995.

Retallack, Dorothy L. *The Sound of Music and Plants*. Marina del Ray, CA: DeVorss, 1973.

Rheingold, Howard. *Tools for Thought*. New York: Simon & Schuster, 1985.

Rhodes, Frank H.T. *Geology*. New York: Golden Press, 1972.

Rhodes, Richard. *The Making of the Atomic Bomb*. New York: Simon and Schuster, 1986.

Ricciuti, Edward R. *The Devil's Garden: Facts and Folklore of Perilous Plants*. New York: Walker, 1978.

Richardson, Robert O. *The Weird and Wondrous World of Patents*. New York: Sterling, 1990.

Richter, H. P. *Practical Electrical Wiring*. 16th ed. New York: McGraw-Hill, 1993.

Rickard, Teresa. *Barnes & Noble Thesaurus of Physics*. New York: Harper & Row, 1984.

Ringler, Carol Ann. *Are You at Risk?* New York: Facts On File, 1991.

Roberts, Kenneth L. *The Seventh Sense*. New York: Doubleday, 1953.

Roberts, Royston M. *Serendipity: Accidental Discoveries in Science*. New York: John Wiley & Sons, 1989.

Robertson, Patrick. *The Book of Firsts*. New York: Clarkson N. Potter, Inc., 1974.

Robinson, Katherine. *The Clothing Care Handbook*. New York: Fawcett Columbine, 1985.

Rochester, Jack B. *The Naked Computer*. New York: Morrow, 1983.

Rodale, Robert. *The Best Gardening Ideas I Know*. Emmaus, PA: Rodale Press, 1978.

Rodale's Book of Hints, Tips & Everyday Wisdom. New York: Smithmark, 1994.

Rodale's Complete Home Products Manual. Emmaus, PA: Rodale Press, 1989.

Rodale's Illustrated Encyclopedia of Gardening and Landscaping Techniques. Emmaus, PA: Rodale Press, 1990.

Rombauer, Irma S. *Joy of Cooking*. New York: Bobbs-Merrill, 1975.

Room, Adrian. *Dictionary of Astronomical Names*. New York: Routledge, 1988.

Room, Adrian. *Dictionary of Trade Name Origins*. London: Routledge & Kegan Paul, 1982.

Root, Waverly L. *Food*. New York: Simon and Schuster, 1980.

Rosenberg, Jerry M. *Dictionary of Computers, Data Processing, and Telecommunications*. New York: John Wiley & Sons, 1984.

Rosenfeld, Sam. *Science Experiments With Water*. Irvington-on-Hudson, NY: Harvey House, 1965.

Ross, Frank Xavier. *The Metric System—Measures for All Mankind*. New York: Phillips, 1974.

Roth, Charles E. *The Plant Observer's Guidebook*. Englewood Cliffs, NJ: Prentice-Hall, Inc., 1984.

Rothenberg, Mikel A. *Dictionary of Medical Terms for the Non-Medical Person*. 2nd ed. Hauppauge, NY: Barron, 1989.

Rovin, Jeff. *Laws of Order*. New York: Ballantine, 1992.

Rupp, Rebecca. *Blue Corn and Square Tomatoes*. Pownal, VT: Garden Way, 1987.

Rush to Burn. Washington, DC: Island Press, 1989.

The Safe Food Book. Washington, DC: U.S. Department of Agriculture, 1985.

Sagan, Carl. *Broca's Brain*. New York: Random House, 1979.

Sagan, Carl. *Cosmos*. New York: Random House, 1980.

Sagan, Carl, and Ann Druyan. *Comet*. New York: Random House, 1985.

Sammons, Vivian O. *Blacks in Science and Medicine*. New York: Hemisphere Publishing, 1990.

Sanders, Dennis. *The First of Everything*. New York: Delacorte, 1981.

Sanders, Ti. *Weather*. South Bend, IN: Icarus Press, 1985.

Sattler, Helen Roney. *Recipes for Art and Craft Materials*. New York: Lothrop, Lee & Shepard, 1987.

Savageau, David. *Places Rated Almanac*. New York: Prentice Hall Travel, 1993.

Savitskii, E.M. *Handbook of Precious Metals*. New York: Hemisphere Publishing Corp., 1989.

Sawyer, L.A., and W.H. Mitchell. *The Liberty Ships*. Cambridge, MD: Cornell Maritime Press, 1970.

Schaefer, Vincent J., and John A. Day. *A Field Guide to the Atmosphere*. Boston, MA: Houghton Mifflin Company, 1981.

Schnaser, Gene. *The Home Repair Emergency Handbook*. Dallas, TX: Taylor Publishing, 1992.

Schneck, Marcus. *Butterflies*. Emmaus, PA: Rodale Press, 1990.

Schneck, Marcus, and Jill Caravan. *Cat Facts*. New York: Dorset Press, 1990.

Schneck, Marcus. *Elephants*. Stamford, CT: Longmeadow Press, 1992.

Schneider, Herman. *The Harper Dictionary of Science in Everyday Language*. New York: Harper & Row, 1988.

Schodek, Danie L. *Landmarks in American Civil Engineering*. Cambridge, MA: MIT Press, 1987.

Schorger, A.W. *The Passenger Pigeon*. Madison, WI: University of Wisconsin Press, 1955.

Schremp, Gerry. *Kitchen Culture*. New York: Pharos, 1991.

Schutz, Walter E. *How to Attract, House, and Feed Birds*. New York: Collier, 1974.

Schwartz, Herbert F. *Patent Law and Practice*. 2nd ed. Washington, DC: Federal Judicial Center, 1995.

Schweighauser, Charles A. *Astronomy from A to Z*. Springfield, IL: Illinois Issues, 1991.

Schweitzer, Glenn E. *Borrowed Earth, Borrowed Time*. New York: Plenum, 1991.

Science and Technology Illustrated. Chicago, IL: Encyclopaedia Britannica, Inc., 1984, 28 vols.

Scientific Quotations: The Harvest of a Quiet Eye. New York: Crane, Russak, 1977.

Scott, John S. *Dictionary of Civil Engineering*. New York: Halsted Press, 1981.

Seager, Spencer. *Introductory Chemistry for Today*. 2nd ed. St. Paul, MN: West Publishing, 1994.

Search for Immortality. New York: Time Life Books, 1992.

Sedenko, Jerry. *The Butterfly Garden*. New York: Villard Books, 1991.

Seldon, Philips. *The Vintage Magazine Consumer Guide to Wine*. New York: Doubleday, 1983.

Self, Charles. *Wood Heating Handbook*. Blue Ridge Summit, PA: TAB, 1977.

Selkurt, Ewald E. *Physiology*. 5th ed. Boston, MA: Little, Brown, 1984.

Seranne, Ann. *The Complete Book of Egg Cookery*. New York: Macmillan, 1983.

Shacket, Sheldon R. *The Complete Book of Electric Vehicles*. Northbrook, IL: Domus Books, 1979.

Shafritz, Jay M. *The Facts on File Dictionary of Military Science*. New York: Facts On File, 1989.

Shapiro, Max S. *Mathematics Encyclopedia*. New York: Doubleday, 1977.

Sherman, Irwin W. *Biology: A Human Approach*. 4th ed. New York: Oxford University Press, 1989.

Sherwood, Gerald E., and Robert C. Stroh. *Wood-Frame House Construction*. Rev. ed. Washington, DC: U.S. Department of Agriculture. Forest Service, 1989.

Shipley, Robert M. *Dictionary of Gems and Gemology*. 6th ed. Santa Monica, CA: Gemological Institute of America, 1974.

Shipman, James T., and Jerry D. Wilson. *An Introduction to Physical Science*. 6th ed. Lexington, MA: D.C. Heath and Company, 1990.

Shore, John. *The Sachertorte Algorithm*. New York: Viking Penguin, Inc., 1985.

Shores, Christopher F. *Fighter Aces*. London: Hamlyn, 1975.

Shorrocks, Bryan. *Drosophila*. London: Ginn, 1972.

Siegman, Gita. *Awards, Honors, & Prizes*. 9th ed. (1991-92). Detroit, MI: Gale Research Inc., 1991.

Sikorsky, Robert. *How To Get More Miles Per Gallon in the 1990's*. Blue Ridge Summit, PA: TAB, 1991.

Silverman, Sharon H. *Going Underground*. Philadelphia, PA: Camino Books, 1991.

Simon, Andre L., and Robin Howe. *Dictionary of Gastronomy*. 2nd ed. Woodstock, NY: The Overlook Press, 1978.

Simon, Gilbert. *The Parent's Pediatric Companion*. New York: Morrow, 1985.

Simpson, George Gaylord. *Penguins*. New Haven, CT: Yale University Press, 1976.

Sinclair, Ian R. *The HarperCollins Dictionary of Computer Terms*. New York: HarperPerennial, 1991.

Singleton, Paul, and Diana Sainsbury. *Dictionary of Microbiology*. New York: John Wiley and Sons, 1978.

Sinnes, A. Cort. *All About Perennials*. San Ramon, CA: Ortho Books, 1981.

Skinner, Brian J. *The Dynamic Earth*. New York: John Wiley & Sons, 1989.

Smallwood, Charles A., et al. *The Cable Car Book*. Berkeley, CA: Celestial Arts, 1980.

Smith, Anthony. *The Body*. New York: Viking Press, 1986.

Smith, Marcia. *Space Activities of the United States and Other Launching Countries/Organizations: 1957-1991*. Washington, DC: Library of Congress, Science Policy Research Division, 1992.

Smith, Michael D. *All About Bulbs*. San Ramon, CA: Ortho Books, 1986.

Smith, Michael D., ed. *The Ortho Problem Solver*. 2nd ed. San Francisco, CA: Ortho Information Services, 1984.

Smith, Richard Furnald. *Chemistry for the Million*. New York: Charles Scribner's Sons, 1972.

Smithsonian Institute. *Annual Report, 1939*. Washington, DC: U.S. Government Printing Office, 1940.

Snyder, Carl H. *The Extraordinary Chemistry of Ordinary Things*. New York: John Wiley & Sons, 1992.

Solinger, Jacob. *Apparel Manufacturing Handbook*. New York: Van Nostrand Reinhold, 1980.

Solomon, Eldra Pearl, and Gloria A. Phillips. *Understanding Human Anatomy and Physiology*. Philadelphia, PA: W.B. Saunders Company, 1987.

Somer, Elizabeth. *Nutrition for Women*. New York: Henry Holt, 1993.

Space Flight: The First 30 Years. Washington, DC: NASA, 1991.

Spangenburg, Ray, and Diane Moser. *Space People From A-Z*. New York: Facts On File, 1990.

Spar, Jerome. *The Way of the Weather*. Mankato, MN: Creative Educational Society, 1967.

Spencer, Donald D. *Computer Dictionary*. 4th ed. Ormond Beach, FL: Camelot, 1993.

Springer, Sally P. *Left Brain, Right Brain*. Rev. ed. New York: W.H. Freeman, 1985.

Stacey, Tom. *The Hindenberg*. San Diego, CA: Lucent, 1990.

Stamper, Eugene. *Handbook of Air Conditioning, Heating and Ventilating*. New York: Industrial Press, 1979.

Standard Guide to Cat Breeds. New York: McGraw-Hill, 1979.

Standard Handbook for Civil Engineers. 3rd ed. New York: McGraw-Hill, 1983.

Stark, Norman. *The Formula Book*. Kansas City, MO: Sheed and Ward, 1975.

Starr, Cecie, and Ralph Taggart. *Biology*. 6th ed. Belmont, CA: Wadsworth Publ. Co., 1992.

Stedman's Medical Dictionary. 25th ed. Baltimore, MD: Williams & Wilkins, 1990.

Stein, Edwin I. *Arithmetic for College Students*. Rev. ed. Needham Heights, MA: Allyn and Bacon, 1961.

Stein, Gordon. *Encyclopedia of Hoaxes*. Detroit: Gale Research, 1993.

Stephens, John H. *The Guinness Book of Structures*. London: Guinness Superlatives, Ltd., 1976.

Stephenson, D.J. *Newnes Guide to Satellite TV*. London: Newnes, 1991.

Stevenson, Katherine Cole. *Houses by Mail*. Washington, D. C.: Preservation Press, 1986.

Stevenson, L. Harold. *The Facts On File Dictionary of Environmental Science*. New York: Facts On File, 1991.

Stewart, David. *The Earthquake America Forgot*. Marble Hill, MO: Gutenberg-Richter Publications, 1995,.

Stiegeler, Stella F. *A Dictionary of Earth Sciences*. Cavaye Place, London: Pan Books, Ltd., 1978.

Stilwell, E. Joseph, et al. *Packaging for the Environment*. New York: AMACOM, 1991.

Stimpson, George. *Information Roundup*. New York: Harper, 1948.

Stobart, Tom. *The Cook's Encyclopedia*. New York: Harper & Row, 1981.

Stokes, Donald. *The Bluebird Book*. Boston, MA: Little, Brown, 1991.

Stokes, Donald. *The Complete Birdhouse Book*. Boston: Little, Brown, 1990.

Stories Behind Everyday Things. Pleasantville, NY: Reader's Digest, 1980.

The Straight Dope. New York: Ballantine, 1986.

Strasser, Alex. *The Work of the Science Film Maker*. New York: Communication Arts Books, 1972.

Subramanyam, Krishna. *Scientific and Technical Information Resources*. New York: Dekker, 1981.

Sussman, Lesley. *The Ultimate Dog Catalog*. Chicago, IL: Contemporary Books, 1985.

Sussman, Martin. *Total Health at the Computer*. Barrytown, NY: Station Hill, 1993.

Sutton, Caroline, and Duncan M. Anderson. *How Do They Do That?* New York: Quill, 1982.

Swank, James M. *History of the Manufacture of Iron in All Ages*. New York: Burt Franklin, 1965.

Swartz, Delbert. *Collegiate Dictionary of Botany*. Ridgefield, CT: Ronald Press, 1971.

Taber, Robert W. *1001 Questions Answered About the Oceans and Oceanography*. New York: Dodd, Mead, 1972.

Taber's Cyclopedic Medical Dictionary. 17th ed. Philadelphia, PA: Davis, 1993.

Taylor, David. *You & Your Cat*. New York: Alfred Knopf, 1988.

Taylor, David, and Daphne Negus. *The Ultimate Cat Book*. New York: Simon and Schuster, 1989.

Taylor, Michael J.H., and John W.R. Taylor. *Encyclopedia of Aircraft*. London: Weidenfeld & Nicolson, 1978.

Taylor, Walter H. *Concrete Technology and Practice*. New York: McGraw-Hill, 1977.

Teitelman, Robert. *Profits of Science*. New York: Basic Books, 1994.

Temple, Robert K.G. *The Genius of China*. New York: Simon and Schuster, 1986.

Tenney, Deanne. *Introduction to Natural Health*. Provo, Utah: Woodland Books, 1992.

Terres, John K. *The Audubon Society Encyclopedia of North American Birds*. New York: Wings Book, 1991.

Thermal and Sound Control. Valley Forge, PA: Certainteed Corporation, 1991.

Thomas, David A. *Math Projects for Young Scientists*. New York: Franklin Watts, 1988.

Thomas, Dirk. *The Harrowsmith Country Life Guide to Wood Heat*. Charlotte, VT: Camden House, 1992.

Thomas, Lowell J. *First Aid for Backpackers and Campers*. Fort Worth, TX: Holt, Rinehart and Winston, 1978.

Thomas, Robert B. *The Old Farmer's Almanac 1988*. Dublin, NH: Yankee Publishing, 1989.

Thro, Ellen. *Genetic Engineering*. New York: Facts on File, 1993.

Thrush, Paul W. *A Dictionary of Mining, Mineral, and Related Terms*. Washington, DC: U.S. Bureau of Mines, 1968.

Thygerson, Alton L. *First Aid Essentials*. Boston, MA: Jones and Bartlett, 1989.

Tichy, William. *Poisons: Antidotes and Anecdotes*. New York: Sterling, 1977.

Tidwell, William D. *Common Fossil Plants of Western North America*. Provo, UT: Brigham Young University Press, 1975.

Tilling, Robert I. *Eruptions of Mount St. Helens*. Rev. ed. Washington, DC: U.S. Department of the Interior, 1990.

Tilling, Robert I. *Volcanoes*. Washington, DC: U.S. Geological Survey, 1992.

Time-Life Books Complete Home Repair Manual. New York: Prentice Hall, 1987.

The Timetable of Technology. San Diego, CA: Harvest Books, 1982.

Toothill, Elizabeth. *The Facts On File Dictionary of Biology*. New York: Facts On File Publications, 1988.

Tortora, G.J. *Introduction to the Human Body*. New York: HarperCollins, 1991.

Tortora, G.J. *Principles of Anatomy and Physiology*. 4th ed. New York: Harper & Row, 1984.

Tortora, G.J. *Principles of Human Physiology*. 2nd ed. New York: Harper & Row, 1986.

Towle, Albert. *Modern Biology*. Austin, TX: Holt, Rinehart and Winston, 1989.

Toxics in the Community. Washington, DC: U.S. Environmental Protection Agency, 1990.

Traffic Engineering Handbook. 2nd ed. Washington, DC: Institute of Traffic Engineers, 1959.

Trask, Maurice. *The Story of Cybernetics*. London: Studio Vista, 1971.

Trease, George E. *Pharmacogsy*. 11th ed. London: Bailliere Tindall, 1978.

Treasures of the Tide. Vienna, VA: National Wildlife Federation, 1990.

Trefil, James. *1001 Things Everyone Should Know About Science*. New York: Doubleday, 1992.

True, Dan. *Hummingbirds of North America*. Albuquerque: University of New Mexico Press, 1993.

Truman, Margaret. *White House Pets*. New York: David McKay, 1969.

Tufty, Barbara. *1001 Questions About Earthquakes, Avalanches, Floods and Other Natural Disasters*. New York: Dover Publications, Inc., 1978.

Tufty, Barbara. *1001 Questions Answered About Hurricanes, Tornadoes and Other Natural Air Disasters*. New York: Dover Publications, Inc., 1987.

Tunnell, James E. *Latest Intelligence*. Blue Ridge Summit, PA: TAB, 1990.

Tyler, Sharon. *The Food Lover's Tiptionary*. New York: Hearst Books, 1994.

Tyning, Thomas F. *A Guide to Amphibians and Reptiles*. Boston, MA: Little, Brown & Co., 1990.

Tzimopoulos, Nicholas D., et al. *Modern Chemistry*. Fort Worth, TX: Holt, Rinehart and Winston, 1990.

Ulene, Art. *Count Out Cholesterol*. Berkeley, CA: Ulysses Press, 1994.

Understanding Computers: Computer Languages. New York: Time-Life Books, 1986.

Understanding Computers: Illustrated Chronology and Index. New York: Time-Life Books, 1989.

U.S. Bureau of Mines. *Bulletin No. 42, 1913*. Washington, DC: U.S. Bureau of Mines, 1913.

U. S. Department of Agriculture. *Farmers' Bulletin no. 1500*. Washington, DC: U. S. Department of Agriculture, 1926.

U.S. Department of Agriculture. *Growing Vegetables in the Home Garden*. Rev. ed. Washington, DC: U.S. Department of Agriculture, 1985.

U.S. Department of Commerce. Patent and Trademark Office. *General Information Concerning Patents*. Washington, DC: U.S. Department of Commerce, 1992.

U. S. Department of Commerce. Patent and Trademark Office. *Basic Facts about Registering a Trademark*. Washington, D. C.: U. S. Department of Commerce, 1994.

U.S. Department of the Army. Headquarters. *Carpenter*. Washington, DC: U.S. Department of the Army. Headquarters, 1971.

U.S. Department of Health and Human Services. *Marijuana* (Pamphlet). Washington, DC: U.S. Dept. of Health and Human Services, 1984.

U.S. Department of the Interior. *The Story of the Hoover Dam*. Washington, DC: U.S. Department of the Interior, 1971.

U.S. Fish and Wildlife Service. *Backyard Bird Feeding*. Washington, DC: U.S. Fish and Wildlife Service, 1989.

U.S. Forest Products Laboratory. *Encyclopedia of Wood*. New York: Drake, 1977.

U.S. Geological Survey. *Our Changing Continent* (Pamphlet). Washington, DC: U.S. Geological Survey, 1991.

U.S. Office of Technology Assessment. *Changing by Degrees*. Washington, DC: U.S. Government Printing Office, 1991.

U. S. Patent and Trademark Office. *Basic Facts About Patents*. Washington, D. C.: U. S. Patent and Trademark Office, 1994.

U. S. Patent and Trademarks Office. *Working for Our Customers: A Patent and Trademark Office Review*. Washington, D. C.: U. S. Patent and Trademarks Office, 1995, pp.

United States Patents [microfilm]. Stamford, CT: Research Publications [n.d.].

The Universal Almanac 1992. Kansas City, MO: Andrews and McMeel, 1991.

The Universal Healthcare Almanac. Phoenix, AZ: Silver & Cherner, Ltd., 1995.

USDA's Food Guide Pyramid. Pamphlet. Washington, DC: U.S. Department of Agriculture, Human Nutrition Information Service, 1992.

Used Car Buying Guide. Yonkers, NY: Consumers Union of United States, 1994.

Van Amerogen, C. *The Way Things Work Book of the Body*. New York: Simon and Schuster, 1979.

Van Andel, Tjeerd H. *New Views on an Old Planet*. New York: Cambridge University Press, 1985.

Van der Leeden, Frits. The Water Encyclopedia. *2nd ed. Chelsea, MI: Lewis, 1990.*

Van Nostrand Reinhold Encyclopedia of Chemistry. 4th ed. New York: Van Nostrand Reinhold, 1984.

Van Nostrand's Scientific Encyclopedia. 8th ed. New York: Van Nostrand Reinhold, 1995.

Vare, Ethlie Ann. *Mothers of Invention*. New York: Morrow, 1988.

Vengris, Jonas. *Lawns*. 3rd ed. Fresno, CA: Thomson Publications, 1982.

Vergara, William C. *Science in Everyday Life*. New York: Harper & Row, Publishers, 1980.

Versatility of Trucks. Detroit, MI: Motor Vehicle Manufacturers Association, 1991.

Villee, Claude. *Biology*. New York: CBS College Publishing, 1985.

Vincoli, Jeffrey. *Basic Guide to Environmental Compliance*. New York: Van Nostrand Reinhold, 1993.

Vine, Richard P. *Commercial Winemaking, Processing and Controls*. Westport, CT: AVI, 1981.

Voelker, William. *The Natural History of Living Mammals*. Medford, NJ: Plexus, 1986.

Vogel, Steven. *Vital Circuits*. New York: Oxford University Press, 1992.

Von Wiesenberger, Arthur. *The Pocket Guide to Bottled Water*. Chicago, IL: Contemporary Books, 1991.

Walkowicz, Chris. *The Complete Question and Answer Book on Dogs*. New York: Dutton, 1988.

Wallace, Irving. *The Book of Lists #2*. New York: Morrow, 1980.

Wallechinsky, David. *The Book of Lists*. New York: Morrow, 1977.

Walters, Michael. *Birds' Eggs*. New York: Dorling Kindersly, 1994.

Ward, Jack. *Biology Today and Tomorrow*. St. Paul, MN: West, 1980.

Warm House, Cool House. Yonkers, NY: Consumers Reports Books, 1991.

Weapons: An International Encyclopedia from 5000 B.C. to 2000 A.D. New York: St. Martin's Press, 1990.

The Weather Almanac. 6th ed. Detroit: Gale Research, 1992.

The Weather Book. Boston, MA: Little, Brown & Company, 1982.

Webster, John G. *Encyclopedia of Medical Devices and Instrumentation*. New York: John Wiley & Sons, 1988.

Webster's College Dictionary. New York: Random House, 1991.

Webster's New Geographical Dictionary. Springfield, MA: Merriam-Webster, 1988.

Webster's Ninth New Collegiate Dictionary. Springfield, MA: Merriam-Webster, Inc., Publishers, 1989.

Weesner, Frances M. *Termites of the United States*. Elizabeth, NJ: National Pest Control Association, 1965.

Weider, Ben, and David Hapgood. *The Murder of Napoleon*. New York: Congdon & Lattès, Inc., 1982.

Weik, Martin H. *Communications Standard Dictionary*. New York: Van Nostrand, Reinhold, 1989.

Weisert, Conrad. *Que's Computer Programmer's Dictionary*. Indianapolis, IN: QUE Corporation, 1993.

The Wellness Encyclopedia of Food and Nutrition. New York: Rebus, 1992.

When Technology Fails. Detroit, MI: Gale Research Inc., 1994.

Whitman, Roger C. *More First Aid for the Ailing House*. New York: McGraw-Hill, 1977.

Whittick, Arnold. *Symbols, Signs and Their Meaning*. London: Leonard Hill Books Limited, 1960.

Who Was Who in American History: Science and Technology. Wilmette, IL: Marquis Who's Who, 1976.

Wilford, John N. *The Riddle of the Dinosaur*. New York: Knopf, 1986.

Williams, Gene B. *Nuclear War, Nuclear Winter*. New York: Franklin Watts, 1987.

Williams, Jack. *The Weather Book*. New York: Vintage Books, 1992.

Williams, Michael R. *A History of Computing Technology*. New York: Prentice-Hall, 1985.

Williams, Robin. *Jargon*. Berkeley, CA: Peachpit Press, 1993.

Williams, T. Jeff. *Greenhouses*. San Ramon, CA: Ortho Books, 1991.

Williams, Trevor. *A Biographical Dictionary of Scientists*. London: Adam & Charles Black, 1969.

Wilson, Edward O. *The Diversity of Life*. New York: Norton.

Wilson, Mitchell. *American Science and Invention*. New York: Simon and Schuster, 1954.

Winburne, John N. *A Dictionary of Agricultural and Allied Terminology*. East Lansing, MI: Michigan State University Press, 1962.

Winkler, Connie. *Careers in High Tech*. Englewood Cliffs, NJ: Prentice Hall Press, 1987.

Winter, Ruth. *A Consumer's Dictionary of Household, Yard and Office Chemicals*. New York: Crown Publishers, Inc., 1992.

Wise, David Burgess. *The Motor Car*. New York: Putnam, 1979.

The Wise Garden Encyclopedia. New York: HarperCollins, 1990.

Wolf, Nancy. *Plastics*. Washington, DC: Island Press, 1991.

Wolke, Robert L. *Chemistry Explained*. Englewood Cliffs, NJ: Prentice-Hall, Inc., 1980.

Woman's Day Encyclopedia of Cookery. New York: Fawcett, 1966-67. 12 vols.

Wood, Gerald L. *The Guinness Book of Animal Facts and Feats*. 3rd ed. London: Guinness Superlatives, Ltd., 1982.

Wood, Gerald L. *Guinness Book of Pet Records*. London: Guinness Books, 1984.

Woods, Geraldine. *Pollution*. New York: Franklin Watts, 1985.

The World Almanac and Book of Facts 1995. New York: World Almanac, 1994.

World and United States Aviation and Space Records. Washington, DC: National Aeronautic Association of the USA, 1995.

World Book Encyclopedia. Chicago, IL: World Book, 1994. 22 vols.

World of Invention. Detroit, MI: Gale Research, 1994.

World of Scientific Discovery. Detroit: Gale Research, 1994.

World Who's Who in Science. Chicago, IL: Marquis - Who's Who, Inc., 1968.

Wragg, David W. *A Dictionary of Aviation*. Reading, Eng.: Osprey, 1973.

Wright, R. Thomas. *Understanding Technology*. South Holland, IL: Goodheart-Willcox, 1989.

Wyatt, Allen L. *Computer Professional's Dictionary*. New York: McGraw-Hill, 1990.

Wyel, Kenneth R. *The Encyclopedia of Shells*. New York: Facts on File, 1991.

Wylie, Harriet. *420 Ways to Clean Everything*. New York: Bonanza Books, 1989.

Wyman, Donald. *Wyman's Gardening Encyclopedia*. 2nd ed. New York: Macmillan, 1986.

Wynbrandt, James. *The Encyclopedia of Genetic Disorders and Birth Defects*. New York: Facts On File, 1991.

Wyngaarden, James B., and Lloyd H. Smith. *Cecil Textbook of Medicine*. 18th ed. Philadelphia, PA: Saunders, 1988.

Wynter, Harriet, and Anthony Turner. *Scientific Instruments*. New York: Charles Scribner's Sons, Inc., 1975.

Yarwood, Doreen. *Five Hundred Years of Technology in the Home*. London: B.T. Batsford, Ltd., 1983.

Yearbook of Science and the Future 1991. Chicago, IL: Encyclopaedia Britannica, Inc., 1990.

Yearbook of Science and the Future 1993. Chicago: Encyclopaedia Britannica, Inc., 1992.

Yost, Graham. *Spy Tech*. New York: Facts On File, 1985.

Zahradnik, Jiri. *A Field Guide In Color To the Animal World*. London: Octopus, 1979.

Zakrzewski, Sigmund F. *Principles of Environmental Toxicology*. Washington, DC: American Chemical Society, 1991.

Zim, Herbert S., and Paul R. Shaffer. *Rocks and Minerals*. New York: Golden Press, 1957.

Zimmerman, O.T. *Conversion Factors and Tables*. 3rd ed. Durham, NH: Industrial Research Service, 1961.

Journals and Periodicals

American Druggist. Published monthly by Hearst Corp., 1790 Broadway, Ste. 6, New York, NY 10019-1412.

American Forests. Published bi-monthly by American Forestry Association, Box 2000, Washington, DC 20013.

American Health. Published monthly by Reader's Digest Association, Inc., 28 West 23rd St., New York, NY 10010.

American Heritage of Invention and Technology. Published quarterly by Forbes, Inc., Forbes Building, 60 Fifth Ave., New York, NY 10010.

American Scientist. Published bi-monthly by Scientific Research Society, Box 13975, 99 Alexander Dr., Research Triangle Park, NC 27709.

American Transportation Builder (now called *Transportation Builder*). Published six times a year by Transportation Builder, American Road & Transportation Builders Association, 501 School St. S.W., Washington, DC 20024.

Annual Energy Review. Published annually by the U.S. Energy Information Administration, James Forrestal Bldg., Rm 1F-048, 1000 Independence Ave., S.W., Washington, DC 20585.

Astronomy. Published monthly by Kalmbach Publishing Co., P.O. Box 1612, Waukesha, WI 53187.

Audubon Magazine. Published bi-monthly by National Audubon Society, 950 Third Ave., New York, NY 10022.

Automotive Industries. Published monthly by Chilton Co., Chilton Way, Radnor, PA 19089.

Automotive News. Published weekly by Crain Communications, 1400 Woodbridge Ave., Detroit, MI 48207-3187.

Aviation Week and Space Technology. Published weekly by McGraw-Hill, Inc., Aviation Week Group, 1221 Ave. of the Americas, New York, NY 10020.

Biocycle. Published monthly by J.G. Press, Inc., 419 State Ave., Emmaus, PA 18049.

Bioscience. Published monthly by the American Institute of Biological Sciences, 730 11th Ave., N.W., Washington, DC 20001-4521.

Blair & Ketchum's Country Journal (now called *Country Journal*). Published monthly by Cowles Magazines, Inc., 6405 Flank Dr., Box 8200, Harrisburg, PA 17105-8200.

Buzzworm: The Environmental Journal. Published six times a year by Buzzworm, Inc., 2305 Canyon Blvd., Ste. 206, Boulder, CO 80302.

California Geology. Published monthly by Division of Mines and Geology, 660 Bercut Dr., Sacramento, CA 95814-0131.

Cat Fancy. Published monthly by Fancy Publications, Inc., Box 6050, Mission Viejo, CA 92690.

Cats Magazine. Published monthly by Cats Magazine, Inc., Box 290037, Port Orange, FL 32129.

Ceramics Monthly. Published monthly by Professional Publications, Inc. (Columbus), Box 12448, 1609 Northwest Blvd., Columbus, OH 43212.

Chemical & Engineering News. Published weekly by American Chemical Society, 1155 16th St. N.W., Washington, DC 20036.

Chilton's Automotive Industries. Published monthly by Chilton Co., 2600 Fischer Bldg., 3011 W. Grand River Blvd., Detroit, MI 48202.

Compute. Published monthly by Compute Publications International, Ltd., 324 W. Wendover Ave., Ste 200, Greensboro, NC 27408.

Consumers' Research Magazine. Published monthly by Consumers' Research, Inc., 800 Maryland Ave. N.E., Washington, DC 20002.

Cornell Animal Health Newsletter. Published monthly by W.H. White Publications, 53 Park Place, New York, NY 10007.

Country Journal. Published bi-monthly by Cowles Magazines, Inc., 6405 Flank Dr., Box 8200, Harrisburg, PA 17105-8200.

Current Health. Published monthly, September through May, by General Learning Corporation, Curriculum Innovations Group, 60 Revere Dr., Northbrook, IL 60062-1563.

Detroit Free Press. Published daily by Detroit Free Press, 321 W. Lafayette, Detroit, MI 48226.

Discover. Published monthly by Walt Disney Magazine, Publishing Group, 500 S. Buena Vista, Burbank, CA 91521-6012.

Endangered Species Technical Bulletin Reprint. (Now called *Endangered Species Update*). Published monthly by University of Michigan, School of Natural Resources, 430 E. University, Dana Bldg., Ann Arbor, MI 48109-1115.

Environment. Published ten times a year by Heldref Publications, 4000 Albemarle St. N.W., Washington, DC 20016.

EPA Journal. Published bi-monthly by U.S. Environmental Protection Agency, Office of Public Affairs, Waterside Mall, 401 M St. S.W., Washington, DC 20460.

E: The Environmental Magazine. Published bi-monthly by Earth Action Network, Box 5224, Westport, CT 06881.

FDA Consumer. Published ten times a year (July-Aug. & Jan.-Feb. issues combined) by U.S. Food and Drug Administration Office of Public Affairs, 5600 Fisher Lane, Rockville, MD 20857.

Facts On File World News Digest with Index. Published weekly by Facts On File, Inc., 460 Park Ave., New York, NY 10016.

Fine Gardening. Published bi-monthly by Taunton Press, Inc., 63 S. Main St., Box 5506, Newtown, CT 06470-5506.

Fine Woodworking. Published bi-monthly by Taunton Press, Inc., 63 S. Main St., Box 5506, Newtown, CT 06470-5506.

Fire Management Notes. Published quarterly by USDA Forest Service, Box 96090, Washington, DC 20090-6090.

Flower and Garden. Published bi-monthly by KC Publishing Inc., 4251 Pennsylvania Ave., Kansas City, MO 64111-9990.

Fortune. Published bi-weekly by Time, Inc., Time & Life Bldg., Rockefeller Center, New York, NY 10020-1393.

Garbage. Published six times a year by Old-House Journal Corp., 2 Main St., Glouchester, MA 01930-5726.

Garden. Published bi-monthly by Garden Society, New York Botanical Garden, Bronx, NY 10458.

Good Housekeeping. Published monthly by Hearst Corporation, Good Housekeeping, 959 Eighth Ave., New York, NY 10019.

Harrowsmith Country Life. Published bi-monthly by Camden House Publishing, Ferry Rd., Charlotte, VT 05445.

Harvard Health Letter. Published monthly by Harvard Medical School, HMS Health Publications Group, 164 Longwood Ave., 4th Floor, Boston, MA 02115.

Harvard Medical School Health Letter (now called *Harvard Health Letter*). Published monthly by Harvard Medical School, HMS Health Publications Group, 164 Longwood Ave., 4th Floor, Boston, MA 02115.

Health. Published seven times a year by Health Magazine, 275 Madison Ave., Ste. 1314, New York, NY 10016.

Home Mechanix. Published by Times Mirror Magazines, Inc., 2 Park Ave., New York, NY 10016-5601.

Horticulture. Published monthly by Horticulture Limited Partnership, 20 Park Plaza, Ste. 1220, Boston, MA 02116-8241.

Human Behavior (ceased publication). Was published monthly by Manson Western Corp., 12031 Wilshire Blvd., Los Angeles, CA 90025.

International Wildlife. Published bi-monthly by the National Wildlife Federation, 1400 16th St., N.W., Washington, DC 20036-2266.

International Energy Outlook. Published annually by the U.S. Energy Information Administration, James Forrestal Bldg., Rm 1F-048, 100 Independence, Ave., S.W., Washington, DC 20588.

The Journal of the American Medical Association. Published weekly by JAMA (The Journal of the American Medical Association), 535 N. Dearborn St., Chicago, IL 60610.

Life. Published monthly by The Time Inc., Magazine Company, Time & Life Bldg., Rockefeller Center, 1271 Ave. of the Americas, New York, NY 10020.

McCall's. Published monthly by McCall's Magazine, 110 5th Ave., New York, NY 10011.

Mechanix Illustrated (now called *Home Mechanix*). Published monthly by Times Mirror Magazines, Inc., 380 Madison Ave., New York, NY 10017.

Mineral Information Service (now called *California Geology*). Published monthly by Division of Mines and Geology, 1516 Ninth St., Fourth Floor, Sacramento, CA 95814.

MMWR: Morbidity and Mortality Weekly Report. Published weekly by the U.S. Department of Health and Human Services, Centers for Disease Control, Epidemiology Program Office, 1600 Clifton Rd., N.E., Atlanta, GA 30333.

Motor Trend. Published monthly by Petersen Publishing Co., 8490 Sunset Blvd. Los Angeles, CA 90069.

National Geographic. Published monthly by National Geographic Society, 17th & M Sts. N.W., Washington, DC 20036.

National Geographic World. Published monthly by National Geographic Society, 17th & M Sts. N.W., Washington, DC 20036.

National Wildlife. Published bi-monthly by National Wildlife Federation, 1400 16th St. N.W., Washington, DC 20036-2266.

Natural History. Published monthly by American Museum of Natural History, Central Park W at 79th St., New York, NY 10024-5192.

Nature and Science (ceased publication). Was published bi-weekly by American Museum of Natural History, Central Park West at 79th St., New York, NY 10024-5124.

Nature Magazine (now incorporated into *Natural History*). Published monthly by American Museum of Natural History, Central Park W at 79th St., New York, NY 10024-5192.

New Scientist. Published weekly by IPC Magazines, Ltd., Holborn Group, King's Reach Tower, Stamford St., London SE9LS, England.

The New York Times. Published daily by The New York Times, 229 W. 43rd St., New York, NY 10036.

Newsweek. Published weekly by Newsweek, Inc., 444 Madison Ave., New York, NY 10022.

Nuclear News. Published monthly by American Nuclear Society, 555 N. Kensington Ave., LaGrange Park, IL 60525.

Organic Gardening. Published nine times a year by Rondale Press, Inc., 33 E. Minor St., Emmaus, PA 18098.

Parents. Published monthly by Gruner & Jahr, U.S.A. Publishing, 685 Third Ave., New York, NY 10017.

Pennsylvania Forests. Published quarterly by Pennsylvania Forestry Association, 56 E. Main St., Mechanicsburg, PA 17055-3851.

Pennsylvania Woodland News. Published bimonthly by Penn State University, Forest Resources Extension, 110 Ferguson Bldg., University Park, PA 16802.

People Weekly. Published weekly by The Time Inc., Magazine Company, Time & Life Bldg., Rockefeller Center, 1271 Ave. of the Americas, New York, NY 10020-1393.

Physics Today. Published monthly by American Institute of Physics, 335 E. 45th St., New York, NY 10017.

Pittsburgh Press. Published daily by Pittsburgh Press, Box 566, 34 Blvd. of the Allies, Pittsburgh, PA 15230.

The Planetary Report. Published bi-monthly by The Planetary Society, 65 North Catalina Ave., Pasedena, CA 91106.

Popular Mechanics. Published monthly by Hearst Magazines, Popular Mechanics, 224 W. 57th St., New York, NY 10019.

Popular Science. Published monthly by Times Mirror Magazines, Inc., 2 Park Ave., New York, NY 10016.

PRLC Technical Bulletin. Published six times a year by Pittsburgh Regional Library Center, 103 Yost Blvd., Pittsburgh, PA 15221.

Progressive Builder (now called *Custom Builder*). Published bi-monthly by Willows Publishing Group, Inc., 38 Laffayette St., Box 998, Yarmouth, ME 04096-0470.

Ranger Rick. Published twelve times a year by National Wildlife Federation, 1400 16th St. N.W., Washington, DC 20036-2266.

Recycling Today. Published monthly by G.I.E., Inc., 4012 Bridge Ave., Cleveland, OH 44113.

Road & Track. Published monthly by Hachette Magazines, Inc., Road & Track, 1499 Monrovia Ave., Newport Beach, CA 92663.

Safety and Health. Published by the National Safety Council, Periodicals Dept., 1121 Spring Lake Dr., Itasca, IL 60143.

Science. Published weekly by American Association for the Advancement of Science, 1333 H St. N.W., Washington, DC 20005.

Science [year] (ceased publication). Was published ten times a year by William Carey, publisher, 1333 H St N.W., Washington, DC 20005.

Science Digest (now called *Breakthroughs in Health & Science*). Published monthly by Family Media, Inc., Men's and In-Home Group, 3 Park Ave., New York, NY 10016.

Science News. Published weekly by Science Service, Inc., 1719 N St. N.W., Washington, DC 20036.

Science News-Letter (now called *Science News*). Published weekly by Science Service, Inc., 1719 N St. N.W., Washington, DC 20036.

The Science Teacher. Published nine times a year by National Science Teachers Association, 1742 Connecticut Ave. N.W., Washington, DC 20009.

Scientific American. Published monthly by Scientific American, Inc., 415 Madison Ave., New York, NY 10017.

Sky and Telescope. Published monthly by Sky Publishing Corporation, Box 9111, Belmont, MA 02178.

Smithsonian. Published monthly by Smithsonian Institution, Arts & Industries Bldg., 900 Jefferson Dr., Washington, DC 20560.

Status Report. Published bi-weekly by Insurance Institute for Highway Safety, Watergate 600 Ste. 300, Washington, DC 20037.

Stone. Published irregular by Stone Press 1112-B, Ocean St., Santa Cruz, CA 95060.

Technology and Culture. Published quarterly by Society for the History of Technology, Duke University, Department of History, Durham, NC 27706.

Time. Published weekly by The Time, Inc. Magazine Company, Time & Life Building, Rockefeller Center, 1271 Ave. of the Americas, New York, NY 10020-1393.

Today's Chemist at Work. Published nine times a year by American Chemical Society, 1155 16th St., N.W., Washington, DC 20036.

Today's Health (incorporated into *Health*). Published monthly by Health Magazine, 275 Madison Ave., Ste. 1314, New York, NY 10016.

Traffic Safety. Published bi-monthly by National Safety Council, Periodicals Dept., 1121 Spring Lake Dr., Itasca, IL 60143.

USA Today. Published daily by Gannett Co., Inc., P.O. Box 500, Washington, DC 20044.

Vegetarian Times. Published twelve times a year by Vegetarian Times, Inc., Box 570, Oak Park, IL 60303.

546 *Weatherwise*. Published bi-monthly by Heldref Publications, 1319 Eighteenth St. N.W., Washington, DC 20036-1802.

Index

A

Abacus 491, 509
Abbreviations 379
Able 63
Abrasion to remove tattoos 335
Abrasives, coated 151
Absolute zero 1
Accelerated mass spectrometer 223
Accidents 166
    Airplane 469
    Automobile 462
    Space-related 68
Acid rain 196, 197
Acids, sulfuric 144
Acre 514
Activated charcoal 353
Active solar energy See Solar energy
Addition
    Abacus versus calculator 509
Adiabatic process 5
Adrenal glands, functions 329
Aerodynamics
    Automobiles 174
Aerogels, Silica 145
Aesculapius 373
Africa
    Endangered mammals 191
    Extinct mammals 188, 189
    Mastodons 188
    Rate of deforestation 181
Age of the universe 29
Agent Orange 199

AIDS (acquired immunodeficiency syndrome) 358
AIDS-related complex See ARC
Air
    Classical element 330
    Composition of 71
    Drag See Drag—Air
    Layers 71
Air bags 465
Air conditioning
    Automobiles 174, 459
    Determining fuel requirements 170
    Energy conservation 172, 174
Air Conditioning Engineers (ASHRAE) 348
Airborne Imaging Spectrometer 102
Airplanes 467, 469
    See also Dirigibles
    Avionics 469
    Black box 469
    Over-water planes 471
    Seating capacity 471
    Supersonic Flight 468
    Tires 470
    Transatlantic flights 468
    Wind tunnel testing 470
    Wooden 470
Akashi-Kaikyo Bridge 440
Alarm clock 415
Alchemy
    Aqua water 144
Alcock, John W. 468

Alcohol
    Breathalyser 422
    Gasohol 162
Alcohol poisoning 350
Alcoholic beverages
    Effects 350
Aldrin, Jr., Edwin E. 64, 65
Algae
    Diatoms 227
Algorithm 490
Alkali metals 16
Alkaline Earth metals 16
Alligators
    Sex determination 281
Alpha Centauri 31, 37
Alpha particles 10
Alphabets 475, 476
    For the blind 476
    International Morse codes 476
ALS See Lou Gehrig's disease
Altair 34
Aluminum 133
    Alzheimer's disease 369
    Components in human body 311
    Health hazards 369
Alvarez, Luis 189
Alvarez, Walter 189
Alzheimer's disease
    Numbers affected 369
    Stages 369
AM radio See Radio, AM
Amanita phalloides
    Mushrooms 355

Amazon River
    Length 83
Ambergris 142
America, North
    Diamond mine 130
    Extinct mammals 188
    Extinctions 190
    Mammoths 188
    Mastodons 188
America, South
    Earliest map 100
    El Nino 180
    Extinct mammals 188
    Mastodons 188
American Lung Association 347
American shorthair cats 306
American Telephone and
    Telegraph 486
Ammonia
    Manufacture 144
Amor asteriods 52
Ampere 26
Ampere, Andre Marie 26
Amphibian planes 471
Amphibians and reptiles
    Comparison 281
    Crocodiles 281
    Endangered species, U.S. 193
    Gestation period 259
    Life span 259
    Names for groups 269
    Names for the young 267
    Regeneration 264
    Sex determination of alliga-
        tors 281
    Tadpoles 309
    Threatened species, U.S. 193
    Turtles 282
Amyotrophic Lateral Sclerosis
    (ALS) See Lou Gehrig's disease
Anabolic steroids
    Effects 384
Analytical engine 491, 498
AND (logical operators) 512
Angel Falls 83
Angel, Jimmy 83
Angstrom, Anders 7
Animals
    Aquatic life See Aquatic life
    Birds See Birds
    Blood types 264
    Breath-holding capacity 292
    Classification 224, 226
    Cloning 217
    Color vision 263
    Disease 358

First in orbit 63
Gestation period 259
Health care 345
Heart rate comparison 293
In space 63
In zoos 263
Insects See Insects
Intelligence 263
Kingdom category 224
Largest 262
Life span 259
Mammals See Mammals
Mimicry 214
Names for groups 269
Names for males and females
    266
Names of the young 267
Regeneration 263
Running speed 264
Snoring 265
Used to detect carbon
    monoxide 158
Vectors 358
Anise 243
Anorexia 369
Answering machine 486
Antarctica
    First person 87
    Ice thickness 87
Anteaters, banded
    Reproduction 294
Antibodies 313, 314, 383-4
    Diseases 229
    See also Monoclonal antibod-
        ies
Antigen 384
Antimony 19
Antimony glance 130
Antiquarks 12
Ants
    Comparison to termites 274
Anvil bone (ear) 340
Aphelion, Earth 45
Appendix, possible purpose 329
Apple maggot 256
Appleseed, Johnny 253
Appleton Layer 72
April, derivation 410
Aqua regia 144
Aquatic life
    Corals 278
    Eel 279
    Krill 278
    Marine mammals See Marine
        mammals
    Names for Groups 269

Tube worms, Giant 279
Aquifer 76
Arabian camel See Dramedaries
Arabic numerals 491
Arachnids
    Endangered species, U.S. 193
    Harvestman 274
    Threatened species, U.S. 193
Arachnodactyly 363
Aragonite 128
ARC (AIDS-related complex) 358
Arch Bridges 440, 441
Arctic tern 285
Area
    Formulas for calculating
        514, 515
    Measurement units 400
    Skin, human 334
Arithmetic mean 512
Armadillos, nine-banded
    Reproduction 300
Armstrong, Edwin Howard 482
Armstrong, Neil A. 64, 65
Aromatherapy 392
Around the world, first airplane
    flight 469
Arrhenius, Svante 179, 217
Arthritis 354
Artificial heart
    Jarvik-7 389
Artificial immunization See
    Immunization
Artificial intelligence 493
Artillery, Heavy 426
Asbestos 347
Asbestosis
    Causes 347
Asia
    Extinct birds 189
    Extinct mammals 188
    Mammoths 188
    Mastodons 188
    Rate of deforestation 181
Asian mayapple
    Anti-cancer drugs 382
Asklepius 373
Aspdin, Joseph 149
Aspiration of food
    Involuntary muscular
        reflexes 317
Assembly language (computers)
    498
Assembly plant, Largest 433
Asteroids 51
    Collisions with Earth 52
    Naming of 57

Asthma
    Aggravation by ozone 347
Astrolabe 57
Astronauts and cosmonauts 60
    See also Names of individual
        astronauts and cosmonauts
    Blacks 66
    Fatalities 68
    First in space 60
    First words on moon 64
    Married couples 66
    Moon 63, 65
    Moon walks 62
    Most time in space 66
    Physical changes during
        spaceflight 61
    Women 65, 66
Astronomers 56, 58
    See also names of individual
        astronomers
Astronomical unit 56
Astronomy
    Father of systematic astron-
        omy 56
    Measurement units 56
Aten asteriods 52
Atherosclerosis
    Heart attacks 365
Atmosphere
    Composition of 71
    Layers 71
Atmospheric phenomena
    Bishop's ring 105
    Green flash 106
    Lights, mysterious 110
    Saint Elmo's Fire 109
    Thunder *See* Thunder
Atmospheric pressure *See* Air pres-
    sure
Atomic bomb, development 426
Atomic Number 19
Atomic physics
    Founders 11
Atomic time 403
Atoms
    Atomic number 19
    Electrons 11
    Subatomic particles *See*
        Subatomic particles
AU *See* Astronomical unit
August, derivation 410
Aurora Borealis 106
Auroras 106
Australia
    World's largest carved sap-
        phire 132

Automobiles *See* Cars
Autosomal Dominant/Recessive
    Conditions 212
Average height and weight
    U.S. 319
Aviation Gasoline *See* Gasoline,
    Aviation
Avionics 469
Avogadro, Amedeo 27
Avoirdupois ton 399
Avoirdupois weights
    Conversion to troy units 401
Aztec Money 128

B

B cells *See* B lymphocytes
B lymphocytes 313, 329
    Comparison to T lympho-
        cytes 313
B-17 473
Babbage, Charles 491, 498
Babies
    Blue eyes 338
Baboons
    Intelligence 263
Babylonian calendar 404
Back surgery 388
Bacon, Roger 152
Bacteria
    Chemoautropic 279
    Diseases 229, 230
    Origin of life 217
    Stone-eating Microbes 229
Bacteriology
    Founders 229
Bactrian camels *See* Camels—
    Bactrian
Baekeland, Leo Hendrik 153
Baikal, Lake 81
Baily's beads 38
Baird, John Logie 484
Bakelite 153
Baker 63
Bald eagle *See* Eagle, Bald
Ball Lightning 108
Balled-and-burlapped plants 249
Balsa tree, density of 141
Bandicoots
    Reproduction 294
Banyan tree 235
Bar code 479
Barbier, Charles 476
Bare-rooted plants 249
Barium 16
Barnard, Christiaan 389
Barometric pressure 124

Barrel, Oil
    Measurement units 167
    Weight 167
Barry, John A. 503
Bartholdi, Frederic-Auguste 444
Baseball, probability of a triple play
    519
Basenji dogs 304
Basic oxygen process, steelmaking
    137
Basketball
    Injuries 346
Bates, Henry Walter 214
Batesian Mimicry 214
Bateson, William 213
Bats 293
Battle of the gauges 452
Bay of Fundy *See* Fundy, Bay of
Bazooka 425
Bead lightning 109
Bean moths 276
Bears
    Hibernation of 263
    Malayan sun bear 299
Beaufort, Francis 115
Beaufort Scale 115
Beaumont, William 316
Beekeepers 273
Bees 270, 273
    Africanized 273
    Dance 273
    Stings 355
Belgian block 149
Bell, Jocelyn 32
Bell, Lawrence 469
Bells (time) 415
Bench mark 402
Bends
    Deep-sea divers 369
Benedictus, Edouard 147
Benz, Karl 456
Bernard, Claude 318
Beryl
    Emeralds 132
Beryllium 16
Berzelius, Jöns Jakob 15
Beta lymphocytes *See* B lympho-
    cytes
Beta particles 10
Bible
    Largest number mentioned
        506
Bicycles 346
Bifocal lenses 338
Big Bang 29, 31
Big Bertha 426

Big Dipper 33
Bile, yellow and black (as humors) 330
Binary digit See Bit
Binary star 31
Binomial coefficients 515
Biochemistry
    Coining of term 221
    Founders 221
Biological Clock 220
Biology
    Classification 224, 226
    Events in geological time periods 209
    Evolution See Evolution
    Genetics See Genetics
    Life structures See Cell structures
    Term 223
Bioluminescence 277
Biomass energy 156
    Gasohol 162
    Gopher plant 157
    U.S. energy production 170
Biome 177
Birdhouses 290
    Bluebirds 290
Birds 283
    Arctic tern 285
    Blood types 264
    Bluebirds 290
    Color vision 263
    Egg size 284
    Endangered species, U.S. 193
    Feeding 290
    Flight 286
    Flight of 287
    Geese 286
    Homing pigeon 289
    Humans and 290
    Hummingbirds 287, 288
    Life span 259
    Migration 285, 286, 288
    Names 283
    Names for males and females 266
    Names for the young 267
    National bird 289
    Nesting habits 290
    Oxpecker 289
    Penguins 288
    Pets 309
    Recently extinct 189, 190
    Sanctuaries 185
    Speed 287
    Swallows 286

Threatened species, U.S. 193
Birth defects 385
Birthday, shared
    Probability 518
Bishop's ring 105
Bismuth
    Density 12
Bit (a binary digit) 499
Bites, black widow spiders
    Symptoms 356
Bivalves 280
Black bile See Humors (theory of health and illness)
Black box 469
Black Death 357
Black diamonds 130
Black holes 30, 31
Black ironwood 141
Black widow spider 356
Blackdamp 138
Blacks
    First American in space 66
    First in space 66
    First woman in space 66
Blackwell, Elizabeth 375
Bladderwort 240
Bleeding to death 352
Blenny (fish)
    Speed 278
Blind
    Alphabet 476
Blinking rate 338
Blood 264
    Alcohol levels 350
    As humor 330
    Bank (first) 375
    Carbon dioxide content 333
    Chemistry 313
    Cholesterol 378
    Circulation (skin) 334
    Color of animal blood 264
    Comparison to sea water 331
    Loss 352
    Normal pH 331
    Optical effect 336
    Oxygenation 331
    Pressure 377
    Temperature of human blood 26
    Types, human, most common U.S. 332
    Types, human, rarest 333
    Vessels (in skin) 334
Blood cells, White See White blood cells
Blood clotting

Christmas factor 365
Blood pressure
    Measurement units 377
    Normal range 377
Blue moon 50
Blue People 362
Blue shift 8
Bluebirds 290
Bluford, Jr., Guion S. 66
Boats
    Hospital ships 450
    Largest 451
    Nuclear-powered boats 452
    Parts 447
    Riverboat measurements 448
    Titanic 450
BOCA Code 430
Body
    Alcohol 422
    Chemical composition 311
    Functions of chemical elements 311
    Internal environment 330, 335
    Number of bones 322
    Number of muscles 324
    Remains after cremation 322
    Shapes, human 320
Body heat
    Lost through the head 318
Bombs, logic 501
Bone repair
    Cigarette smoking 351
Bones
    In the ear 340
    Most commonly broken 323
    Number in human body 322
    Smallest in the body 340
Bonsai 254
Books, codes 480
Boole, George 512
Boomerang 3
Boot, cold (computers) 500
Boot, warm (computers) 500
Booting a computer 499
Borglum, Gutzon 93
Borglum, Lincoln 93
Boron
    Components in human body 311
Bosch, Karl 144
Bosenberg, Henry F. 258
Botany, founder of 238
Botulinal toxin 353
Botulism 353
Boulder Dam 443

Bowie, Jim 424
Bowie knife 424
Boxwork 90
Boyle, Robert 15
Brackish Water 80
Braille 476
Braille, Louis 476
Brain
    Effect of color on activity
        339
    Neurons 326
    Size comparison 327
Braking distance of cars 461
Braun, Ferdinand 483
Brazil
    World's largest cut emerald
        found 132
Breast surgery 388
Breathalyser 422
Breathing 317
Brickwedde, F.G. 145
Bridge (game), number of possible
    games 518
Bridge-tunnels
    Longest 439
Bridges
    Covered U.S. briges 440
    Floating 441
    Kissing 440
    Longest bridges 440
    Longest in U.S. 441
    Place with most 441
    Suspension See Suspension
        Bridges
    Testing 437
    Types 439
Bridges, Robert 136
A Brief History of Time 30
British measurements of water
    400
Broadcast range
    AM radio 482
    FM radio 482
Bromine
    Liquid state 19
Brompton's cocktail 385
Brooklyn Bridge 442
Brown Mountain Lights of North
    Carolina 110
Brown, Arthur W. 468
Bruhn, Wilhelm 467
Brunel, Isambard K. 452
BTU 169
    Comparison of different fuels
        169
    Cooling capacity 170

Gas, Natural 169
Buckminsterfullerenes 145
Bug (computer term) 500
Building Officials and Code
    Administrators Code 430
Building Parts
    Chimneys and flues 429
    Doors 429
    Nails, screws, hardware 431
    Roofs 435
Buildings
    Codes 430
    Dams See Dams
    Eiffel Tower 444
    Geodesic Dome 434
    Houses and house construc-
        tion See Houses
    Largest 433
    Leaning tower of Pisa 433
    Microbe damage 229
    Parts See Building Parts
    Shopping Centers 433
    Skyscraper, first 432
    Solar energy systems 156
    Sound barrier measurements
        431
    Statue of Liberty 444
    Tallest 434
    "Topping Out" 436
    Yurts 432
Bulb (flower) 239
Bulletin of the Atomic Scientists
    416
Bulletproof glass 147
Bunion removal
    Second opinions 388
Burns
    Causes 371
    Classification 371
Bushnell, David 424
Butterflies 270
    Gardens 272
    Life span 259
    Plants that attract 251
Butterwort 240
Buzzard Day 286
Byron, Augusta Ada 498
Byte (computer term) 499

C
C, computer language 499
Cable cars 455
Cabs See Taxicabs
Caduceus 373
Caesar, Julius 404
Caisson disease See Bends

Calcite
    Structure 13
Calcium 16
Calcium carbonate 90, 91
Calculator
    Comparison to abacus 509
Calculus
    Binomial coefficients 515
Calendar
    Days of week 409
    Leap year 409
    Value of year 403
    Week 409
Calendars 408
    Babylonian 404
    Chinese 408
    Coptic 404
    Egyptian 404
    French Republican calendar
        404
    Gregorian 404
    Indian 404
    Islamic 404
    Japanese 404
    Jewish 404
    Julian Day Calendar 404
    Lunar 404
    Months 407
    Roman 404
    Solar 404
    Thirteen-month calendar
        404
Call letters, radio station 481
Calories, food
    Burned in specific activities
        315
Calories, nonfood
    Comparison of different fuels
        169
Calvin Cycle 222
Calvin, Melvin 222
Cambrian Era
    Fossils 128
Camels
    Arabian camels 299
    Bactrian camels 299-300
    Mail Delivery 475
    Water storage 299
Canada
    Acid rain 197
Canaries 288
    Used to detect carbon
        monoxide 158
Canary Islands 288
Cancer 358
    Carcinogens 348

Classification 366
Nuclear reactor safety 165
Plant origins 182
Research 216, 367
Smoking 351
Treatment 384
Cannon King 426
Cannon, Walter Bradford 318
Cantilever Bridges 440, 441
Canyons
Deepest 92
Largest 92
Longest 92
Cape May diamonds 130
Capillaries
In skin 334
Capybara 300
Car companies *See* Cars
Manufacturing 457
Carats
Measurement units 132
Carbon black 150
Carbon dioxide
Concentration in normal
blood 333
Removal from blood 331
Carbon products
Fullerenes 146
Carbon-14 Dating 223
Carboniferous Period
Coal 157
Carcinogens
Asbestos 347
Classifications 348
PCBs 194
Radon 347
Cardiac muscles 324
Carnivorous plants 240
Carotenoids 234
Carpal tunnel syndrome 363, 500
Carroll, Lewis 513, 519
Cars
Accident 462
Air conditioning 174, 459
Airbags *See* Cars—Safety
Automatic transmission 459
Braking distance 461
Catalytic convertors 160
Economy 174, 175
Effect of speed on economy
174
Electric cars 457
Energy conservation 174,
175
Engine measurements 455
Fuel comparisons 162

Gasoline 160
Lead-free gasoline 160
License plates 460
Manufacture 458
Nuclear-powered cars 460
Radar detection devices 464
Safety 462, 465
Safety recalls 461
Sales 461
Seat belts 462
Speed detection devices 463,
464
Stolen cars 455
Tires *See* Tires
U.S. registration 460
VIN number 460
Carver, George Washington 257
Casting out nines 511
Casts (Fossils) 128
CAT Scan
Medical tests 378
Catamount *See* Cougar
Cataract removal
Second opinions 388
Caterpillars
Weather prediction 124
Catgut 388
Catnip 244, 257
Cats 298
Age 305
American shorthair 306
Breeds 306
Color vision 263
Desert cats 298
Diseases transmitted to
humans 358
Eyes 307
Gestation 291
Life span 259
Mail delivery 475
Memory ability 306
Names for males and females
266
Poisonous plants 308
Purring 308
Sand cat 298
Siamese cats 307
Speed 264
Tabby 306
Whiskers 308
Caves 90
Coral 90
Deepest 90
Exploring 90
Longest cave system 90
Pearls 90

Structures 90, 91
CC in engine sizes 418
CD-ROM
Life span 489
Celestial objects
Naming of 56
Cell Division 219
Cloning 217
Cell Fusion 215
Cell Structure
DNA *See* DNA
Mitchondra 220
RNA *See* RNA
Cellular telephone 487-8
Celluloid 153
Celsius scale 25
Comparison to Kelvin and
Fahrenheit scales 25
Conversion to Fahrenheit
scale 25
Celsius, Anders 25
Cement 148
Census, Tabulating machines 492
Centigrade temperature scale *See*
Celsius scale
Centipede 276
Century 403
Cephalopods 280
Ceres 51
Cervix
Pelvic inflammatory disease
370
Cesium 16
Isotopes 20
Chain, Ernest 383
Chain lightning 109
Challenger disaster *See* Space
flights—Challenger disaster
Chamois 301
Chaos, Science of 520
Chapman, John 253
Charcoal, activated *See* Activated
charcoal
Charles, Jules 258
Charon 47
Check bit 499
Chemical elements
Abundancy 20
Group I elements 15
Metals *See* Metals
Noble metals 23
Periodic Table 15, 16, 23
Transition elements 16
Transuranic elements 17
Chemical garden
Formula 14

Chemicals
    Ammonia 145
    Aqua water 144
    Hydrogen peroxide 145
    Sulfuric acid 144
Chemicals, Toxic *See* Toxic chemicals
Chemistry
    Founders 15
    Periodic table *See* Chemical elements—Periodic table
Chemistry, Body
    Role of liver 326
Chemoautotropic bacteria 279
Chemotherapy 384
Chemotropism 233
Chernobyl 166, 194
    Nuclear reactor safety 165
Chesapeake Bay Bridge-Tunnel 439
Chess-playing computer (MADAM) 494
Chicago
    Winds 112
Childhood poisoning death rate 354
Childproof packaging 354
Chimneys 429
Chimpanzees
    First in orbit 63
    In space 63
    Intelligence 263
China, People's Republic of
    Abacus 509
    Chinese calendar 404
    Earthquake detector 95
    Pascal's triangle 515
    Relief maps, Invention 100
    Space launches 67
    Zero 505
China Syndrome 166
Chinese fighting dog 304
Chinese restaurant syndrome
    Causes 371
    MSG 371
Chips, Silicon *See* Silicon chips
Chiron 52
Chiropractic 375
Chitons, 280
Chlorine
    Components in human body 311
Chlorofluorocarbons *See* CFCs
Chlorophyll 234
Chloroplasts 232
Choking treatment

Heimlich maneuver 352
Cholesterol
    Effects of 349
    Sources 349
    Types 349
Cholesterol, blood *See* Blood cholesterol
Christmas factor 365
Christmas trees
    Fire resistance 255
    Preserving 254
Christy, James 47
Chromium
    Components in human body 311
Chromosomes
    Number in human cells 311
Chronobiology 221
Chudnovksy, Gregory and David 508
Cigar smoking
    Oral cavity cancers 351
Cigarette smoke
    Composition 351
Cigarette smoking
    Lung cancer 351
    Number in U.S. 351
    Quitting 351
Circadian Rhythm 221
    Jet lag 364
Circle
    Area 514
    Pi 508
Circle of Fire 94
Circle, Squaring the 516
Circular cylinder
    Volume 513
CITES *See* Convention in International Trade in Endangered Species
Civil Engineering
    Founders 437
Civil War, American
    Innovations 424, 425
    Machine gun 425
Clams
    Threatened and endangered species, U.S. 193
Clark, Barney B.
    Artificial heart 389
Clarke, Arthur C. 487
Clarke belt 487
Clavicle
    Most commonly broken 323
Clays
    Fuller's earth 139

Clean Air Act 196
Clemens, Samuel L. 449
Cleveland, Ohio
    Electric traffic light 438
Clocks
    Atomic clock 413
    Doomsday clock, Nuclear 416
    Grandfather clock 415
    Numbers 414
Cloning 217
Cloning in medicine 384
Close Encounters
    Of the First, Second, Third, and Fourth Kind 60
Clouds
    Types 106
Clover
    Greatest number of leaves 243
Clydesdale horses 297
CN Tower 434
Coal
    Composition 157
    Energy consumption, by country 171
    Energy output compared to other fuels 169
    Mining 138
    Mining methods 158
    Reserves, U.S. 172
    U.S. energy production 170
Coal dumps
    Products 138
Coal tar
    Use 150
Coatings, surface
    Teflon 154
Cobalt
    Components in human body 311
COBOL (common business oriented language) 499
Cocaine 387
Cockroaches
    Age 276
Cogeneration energy production process 163
Coherent light 419
College of Philadelphia
    Department of Medicine 374
Color
    Light 72
    Planets 42
    Sky 72
    Stars 32

Sun 38, 72
Color vision
    Animals 263
Colors
    Effect on moods 339
    Perception 337
    Primary colors 6
Colossus 492
Colt revolver 424
Colt, Samuel 424
Columbus, Christopher
    Map of America 100
Combustion
    Kindling point of paper 5
    Oxygen 4
    Phlogiston 4
    Spontaneous *See*
      Spontaneous combustion
Comet Encke 52, 53
Comet Halley 53
Comets 53
    Collisions with Earth 52
    Composition 53
    Naming of 57
    Orbits 53
    Short-period 53
Common cold 357
Common warts *See* Warts
Communications
    Criminal activities 502
    E mail 502
    Fax 502
    Space shuttle 483
    Submarines 481
    Telegraph 476
Communications satellite *See*
  Satellites, communication
Compact discs (CDs) 488
Comprehensive Drug Abuse
  Prevention and Control Act 386
Computerized axial tomography
  See CAT scan
Computers
    See also Disks, computer
    Booting 499
    Communications 501, 502
    Correct positioning 500
    Criminal activities 501
    Data storage 497, 501
    E mail 502
    Errors 500
    Fuzzy search 501
    Innoculation 501
    Input devices 497
    Logic bombs 501
    Mouse 497

Pixels 501
Sabotage 501
Starting 499
Video display 497, 501
Viruses 500
When to turn off 499
Worms 501
Concrete 149
Condoms 391
Conifers (dwarf) *See* Trees—Dwarf
  conifers
Constellations 34
Container-grown plants 249
Continental divide 91
Continental drift 84
Contraception
    Condoms 391
Controlled substance 386
Cooling capacity in BTUs 170
Cooling degree day 170
Copper 16, 19
    Components in human body
     311
Coptic calendars 404
Coral reefs 278
Corals (animals) 278
Cord of wood 170
Coriolis effect 5, 110
Coriolis, Gaspard C. 110
Corm (flower) 239
Corn
    Ethanol production 162
Corvair 462
Coryza *See* Cold, common
Cosmonauts *See* Astronauts and
  cosmonauts
Cougar 298
Counting boards 509
Cove molding 430
Covered bridges in United States
  440
Cows
    Mail delivery 475
CPU 498
Crack 387
Cracking, Hydrocarbon *See*
  Hydrocarbon cracking
Cranefly 275
Crayfish
    Regeneration 264
Creosote 150
Crescent moon 49
Cretaceous Period 187-189

Crick, Francis 218
Crocodiles
    Speed of motion 281
Cross-pollination 231
Crown glass 146
Crown jewels 132
Crown molding 429
Crude oil *See* Oil, Crude
Cruise ship, largest 451
Crustaceans
    Blood color 264
    Regeneration 264
    Threatened and endangered
     species, U.S. 193
Cryonic suspension 322
Crystal garden
    Formula 14
Crystallography
    Founders 13
Crystals
    See also Snow
    Snowflakes 122
Cube
    Volume 513
Cubic centimeters in engine sizes
  418
Cucumbers
    Products 143
Cuisenaire, Emile-Georges 511
Cuisenaire rods 511
Culin device on a tank 472
Cullinan Diamond 132
Curare
    Poison 355
Curie (lunar crater) 51
Curie, Marie 51
Curie, Pierre 10, 51
Cybernetics
    Founder 421
Cycles, Life 221
Cyclones 113
Cygnus X-1 31
Cylinder
    Volume 513
Cypress
    Mediterranean 448
    Monterey 448
Cyprus
    Solar energy 155

D

D&C *See* Dilatation and curettage
Daddy longlegs 274
Daffodils
    Perennials 252
Daimler, Gottlieb 456

Dalton, John 15
Damadian, Raymond 378
Damp, in coal mines 138
Dams
    Highest dams 443
    Hoover Dam 443
    U.S. 443
Dance of the bees 273
Dark perception 337
Darval, Denise Ann
    First heart transplant 389
Darwin, Charles 213
Darwinism 213
Dating of prehistoric objects, etc. 223
Davis, Jan 66
Dawn 403
Dawn redwood tree 236
Day, Length of on Earth 45
Day, Length of on planets 44
Daybreak 403
Daylight Savings Time 412
Days of week 409
DDT 257
Dead body, growth of nails and hair 336
Dead reckoning 447
Dead Sea 75
    Salt content 80
Deadly nightshade See Strychnine
Deadweight tonnage 449
Death of the sun 37
Death, causes of
    In the U.S. 345
Deaths
    In space 68
December, derivation 410
Decibels 341
Deer
    Garden fences 256
Deer ticks See Ticks
DeForest, Lee 480
Delamain, Richard 511
Deneb 34
Density
    Woods 141
Density of matter
    Solids and liquids 12
    Water 13
Dental care
    X-rays 348
Deoxyribonucleic Acid See DNA
Dermis 334
Desert cat
    Habitat 298
Deserts 177

Largest 89
Deuterium 145
Deutsches Institut fur Normung standards 402
Development
    Polio vaccine 383
Deville, Sainte-Claire 133
DeVries, William
    Artificial heart 389
Dexter, Thomas 136
Diagnosis of disease 374
Diameters of the planets 42
Diamonds
    Authenticating 131
    Cap May 130
    Carats 132
    Composition 130
    Largest 132
    Mines, United States 130
    Measurement units 132
    Points 132
    Properties 130
    Valuing 131
    Weighing 132
Diaphorase
    "Blue People" 362
Diastolic blood pressure 377
Diatomaceous Earth 139
Diatomite 139, 228
Diatoms 227
    Products 139
Digestion
    First direct studies 316
Digital audio tape (DAT) 488
Digitate warts See Warts
Dilatation and curettage
    Second opinions 388
DIN standards 402
Dinosaurs 187
    Largest 187
    Life spans 188
    Reason for extinction 188
    Smallest 187
Dioxin
    Comparison to PVC 205
Dirigibles 467
Disasters
    Greatest in U.S. 118
Discoveries
    Antarctica 87
    Deuterium 145
    Electrons 11
    Fullerenes 146
    Penicillin 383
    Spontaneous combustion 4
    Streptomycin 383

Superconductivity 2
Diseases
    Caught from animals 358
    Causes 229, 230
    Common cold 357
    Immunity See Immunity
    Inherited diseases 212
    Periodontal 357
Disk operating system See DOS
Diskettes, computer See Floppy disks
Displacement in engines 418
Display, video 497, 501
Distance
    Horizon measurement 401
    Of planets from the sun 41
Diver's paralysis See Bends
Diving ability of marine mammals 295
Division
    Abacus versus calculator 509
DNA 218, 312
    Fingerprinting 423
    Recombinant See
      Recombinant DNA/RNA
    Sampling in hair 336
"Do not fold, spindle, or mutilate" 493
Dodgson, Charles See Carroll, Lewis
Dodos, extinction 189
Dog days 105
Dog star See Sirius
Dog watches (time) 415
Dogs
    Dalmatians 299
    Age 305
    Basenji 304
    Biting propensity 303
    Breeds 302, 305
    Classification 301
    Color vision 263
    Dangerous 303
    First in orbit 63
    Foxhound 302
    In space 63
    Medical contribution 305
    Memory ability 306
    Pugs 305
    Saluki 302
    Shar-pei 304
    Shedding 304
    Tagging 306
    Voiceless 304
    Wrinkled 304
Dogwood tree 254

Dolby noise reduction system 488
Dolby, R.M. 488
Dolphin-safe tuna 193
Dolphins
    Comparison to porpoises 296
    Intelligence 263
    Speed 278
Donkey engine 418
Donkeys, number 296
Doomsday clock for nuclear anni-
    hilation 416
Doorjamb 429
Doors
    Parts 429
Doppler effect 8, 464
Doppler, Christian 8, 464
DOS (disk operating system) 501
Double-blind study 381
Double-digging 245
Drag
    Air 2
    Golf balls 2
Drake, Frank 58, 59
Drake's equation 58
Dramedaries 300
Dreaming 315
Drew, Richard C. 375
Driest place 119
Drilling
    Deepest 74
Dromedaries
    Water storage 300
Drowning treatment
    Heimlich maneuver 352
Drug testing
    Cocaine 386
    Using hair 336
Drugs
    Childproof packaging 354
    Measurement units 401
    Overdose treatment 353
Drugs, prescription See
    Prescription drugs
Dry ice 143
Dry measures
    U.S. customary units 398
Ducks
    Life span 259
    Names for males and females
        266
    Names for the young 267
Duhamel, J.P.F. 4
Duryea, Charles 457
Dusk 403
Dust mites 367

Dwarf conifers See Trees—Dwarf
    conifers
Dynamic time 402
Dynamite 152
Dyslexia
    Causes 368
    Symptoms 368

E

E mail 502
Eagles
    American 289
    Bald 289
    National bird 289
    Sanctuaries 185
Earhart, Amelia 468
Early Bird 486
Ears
    Bones 340
    Hearing range 341
    Loudness 341
Earth 44
    Aphelion 45
    Circumference 46
    Classical element 330
    Continents 84
    Core temperature 74
    Crust composition 74
    Crust movement 84, 94
    Deepest drilling 74
    Distance from sun 45
    Highest points 75
    Land 76
    Lowest points 75
    Mass 73
    Perihelion 45
    Revolutional effects 5
    Rotation speed 45
    Rotational effects 409
    Shape of 46
    Surface 76
    Temperature, Air See
        Temperaure Air
    Temperature underground
        74
    Water surface 76
    Weight 73
Earth Resources Technology
    Satellite (ERTS) See Landsat
Earth stations 484
Earthquakes
    Measurement devices 95, 96
    Measurement units 96
    Most severe in U.S. 97
    New Madrid 97
    San Francisco 98

    Severity 98
    Tsunami 95
Easter
    Date determination 411
ECG (electrocardiograph)
    Medical technology 377
    Mobil 377
Echidna 295
Eckert, John Prosper, Jr. 494
Eclipses
    Annular 38
    Lunar 30, 50
    Partial lunar 50
    Partial solar 38
    Penumbral 50
    Solar 30, 38, 521
    Total lunar 50
    Total solar 38
Ecliptic 37
Ecology 177
    See also Biomes
Economy, law of 521
Ecorche 325
Ectomorph
    Human body typing 320
Eels, electric See Electric eels
Efficiency research 519
Egg-laying Mammals 295
Eggs
    Birds 285
    Spiders 275
Egyptian calendars 404
Ehrlich, Paul 384
Eiffel Tower 444
Einstein, Albert 521
EKG See ECG
Electric cars 457
Electric eels, voltage 279
Electricity
    Appliances, Household 173
    Comparison to different fuels
        162
    Eels 279
    Energy output compared to
        other fuels 169
    From geothermal energy
        155
    From solar energy 155
    From water power 155
    Generation methold 163
    Leyden jar 5
    Meters 170
    Speed 498
Electrocardiograph See ECG
Electromagnetic radiation 10
    Measurements 7

Health hazards 346
Electromagnetism *See* Magnetism
Electronic mail *See* E mail
Elements
        Classical 330
        Most abundant in the Earth's
                crust 74
Elephant bird
        Egg size 284
Elephants
        Comparison 297
        Gestation period 291
        Intelligence 263
        Legal status 191
        Monetary value 191
Embalming fluids 23
Embryo
        Development 220
Embryology
        Founder 220
Emeralds
        Coloring 132
        Composition 132
        Largest 132
Empedocles of Agrigentum 330
Emperor penguin 288
Empire State Building 433, 434
Encke's comet *See* Comet Encke
Endangered species 191
        See also Threatened species;
                Vulnerable species; Extinct
                species
        Bears 299
        Blue whales 192
        Determining status 190
        Elephants 191
        Horses 297
        Manatee 296
        Right whales 192
        Turtles 192
        U.S. 193
        Wolves 298
Endangered Species Act 191
        Provisions for assigning
                endangered label 190
Endless ropeway 455
Endocrine glands 329
Endomorph
        Human body typing 320
Endorphins 314
Energy
        Appliances, Household 173
        Comparison of different fuels
                169
        Conservation 163, 172-175
        Consumption 170-173

Consumption, by country
        171
Consumption, U.S. 172
Economy 163
Electricity *See* Electricity
Lighting 173, 174
Loss through drag *See*
        Drag—Air
Magnetism *See* Magnetism
Meters 170
Production 170
Quantum mechanics *See*
        Quantum mechanics
Reserves, U.S. 172
Engineering, civil 437
Engineering psychology 520
Engines
        cc 418
        Four-stroke comparison to
                two-stroke 417
        Internal combustion 418
        Measurement units 418
Engines, Donkey 418
England
        Water power 156
Englehart, Douglas C. 497
ENIAC (electronic numerical inte-
        grator and computer) 494
Enigma 478, 492
Enola Gay 474
Enos 64
Environmental Protection Agency
        (EPA) 346-8
EPA *See* Environmental Protection
        Agency
Epicondylitis 363
Epidemiology
        Founder 374
Epidermis 334
Epstein-Barr
        Herpes 361
Ergonomics 520
Erie, Lake
        Acid rain 197
Esophagus
        Involuntary muscular
                reflexes 317
Espaliering 253
Essential oils 142
Ethanol
        Gasohol 162
        Yields of different crops 162
Ether theory 7
Euclid 506
Europe
        Acid rain 197

Biomass energy 156
Extinct mammals 188
Fifth generation computers
        492
Mammoths 188
Mastodons 188
Europe, Eastern
        Acid rain 197
Eutrophication 178
Evening 403
Everest, Mt. 75
Evolution
        Darwinism 213
        Humans 212
        Mimicry 214
        Ontogeny 220
        Origin of life 217
        Survival of the Fittest 214
        Trials 214
Ewing, William Maurice 85
Exercise
        Sore muscles 325
Exosphere 72
Expert system 494
Exploration of Space *See* Space
        flight
Explorer 1 67, 72
Explosives
        Dynamite 152
        TNT 152
Extinct species 188, 191
        Dodos 189
        Mammoths 188
        Mastodons 188
        Passenger pigeons 190
        Quagga 189
        See also Endangered species;
                Threatened species;
                Vulnerable species
Extraterrestrial life
        Encounters with 60
        Mars 46
        Probability of 58
        Search for 59
Extremely Low Frequency (ELF)
        Electromagnetic fields
                Health hazards 346
Exxon Valdez 198
Eyes
        Blinking rate 338
        Blood leakage 336
        Color of eyes 338
        Color perception 337
        Farsightedness 338
        Floaters 336
        Iris color 338

Lenses 338
Light and dark perception 337
Nearsightedness 338
Optical illusion 338
Phosphenes 338
Practioners 376
Relation to moods 339
Retina abnormalities 338
Transplants 390
Vision correction 338
Visual clarity 338

F

Factor VIII 364
Factorials 513
Fahrenheit scale
Comparison to Kelvin and Celsius scales 25
Conversion to Celsius scale 25
Fahrenheit, Daniel 24
Fairy ring 228
Fall of the Roman Empire
Lead 357
Fallopian tubes
Pelvic inflammatory disease 370
Fantus, Bernard 375
Farnsworth, Philo T. 483
Farsightedness 338
Fatalities
In space 68
Fax machine 486, 487
February, derivation 410
Federal Communications Commission (FCC) 485
Ferris, George Washington Gale 445
Ferris wheel 445
Fiber optic cable 487
Fiberglass 148
Fibonacci, Leonard 506
Fibonacci numbers 506
Fifth generation computers 492, 493
Previous generations See Generation number, i.e., Second generation computers
Figure head 448
Filiform warts See Warts
Finger nails, growth rate 336
Fingerprints 334-5
Fire (Classical element) 330
Firedamp 138

Fireflies 277
Fireplaces
Making logs from newspaper 172
Fires, prevention
Smokey the bear 182
Fireworks, colored 152
First aid 352
Heimlich maneuver 352
First American car company 457
First American in orbit 60
First American in space 60
First American railroad 454
First American to walk in space 64
First American woman in space 65
First American woman to walk in space 64
First animal in orbit 63
First asteriod discovered 52
First atomic bomb 474
First battery 26
First bifocal lenses 338
First Black American in space 66
First Black in space 66
First Black surgeon to do heart surgery 389
First Black woman in space 66
First blood bank 375
First car 455
First car air conditioners 459
First car license plates 460
First car with automatic transmission 459
First chimpanzee in orbit 63
First chimpanzee in space 63
First color standardization scheme of minerals 129
First commerical communications satellite 486
First computer programmer 498
First continuously cultured human malignant cells 367
First direct studies of digestion 316
First dog in orbit 63
First finger prints classification for identification 335
First generation computers 492
First geothermal power station 155
First golf shot on the moon 63
First heart transplant 389
First large tidal electric generation plant 156
First major oil spills 198

First major oil tanker accident 198
First man in space 60
First man on the moon 62
First map of America 100
First married couple in space 66
First meal on moon 65
First microcomputer 495
First monkey in space 63
First nail-making machine 432
First nonstop transatlantic flight 468
First nuclear-powered aircraft carrier 452
First nuclear-powered vessels 452
First oil well in the United States 159
First person
Antarctica 87
South Pole 87
First plant patent 257
First programmable electronic computer 491
First radial-ply tire 458
First radio broadcasting station 481
First satellite 67, 68
First service station 161
First shopping center 433
First skyscraper 432
First solo crossing flight 468
First space walk 64
First speed trap 463
First Star of Africa diamond 132
First successful offshore oil wells 159
First successful round-the-world flight 469
First surgical appendix removal 329
First suspension bridge 442
First taxicabs 467
First test-tube baby 390
First tidal-powered mill 156
First traffic lights 438
First U.S. coast-to-coast highway 437
First U.S. female physician 375
First U.S. satellite 67
First untethered space walk 64
First use of chemotherapy 384
First weather forecasting 124
First woman in space 65
First woman to fly solo across the Atlantic 468
First woman to walk in space 64

First words on the moon 64
First zoo in the United States 185
Fish
    Age, determining 277
    Life span 259
    Names for groups 269
    Names for the young 267
    Speed 277
    Threatened species, U.S.;
      Endangered species, U.S.
      193
Fitzgerald, William
    Relexology 392
Five-in-one tree 252
Flail 423
Flashlight battery
    Voltage 26
Flat warts See Warts
Fleas
    Disease 359
    Jumping ability 276
    Vectors 359
Fleming, Alexander 383
Flesh-eating bacteria 361
Flies 270
    Disease 359
    Vectors 359
Flint tools, Neanderthal 416
Float-glass process 147
Floaters, optical effect 336
Floating bridges See Bridges,
  Floating
Floppy disks
    Comparison to hard disks
      496
    Formatting 496
    Storage capacity 497
Floral clock 414
Florey, Howard 383
Flowers
    First spring wildflower to
      bloom 243
    Floral clock 414
    "Imperfect" 239
    National 242
    Parts of 238
    Symbolic of months 241
    Unisexual 239
Flowers, T.H. 492
Flue gas scrubbers 196
Flues 429
Fluorescent lighting 173
    Colors 6
    Energy conservation 174
Fluorine

Components in human body
    311
Fluorocarbon 154
Flying fish
    Speed 278
Flying Fortress 473
"Flying Tigers" 473
Food and Drug Administration
    354, 356, 389
Food chains 177
Food on the moon 65
Fool's gold 131
Football
    Injuries 346
Force
    Magnetism See Magnetism
Ford, Henry 458
Forest fires
    Causes 183
    Prevention 182
    Smokey the bear 182
    United States, western 183
Forests
    Rate of destruction 182
    See also Tropical forests;
      Rain forests
Formaldehyde 23
    Contamination 199
Fossil Fuel
    Composition 157
Fossils 92
    Age 128
    Formation 128
Foucault Pendulum 99
Foucault, Jean 99
Founder of conservation 186
Founder of systematic astronomy
  56
Founder of the Soviet space pro-
  gram 67
Four-horned antelope 296
Fourth generation computers 492
Four–stroke eninges 417
Foxhound, American 302
France
    Hydroelectricity 156
    Water power 156
Francium 16
Franco-German War—Artillary 426
Frankincense 143
Franklin, Benjamin 101, 338
Freebase 387
Freezing human bodies for revival
  322
Freezing of water 1
Freezing rain 122

French Republican calendar 406
Frogs
    Tadpoles 309
Frost 123
Frown
    Number of muscles used 325
Frozen ground See Permafrost
Fruit fly 256, 276
Fruit trees 253
    Chilling requirement 252
    Espaliering 253
    Protection from mice 256
Fuel 167
    See also specific fuel, i.e.,
      Gasoline
    Comparison of alternatives
      162
    Plant sources 157
    Weight 167
Fugate, Martin 362
Fujita and Pearson Tornado Scale
  114
Fujita, T. Theodore 114
Fulgurites 109
Full moon 50
Fuller, R. Buckminster 145, 435
    Spaceship Earth 186
Fuller's earth 139
Fullerenes 146
Fungus 228
    Kingdom 226
Fungus ring 228
Funicular railway 455
Furnace
    Energy conservation 172
Fuzzy search (computers) 501

G

Gabor, Dennis 420
Gagarin, Yuri 60, 68
Galaxies
    Classification 58
    Milky Way 33
    Recession of 58
Galena 130
Galileo spacecraft 67
Gall bladder removal 388
Gallium
    Liquid state 19
Galton, Francis 335
Gametes (sex cells) 312
Gamma radiation 10
Gandy dancer 454
Garbage
    See also Solid waste
    Biodegrable plastic 153

Gardening
  Best soil pH 245
  Best time to weed 251
  Catnip 257
  Container 249
  Deer fences 256
  Lunar 246
  Shakespeare garden 250
  Squirrel fences 256
  Vegetables 250
  Working the soil 245
Gardens, butterfly 272
Gas, Natural
  Comparison to different fuels
    162
  Composition 157
  Energy consumption, by
    country 171
  Energy output 169
  Energy output compared to
    other fuels 169
  Heating 169
  Largest fields 159
  Meters 170
  Reserves, U.S. 172
  U.S. energy production 170
Gases 11
Gasohol 162
  Comparison to different fuels
    162
Gasoline
  Additives 160
  Comparison to different fuels
    162
  Energy output compared to
    other fuels 169
  Gasohol 162
  Hydrocarbon crackig 160
  Knocking 160
  Measurement units 161
  Octane ratings 160-161
  Pollution 161
  Production for petroleum
    160
  Pump 161
  Reformulated 161
  Service 161
Gasoline engines
  Economy 174, 175
  Emissions 196
  Energy consumption 174
  Knocking 161-2
  Lead affecting performance
    160
  Smog 195
Gastropods 280

Gatlefosse, Rene Maurice 392
Gatling gun 425
Gatty, Harold 469
Geese, migration 286
Gell-Mann, Murray 11
Genes
  Cloning 217
  DNA See DNA
  RNA See RNA
  Sex cells 312
  Splicing 215
Genesis rock 51
Genetic engineering 215, 384
Genetic fingerprinting 336, 422
Genetic relationship
  Using DNA 422
Genetics 214
  Cloning of genes 217
  Coining of term 213
  DNA See DNA
  Engineering See Genetic
    Engineering
  Founders 213
  Heredity 212
  See also Evolution
Geneva Medical College 375
Genital warts See Warts
Genome Project 216
Geodesic dome 434
Geologic clocks 223
Geological time 98
  Biological events 209
Geology
  Caves See Caves
  Craters 90
  Founder 100
  Moraine 89
  Rock formations 89
Geometry
  Area 514
  Circle 508
  Cylinder core 508
  Squaring the circle 516
  Volumes 513
Geostationary orbits 488
Geothermal energy 155
Geothermal power
  U.S. energy production 170
Geotropism 233
Geraniums
  Surviving the winter 252
German silver 136
Gestation period
  Longest 259
  Mammals 291
  Marsupials 294

Geysers
  As energy sources See
    Geothermal energy or
    Hydrothermal energy
Gibbons, intelligence 263
Gibbous moon 49
Gibraltar, Rock of 93
Gibraltar, Strait of 93
Gilbert, William 4
Gilbreth, Frank Bunker 519
Glaciers
  Effect on terrain 88-90
  Ice Ages 89
  United States 88
Glands 329
  Effect of visual stimuli 339
  Endocrine 329
  Largest 329
  See also Individual glands,
    i.e., Pituitary glands
Glass
  Bulletproof glass 147
  Composition and viscosity 146
  Crown glass 147
  Flat glass process 148
  Glass blocks 147
  Movie stunt glass 148
  Thermopane glass 147
Glass-fiber-reinforced plastics 148
Glaze 122
Glenn, Jr., John H. 61
Global temperature 103
Global warming, threat of 193
Glycerine
  as leaf preserver 237
Gold 16, 19
  24 karat gold 134
  Gold leaf 135
  Production 135
  Weight measurements 401
  White gold 135
Golden Gate Bridge 442
Golf balls
  Reason for dimples 2
Golf on the moon 63
Gondwanaland 84
Googol 507
Googolplex 507
Goose-bumps 335
Gopher plant as a petroleum
  source 157
Gopher Wood 448
Gorgas, William C. 359
Gorillas
  Intelligence 263
Graf Zeppelin 467

Grafting, skin to remove tattoos 335
Gram atomic weight 27
Gram formula weight 27
Grand Canyon
    Length 92
Grand Canyon of the Snake 92
Grand tour of the solar system 61
Grandfather clock 415
Grapes
    Seedless 253
Grasshopper, short-horn
    Pest 270
Gravitational force 43
Gravitropism 233
Gray
    Radiation measurement 348
Great Lakes
    Largest 81
Great white shark 280
Greater Star of Africa diamond 132
Green flash phenomenon 106
Green products 186
Greenhouse
    First practical 258
Greenhouse effect 179, 193
Greening of the galaxy 60
Greenwich Mean Time 413
Gregoire, Marc 154
Gregorian calendar 403, 405, 407, 408
Gross tonnage 449
Ground, Frozen See Permafrost
Groundhogs
    Weather prediction 124
Group I elements 16
Group II elements 16
Group names See Names, Group
Growth rate 518
GSI (Silicon chip size) 495
Gulf Stream 101
Gun, Gatling 425
Gun, machine 425
Gun, Tommy 425
Gunpowder 151
Gunter, Edmund 511
Gutenberg, Beno 74
Gypsy moth 238
    Caterpillars, predators 237

H

Haber, Fritz 144
Hacker (computer term) 502
Hahneman, Christian F.S. 375
Hail

Formation 121
Largest stones 121
Hair, Human
    Average number on head 336
    Follicles 334
    Forensics 336
    Growth in dead body 336
    Growth rate 335
Halcyon days 111
Half-life of radioactive isotopes
    Dating agent 223
Half-life of radioactivity material 13
Hall, Charles Martin 133
Halley, Edmund 53
Halley's comet See Comet Halley
Hallidie, Andrew S. 455
Ham 63
Hammer bone (ear) 340
Hamstring muscles, function 324
Hansen's disease
    Leprosy 360
Happy Giant 451
Hard disks 496
    Comparison to floppy disks 497
Hardwood as fuel See Wood as fuel
Harkin's rule 19
Harvest moon 50
Hat
    Conserving body heat 318
Hatters 357
Haüy, Rene-Just 13
Haüy, Valentin 476
Haven, C.D. 147
Hawk Mountain Sanctuary 185
Hawking, Stephen 30
Hawking's radiation 30
Hawks, sanctuaries 185
Hazardous waste sites, U.S. 202
HDL See High density lipoproteins
HDPE plastic
    Recycling 206
HDTV See High definition television
Health
    Cigarette smoking 351
    Ozone levels 347
    Risk factors 343
Health care
    Negative ion generator 391
    Nursing homes 376
    Pets 345
    Reflexology 391
Health hazards
    Aluminum 369

Asbestos 347
Chernobyl accident 166
Nuclear power 166
PCBs 194
Radon 347
Hearing
    Loudness 341
    Range of sound frequency, humans 341
Heart
    Attacks 365
    Attacks, Pets 345
    Blood volume 328
    Muscles 324
    Pacemakers 390
    Pumping process 328, 331
    Rate See Heart rate
    Surgery 388
Heart rate 328
    Comparison of animals 293
    Effect of color 339
Heat
    Combustion See Combustion
    Maxwell's demon 3
    Measurement of heat flow 430
    Measurement of temperature See Temperature scale
    Spontaneous combustion See Spontaneous combustion
    Thermodynamic laws 3
Heat exhaustion 366
Heat lightning 109
Heat stroke 366
Heating
    Determining fuel requirements 169
    Fuel comparison 157
    Geothermal energy 155
    Home, Energy conservation 172
    Solar energy 156
    Wood as fuel 157
Heating degree day 169
Heaviside-Kennelly Layer 72
Heimlich, Henry J. 352
Heimlich maneuver 352
Heineken, Albert 208
Heisenberg, Werner Karl 24
HeLa cells 367
Helium
    Abundancy 20
Hell's Canyon 92
Helmont, Jan Baptista van 221
Hemophilia 365
    Factor VIII 364

Hemorrhoid removal
    Second opinions 388
Henriette Lacks
    HeLa cells 367
Henry, Edward 335
Henry, Joseph 477
Herbs
    Symbolic meanings 240
Hermes 373
Hermit crab (pet) 310
Hernia repair 388
Herodotus 491
Heron (or Hero) of Alexandria 515
Heroult, Paul 133
Herpes 358
    Causes 360
    Symptoms 360
Hess, Harry Hammond 85
Hibernation, bears 263
High definition television (HDTV) 484
High density lipoproteins (HDL)
    Good cholesterol 349
High density lipoproteins See HDL cholesterol
High speed steels 137
High Technology (High Tech) 519
Highways See Roads
Higinbotham, William 494
Hindenburg 467
Hindu numerals 491
    Zero 505
Hip reconstruction 388
Hipparchus 56
Hippocrates 374
Hippocratic Oath 373
Hiroshima, Japan
    Atomic bomb 427
HIV (human immunodeficiency virus) 358
Hogs 298
Hollerith cards 492, 493
Hollerith, Herman 492
Holmes, Thomas H. 343
Holography 420
Holter, J.J. 377
Holter monitor
    Medical technology 377
Home Insurance Company Building 432
Homeopathy 375
Homeostasis 318, 330
Homing pigeons
    Homing ability 289
Homo Erectus 212
Homo Habilis 212

Homo Sapiens 187, 212
    Brain size compared to Neanderthal 327
Honeybees See Bees
Hoodoo 89
Hooke, Robert 419
Hoover Dam 443
Hopper, Grace Murray 498-9
Hopper's rule 497
Horizon, Distance measurement 401
Horse latitudes 110
Horsehair, products 143
Horsepower 455
Horses
    Clydesdale 297
    Horsehair 143
    Number 296
    Przewalski's horse 297
    Thoroughbred names 297
Hospital Ships 450
Household receptacles
    Voltage 26
Houseplants
    Poisonous to cats 308
Houses
    Amount of wood 429
    Mail-order houses 436
Howard, Luke 106
Hubble, Edwin Powell 29, 58
Hubble Space Telescope 58
Hubble's Constant 29
Hubble's Law 58
Hughes, Howard 470
Human factors engineering 520
Humans 264
    Blood 26
    Cell structure 220
    Cloning 217
    Effect of spaceflight on body 61
    Evolution 212
    Ingerited traits 212
    Life span 259
    Swimming speed 278
Humber Estuary Bridge 440
Hummingbirds
    Feeding 288
    Flight of 287
    Plants that attract 251
    Speeds 287
    Vervain, egg size 285
Hummve 472
Humors (theory of health and illness) 330, 374
Hunter's moon 50

Hunting
    Elephants 191
    Endangered species 191
Hurricanes 113
    Measurement 116
    Names 117
    U.S. 118
Hutchins, Levi 415
Hutchinson-Gilford syndrome 369
Huygens, Christiaan 42
Hyatt, John Wesley 153
Hydrocarbon cracking 160
Hydrochloric acid gases
    From burning PVC 205
Hydroelectric power
    U.S. energy production 170
Hydroelectricity See Electricity— from water power
Hydrogen
    Abundancy 20
    Isotopes 20
Hydrogen peroxide 145
Hydrogen power
    Comparison to different fuels 162
Hydroponics 246
Hydrotropism 233
Hynek, J. Allen 60
Hysterectomy
    Second opinions 388

I

Iatrogenic illnesses 370
IBM
    DOS 502
    PC 502
    Punched card 492, 493
Ice
    Dry 144
    Glaze 122
    Thickness in Antarctica 87
Ice Age 88
    Post-nuclear war 427
Iceland
    Biothermal energy 155
Igneous rocks 127
Immune system 313
    Possible role of appendix 329
Immunity
    Antibodies 229
Immunization 313
Imported cars
    Sales 461
Impossiblity of motion 519
In vitro fertilization (IVF) 390
Incandescent lighting 173

Increase, Percentage of 518
Incus bone (ear) 340
Indian calendars 405
Indian dollars 128
Industrial waste 194
     Air pollution 196
Inertia 2
Inertial navigation 447
Infectious disease 357
     Zoonosis 358
Inferior planets 44
Infinity 509
Information highway 489
Infrared coagulation treatment to
     remove tattoos 335
Ingham, Eunice D.
     Reflexology 392
Injuries 346
Insecticides
     DDT 257
Insects
     See also Spiders
     Ants 274
     Bean moths 276
     Bees 273
     Beneficial 270
     Butterflies *See* Butterflies
     Centipede 276
     Cockroaches 276
     Cranefly 275
     Disease 358
     Fireflies 277
     Fleas 276
     Fruit fly 276
     Life span 259
     Locust 270
     Metamorphoses 271
     Mimicry 214
     Mosquitos 274
     Moths 272
     Names 269
     Names for males and females
          266
     Names for the young 267
     National insect 272
     Number of species 270
     Products from 270
     Regeneration 263
     Termites 274
     Threatened or endangered
          species, U.S. 193
     Vectors 358
Insulin 329
Intelligence
     Animals 263

Artificial *See* Artificial intelli-
     gence
Intelligent life on other planents
     58
Intelsat (International
     Telecommunications Satellite
     Organization) 486
Internal environment, human
     body 318, 330, 335
International Astronomical Union
     34, 56
International atomic time 413
International date line 413
International morse code 476
International phonetic alphabet
     475
International system of units 348,
     394
Internet 490
Interstate roads *See* Roads
Intestine 318
Intoxication *See* Blood—Alcohol
     levels
Inventions
     Alphabets for the blind 476
     Aluminum process 133
     Ammonia process 145
     Atomic bomb 426
     Bowie knife 424
     Cars 455
     Cement 148
     Chemotherapy 384
     Civil War, American 424, 425
     COBOL 499
     Colt revolver 424
     Computer 491
     Dry ice 144
     Dynamite 152
     ECG, mobile 377
     Fiberglass 148
     Fireworks 152
     Gasoline pump 161
     Glass 146, 147
     Glass blocks 147
     Glass, bulletproof 147
     Glass process 148
     Gun powder 151
     Jarvik-7 artificial heart 389
     Logarithms 510
     Macadam roads 149
     Machine gun 425
     Mine barrage 424
     Morse code, International
          476
     Mouse, computer 497
     Plastic 153

Relief maps 100
Revolver 424
Sandpaper 151
Silicon chips 495
Slide rule 511
Solder 150
Technetium 138
Teflon 154
Television 483
Thermopane glass 147
TNT 152
Warfare 424
Invertebrates
     Regeneration 263
Involuntary muscles 324
     Controlling swallowing 317
Iodine
     Components in human body
          311
Ionosphere 72
Iridology 392
Iron 16, 19
     Components in human body
          311
     Ironworks in U.S. 136
Iron pyrite 131
Ironwood 141
Irrational number, Pi 508
ISBN (International Standard
     Book Number) 480
Isinglass 143
Islamic calendar 404
Isotopes
     Dating agent 223
     In elements, most 20
Israel
     Space launches 67
Italy
     Biothermal energy 155
IVF *See* In vitro fertilization
Ivory Trade Ban 191
Ivy, damage caused to walls 244

J

Jacquard, Joseph Marie 492
Janssen, Hans 418
Janssen, Zacharias 57, 418
January
     Derivation 410
     January 1 404
Japan
     Abacus 509
     Fifth generation computers
          492
     Neural networks 492
     Robots, industrial 420

Solar energy 155
    Television development 485
Japanese calendars 405
Jarvik-7
    Artificial heart 389
Jeffreys, Alec 423
Jemison, Mae C. 66
Jenner, Edward 229
Jenney, William Le Baron 432
Jersey barrier 438
Jesse H. Jones Memorial Bridge 441
Jet lag 364
Jet stream 110
Jewelry
    Gold content 134
    Gold leaf 135
    White gold 135
Jewish calendar 404
Jimson weed 244
Johnny Appleseed 253
Joliot (lunar crater) 51
Joliot-Curie, Frederic 51
Jovian planets 44
Julian Day
    Calendar 405, 408
    Count 406
July, derivation 410
Jumping beans 276
June, derivation 410
Jupiter 44
    Galileo mission 67
    Rings 42

K

Kaiser, Henry J. 450
Kangaroos
    Reproduction 294
Kantrowitz, Adrian
    First heart transplant in
        United States 389
Kasner, Edward 507
Kasperak, Mike
    First heart transplant in
        United States 389
KDKA, Pittsburgh 482
Kelvin, Lord 217
    See also Thomson, William
Kelvin temperature scale 25
Kennelly-Heaviside Layer
    Effect on radio transmission
        482
Kerosene
    Pump 161
Kharizmi, Muhammad ibn Musa al
    491

Kidney stones
    Composition 370
Kilby, Jack 495
Killer bees See Bees—Africanized
Killing frost 248, 249
Kissing Bridge 440
Kleist, E. Georg van 5
Kludge (computer term) 502
Knee surgery 388
Knife, Bowie 424
Knoll, Max 420
Koalas, reproduction 294
Koch, Robert 229, 230
Korolev, Sergei P. 67
Kowal, Charles 52
Krill 278
Krupp family, gun manufacturers
    426

L

LaBrea tar pits 92
Lactic acid, role in sore muscles
    325
Lactose intolerance 362
Laika 63
Lakes
    Largest 81
Lamarck, Jean Baptiste 106, 223,
    224
Landsat 101
Language difficulties
    Dyslexia 368
Languages, computer
    Ada 498
    COBOL 499
Larboard 448
Lasers 419
    Applications 419
    Compact discs 489
Latex, as petroleum source 157
Latin America
    Rate of deforestation 181
Latitudes, Horse 110
Laurasia 84
Lauterbar, Paul 378
Lavoisier, Antoine-Laurent 5, 15
Lawn clippings 251
LDL See Low density lipoproteins
LDPE plastic, recycling 206
Lead 19
    Emmissions, sources 356
    Poisoning 356, 357
    Sulphide 130
Leaning Tower of Pisa 433
Leap second 409
Leap year 409

Leaves turning color 234, 235
Lee, Mark 66
Left turn 463
Left-handedness, footedness, etc.
    Percentage in population
        321
Legionnaire's disease 359
Leibniz, Gottfried Wilhelm 491
Leith, Emmet 420
Length
    Biblical units 393
    Metric units See Metric units
    U.S. customary units 395
Lenses, for vision correction 338
Leonard of Pisa 506
Leonov, Alexei 64
Leprosy 360
Leyden jar 5
Libby, Willard 223
Liberty garden 250
Liberty Ships 450
Lice
    Disease 359
    Vectors 359
License Plates 460
Lichens 228
Lichtenberg figures 422
Life
    On Mars 46
    On other planets 58
Life spans
    Animals 259
    Humans 259
    Nuclear power plant 163
    Oldest authenticated human
        322
Light
    Coherent 419
    Colors 6
    Doppler effect 8
    Perception 337
    Speed of light 7
Light Amplification by Stimulated
    Emission of Radiation See Lasers
Light year 56
Lighting
    Incandescent compared to
        fluorescent 173
Lightning
    Amperes 108
    Ball Lighting 108
    Bead lightning 108
    Chain lightning 108
    Distance calculation 108
    Effects 121
    Heat lightning 108

Length 108
Number of deaths 120
Odds against being struck 344
Product 109
Repetition 108
Ribbon lightning 108
Sheet lightning 108
Speed 108
Streak lightning 108
Temperature 107
Types 108
Victims 107
Voltage 108
Lightning bugs 277
Lights
Brown Mountain 110
Traffic *See* Traffic lights
Lincoln, Abraham 363
Lincoln Highway 437
Lindbergh, Charles A. 468
Linnaeus, Carolus 25, 224, 226
Lippershey, Hans 57, 419
Liquid measures
U.S. customary units 398
Liquid state, Chemical elements at room temperature in 19
Liquids 11
Lisa (microcomputer) 494
Listing, Johann Benedict 517
Lithium 16
Lithotripsy
Kidney stones 390
Liver function 326
PCBs 194
Living stones 244
Loadline in shipping 450
Lobsters 278
Locust, desert 270
Lodestone 138
Logarithms 510, 511
Logical operators 512
London
First traffic light 438
Lone Star, The 132
Long ton 399
Longevity *See* Life spans
Lost wax process 421
Lou Gehrig's disease 364
Low density lipoproteins (LDL)
Bad cholesterol 350
LSI (Silicon chip size) 495
Lucky numbers, 7 508
Luffa sponge 143
Lumber, house construction amount 429

Lunar eclipses *See* Eclipses—Lunar
Lungs
Role in oxygenating blood 331
Size 329
Lyme disease
Causes 359
Symptoms 359
Lymphocytes 313
See also B lymphocytes, T lymphocytes
Lymphokines 314

M

MacAdam, John Louden 149
Macadam roads 149
Mace 423
Machine guns 425
Machine language (computers) 498
Machines
Power take-off 418
Six simple 416
Macintosh microcomputer (first) 494
Maclure, William 100
Macrophage *See* White blood cells
MADAM (Manchester automatic digital machine) 494
Magee, Carlton C. 466
Magical numbers, 7 508
Magnesium 16
Components in human body 311
Magnetic declination 99
Magnetic recording 488
Magnetic resonance imaging *See* MRI
Magnetism
Founders 4
Homing pigeons 289
Lodestone 138
Magnetosphere 72
Mail delivery
Animals 475
Maiman, Theodore 419
Mainframe computers
Booting 499
Malaria
Causes 359
Panama Canal 359
Malayan sun bear 299
Malleus bone (ear) 340
Mallon, Mary 360
Mammals

Armadillos 300
Bats 293
Bears 263, 299
Blood types 264
Camels 299
Capybaras 300
Cats *See* Cats
Chamois 301
Color vision 263
Cougar 298
Dogs *See* Dogs
Echidna 295
Egg-laying mammals 295
Elephants 297
Flying mammals 293
Gestation period 291
Horses 296, 297
Intelligence 263
Life span 259
Marsupials *See* Marsupials
Mules and donkeys 296
Names for groups 291
Names for males and females 266
Pigs, potbellied 309
Platypus 294, 295
Porcupines 300
Recently extinct 189
Rhinoceros 289
Skunks 301
Speed 264
Threatened and endangered species U.S. 193
Venomous 294
Whales *See* Whales
Wolves 298
Mammoth Cave 91
Mammoths
Comparison to mastodons 188
Man in orbit
First 60
First American 60
Man in space
First 60
First American 60
Manatee 296
Manganese
Components in human body 311
Manhattan Project 426
Manhole covers' shape 439
MANIAC (mathematical analyzer, numerator, integrator, and computer) 493
Manned space flight

Longest 63
Longest American 63
Mantle 74
Maps
    Earliest map of America 100
    Relief 100
March, derivation 410
Marconi, Guglielmo 480
Marianas Trench 75
Marijuana 388
    Legally grown 388
Marine Mammal Protection Act
  193
Marine mammals
    Breath-holding capacity 292
    Diving ability 295
    Intelligence 263
    Life span 259
    Manatee 296
    Names for males and females
      266
    Names for the young 267
    Names, Group 291
    Porpoises and dolphins 296
    Size 295
    Smallest 262
    Weight 295
Mark I computers 498
Mark twain 448
Married couple in space 66
Mars 44
    Life on 46
Marsupials
    Anteaters 294
    Bandicoots 294
    Gestation period 291
    Kangaroos 294
    Koalas 294
    Life span 259
    Names for males and females
      266
    Names for the young 267
    Names, Group 291
    Opossums 294
    Reproduction 294
    Tasmanian devils 294
    Wallabies 294
    Wombats 294
Mass
    Of the Earth 73
Mastodons
    Comparison to mammoths
      188
Mathematics
    Calculation speeds 509

Atoms *See* Atoms
Density *See* Density of matter
Inertia *See* Inertia
Motion *See* Motion
Quantum mechanics *See*
  Quantum mechanics
Solids 145
States of matter 10
Structure 13
Subatomic particles *See*
  Subatomic particles
Superconductivity 2
Mauchly, John William 494
Maxwell's demon 3
May, derivation 410
May, Gene 469
McCandless, II, Bruce 64
Mean (definition) 512
    Comparison to median 512
Meander 82
Measurement
    Energy 455
    Horizon 401
    Light 7
    Riverboat depths 448
    Sound barrier (STC) 431
    Temperature *See*
      Temperature scales
    Time *See* Time
    U.S. customary linear mea-
      sures *See* U.S. customary
      measurements
    Weight *See* Weight
    Wind 115
Measurement devices
    Astrolabe 57
    Calendar *See* Calendar
    Radiocarbon dating 223
    Theodolite 402
    Time *See* Calendar
Measurement units
    Area 400
    Astronomical unit 56
    Astronomy 56
    Avoirdupois weights 401
    Biblical units 393
    Length 395
    Light year 56
    Parsec 56
    SI system of measures 394
    Time *See* Time—
      Measurement units
    Troy weights 401
    U.S. customary dry and liquid
      units 398
    Water 400

Median (definition) 512
    Comparison to arithmetic
      mean 512
Medical branches
    Comparisons 376
Medical care
    Hospital ships 450
Medical equipment
    Fiber optics 487
Medical instruments
    Viewing internal organs and
      functions 378
Medical research 388
Medical schools 375
Medications
    Plant origins 182, 382
Megachannel Extraterrestrial Assay
    See META
Meiosis 219
Melanin
    Color of eyes 338
Meltdown 166
Men
    Desirable weight 319
    Heaviest man 320
    On the moon 62
Mendel, Gregor 212, 213
Mendeleyev, Dmitri Ivanovich 15
Mendelian Inheritance 212
Mercalli, Guiseppe 96
Merck and Company 383
Mercury 19, 44, 373
    Naming of surface features
      56
Mercury poisoning 357
Mermaid's purse 280
Mesomorph
    Human body typing 320
Mesons 12
Mesopotamia, Abacus 509
Mesosphere 71
Messing Bridge 440
META 59
Metallurgy, powder 421
Metals
    Alloys 136
    Aluminum 133
    Gold *See* Gold
    Iron 136
    Noble metals 23, 134
    Pewter 136
    Precious metals 134
    Silver 136
    Solder 150
    Steel *See* Steel
    Superconductivity 2

Technetium 138
Metals, precious
    Measurement units 401
Metamorphic rocks 127
Meteor showers 54
Meteoriod theory of dinosaur
    extinction 189
Meteoroids 54
Meteorites 54
    Largest 55
Meteors 54
    Showers 54
Meter (length) 395
Methanol
    Comparison to different fuels
    162
Metius, Jacob 57
Metric ton 399
Metric units
    Area measures 400
    Conversion to U.S. customary
    units 396
    Meter 395
    Prefixes 506
    SI system 394
    U.S. customary units 395,
    398
Metropolis, Nicholas C. 493
Mexican jumping beans 276
Mice
    Heart rate 293
    Used to detect carbon
    monoxide 158
Michelin, Andre and Edouard 458
Michelin tires 458
Michelson, Albert A. 7
Michelson-Morley experiment 7
Microcomputers
    Booting 499
    DOS 502
    First 494
    IBM 502
    Operating systems 502
Microscopes
    Compound 418
    Electron 420
Microsoft
    DOS 502
Microwave signals
    Effect of weather 484
Midnight 403
MiG 473
Migration
    Arctic tern 285
    Geese 286
    Hummingbirds 288

Swallows 286
Milieu Interieur 318, 330
Military time 416
Milk
    Inability to digest 362
Milky Way galaxy 33
Mimicry, insects 214
Mine barrage 424
Miner's canary 158
Minerals
    Antimony glance 130
    Aragonite 128
    Aztec money 128
    Beryls 132
    Calcite 128
    Classification by external
    characteristics 129
    Color 129
    Comparison to rocks 129
    Diamonds 130-132
    Emeralds 132
    Fool's gold 131
    Galena 130
    Gold *See* Gold
    Hardness scale 129
    Indian dollars 128
    Iron pyrite 131
    Lead sulphide 130
    Pioneer dollars 128
    Pitchblende 130
    Precious stones 132
    Pyrite, Iron 131
    Quartz 130
    Rubies 132
    Sapphires 132
    Star rubies 132
    Star sapphires 132
    Stibnite 130
Minerals, strategic 129
Mines
    Coal 158
    Temperature 74
Minicomputers
    Booting 499
Minuteman missile, range 427
Missiles, U.S. range 427
Mississippi Valley
    Acid rain 197
Mississippi-Missouri River system
    Length 83
Mississippian Period
    Coal 158
Mistletoe poisoning, symptoms
  355
Mitchondria
    Number in cells 220

Mitosis 219
Möbius, August Ferdinand 517
Möbius strip 517
Mode (mathematics) 512
Moho 74
Mohorovicic, Andrija 74
Mohs, Friedrich 129
Mohs scale 129
Mojave Desert
    Size 89
    Solar energy 155
Molding, sintering 421
Molds (Fossils) 128
Mole 27
Mollusks
    Bivalves 280
    Cephalopods 280
    Chitons 280
    Gastropods 280
    Monoplacophora 280
    Threatened and endangered
    species, U.S. 193
    Tooth shells 280
Molybdenum, components in
  human body 311
Monera, kingdom 225
Monkey ball tree 237
Monkey Trial 214
Monkeys
    In space 63
    Intelligence 263
Monoclonal antibodies 384
Monoplacophora 280
Months
    Derivation of names *See* indi-
    vidual months
    Symbolic flowers 241
Moods
    Effect of color 339
Moon
    Apogee 49
    Blue moon 50
    Circumerence 49
    Color 50
    Craters named for Curie fam-
    ily 51
    Diameter 49
    Distance form Earth 49
    First golf shot on 63
    First man on 62
    First meal on 65
    First word on 64
    Full *See* Full moon
    Genesis rock 51
    Harvest moon 50
    Hunter's moon 50

Lunar calendar *See*
    Calendars—Lunar
Men on 62
New *See* New Moon
Perigee 49
Phases 49
Relation to incidents of vio-
    lence 344
Rotation 49
Side facing Earth 49
Size 49
Tail 51
Moons
    Naming of surface features
    56
    Of the planets 48
Moraine 89
Moreno, Jacob L. 392
Morgan, Augustus de 512
Morley, E. W. 7
Morning Star Flail 423
Morse, Samuel F. B. 477
Mortality rates
    Black widow spider bites 356
    Botulism 353
    Heart attacks 365
    Poison mushrooms 355
Mosquitoes
    Bite 274
    Disease vectors 359
Moths 270
    Gypsy moth 238
Motion
    Coriolis effect *See* Coriolis
    effect
    Drag *See* Drag—Air
    Inertia 2
    Laws of motion 2
    Quantum mechanics *See*
    Quantum mechanics
Motion study 519
Motor vehicles
    Accidents, fatalities 344-346
    Cars *See* Cars
    Taxicabs 466
    Trucks 466
Motorcycle accidents
    Fatalities 344
Mount
    For individual mountain *See*
    significant portion of name,
    i.e., Rushmore, Mount
Mouse, computer 497
Mountain lion *See* Cougar
Movie stunts, glass 148
Mowing 251

Mr. Yuk 354
MRI
    Comparison with x-ray 378
    Medical technology 378
MS-DOS *See* DOS
MSG, allergies 371
MSI (Silicon chip size) 495
Muir, John (Father of conserva-
    tion) 186
Mules, number 296
Müller, Fritz 214
Müller, Paul 257
Multiplication
    Abacus versus calculator 509
Murphy, G.M. 145
Muscles
    Hamstring, function 324
    Jaw 325
    Model to depict 325
    Number in human body 324
    Number used to smile or
    frown 325
    Role in goose bumps 335
    Sore from exercise 325
Mushrooms
    Poisonous 355
Musical scale
    Sound frequency 9
Musschenbroek, Pieter van 5
Mustard plaster 391
Mutualism 290
Mycology 228
Myocardial infarction *See* Heart
    attack
Myrrh 143

N

Nader, Ralph 462
Nagasaki, Japan
    Atomic bomb 427
Nails 431
    See also Screws
Nails
    Growth in dead body 336
    Growth rate 336
Names
    Horses, thoroughbred 297
    Hurricanes 115
    Male and female animals 266
Names, Group
    Animals 267, 269
    Birds 283
    Insects 269
    Mammals 291
Naming of celestial objects 56
Nanosecond 498

Napier, John 491, 510, 511
Napier's bones (or rods) 491, 510
Napoleon Bonaparte, cause of
    death 372
Narcolepsy 364
Nasal septum repair
    Second opinions 388
National Archives and Records
    Administration 489
National Cancer Institute 382
Natural attractions
    Most popular in U.S. 91
Natural drugs
    Pharmacognosy 379
Natural gas *See* Gas, Natural
Natural Selection 213
Naturopathy 375
Navel orange 253
Neanderthal man
    Brain size compared to
    Homo sapiens 327
    Tools 416
Neap tides 84
Nearsightedness 338
Necrotizing fasciitis 361
Nectar 238
Negative ion generator 391
Neptune 44, 47
    Position in solar system 47
    Rings 42
Nerves
    In skin 334
    Largest 325
Nesting boxes *See* Birdhouses
Net registered tonnage 449
Netplex 490
Neumann, John von 494
Neural networks 493
Neurons 326
Neutron stars 32
Neutrons 12
New Madrid earthquakes 97
New moon 49
New Year's Day 404
    Sea time determination 415
New York Infirmary for Women
    and Children 375
Newman, Max 492
Newspapers
    Recycling 172, 205
    Waste paper 205
Newton, Isaac 2
Niagara Falls
    Erosion 84
Nickel silver 136
Night 403

Nightshade 354
  Deadly *See* Strychnine
Nile River, length 83
NIMBY/NIMFY syndromes 201
Niño, El, environmental effects 180
Nitric oxide
  Pollution 196
Nitrocellulose 153
Nitrohydrochloric acid 144
NMR *See* MRI
Noah's Ark, wood of 448
Nobel, Alfred 152
Nobel Prize 383
  Chemistry 145, 222
  Physiology or medicine 218
Noble metals 18, 134
Nonrapid eye movement *See* NREM sleep
Noon 403
North Star *See* Polaris
Northern Lights 106
Northernmost points of land 86
NOT (logical operators) 512
"Not In My Back Yard" 201
"Not In My Front Yard" 201
November, derivation 410
Nowcasting 124
Noyce, Robert 495
NREM sleep 315
  See also REM sleep
Nuclear autumn 427
Nuclear chain reaction, contained 426
Nuclear fuel
  Energy output compared to other fuels 169
Nuclear magnetic resonance imaging *See* MRI
Nuclear power/Nuclear reactors
  Accidents 165
  By country 164
  Chernobyl accident 166
  Life span compared to other types of power 163
  Life span of power plant 163
  Meltdown 166
  Oldest operational plant in U.S. 163
  Safety 165-6
  U.S. energy production 170
Nuclear transfer 217
Nuclear war
  Doomsday clock 416
Nuclear waste 204
  Storage 202

U.S. dump sites
Nuclear Waste Policy Act 202
Nuclear winter 427
Nuclear-powered cars 460
Numbering of U.S. roads 437
Numerals *See* Numbering system, i.e., Arabic numerals, Hindu numerals
Nursing homes
  Number in U.S. 376

O

Obsidian tools, Neanderthal 416
Ocean Liners
  Queen Elizabeth 451
  Titanic 450
Oceans
  Composition 77
  Deepest points 75
  Tides 84
Ockham's razor 521
Octane
  Octane rating 161
  See also Gasoline
October, derivation 410
Octopi, life span 259
Odor maps, Homing pigeons 289
Off-shore platform 443
Office Buildings 433
  First 432
Oil fields
  Largest 159
Oil of vitriol 144
Oil wells
  First in the U.S. 159
  First offshore drilling 163
Oil, crude 170
  See also Petroleum
  Energy output compared to other fuels 169
  First well in the U.S. 159
  Grades 160
  Measurement units 167
  Pennsylvania 159, 160
  Production levels 159
  U.S. energy production 170
  Weight 167
Oil, heating
  Energy output compared to other fuels 169
Oils, essential 142
Old Reliable 63
Oldest person 322
Olds, Ransom Eli 457
On the Origin of Species 213
Onager 423

Ontario, Lake
  Acid rain 197
Ontogeny Recapitulates Phylogeny 220
Oort, Jan 53
"Open Sesame" 243
Operating system, Computer 499
Operation Ranch Hand 199
Ophthalmologists 376
Opossums
  Gestation period 291
  Reproduction 294
Opposition 30
Optical illusion 338
Opticians 376
Optometrists 376
OR (logical operators) 512
Orange
  Navel 253
Orangutans
  Intelligence 263
Organic compounds
  Synthesization 13
Organs, largest 326, 329
Orient Express 454
Origin of Life 217
Oroville Dam 443
Orphan drugs 381
Osteopathic medicine 375
Ostrich, North African
  Egg size 285
Oughtred, William 511
Outer Space Treaty 60
Ovaries
  Functions 329
  Pelvic inflammatory disease 370
Owens Illinois Glass Company 148
Oxbow Lake 82
Oxidation
  Spontaneous combustion 4
Oxpecker 289
Oxygen
  Abundancy 20
  Addition to blood 331
Ozone
  In the upper atmosphere 179
  Levels, symptoms 347

P

Pacemakers
  Weight 390
Packaging
  Average American's contribution to solid waste 203
  Municipal solid waste 204

Pain relief 385
Painter *See* Cougar
Paints
    White pigment 151
Paleontology
    Tools 416
Palitzsch, Johann 53
Pallas 51
Palmer, Daniel David 375
Panama Canal 359
Pancreas, functions 329
Pangaea 84
Panspermia 217
Paper 205
    Newspaper waste 205
    Wood content 139
Paraheliotropism 233
Paralysis
    Lou Gehrig's disease 359
Parasitic disease
    Zoonosis 358
Parathyroid glands, functions 329
Parity bit 499
Parker, James 149
Parkes, Alexander 153
Parking meter 466
Parks
    Canyons 92
    Hancock Park 92
    LaBrea tar pits 92
    Most popular in U.S. 91
    Mount Rushmore National
        Monument 93
Parrots
    Diseases transmitted to
        humans 358
Parsec 56
Parsimony, law of 521
Pascal, Blaise 491, 515
Pascal's triangle 515
Passenger pigeon, extinction 190
Passionflower 242
Passive solar energy *See* Solar
    energy
Passover
    Date determination 412
Pasteur, Louis 229
Pasteurization 230
Paternity testing 422
Patient care
    Iatrogenic illnesses 370
Patient-controlled analgesia (PCA)
    385
PC-DOS *See* DOS
PCA *See* Patient-controlled analge-
    sia

PCBs
    Health hazards 194
Peacemaker missile, range 427
Pearl of Allah 132
Pearl of Lao-tze 132
Pearl, largest natural 132
Pedicar 175
Pelvic inflammatory disease 370
Penguins, Predators of 288
Penicillin 383
Pennsylvania crude oil *See* Oil,
    crude—Pennsylvania
Pennsylvania Hawk Mountain
    Sanctuary 185
Pennsylvanian period, coal 158
Penny nails 431
Pentagon building 433
Penzias, Arno A. 29
Percentage of increase 518
Perfect number 505
Perihelion, Earth 45
Periodic table 15
Periodontal disease 357
Permafrost 86, 123
Perpetual calendar 405
Perrier, C. 138
Perscription drugs 386
Pershing missile range 427
Pesah, Date determination 412
PET, Comparison to PVC 205
PET plastic
    Recycling 206
Petals 238
Petrification (Fossils) 128
Petrified lightning 109
Petrified wood 141
Petroleum
    Composition 157
    Energy consumption, by
        country 171
    Gasoline Production 160
    Hydrocarbon cracking 160
    Plant sources 157
    Reserves, U.S. 172
Petrology 128
Pets
    Birds 309
    Health care 345
    Hermit crab 310
    White House 310
Pewter 136
pH
    Blood 331
    Saliva 331
    Urine 331
Pharmacognosy 379

Phases of the moon 49
Philadelphia Zoological Garden
    185
Philippines
    World's largest natural pearl
        found 132
Phillips Company 489
Phillips screws 431
Philosopher's stone 19
Phlegm (as humor) 330
Phlogiston 4
Phobias 369, 372
Phosphenes (optical effect) 338
Photochemical air pollution *See*
    Smog
Photons 419
Photosynthesis 222, 232, 234
Phototropism 233
Photovoltaic energy
    U.S. energy production 170
Physical effects of spaceflight 61
Physical science
    Founders 27
Physicians 374
    Ancient 374
    Female 375
    Ophthalmologists 376
Physics, Atomic *See* Atomic
    physics
Physiology
    Founder 318
Pi (value) 508
Piazzi, Giuseppe 51
Pica 371
Piccard, Jacques 78
Picture element 501
PID *See* Pelvic inflammatory dis-
    ease
Pigeons
    Homing 289
Pigments
    Titanium dioxide 151
Pigs 298
    Diseases transmitted to
        humans 358
    Intelligence 263
    Pets 309
Pilkington, Alistair 147
Pioneer 3 72
Pioneer Dollars 128
Piri Re'is map 101
Pisa, Leaning tower 433
Pisano, Bonanno 433
Pisé 432
Pistil 239
Pitchblende 130

Pitcher plant 240
Pittsburgh
    Bridges 441
Pituitary glands, functions 329
Pixel 501
Planes *See* Airplanes
Planet X 47
Planets
    Color 42
    Day, Length of 44
    Diameter 42
    Distance from sun 41
    Gravitational force 43
    Inferior 44
    Jovian 44
    Moons 48
    Naming of surface features
        56
    Revolution, Period of 41
    Rings 42
    Rotation 44
    Superior 44
    Terrestrial 44
    Time to orbit sun 41
Planktonic crustaceans
    Krill 278
Plantar warts *See* Warts
Plants
    Balled-and-burlapped 249
    Bare-rooted 249
    Carnivorous 240
    Cells 232
    Classification 224, 226
    Cloning 217
    Container-grown 249
    Growth, exposure to music
        233
    Kingdom category 224, 226
    Patent (first) 258
    Photosynthesis 222
    Poisonous to cats 308
    Products *See* Essential oils;
        Luffa sponge
    Symbolic meanings 240
    Threatened and endangered
        species, U.S. 193
Plants, poisonous
    Poison ivy 255
    Poison oak 255
    Poison sumac 255
Plants as energy sources
    U.S. energy production 170
Plants as fuel *See* Biomass energy
Plasmas 10
Plastics 153
    Biodegrable 153

Glass-fiber-reinforced plastics
    148
    Recycling 206
Plate glass 147
Plate tectonics 84
Platinum 16
Platypus, duck-billed 294-5
Pleaching 254
Pleistocene Epoch
    Great Ice Age 88
Plessor
    Medical instruments 379
Plimsoll line 450
Plimsoll mark 450
"Plumber's" solder 150
Plunkett, Roy J. 154
Pluto 44, 48
    Discovery 47
    Position in solar system 47
    Retrograde motion 44
    Rotation 44
Pneumonia 358
Pochon, Henri 229
Points, Measurement units 132
Poison control centers 354
Poison ivy 255
    Causes and Symptoms 368
Poison oak 255
Poison sumac 255
Poisoning 354
    Alcohol 350
    Children 354
    Red tides 181
    Treatment, activated charcoal
        353
Poisonous snakes
    Habitat 282
Poisons
    Black widow spider 356
    Curare 355
    Damp in coal mines 138
    Lead 356
    Mushrooms 355
    Ozone 179
    Strychnine 355
Polaris 33
Polaris missile, range 427
Police radar 464
Poliomyelitis vaccine 383
Pollination 231
Pollution
    Acid rain 196, 197
    Alternative fuels 162
    Detergents 178
    Eutrophication 178
    Fertilizers 178

Gasoline emissions 162, 195
Greenhouse effect 193
Health hazards 181
Indoor air 200
Industrial wastes 178
Ozone destruction in the
    upper atmosphere 179
Ozone in the lower atmos-
    phere 179, 347
Reformulated gasoline 161
Sewage 178
Water 76, 178
Pollution, Air
    Acid rain 196, 197
    Gasoline engine emissions
        162, 195
    Smog 195
Polychlorinated biphenyls *See*
    PCBs
Polydipsia (excessive thirst) 320
Polyethylene
    Comparison to PVC 205
Polystyrene
    Comparison to PVC 205
Polyvinyl chloride *See* PVC Plastics
Pong 494
Pontiac Silverdome Stadium 436
Pontoon bridges 441
Porcupine
    Quills 300
Porpoises, comparison to dolphins
    296
Port 448
Portland cement 149
Post, Wiley 469
Potatoes 354
Potassium 16, 19
    Components in human body
        311
Potbellied pigs 309
Powder metallurgy 422
Power take-off 418
Precious metals 134
    Gold *See* Gold
Precious stones
    Largest 132
    Weight units 401
Precipitation
    Clouds *See* Clouds
    Freezing rain 122
    Hail 121
    Rain *See* Rain
    Sleet 122
Predation 274
Premature old age
    Progeria 369

Prescription drugs 379
    Frequency prescribed 381
    Shelf life 380
Pressure, blood *See* Blood pressure
Prime meridian 100
Prime numbers 506
Probability
    Of a triple play 519
    Shared birthday 518
Progeria 369
Programming, computer 498
Prohibition
    Machine guns 425
Project Sentinel 59
Proper divisors 505
Prostate removal
    Second opinions 388
Protista
    Kingdom 225
Protons 12
Protruding ears
    Causes 321
Przewalski's horse 297
Psychodrama 389
    Developed 392
Pug dogs 305
Pulsars 32
Pulsating radio sources *See*
    Pulsars
Puma *See* Cougar
Punched cards 491, 493
Purple 478
Purring of cats 308
PVC plastics
    Air pollution 205
Pyramid
    Volume 513
Pyrite, Iron 131
Pythagoras 516

Q

Q-BOP process 137
QB 222
Quad
    Comparison of different fuels
    169
Quagga 189
Quantum mechanics
    Founders 24
Quarks 11
Quartz, Cap May diamonds 130
Quasars 30
Quasi-stellar radio source *See*
    Quasars
Quebec Bridge 441
Queen Elizabeth 451

Quills, porcupines 300

R

R-value 430
Rabies in humans 357
RAD *See* Radiation absorbed dose
    (rad)
Radar
    Detection devices 464
    Police radar 464
Radial tires 459
Radiation
    Dental x-rays 348
    Measurement units (expo-
    sure) 348
Radiation absorbed dose (rad) 348
Radio
    AM/FM Broadcast ranges 482
    Invention 480
    Time signal 414
    Transmission codes 478
Radio station, First 481
Radioactive materials
    Pitchblende 130
Radiocarbon dating 223
Radium 16
    Pitchblende 130
    Radon 347
Radon 347
Rahe, Richard H. 343
Railroad ties 139
Railroad worm 256
Railroads, First in U.S. 454
Railway, Funicular 455
Rain
    Freezing rain 122
    Frog and Toad showers 121
    Rainiest place 119
    Shape 119
    Speed 119
    Thunder *See* Thunder
Rain forests 177
Rain shadow (gardening) 247
Rainbow colors 109
Rammed earth 432
Rapid eye movement sleep *See*
    REM sleep
Rasmussen report 165
Read only memory *See* ROM
Recombinant DNA/RNA 215
Rectangle, area 514
Recycling
    Building materials 208
    Newspaper 172
    Plastics 206
    Symbol on plastic 206

"Red Baron" 473
Red dog 138
Red shift 8
Red tides 181
Redier, Antoine 415
Reflexology 391
Refraction, light 109
Regeneration
    Animals 263
Reindeer
    Mail delivery 475
Relativity, theory of 7
Relief Maps *See* Maps—Relief
REM *See* Roentgen equivalent man
    (rem)
REM sleep 315
Reproduction
    Emperor penguin 288
    Embryo 220
    Marsupials 294
    Virus 222
Reptiles *See* Amphibians and rep-
    tiles
Réseau, Jean Bernard 91
Reservoirs, Water 76
    See also Aquifers
Resins
    Frankincense 143
Retina 336, 338
    Optical illusion 338
    Phosphenes 338
Revetment 443
Revolution of planets around sun
    41
Revolver, Colt 424
Rhinoceros, black
    Bird on back 289
Rhizome (flower) 239
Rhythms in life 220
Ribbon lightning 109
Ribonucleic Acid *See* RNA
Richter, Charles W. 96
Richter scale 96
Richthofen, Manfred von 473
Ride, Sally K. 65, 66
Right turn 463
Right-handedness, footedness, etc.
    Percentage in population
    321
Rigid Beam Bridge 439
Ring of Fire *See* Circle of Fire
Ringed planets 42
Risk factors (health) 343
Riverboats
    Measurement of depth 448
Rivers, longest 83

RNA 218
Road Tunnels 439
Roads
    Belgian block materials 149
    First U.S. transcontinental
      road 437
    Macadam roads 149
    Manhole covers' shape 439
    Numbering of U.S. roads 437
    Speed limits 345
    Traffic light installation 438
    U.S. road mileage 437
Robots, industrial 420
Roc 284
    Egg size 284
Rock of Gibraltar *See* Gibraltar,
  Rock of
Rocks
    Classification 127
    Comparison to minerals 129
    Formations 89
    Products *See* Diatomite
Rockville Bridge 441
Rodents
    Capybaras 300
    Gestation 291
    Life span 259
Roebling, John A. 442
Roentgen equivalent man (rem)
  348
Roger Commission 69
Rogers, William 69
Roget, Peter Mark 511
Rogunskaya Dam 443
Roller Coasters 446
ROM 499
Roman calendars 405
Roman numerals 505
Roman pewter 136
Roofs
    Largest building 435
Rootstock (flower) 239
Roses, symbolic colors 242
Rosin 141
Rosing, Boris 483
Rosy periwinkle
    Anti-cancer drugs 382
Rotation of planets 44
Rotation speed of the Earth 45
Rotational time 402
Round-the-world airplane flights
  469
Route numbers *See* Roads
Royal water 144
Rubidium 16
Ruby, largest 132

Rule of 70 518
Rule, slide *See* Slide rule
Rumble seat 459
Running speed of animals 264
Rushmore, Mount, National
  Monument 93
Rutan, Dick 469
Rutherford, Ernest 10

S

Sabin, Albert 384
Saffir, Herbert 116
Sailfish, Cosmopolitan
    Speed 277
Sailing 447
Saint Elmo's Fire 109
St. Helens, Mount
    Eruption 94
St. Martin, Alexis 316
Salamanders
    Gestation period 259
Saliva
    Normal pH 331
Salk, Jonas E. 383
Salmon, spawning 280
Saluki 302
San Francisco earthquakes, sever-
  ity 98
Sand cats, habitat 298
Sandpaper 151
Sandstone
    Weathering 89
Santorio, Santorio 24
Sapphire, largest carved 132
Satellite dish 484, 485
Satellites 67
    Communications 486
    Communications, shortwave
      radio 483
    Geostationary 488
    Images of the Earth 75
    Orbits 488
    Solar energy 155
    Studying environmental
      impacts 181
Saturn 44
    Rings 42
Saudi Arabia
    Oil and gas fields 159
Savitskaya, Svetlana 64
Scaliger, Joseph Justus 406
Scandinavia
    Acid rain 197
Scavenger cells *See* White blood
  cells
Schade, Otto 485

Schwartz, Berthold 152
Sciatic nerves 325
Scientific instruments
    Astrolabe 57
Scientific standards
    DIN standards (German) 402
Scopes, John T. 214
Scopes (Monkey) Trial 214
SCP-DOS *See* DOS
Screamer *See* Cougar
Screws 431
Seaplanes 471
Search for Extraterrestrial
  Intelligence *See* SETI
Sears, Roebuck and Company
  mail-order houses 436
Sears Tower 434
Seashells
    See also Shells
    Sound resonance 8
Seasons
    Cause 45, 410
    Dates 411
    Lengths 410
    Summer 105
Seat belts 462
Seawalls 442
Second generation computers 492
Second Star of Africa diamond 132
Sedimentary rocks 127
Seedlings, hardening off 247
Seeds
    Chia 255
    How long to keep 247
Segre, Emilio 138
Seismograph 95, 96
Selenium
    Components in human body
      311
Sepal 238
September, derivation 410
Serpents as symbol of healing 373
Sesame seeds 243
Set theory (Venn diagrams) 512
SETI 59
Seven (magical number) 508
Sewer manhole covers 439
Sex-linked dominant/recessive
  212
Shakespeare garden 250
Sharks 280
Shar-pei 304
Sheet lightning 109
Shekel
    Conversion to modern units
      393

Sheldon, William Herbert 320
Shellfish as food
    Health hazards 181
Shells
    Mollusk 280
Shepard, Alan, Jr. 61, 63
Ships *See* Boats
Shock
    Due to blood loss 352
    Due to burns 371
Shooting star 54
Shopping centers 433
Short ton 399
Short-period comets 53
Shortwave radio
    Receiving space communica-
        tion 482-3
Shumway, Norman
    First heart transplant in
        United States 389
SI measurement system 348, 394
Siamese cats
    Color points 307
    Eyes 308
Siamese twins 321
Siberia
    Explosion 52
Sick building syndrome 359
    See also Pollution, indoor air
Sierra Club
    Founder 186
Sievert
    Radiation measurement 348
Silica aerogels 145
Silicon
    Abundancy 20
    Components in human body
        311
Silicon chips 494
    See also Circuit chips
    Sizes 495
Silver 16, 19
    German silver 136
    Weight measurements 401
Silver ghost *See* Cougar
Simpson, Robert 116
SINS system 447
Sintering 422
Siple, Paul A. 113
Sirius 31, 56, 105, 404
Six-shooter 424
Skeletal muscles 324
Skill, Andrew 375
Skin
    Goose-bumps 335
    Human 326

Ridge patterns 334
Size in average human 334
Tattoo removal 335
Sklodowska (lunar crater) 51
Skunks
    Odor of spray 301
    Removing odor 308
Sky, Reason for blue color 72
Slate, Thomas Benton 144
Sleepiness *See* Narcolepsy
Sleeping
    Average time per night 315
    Changing needs with age
        315
    Food calories burned 315
Slide rule 511
Smalley, Richard 145
Smeaton, John 149
Smile, number of muscles used
    325
Smith, Robert Angus 196
Smog, composition 195
Smoking
    Health hazards 351
    See also Specific type, i.e.,
        Cigarette smoking
Smooth muscles 324
Snails
    Threatened and endangered
        species, U.S. 193
Snakes, poisonous 282
Snoring
    Animals 265
    Humans 315
    Sound level 315
Snow
    Classification 122
    Conditions 123
    Formation 122
    Snowfall in U.S., greatest
        123
    Snowflakes 122
    Water content 122
Snowmold 251
Soda straws 90
Sodium 16, 19
    Components in human body
        311
Softwood as fuel *See* Wood as fuel
Soil
    Best time to work 245
    Garden soil 245
    Potting soil 245
Soil pH 245
Solar calendars *See* Calendars—
  Solar

Solar cycle 38
Solar eclipses *See* Eclipses—Solar
  38
Solar energy 155
    Passive systems compared to
        active systems 156
    U.S. energy production 170
Solar flares 38
Solar system
    Age 40
    Formation 40
Solar winds
    Aurora effect 106
Solder 150
Solid waste 203
    Generated annually in the
        United States 203
    Generated by average
        American 202
Solids 11
    Density 12, 141
    Lightest material 145
Somatotyping 320
Sonar
    Bats 293
Sonic booms 7
Sony 489
Sopwith Camel 472
Sound
    Doppler effect 8
    Sound barriers in buildings
        431
    Speed of 7, 10
Sound Transmission Class 431
South Africa
    World's largest diamond 132
South Pole
    First person 87
Southern polar aurora 106
Southernmost points of land 86
Soviet Union, Space program in
  See Space flight—U.S.S.R.
Space flights
    Accidents 68, 69
    Animals 63
    Astronauts and cosmonauts
      See Astronauts and cosmo-
      nauts
    Blacks 66
    Challenger disaster 69
    Chimpanzees 63
    Dogs 63
    Fatalities 68, 69
    First American in space 60
    First man in space 60
    Galileo 67

Launches 67
Longest manned flight 63
Monkeys 63
Moon 62-4
Satellites 67
Space walks 64
U.S.S.R. 67
Voyager 61
Women 66
Space law 60
Space shuttles
    Radio transmissions 482
Space walks, see Space flights—
    Space walks
Spacecraft
    Solar energy 155
Spaceship Earth 186
Spawning
    Salmon 280
Spectroscopy
    Founders 7
Speed (cars)
    Detection devices 463, 464
    Speed limits 345
    Speed traps 463
Speeds
    Blenny (fish) 278
    Dolphins 278
    Flying fish 278
    Humans 278
    Of light 6-7
    Of sound 7, 10
    Sailfish, Cosmopolitan 277
    Trout 278
    Tuna 277, 278
    Wahoe (fish) 278
Speleology 90
Speleothem 90
Spelunking 90
Spencer, Herbert 214
Sphere
    Surface area 514
    Volume 513
Sphygmomanometer (medical
    instrument) 377
Spiders 356
    See also names of individual
        spiders, i.e., Black Widow
    Eggs 275
    Webs 275
Spiegelman Monster 222
Spiegelman, Sol 222
Spiny anteater See Echidna
Spirit of St. Louis 468
Sponges, luffa 143
Spontaneous combustion 4

Sport injuries 346
Spring tides 84
Spruce Goose 470
Sputnik 1 67
Squaring the circle 516
SSI 495
Stack, John 469
Staff of Aesculapius 373
Stalactites 90-1
Stalagmites 90-1
Stamen 238
Standard gauge railroad 452
Standard temperature and pres-
    sure 26
Stapes bone (ear) 340
Star of Africa diamond 132
Star ruby, largest 132
Star sapphire
    Largest 132
    Source of star effect 133
Starboard 448
Stars
    Age 32
    Binary 31
    Brightest 32
    Closest to Earth 36
    Color 32
    Magnitude 32
    Naming of 56
    Neutron stars 32
    Temperature 32
Statue of Liberty 444
STC Rating 431
Steam
    Energy output compared to
        other fuels 169
Steel
    High speed steel 137
    Production process 137
Stephenson, George 452
Steroids See Anabolic steroids
Stibnite 130
Stirrup bone (ear) 340
Stitches 356
Stomach
    First direct studies 316
Stone-eating Bacteria 229
Stones, living 244
Storms, thunder See Thunder
Stove, woodburning 157
STP 26
Strait of Gibraltar See Gibraltar,
    Strait of
Strategic minerals 129
Stratosphere 71
Strauss, Joseph B. 442

Strawberry cultivation
    Problem insects 256
Streak lightning 108
Streptococcus 361
Streptomycin 383
Strontium 16
Strychnine poison 355
Sturgeon
    Products 143
Subatomic particles
    Electrons 11
    Quantum mechanics See
        Quantum mechanics
    Quarks 11
Submarines
    Communication 485
Subtraction
    Abacus versus calculator 509
Sugar
    Ethanol production 162
Sulfites 366
Sulfur
    Components in human body
        311
Sulfur Dioxide
    Environmental damage 229
    Pollution 196
Sulfuric acid 144
Sullivan, Kathryn D. 64, 66
Sulphide, Lead 130
Summer
    Dog days 105
Summer Triangle 34
Sun 36
    Age 37
    Color of 38
    Composition 37
    Death of 37
    Light See Sunlight
    Mass 37
    Reason for yellow color 72
    Rings 105
    Solar calendars See
        Calendars—Solar
    Star type 32
    Temperature 37
Sun spots 38
Suncoast Dome 435
Sundew 240
Sunlight
    Color of 38
    Colors 6
    Time to reach Earth 38
Sunset 403
    Green flash 106

Reason for orange and red
color 72
Sunspots 38
Aurora effect 106
Super High Frequency (SHF) 481
Super Outbreak 116
Superconductivity 2
Supergiants 32
Superior planets 44
Supernovas 32
Supersonic Flight 468
Surface coatings
Teflon 154
Surface to surface missiles, range
427
Surgical ligature
Catgut 388
Surgical procedures
Second opinions 388
Surveying
Instruments 402
Survival of the Fittest
Coining of phrase 214
Suspended animation 322
Suspension bridges 440
Brooklyn Bridge 442
Golden Gate 442
Longest in U.S. 441
Verrazano-Narrows Bridge
441
Swallowing
Involuntary muscular
reflexes 317
Swallows
Migration return 286
Sweat glands 334
Swine 298
Sydenham, Thomas 374
Symbiosis 229, 279, 290
Symptoms
AIDS 358
Alzheimer's disease 369
Anorexia 369
ARC 358
Bends 369
Black widow spider bites 356
Botulism 353
Chinese restaurant syndrome
371
Classes of burns 371
Excess ozone 347
Herpes 361
Jet lag 364
Lactose intolerance 362
Legionnaire's disease 359
Lou Gehrig's disease 359

Lyme disease 359
Marfan's syndrome 363
Narcolepsy 364
Pelvic inflammatory disease
370
Pollution, indoor air 200
Progeria 369
Retinal detachment 336
Strychnine 355
A Synopsis of the Astronomy of
Comets 53
Synthetic gemstone 154
Synthetic skin See Skin, synthetic
Synthetic soil, composition of 245
Système Internationale d'Unites
348, 394
Systolic blood pressure 377
Syzygy 30

T

Tabby cats 306
Tadpoles, care 309
Tamayo-Mendez, Arnoldo 66
Tankers, largest 451
Tanks 472
Culin device 472
Tap water See Water, tap
Tapetum lucidum 307
Tasmanian devils
Reproduction 294
Taste sensations 341
Tattoos, removal 335
Taxicabs 466
Taxol 382
Technetium 138
Technobabble 503
Technology, High 519
Teflon 154
Telefacsimile 486
Telegraphy
Morse code, International
476
Wireless radio 480
Telephones 486
Answering machine 487
Cellular telephone 488
Fax machine 487
Telephone poles 139
Telescopes
Hubble Space Telescope 58
Invention of 57
Television 485, 486
Founder of 483
Reception, effect of weather
483
Satellite dish 484, 485

Telford, Thomas 437
Telstar 1 486
Temperature
Absolute zero See Absolute
zero
Air 103, 113
Effects on freezing water 1
See also Air temperature
Temperature scales
Celsuis scale 25-6
Fahrenheit scale 26
Kelvin scale 25
Temperature, body 330
Regulation in humans 330,
335
10-codes 478
Tennis elbow 363
Tereshkova-Nikolaeva, Valentina V.
65
Termites 274
Terrestrial planets 44
Tertiary Period 189
Testes, functions 329
Tests for drug use 386
Tetrahydrocannabinol (THC) 388
Texas tower 443
Thalidomide 385
Theodolite 402
Theophrastus 238
Therblig 519
Thermal cracking See
Hydrocarbon cracking
Thermal energy, generation
method 163
Thermodynamics See Heat
Thermometer 24
Thermopane glass 147
Thermosphere 72
Thermotropism 233
Thigmotropism 233
Third generation computers 492
Thirteen-month calendar 406
Thomson, Sir Joseph John 11
Thomson, William 25
Threatened species 191
In the U.S. 193
See also Endangered species;
Extinct species; Vulnerable
species
Three Mile Island accident 165
Thunder
Distance 121
Distance calculation 108
Thunderstorms 352
Occurences 120
Thyroid glands, functions 329

Ticks
    Disease and vectors 359
Tidal bore 79
Tidal energy See Water power
Tides 84
Timber 237
Timber wolf 298
Time
    See also Calendars
    Abbreviations 414
    Atomic time 402
    Calendars 408
    Century 403
    Correct time radio signal
        414
    Correct U.S. time 413
    Daylight Savings Time 412
    Dynamic time 402
    Geologic See Geological time
    Leap second 409
    Measurement 402-3, 408-9
    Military 416
    Radiocarbon dating 223
    Rotational time 402
    Seasons See Seasons
    Universal time 413
    Year 408
Time and motion study 519
Time zones 413
Tin 19
Tire, Michelin 458
Tires
    Airplane 470
    Effect of underinflation on
        gasoline consumption 175
    Numbering for tire sizes and
        types 466
    Radial 458
    Tubeless 459
Tissue Culture 217
Titanic 450
Titanium dioxide 151
TNT 152
Toe nails, growth rate 336
Tomahawk missile, range 427
Tombaugh, Clyde 47
Tombs
    Microbe damage 229
Tommy gun 425
Tonnage of Boats 449
Tonne 399
Tonsillectomy
    Second opinions 388
Tonsils, possible purpose 329
Tools, Neanderthal 416
Tooth shells 280

"Topping Out" 436
Tornadoes 113, 114
    U.S. activity 115-6
Townes, Charles 419
Toxic Release Inventory (TRI) 194
Tracheal
    Involuntary muscular
        reflexes 317
Traffic
    Laws 464
    Lights, first installed 438
Trains
    Orient Express 454
Trans-Siberian Railway 453
Transatlantic airplane flights, First
    468
Transcendental number, Pi 508
Transistors 495
    On circuit chips 495
Transit 402
Transition chemical elements 16
Transportation
    Human-powered 175
Treaties
    Space 60
Treatment
    Black widow spider bites 356
    Drug overdose 353
    Insufficient or irregular heart
        beat 390
    Lactose intolerance 362
    Legionnaire's disease 359
    Leprosy 360
    Lyme disease 359
    Poisoning 353
    Tattoo removal 335
    Using activated charcoal 353
    Using botulinal toxin 353
    Using Heimlich maneuver
        352
    Using negative ion generators
        391
Trees
    Banyan tree 235
    Bonsai 254
    Conifers 236
    Dawn redwood 236
    Deciduous 236
    Dogwood 254
    Dwarf conifers 254
    Fir, pine, spruce (differences)
        236
    Fruit trees 253
    Greatest number 235
    Leaves turning color 234,
        235

    Longest-lived species 233
    Monkey ball tree 237
    Number used for home con-
        struction 429
    Pleaching 254
    Products See Tropical forests
    Rings 234
    Rose family 237
    Tallest 235
    Wood See Wood
Trials
    Evolution 214
Triangle
    Area 514, 515
    Pascal's 515
Triassic Period 187
Trident missile, range 427
Triestes bathyscaphe 78
Trinitrotoluene 152
Triple play probability 519
Trojan asteriods 52
Tropical forests
    See also Rain forests
    Products 140
    Rate of destruction 181-2
Tropism 233
Troposphere 71
Trout, speed 278
Trouvelot, Leopold 238
Troy weights
    Conversion to avoirdupois
        units 401
Tsunami 95
Tube worms, Giant 279
Tubeless car tires 459
Tuber (flower) 239
Tuberculosis 230
    Streptomycin 383
Tuberous root (flower) 239
Tufa 90
Tuna, speed 277
Tundras 177
Tungsten 19
Tunguska Event 52
Tunnel disease See Bends
Tunnels (road)
    Longest 439
Turco, Richard P. 427
Turing, Alan M. 492, 494
Turkey vultures
    Migration 286
Turtles
    Endangered species 192
    Shell 282
20/20 vision 338
24 karat gold 134

Twilight 403
Twins, Siamese 321
Two-stroke engines, comparison to four-stroke engines 417
Tyndall, John 179
Typhoid Mary 360

U

UFOs 60
ULSI (silicon chip size) 495
Ultra High Frequency (UHF) 481
Ultrasound
    Medical instruments 378
Uncertainty, theory of 24
Uncle Sam diamond 130
Unidentified Flying Objects *See* UFOs
United Kingdom
    Crown Jewels 132
    Nuclear reactor accidents 165
United Nations Outer Space Treaty *See* Outer Space Treaty
United States
    Acid rain 197
    Biothermal energy 155
    Blood types, most common 332
    Diamond mine 130
    Endangered species 193
    Endangered species, determining status 190
    Energy consumption 171-2
    Energy reserves 172
    Excess weight 320
    Fifth generation computers 492
    First zoo 185
    Forest fires, causes 183
    Glaciers, Effect on terrain 88
    Gypsy moth infestations 183
    Heaviest persons 320
    Highest Point 75
    Hurricanes 118
    Ice Ages 88
    Landfills 204
    Largest desert 89
    Largest oil and gas fields 159
    Laws regulating toxic chemicals 194
    Lowest point 75
    Northernmost points 86
    Nuclear reactor accidents 165
    Nuclear waste dump sites 202

Nuclear waste storage 202
Oldest operational nuclear power plant 163
Paper manufacturing using waste paper 205
Percentage of population overweight 320
Petroleum imports 170
Robots, industrial 420
Solid waste 204
Southernmost points 86
Space launches 67
Strategic minerals 129
Temperature, air 103
Threatened species 193
Three Mile Island accident 165
Time 413
Tornadoes 115
Toxic chemicals, laws regulating 194
Univax 1 492
Universal Product Code (UPC) 479
Universal time 413
Universe
    Age 29
    Expansion 29
    Origin 29
University of California, Berkeley, student protest 493
University of Pennsylvania School of Medicine 374
Upatnieks, Juris 420
Uranium 137
    Pitchblende 130
Uranus 44, 47
    Retrograde motion 44
    Rings 42
    Rotation 44
Urea, synthesization 13
Urey, Harold C. 145
Urine, normal pH 331
Ursa Major 33
U.S. customary measures
    Conversion to metric units 396
    Length 395
    Water 400
U.S.S.R.
    Chernobyl accident 165-6
    Space program in *See* Space flight—U.S.S.R.
Uterus
    Pelvic inflammatory disease 370
Uvula 325

V

Vaccination 229
    Polio 383
Vacuum tubes 495
Vail, Alfred 477
Van Allen belts or zones 72
Van Allen, James Alfred 72
Van Helmont, Johannes Baptista *See* Helmont, Johannes Baptista van 221
Vapor, Sublimation of water 122
Varicose vein removal 388
VASCAR 464
Vectors, disease 358-9
Vega 34
Vehicle identification number 460
Velocipede 454
Venn diagrams 512
Venn, John 512
Venus 44
    Naming of surface features 56
    Retrograde motion 44
    Rotation 44
Venus fly trap 240
Verneuil, Auguste Victor Louis 154
Verrazano-Narrows Bridge 441
Vertebrates, blood color 264
Very high frequency (VHF) 481
Very low density lipoproteins (VLDL) 350
Victory garden 250
Video-arcade games 494
Video display screen 497, 501
VIN 460
Violence, during full moon 344
Virtual reality 489
Virus 229
    Coining of term 229
    QB 222
    Reproduction 222
    Use in vaccines 229
Virus, computer 501
Vision
    Color 337, 339
    Correction 338
    Effect on moods, heart rate, brain activity 339
    Light and dark perception 337
    Optical illusion 338
    20/20 338
Vision, Color 337, 339
    Animals 263

Visual Average Speed Computer
  Recorder 464
Vitriol, Oil of 144
VLDL *See* Very low density
  lipoproteins
VLSI (silicon chip size) 495
Volcanoes 94
    As energy sources *See*
      Geothermal energy
    Atmospheric effect 105
    Composite 94
    Most destructive 94
    Types 93
    U.S. 94
Volt 26
Volta, Alessandro 26
Voltages
    Battery, car 26
    Battery, flashlight 26
    Receptacles 26
Volume
    Biblical units 393
    Formulas for calculating 513
Voluntary muscles 324
Voyager 1 42, 48, 61
Voyager 2 43, 48, 61
Voyager record 61
Vulnerable species 191
    See also Endangered species;
      Extinct species; Threatened
      species
    Bowhead whales 192
    Finback whales 192
    Humpback whales 192
    Right whales 192
    Sei whales 192

W

Wahoe (fish)
    Speed 278
Waksman, Selman A. 383
Wallabies
    Reproduction 294
Walsh, David 78
Waning crescent moon 49
Waning gibbous moon 49
Warhawks 473
Warts 361
Wasps 270
Waste paper *See* Paper, waste
Waste, solid, generated annually in
  the United States 203
Watches (time) 415
Water
    Boiling point 26
    Classical element 330

Content in snow 122
Density 12, 13
Drinking 356
Drinking sources 76
Freezing 1
Freezing point 26
Power *See* Hydroelectric
  power
Sea, comparison to blood 331
    Shortage 76
    Tap, Lead content 356
    Weights 400
Water-lily 244
Watson, James 218
Watt, James 455
Wave energy *See* Water power
Waves, water
    Causes 78
Waxing crescent moon 49
Waxing gibbous moon 49
Weapons, poison 355
Weather
    Barometric pressure 124
    Hot, humid weather 105
    Prediction 123, 124
    Seasons *See* Seasons
    Wind *See* Wind
Weavers, orb 275
Weaving, Jacquard 492
Webs, spider *See* Spiders—Webs
  275
Week
    See also Calendars
    Days 409
    Origin 410
Weight
    Avoirdupois weights 401
    Biblical units 393
    Fuels compared 167
    Heavist person 320
    Metric system 399
    Of the Earth 73
    Oil, Barrel 167
    Pacemaker 390
    Skin, human 334
    Troy weights 401
    U.S. customary units 399
Weight, desirable 319
Weight, excess
    Americans, percentage 320
    Heaviest persons 320
Weights and measures *See*
  Measurement units
Weiner, Norbert 421
Werner, Abraham Gottlob 129
Werner's syndrome

Progeria 369
West Edmonton Mall 433
Western yew
    Anti-cancer drugs 382
Whales
    Breath-holding capacity 292
    Intelligence 263
    Life span 259
    Populations 192
    Weight 295
Wheeler, John 31
Whiskers of a cats 308
White blood cells 313
White damp 138
White, Edward II 64
White gold 135
White pigments 151
Wilbrand, J. 152
Wilkins, Maurice 218
Williams, Daniel Hale 389
Wilson, Robert W. 29
Wind
    Cyclones 114
    Halcyon days 111
    Hurricanes *See* Hurricanes
    Measurement 115
    Temperature effect 113
    Wind chill factor or index
      112, 113
Wind power
    U.S. energy production 170
Wind tunnels 470
Windpipe
    Involuntary muscular
      reflexes 317
Winthrop, John, Jr. 136
WOBO 208
Wohler, Friedrich 13
Wolff, Kasper Friedrich 220
Wolves 298
Wombats 294
Women
    Astronauts and cosmonauts
      64-66
    Blacks 66
    Desirable weight 319
    Heaviest women 320
    In space 65, 66
    Pilots (Amelia Earhart) 468
    Space walkers 64
Wood
    See also Biomass energy
    Amount for a house 429
    As fuel (comparison) 157
    Density 141
    Papermaking 139

Telephone poles 139
Wood preservative 150
World bottle 208
World Trade Center Complex 434
World War I
    Artillery 426
World War II
    Artillery 426
    Bazooka 425
    Oil spills 198
Worms, computer 501
Worms, segmented
    Blood color 264
Wormwood 243
Wright, Orville 467
Wright, Wilbur 467

X

Xenon
    Isotopes 20
Xeriscape 246
X-ray 378

Comparison with MRI 378
Dental 348

Y

Yannas, Ioannis V.
    Development of synthetic
        skin 391
Yapoks
    Gestation period 291
Yard 395
Yazoo 82
Yeager, Charles E. 469
Yeager, Jeana 469
Year
    Chinese year cycle 407
    First day of new year 404
    Leap year 409
    Longest and shortest 408
    Value of calendar year 403
Year without a summer 104
Yellow bile *See* Humors (Theory of
    health and illness)

Yellow fever
    Causes 359
    Panama Canal 359
Yenisei-Angara River system
    Length 83
Yosemite Falls 83
Yudin, Sergei 375
Yurt 432

Z

Zeno of Elea 519
Zeno's paradox 519
Zero
    Absolute *See* Absolute Zero
    Concept 491, 505
Zinc
    Components in human body
        311
Zoo, first in the U.S. 185
Zoonosis 358
Zworykin, Vladimir K. 420, 483
Zygotes 312